Algebra and Trigonometry with Analytic Geometry

A series of books in the mathematical sciences

Editor: Victor Klee

Algebra and Trigonometry with Analytic Geometry

Arthur B. Simon
California State University, Hayward

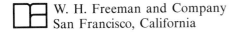 W. H. Freeman and Company
San Francisco, California

This book is dedicated to my parents, Bess and Joe.

Sponsoring Editor: Peter Renz; *Manuscript Editor:* Andrew Kudlacik; *Project Editor:* Patricia Brewer; *Designer:* Marjorie Spiegelman; *Production Coordinator:* Chuck Pendergast; *Illustration Coordinator:* Batyah Janowski; *Artist:* J & R Technical Services, Inc.; *Compositor:* York Graphic Services; *Printer and Binder:* The Maple-Vail Book Manufacturing Group.

Library of Congress Cataloging in Publication Data

Simon, Arthur B
    Algebra and trigonometry with analytic geometry.

    (A Series of books in the mathematical sciences)
    Includes index.
    1. Algebra.   2. Trigonometry.   3. Geometry,
Analytic.   I.   Title.
QA154.2.S53   512′.13   78-23409
ISBN 0-7167-1016-1

Preface

This book has three purposes: to prepare students for calculus, to illustrate the strong relationship between algebra and geometry, and to present some interesting applications of mathematics. The topics are from college algebra, trigonometry, and analytic geometry; the function concept is the unifying theme.

Chapter 1 reviews the fundamental concepts of arithmetic and algebra. The exercises focus on the basic manipulative and analytical skills. Chapter 2, the heart of the book, introduces functions and their graphs. The exercises emphasize evaluation of functions, curve sketching, and the use of functions in applications. Chapters 3 through 5 describe the polynomial, exponential, and logarithmic functions.

Should trigonometry be introduced by the concrete and familiar method of right triangles or by the more abstract and general method of circular functions? I have adopted a careful compromise that offers the advantages of both methods. The sine and cosine are first defined in terms of angles in standard position; these definitions are soon shown to be equivalent to the usual definitions of the circular functions. In Chapter 6 the function concept is emphasized. Chapter 7 deals with triangle trigonometry and its applications; it also includes a discussion of polar coordinates and vectors. Trigonometric inverses, addition formulas, and multiple-angle formulas are described in Chapter 8, which completes the study of trigonometry.

Following trigonometry are chapters on complex numbers and conic sections. There are also two appendixes, one on induction and the Binomial Theorem and another on systems of equations.

Of all the features in this book, I am most proud of the exercises. As we all know, mathematics is not a passive subject; skill in mathematics and a true appreciation of it cannot be acquired without practice. The exercises at the end of each section offer students ample opportunity to participate actively in all kinds of mathematical activity. There are four groups, or categories, of exercises. The problems in the first group develop computational skills. Those in the second group (indicated by a small white box in the margin) require the application of those skills to problems from business, economics, engineering, mathematics, and physics. For the most part, the applications are similar to examples worked out in the text, but many of them require students to forge the concepts into a working tool. The third category (indicated by a gray box) consists of exercises that call for the proof or verification of stated results. The exercises in the final group (a black box) are of a creative nature—generalizations of given statements or open-ended questions—and students are often urged to make up exercises of their own to exchange with each other. The exercises numbered in boldface type are answered in the back of the book and could be used as a reasonable homework assignment.

     Many of the routine computational exercises may be worked with hand calculators. However, calculators should be used to supplement rather than supplant the study of computational skills. Moreover, the use of calculators does not in any way lessen the need for students to understand the theory and the application of concepts. On the contrary, freeing students from tedious computation permits them to study a larger variety of concepts and applications.

     This book is flexible enough to be used for a number of different courses both in semester and in quarter systems. Some possible course outlines are shown below; each one provides ample time for review and examinations. A single asterisk means that students should have studied the equivalent of one and one-half years of high-school algebra and some geometry. Two asterisks mean that students should have studied three years of high-school mathematics, including some trigonometry.

Three lectures per week

	*Two-quarter sequence**	*One semester***
Chapter 1 Preliminaries	6 lectures	5 lectures Combine 1-1 and 1-2
Chapter 2 Functions	5 lectures	5 lectures
Chapter 3 Linear and quadratic functions (and possibly parts of Appendix B)	5 lectures	5 lectures
Chapter 4 Polynomials	6 lectures	4 lectures Combine 4-1 and 4-2 Combine 4-3 and 4-4

Chapter 5
Exponential and   4 lectures   3 lectures
logarithmic   Omit 5-4 (computation   Combine 5-2 and 5-3
functions   with logarithms)   Omit 5-4 (computations)

End of first quarter—total lectures: 26

Chapter 2
Functions   3 lectures
                         Review 2-1, 2-3, and 2-5

Chapters 6, 7, and 8
Trigonometry   15 lectures   10 lectures
                                                       Combine 7-1 and 7-2
                                                       Combine 7-3 and 7-4
                                                       Omit 7-5 (vectors)
                                                       Omit 8-4 (identities)
                                                       Omit 8-5 (equations)

Chapter 9
Complex numbers or   4 lectures   4 lectures
Appendix A
Induction and the
Binomial Theorem

Chapter 10
Analytic geometry   4 lectures   4 lectures
                         Omit 10-5 (rotations)   Omit 10-5 (rotations)

Second quarter—total lectures: 26   Total lectures: 40

Four lectures per week

*Two-quarter sequence**
    First quarter: Chapters 1 through 5 and
    Appendix B.   Total lectures: 31
    Second quarter: Review Chapter 2.
    Chapters 6 through 10 and Appendix A.   Total lectures: 31

*One semester**
    Use the outline for the two-quarter sequence
    with three lectures per week but omit the
    review of Chapter 2.   Total lectures: 49

Five lectures per week

*One quarter***
    Use the outline for the one-semester course
    with three lectures per week.   Total lectures: 40

*One semester**
    Entire book.   Total lectures: 59

I would like to thank Chuck Murray and Harold Palmer (Chabot College), Colbert Purvis and Rangit Sabharwal (Hayward), Jim Staaksted (Cabrillo College), and Don Tucker (University of Utah) for talking with me about the preliminary versions of this book and making many helpful comments. I would also like to thank the many people who reviewed the manuscript and made detailed suggestions for improvement; especially Victor Klee (University of Washington), Stewart Priddy (Northwestern University), and Brandon Wheeler (Sacramento City College).

Credit for the final form of the book must be given to the staff at W. H. Freeman and Company, especially the editor, Peter Renz, the manuscript editor, Andrew Kudlacik, and the project editor, Pat Brewer.

Finally, I want to express a special word of appreciation to my wife, Dolores. She not only typed the manuscript, she was a constant source of support and encouragement. I could not have done it without her.

October 1978   A.B.S.

Contents

Algebra

Trigonometry, Complex Numbers, and Analytic Geometry

Appendixes

Algebra and Trigonometry with Analytic Geometry

Chapter 1

Preliminaries

The concepts and methods explained in this chapter are fundamental to your work in the rest of the book. Even if you have studied the real number system, factoring, exponents, and word problems before, this review will sharpen your basic manipulative and analytical skills.

1-1
Operations with Real Numbers

The **real numbers** are the numbers most familiar to you; they include whole numbers, fractions, and decimals. They are important because they can be used for computing answers to problems that arise naturally in everyday life, not to mention the ones in this book. Certain kinds of real numbers have been given names. The whole numbers, $0, 1, 2, 3, \ldots$, and their negatives, $-1, -2, -3, \ldots$, are known as **integers.** A number that can be written

$$\frac{a}{b}$$

a fraction in which a and b are integers and b is not 0, is called a **rational number** or simply a **rational.** The following are all rational numbers:

$$\frac{1}{2} \qquad \frac{1}{3} \qquad \frac{1}{16} \qquad \frac{3}{2} \qquad \frac{2}{3} \qquad \frac{479}{32} \qquad \frac{-2}{3} \qquad \frac{8}{-5} \qquad \frac{3}{1}$$

Notice that every integer is also a rational number: the last fraction in the row above is just another way of writing the integer 3. There are also many real numbers that cannot be written as such fractions; they are called **irrational numbers.**

In order to compute with real numbers, you need to know the properties of the basic operations, **addition** and **multiplication.** If a and b are real numbers, then their **sum** $a + b$ and their **product** $a \cdot b$ (frequently written ab) are also real numbers.

Commutative property
If a and b are real numbers,

$$a + b = b + a \quad \text{and} \quad ab = ba$$

If you add two numbers, the answer is the same no matter which number you write down first. Likewise, the order in which you multiply two numbers does not affect the answer.

Associative property
If a, b, and c are real numbers,

$$a + (b + c) = (a + b) + c \quad \text{and} \quad a(bc) = (ab)c$$

When you add (or multiply) three numbers, it makes no difference which two you add (or multiply) first.

Distributive property
If a, b, and c are real numbers,

$$a(b + c) = ab + ac \quad \text{and} \quad (b + c)a = ba + ca$$

Identities
If a is a real number,

$$a + 0 = a \quad \text{and} \quad a \cdot 1 = a$$

The number 0 is called the **additive identity,** and the number 1 is called the **multiplicative identity.**

Inverses
For each real number a, there is exactly one number $-a$ such that $a + (-a) = 0$. The number $-a$ is called the **additive inverse** of a.

For each real number a, *except* 0, there is exactly one number a^{-1} such that $aa^{-1} = 1$. The number a^{-1} is called the **multiplicative inverse,** or **reciprocal,** of a. It is also written $\dfrac{1}{a}$ or $1/a$. Notice that the symbol 0^{-1} is not defined: 0 does not have a reciprocal.

Replacement properties
Suppose a, b, c, and d are real numbers.

$$\text{If } a = b \text{ and } c = d, \text{ then } a + c = b + d \text{ and } ac = bd.$$

This is called a replacement (or substitution) property because a is replaced by b and c is replaced by d in the sum $a + c$ to obtain $b + d$. In particular, you can use the fact that $c = c$ to show that

$$\text{if } a = b, \text{ then } a + c = b + c \text{ and } ac = bc.$$

You may recognize this as "adding the same thing to both sides" and "multiplying both sides by the same thing."

All the usual arithmetic manipulations are justified by these basic properties. For example, here is a proof that cancellation is valid; the name of the property that justifies each step is in parentheses at the right.

Cancellation properties
Suppose a, b, and c are real numbers.

(a)   If $a + c = b + c$, then $a = b$.

(b)   If $ac = bc$ and $c \neq 0$, then $a = b$.

Proof

(a)
$$a + c = b + c$$
$$(a + c) + (-c) = (b + c) + (-c) \qquad \text{(Add } (-c) \text{ to both sides.)}$$
$$a + (c + (-c)) = b + (c + (-c)) \qquad \text{(Associative)}$$
$$a + 0 = b + 0 \qquad \text{(Inverse)}$$
$$a = b \qquad \text{(Identity)}$$

(b) $ac = bc$

$c \neq 0, \quad$ so c^{-1} exists   (Inverse)

$(ac)c^{-1} = (bc)c^{-1}$ (Multiply both sides by c^{-1}.)

$a(cc^{-1}) = b(cc^{-1})$ (Associative)

$a \cdot 1 = b \cdot 1$ (Inverse)

$a = b$ (Identity)

Other arithmetic properties will be stated without proof.

■ **Definition of subtraction**
   If a and b are real numbers, then b *subtracted from* a is written $a - b$, and

$$a - b = a + (-b)$$

The expression $a - b$ is also read "a minus b."

■ **Definition of division**
   If a and b are real numbers and $b \neq 0$, then a *divided by* b is written $a \div b$, and

$$a \div b = ab^{-1}$$

The number ab^{-1} can also be written $a \cdot \dfrac{1}{b}, \dfrac{a}{b}$, or a/b; it is called the **quotient** of a by b. In the expression $a \div b$, the number b is called the **divisor.**

■ *Division by 0 is not defined.*

If a is any real number *except* 0, then

$$a \div a = \frac{a}{a} = 1$$

Notice that subtraction and division do not have the commutative or associative properties. For example, $9 - 3 = 6$, but $3 - 9 = -6$. Also, $8 \div (4 \div 2) = 8 \div 2 = 4$, but $(8 \div 4) \div 2 = 2 \div 2 = 1$.

Multiplication by 0

Suppose a and b are real numbers; then

$$a \cdot 0 = 0$$

$$\text{If } ab = 0, \text{ then } a = 0 \text{ or } b = 0.$$

Example 1

If $3b = 0$, then $b = 0$ (because $3 \neq 0$).

If $(a - 2)(b - 4) = 0$, then $a - 2 = 0$ or $b - 4 = 0$.

Inverse of an inverse

If a is any real number, then

$$-(-a) = a$$

If a is any real number, except 0, then

$$(a^{-1})^{-1} = a$$

To put it another way,

$$1/(1/a) = a$$

Example 2

(a) $-(-3) = 3$ and $-(-(-4)) = -(4) = -4$

(b) $\dfrac{1}{\dfrac{1}{2}} = 2$

Adding and subtracting signed numbers

(a) $(-a) + (-b) = -(a + b)$

(b) $(-a) + b = b - a$

$\qquad\qquad = -(a - b)$

(c) $a - (-b) = a + b$

Example 3

(a) $-3 + (-2) = -(3 + 2) = -5$

  $-4 + (-6) = -10$

(b) $-3 + 4 = 4 - 3 = 1$

  $-3 + 2 = 2 - 3$

  $\qquad = -(3 - 2) = -1$

  $-6 + 4 = -(6 - 4) = -2$

(c) $3 - (-2) = 3 + 2 = 5$

  $-4 - (-6) = -4 + 6 = 2$

Multiplying and dividing signed numbers

(a) $(-a)(-b) = ab$

(b) $(-a)(b) = a(-b) = -ab$

(c) $(-a) \div (-b) = a \div b = \dfrac{a}{b}$ (Assume that $b \neq 0$.)

(d) $(-a) \div b = a \div (-b) = -(a \div b) = -\dfrac{a}{b}$ (Assume that $b \neq 0$.)

Example 4

(a) $(-3)(-2) = (3)(2) = 6$

(b) $(-3)(2) = (3)(-2) = -6$

(c) $(-4) \div (-2) = \dfrac{-4}{-2} = \dfrac{4}{2} = 2$

(d) $\dfrac{-8}{2} = \dfrac{8}{-2} = -\dfrac{8}{2} = -4$

  $\dfrac{-3}{4} = \dfrac{3}{-4} = -\dfrac{3}{4}$

Multiplying and dividing fractions
Suppose that a, b, c, and d are real numbers. If $c \neq 0$ and $d \neq 0$, then

$$\frac{a}{c} \cdot \frac{b}{d} = \frac{ab}{cd}$$

In words, to multiply fractions, multiply the **numerators** (the numbers on top) and multiply the **denominators** (the numbers on the bottom). If also $b \neq 0$, then

$$\frac{a}{c} \div \frac{b}{d} = \frac{a}{c} \cdot \frac{d}{b} = \frac{ad}{cb}$$

In words, to divide one fraction by another fraction, invert the divisor and multiply.

Example 5

(a) $$\left(\frac{1}{3}\right)\left(\frac{-2}{5}\right) = \frac{1(-2)}{3 \cdot 5} = \frac{-2}{15}$$

$$\left(-\frac{1}{5}\right)\left(\frac{4}{3}\right) = -\left(\frac{1}{5}\right)\left(\frac{4}{3}\right) = -\frac{4}{15}$$

(b) $$\frac{1}{3} \div \frac{-3}{4} = \frac{1}{3}\left(\frac{4}{-3}\right) = -\frac{4}{9}$$

$$-\frac{1}{5} \div \frac{4}{3} = -\left(\frac{1}{5}\right)\left(\frac{3}{4}\right) = -\frac{3}{20}$$

Adding and subtracting fractions
Suppose that a, b, and c are real numbers. If $c \neq 0$, then

$$\frac{a}{c} + \frac{b}{c} = \frac{a+b}{c} \qquad \text{and} \qquad \frac{a}{c} - \frac{b}{c} = \frac{a-b}{c}$$

In words, to add or subtract fractions that have the same denominator, add or subtract the numerators and write the result over the denominator.
If also d is a real number and $d \neq 0$, then

$$\frac{a}{c} + \frac{b}{d} = \frac{ad+bc}{cd} \qquad \text{and} \qquad \frac{a}{c} - \frac{b}{d} = \frac{ad-bc}{cd}$$

To add two fractions that have different denominators, multiply the numerator of the first times the denominator of the second, and add this to the numerator of the second times the denominator of the first; then write the result over the product of the two denominators. Subtraction is the same, except that you must *subtract* the numerator of the second times the denominator of the first.

Example 6

(a) $\dfrac{-3}{4} + \dfrac{5}{4} = \dfrac{-3+5}{4} = \dfrac{2}{4} = \dfrac{1}{2}$ *

$\dfrac{-1}{7} - \left(\dfrac{3}{-7}\right) = \dfrac{-1}{7} - \dfrac{-3}{7} = \dfrac{-1-(-3)}{7} = \dfrac{2}{7}$

$\dfrac{2}{-3} - \left(-\dfrac{1}{3}\right) = \dfrac{-2}{3} + \dfrac{1}{3} = \dfrac{-1}{3}$ or $-\dfrac{1}{3}$

(b) $\dfrac{1}{3} + \dfrac{3}{4} = \dfrac{(1 \cdot 4) + (3 \cdot 3)}{3 \cdot 4} = \dfrac{13}{12}$

$\dfrac{7}{6} - \dfrac{1}{3} = \dfrac{7 \cdot 3 - 1 \cdot 6}{6 \cdot 3} = \dfrac{15}{18} = \dfrac{5}{6}$

The first line of Example 6 says that $\frac{2}{4} = \frac{1}{2}$; the last line says that $\frac{15}{18} = \frac{5}{6}$. These pairs are called **equivalent fractions.**

■   **Definition**

Two fractions $\dfrac{a}{b}$ and $\dfrac{c}{d}$ are equivalent if $ad = bc$.

Equivalent fractions represent the same number: they have the same value. Thus, $\frac{2}{4} = \frac{1}{2}$ because $2 \cdot 2 = 4 \cdot 1$, and $\frac{15}{18} = \frac{5}{6}$ because $15 \cdot 6 = 18 \cdot 5$. An easy way to change a fraction into an equivalent one is to multiply it by 1:

$$\frac{1}{2} \cdot 1 = \frac{1}{2} \cdot \frac{2}{2} = \frac{2}{4}$$

$$\frac{1}{2} \cdot 1 = \frac{1}{2} \cdot \frac{3}{3} = \frac{3}{6}$$

$$\frac{5}{6} \cdot 1 = \frac{5}{6} \cdot \frac{3}{3} = \frac{15}{18}$$

$$\frac{5}{6} \cdot 1 = \frac{5}{6} \cdot \frac{4}{4} = \frac{20}{24}$$

---

*Hand-held calculators display rational numbers as decimals. The number $-\frac{3}{4}$ appears as $-.75$; $\frac{5}{4}$ appears as 1.25; and their sum appears as .5.

The **least common denominator,** or **LCD,** of two fractions is the smallest integer that can be divided evenly by each of the two denominators. The easiest way to add or subtract fractions with different denominators is to find the LCD, change each fraction into an equivalent one with the LCD for a denominator, and then add or subtract.

Example 7

(a) The LCD of $\frac{1}{3}$ and $\frac{3}{2}$ is 6,

$\frac{1}{3}$ is equivalent to $\frac{2}{6}$, and $\frac{3}{2}$ is equivalent to $\frac{9}{6}$, so

$$\frac{1}{3} + \frac{3}{2} = \frac{2}{6} + \frac{9}{6} = \frac{11}{6}$$

(b) The LCD of $\frac{7}{6}$ and $\frac{1}{4}$ is 12,

$\frac{7}{6}$ is equivalent to $\frac{14}{12}$, and $\frac{1}{4}$ is equivalent to $\frac{3}{12}$, so

$$\frac{7}{6} - \frac{1}{4} = \frac{14}{12} - \frac{3}{12} = \frac{11}{12}$$

The real line

The real numbers can be pictured as points on a line. Conversely, each point on a line can represent a real number called the **coordinate** of the point. One point is chosen and labeled 0; to the right of 0, another point is chosen and labeled 1. This establishes a unit distance and determines the coordinate of *every* point on the line. This line is called the **real line;** it is like a ruler with no ends (see Figure 1-1). The numbers to the right of 0 are called **positive;** those to the left are called **negative.** The number 0 itself is *neither* positive nor negative.

The real line represents the real numbers in a certain **order:** if you choose any two numbers a and b, one of them is to the right of the other. If the one on the right is b, for example, a is said to be *less than b.* This statement is written in symbols as $a < b$. Algebraically, this means that $b - a$ is a positive number. Another way of saying the same thing is to say that b is *greater than a.* This statement can be written in symbols as $b > a$. Notice that if a is positive, then $a > 0$; if a is negative, then $a < 0$.

Figure 1-1
The real line.

Example 8

(a) $1 < 2$ $2 > 1$ $-1 < \frac{1}{2}$

(b) $-2 < 1$, so $1 - (-2) > 0$.

There are important properties that relate the arithmetic operations to the order.

■   **Ordering properties**

(a)   If $a < b$, then $a + c < b + c$.

(b)   If $a < b$ and $c > 0$, then $ac < bc$;

BUT if $a < b$ and $c < 0$, then $ac > bc$.

(c)   If $a \neq 0$, then $a \cdot a > 0$.

(d)   If $a < b$ and $b < c$, then $a < c$.

Example 9

(a) $3 < 5$, so $3 + (-2) < 5 + (-2)$ and, for any c, $3 + c < 5 + c$.

(b) $-4 < -2$ and $3 > 0$, so $(-4)(3) < (-2)(3)$ and,
for any $c > 0$, $-4c < -2c$;

BUT $-3 < 0$, so $(-4)(-3) > (-2)(-3)$ and, for any $c < 0$,
$-4c > -2c$.

(c) $2 \cdot 2 > 0$ and $(-3)(-3) > 0$

There are two other symbols that express order in the real number system. The
expression $a \leq b$, read "*a is less than or equal to b*," means that a is *either* less than b
or equal to b. Similarly, $a \geq b$ means that a is *either* greater than *or* equal to b.

Example 10

(a) $3 \geq 1$ $1 \leq 3$ $3 \leq 3$ $3 \geq 3$

(b)   If x is *not* a negative number, then $x \geq 0$;

if x is *not* a positive number, then $x \leq 0$.

(c)   If a is *any* real number, then $a \cdot a \geq 0$ [see Ordering Property (c)].

Integer exponents

In solving scientific and mathematical problems, you will often have to multiply a number by itself. It is easy to write the product of a times a as $a \cdot a$, or even a times a times a as $a \cdot a \cdot a$. What about the product of a with itself 8 times? Or x with itself 64 times? You can write

$$a \cdot a \cdot a \cdot a \cdot a \cdot a \cdot a \cdot a \quad \text{and} \quad \underbrace{x \cdot x \cdot x \cdot \ldots \cdot x \cdot x}_{64}$$

but, fortunately, there is an easier way to do this.

■ **Definition of x^n**

If x is a real number and n is a positive integer, the expression x^n means x multiplied by itself n times. Read x^n "x to the nth power" or simply "x to the n"; x is called the **base** and n is called the **exponent.**

Ordinarily, x^1 is written x; x^2 is read "x squared," and x^3 is read "x cubed."

A word of caution about expressions such as $-x^2$. *The exponent applies only to the quantity immediately preceding it.* Thus, in the expression -3^2 only the 3 is squared: $-3^2 = -9$. If you want to square the quantity -3, you must write $(-3)^2$; then $(-3)^2 = (-3)(-3) = 9$.

Example 11

(a) $-4^2 = -(4 \cdot 4) = -16 \qquad (-2)^3 = (-2)(-2)(-2) = -8$

(b)   If $x = -2$ and $y = 3$, then

$$x^3 - y^2 = (-2)^3 - 3^2 = -8 - 9 = -17$$
$$3x^2 - 4y = 3(-2)^2 - 4 \cdot 3 = 12 - 12 = 0$$
$$-x^4y^3 = -(-2)^4 3^3 = -16 \cdot 27 = -432$$

■ **Definition of x^{-n}**

If n is a positive integer and $x \neq 0$, then

$$x^{-n} = \frac{1}{x^n}$$

Example 12

(a) $5^{-1} = 1/5 \qquad 3^{-2} = 1/3^2 = 1/9$

$(-4)^{-3} = 1/(-4)^3 = -1/64$

(b)   It follows from the definition that $\dfrac{1}{x^{-n}} = x^n$.

$$\frac{1}{7^{-1}} = 7 \qquad \frac{1}{2^{-3}} = 2^3 = 8$$

$$\frac{2^{-4}}{3^{-2}} = \frac{3^2}{2^4} = \frac{9}{16}$$

Calculating with exponents can be remarkably easy if you make use of the following properties.

■ Properties of exponents

(a) $x^m x^n = x^{m+n}$ \qquad\qquad\qquad\qquad (b) $(xy)^n = x^n y^n$

(c) $\dfrac{x^m}{x^n} = x^{m-n}$ \quad $(x \neq 0)$ \qquad (d) $\left(\dfrac{x}{y}\right)^n = \dfrac{x^n}{y^n}$ \quad $(y \neq 0)$

(e) $(x^m)^n = x^{mn}$

These properties are not difficult to prove. For instance, if m and n are positive integers, then

(a) $x^m x^n = \underbrace{(x \cdot x \cdot \ldots \cdot x)}_{m}\underbrace{(x \cdot x \cdot \ldots \cdot x)}_{n} = \underbrace{x \cdot x \cdot \ldots \cdot x}_{m+n} = x^{m+n}$

(b) $(xy)^n = \underbrace{(xy)(xy) \ldots (xy)}_{n} = \underbrace{(x \cdot x \cdot \ldots \cdot x)}_{n}\underbrace{(y \cdot y \cdot \ldots \cdot y)}_{n} = x^n y^n$

Notice that, in order to add and subtract exponents in expressions such as (a) and (c), the exponents must have the same base.

Although the definition of x^n stated that n must be a positive integer, these properties of exponents are true even when m and n are negative integers. Always remember, though, that when a number x has a negative integer for an exponent, x *must not be* 0. What if the *exponent* is 0?

■ Definition of x^0

If $x \neq 0$, then $x^0 = 1$.

This definition is quite natural because, if $x \neq 0$ and n is any integer, then $x^n/x^n = x^{n-n} = x^0$ by Property (c) above; on the other hand, x^n divided by itself equals 1.

Example 13

(a) $x^2x^3 = x^{2+3} = x^5$ $\qquad 2^4 2^{-5} = 2^{-1} = 1/2$

(b) $(xy)^3 = x^3y^3$ $\qquad \left(2 \cdot \dfrac{1}{3}\right)^2 = 2^2 \cdot \left(\dfrac{1}{3}\right)^2 = 4 \cdot \dfrac{1}{9} = \dfrac{4}{9}$

(c) $\dfrac{x^5}{x^3} = x^{5-3} = x^2$ $\qquad \dfrac{5^4}{5^6} = 5^{-2} = \dfrac{1}{5^2} = \dfrac{1}{25}$

$\dfrac{4^2}{4^2} = 4^0 = 1$

(d) $\left(\dfrac{x}{y}\right)^{-6} = \dfrac{x^{-6}}{y^{-6}} = \dfrac{y^6}{x^6}$ $\qquad \left(\dfrac{5}{4}\right)^3 = \dfrac{5^3}{4^3} = \dfrac{125}{64}$

(e) $(x^3)^4 = x^{12}$ $\qquad (2^{-2})^3 = 2^{-6} = 1/64$

(f) $5^0 = 1$ $\qquad (-7)^0 = 1$ $\qquad 0^0$ is undefined.

Square roots and cube roots

In a way, subtraction is the reverse of addition, and division is the reverse of multiplication. It is also useful to have an operation that reverses raising a number to a power. For example, if $169 = a^2$, what is a?

■ **Definition**
A **square root** of x is a number whose square is x. The **cube root** of x is the number whose cube is x.

This definition of a square root has a few wrinkles that must be ironed out. First of all, $a^2 \geq 0$ for every real number a [see Ordering Property (c)]. It follows that *negative numbers do not have square roots* in the real number system. Furthermore, each positive number has *two* square roots. For example, $5^2 = 25$ so 5 is a square root of 25; but -5 is also a square root of 25, because $(-5)^2 = 25$. So there can be no doubt about which square root is meant, the positive square root (called the **principal root**) of a positive number x is written $\sqrt{x}$, and the negative square root of x is written $-\sqrt{x}$. The only square root of 0 is 0.

Example 14

$$\sqrt{16} = 4 \qquad\qquad \sqrt{169} = 13 \qquad\qquad \sqrt{\dfrac{1}{9}} = \dfrac{1}{3}$$

$$-\sqrt{16} = -4 \qquad -\sqrt{169} = -13 \qquad -\sqrt{\frac{1}{9}} = -\frac{1}{3}$$

$$\sqrt{0} = 0$$

This problem does not come up with cube roots, because every real number has only one cube root. If x is any number, the expression $\sqrt[3]{x}$ stands for the cube root of x. When x is positive, $\sqrt[3]{x}$ is positive; when x is negative, $\sqrt[3]{x}$ is negative.

Example 15

$$\sqrt[3]{8} = 2 \qquad \sqrt[3]{-8} = -2 \qquad \sqrt[3]{0} = 0$$

$$\sqrt[3]{27} = 3 \qquad \sqrt[3]{-27} = -3$$

Symbols such as $\sqrt{}$ and $\sqrt[3]{}$ are called **radicals.** When you work problems with radicals, remember these facts:

■   If $x \geq 0$, then $(\sqrt{x})^2 = x$.

If x is any number, $(\sqrt[3]{x})^3 = x$.

They follow from the definitions: $\sqrt{x}$ is the nonnegative number whose square is x, so $(\sqrt{x})^2 = x$. Similarly, $\sqrt[3]{x}$ is the number whose cube is x, so $(\sqrt[3]{x})^3 = x$.

Example 16

(a) $\sqrt{2}$ is the number whose square is 2; therefore, $(\sqrt{2})^2 = 2.$*

(b) $\sqrt[3]{4}$ is the number whose cube is 4; therefore, $(\sqrt[3]{4})^3 = 4$.

(c) $(\sqrt{2})^3 = (\sqrt{2})^2\sqrt{2} = 2\sqrt{2} \qquad (\sqrt{3})^5 = (\sqrt{3})^2(\sqrt{3})^2\sqrt{3} = 9\sqrt{3}$

(d) $(\sqrt[3]{7})^4 = (\sqrt[3]{7})^3\sqrt[3]{7} = 7\sqrt[3]{7} \qquad (\sqrt[3]{-5})^4 = -5\sqrt[3]{-5}$

---

*The number $\sqrt{2}$ is irrational. It cannot be written as a quotient of two whole numbers, although its value can be *approximated* correct to any number of places: $\sqrt{2} \approx 1.414213562. \ldots$ Notice, however, that its square *is* a whole number: $(\sqrt{2})^2 = 2$.

Exercises

Perform the indicated operations.

1. $-3 + (-8)$

2. $-9 + (-10)$

3. $-\dfrac{2}{3} - \dfrac{5}{3}$

4. $\dfrac{1}{2} - \left(-\dfrac{7}{2}\right)$

5. $-\dfrac{7}{8} + \left(\dfrac{-9}{4}\right)$

6. $-\dfrac{3}{4} - \dfrac{5}{6}$

7. $\dfrac{8}{3} - \left(-\dfrac{1}{4}\right)$

8. $\dfrac{2}{7} - \dfrac{3}{4}$

9. $4.62 - (-6.81)$

10. $-9.8 - 5.6$

11. $\dfrac{1}{3} \div \dfrac{6}{13}$

12. $\dfrac{4}{5} \div \left(-\dfrac{1}{2}\right)$

13. $-\dfrac{2}{5} \div (-6)$

14. $4 \div \dfrac{3}{2}$

15. $8.2 \div (-4.1)$

16. $4.8 \div 9.6$

17. $\dfrac{3.61}{1.30}$

18. $\dfrac{2.6}{1.2}$

19. $(-3)(2)(-4)$

20. $2(-4)(5)$

21. $\dfrac{1}{3}\left(-\dfrac{2}{5}\right)\left(-\dfrac{1}{6}\right)$

22. $\dfrac{4}{5}\left(-\dfrac{1}{3}\right)\left(\dfrac{2}{3}\right)$

23. $\dfrac{1}{3} - \dfrac{2}{5} - \dfrac{1}{6}$

24. $-\dfrac{1}{2} + \dfrac{1}{6} - \dfrac{1}{12}$

25. $3^2 4^2$

26. $2^3 3^3$

27. $(-1)^2(-1)^5$

28. $(-2)^5(-2)^2$

29. $\left(\dfrac{2}{5}\right)^3$

30. $\left(\dfrac{-3}{4}\right)^2$

31. $\left(\dfrac{-1}{5}\right)^3$

32. $\left(\dfrac{4}{5}\right)^0$

33. $\left(\dfrac{1}{2}\right)^{-4}$

34. $\left(\dfrac{2}{3}\right)^{-3}$

35. $\left(\dfrac{-2}{5}\right)^{-2}$

36. $\left(\dfrac{3}{-8}\right)^{-3}$

37. $(2^2)^{-4}$

38. $(4^{-3})^2$

39. $(8^{-1})^2$

40. $(5^{-1})^{-3}$

41. $\sqrt{36}$

42. $\sqrt{81}$

43. $\sqrt[3]{-64}$

44. $\sqrt[3]{-125}$

45. $-\sqrt{100}$

46. $-\sqrt{169}$

47. $\sqrt[3]{8}$

48. $\sqrt[3]{1000}$

Let $s = -2$ and $t = 3$. Find the value of each of these expressions.

49. $s^3 - t^2$

50. $-3s^2 + t$

51. $(st)^2$

52. $(st)^{-2}$

53. $\left(\dfrac{s}{t}\right)^{-3}$

54. $\left(\dfrac{t}{s}\right)^0$

55. s^t

56. t^s

Let $u = -\dfrac{2}{3}$ and $v = \dfrac{1}{4}$. Find the value of each of these expressions.

57. $-u^2 - 3v$

58. $2u \div v^2$

59. $(uv)^2$

60. $(uv)^{-2}$

61. $\left(\dfrac{u}{v}\right)^0$ **62.** $\left(\dfrac{u}{v}\right)^3$ **63.** $2u^3 + v^{-2}$ **64.** $\dfrac{u^5}{u^3}$

Let $x = \sqrt{2}$ and $y = \sqrt[3]{-4}$. Find the value of each of these expressions.

65. $-x^4$ **66.** y^3 **67.** $x^{-6} + y^{-6}$ **68.** $x^6 + y^9$

69. $-y^7$ **70.** x^5 **71.** x^{y^3} **72.** $x^{16y^{-3}}$

73. $\sqrt{x^2}$ **74.** $\sqrt{y^6}$ **75.** $\sqrt[3]{x^2 - 2}$ **76.** $\sqrt[3]{y^3 + 4}$

77. $\sqrt{x^4 + y^3}$ **78.** $\sqrt[3]{x^2 + 6}$ **79.** $-\sqrt{2x^2 - 3y^3}$ **80.** $-\sqrt{x^6 + 1}$

81. Write the inequalities $-3 < 2$ and $3 > -2$. Perform each of the following operations on both sides of each inequality.
    (a)   add 5   (b)   multiply by 5
    (c)   add -5 (d)   multiply by -5
Which operations change the direction of the inequalities? In each case, what Ordering Property is demonstrated?

82. Divide both sides of each inequality below by 2 and notice what happens to the inequality. Do the same with -2. What is the general rule?
    (a) $2 < 6$ (b) $-6 < 2$ (c) $-2 > -6$

83. Take reciprocals ($1/a$ is the reciprocal of a) of both sides of each inequality in Exercise 82 and notice what happens to the inequality. Formulate a general rule.

1-2
Operations with Algebraic Expressions

In the preceding section, the basic operations and properties of the real number system were described. In this section, we shall apply those operations and properties to algebraic expressions, such as

$$2x^3 \qquad 3\sqrt{y} + 7 \qquad \frac{a}{u^2} + bv^2$$

The ability to manipulate such expressions is a skill useful in practically every area of mathematics. Reading the next few sections carefully will help you to develop this skill.

    A letter that can represent any element of a given set is called a **variable.** In the examples above, x, y, u, and v are variables. Letters toward the end of the alphabet usually denote variables. The real numbers, such as 2 in the first example and 3 and 7 in the second example, are called **constants.** Letters near the beginning of the alphabet, such as a, b, and c, are sometimes used to denote constants, as in the third example above.

    Variables in an expression may be replaced by real numbers; if the resulting value of the whole expression is a real number, we shall call the replacement

allowable. In the expression $2x^3$, every real number is an allowable replacement for x. If x is replaced by -1, then the **value** of $2x^3$ is $2(-1)^3 = -2$; the value of $2x^3$ at $x = \sqrt{5}$ is $2(\sqrt{5})^3 = 10\sqrt{5}$. In the expression $3\sqrt{y} + 7$, only the nonnegative real numbers are allowable replacements for y, because the square root of a negative number is not a real number. The value of $3\sqrt{y} + 7$ at $y = 4$ is $3\sqrt{4} + 7 = 13$; its value at $y = 6$ is $3\sqrt{6} + 7$. In the third example, 0 is the only number that is not an allowable replacement for u, and every real number is an allowable replacement for v. The set of all allowable replacements for a variable is called the **domain** of the variable.

Addition and subtraction

In an algebraic expression, parts that are separated by a plus sign or a minus sign are called **terms** of the expression. Two terms are called **like terms** if they have the same variables raised to the same powers. For example, in the expression $3x^2y - 5x^2y + 4xy^2 + 2xy^2$, the first two terms are like terms, and so are the last two, but $3x^2y$ and $4xy^2$ are not.

The constant part of a term, whether the constant is written as a specific real number or is merely represented by a letter, is called the **coefficient.** In the three examples at the beginning of this section, 2 is the coefficient of x^3, 3 is the coefficient of $\sqrt{y}$, and a is the coefficient of $1/u^2$. When no coefficient is written, it is understood to be 1 or -1. For example, the coefficient in the term $-x^2$ is -1.

We can use the Distributive Property to combine like terms by adding or subtracting their coefficients:

$$4xy^2 + 2xy^2 = (4 + 2)xy^2 = 6xy^2$$

and

$$3x^2y - 5x^2y = (3 - 5)x^2y = -2x^2y$$

■   To add two algebraic expressions, remove the parentheses and combine like terms.

Example 1

(a) $(3x^2 + 2x + 8) + (-5x - 9) = 3x^2 + 2x + 8 - 5x - 9$

$$= 3x^2 + (2 - 5)x + (8 - 9)$$

$$= 3x^2 - 3x - 1$$

The operation with the Distributive Property can usually be performed mentally.

(b) $(-3x + 4y - xy) + (x - 4y + 2xy) = -3x + 4y - xy + x - 4y + 2xy$

$$= -2x + xy$$

Recall the definition of subtraction in Section 1-1: $a - b = a + (-b)$. It follows from this definition that

■   To subtract one algebraic expression from another, change the sign in front of each term in the one to be subtracted, and then add the expressions.

Example 2

(a) $(2x + y) - (3x - 4y)$

$= (2x + y) + (-3x + 4y)$

$= 2x + y - 3x + 4y = -x + 5y$

(b) $(3x^2 + 2x + 8) - (-5x - 9)$

$= (3x^2 + 2x + 8) + (5x + 9)$

$= 3x^2 + 2x + 8 + 5x + 9$

$= 3x^2 + 7x + 17$

There really is no need to rewrite the parentheses in the second line above.

(c) $(2x^2 - 4xy + 5y^2) - (x^2 - 3xy - y^2)$

$= 2x^2 - 4xy + 5y^2 - x^2 + 3xy + y^2$

$= x^2 - xy + 6y^2$

Multiplication

To multiply two terms, multiply the constants and rearrange the variables so you can use the Properties of Exponents.

Example 3

(a) $(3xy^3)(2xy) = (3)(2)(x)(x)(y^3)(y) = 6x^2y^4$

(b) $(-4x^2y^{-5})(xy^3z) = (-4)(x^2)(x)(y^{-5})(y^3)(z) = -4x^3y^{-2}z$

Try to multiply the next one without the middle step.

(c) $(2x^2y^4)(-4x^{-3}y) = -8x^{-1}y^5$

By using the Distributive Property, you can multiply a term by an expression that contains more than one term.

Example 4

(a) $2x^2(3xy + y^2) = (2x^2)(3xy) + (2x^2)(y^2)$
$$= 6x^3y + 2x^2y^2$$

Try to eliminate the middle step by performing the multiplications mentally.

(b) $-xy^2(3 - 4x + y^3) = -3xy^2 + 4x^2y^2 - xy^5$

Repeated application of the Distributive Property will give the following method for multiplying algebraic expressions.

■   To find the product of two algebraic expressions, multiply each term of one by each term of the other and add the results.

Example 5

(a) $(x + 2y)(x + 3y) = (x)(x) + (x)(3y) + (2y)(x) + (2y)(3y)$
$$= x^2 + 3xy + 2xy + 6y^2$$
$$= x^2 + 5xy + 6y^2$$

(b) $(2x - 7)(4x + 2) = (2x)(4x) + (2x)(2) + (-7)(4x) + (-7)(2)$
$$= 8x^2 + 4x - 28x - 14$$
$$= 8x^2 - 24x - 14$$

With some practice, you will be able to perform this operation mentally. Try your hand at these:

(c) $(x - 4)(2x + 3) = 2x^2 - 5x - 12$

(d) $(2x - 3y)(4x + y) = 8x^2 - 10xy - 3y^2$

(e) $(x - \sqrt{2})(x + 3\sqrt{2}) = x^2 + 2\sqrt{2}x - 6$

The multiplication problems in Example 5 contain expressions with two terms each. If a problem contains an expression with more than two terms, it is usually wise to perform "long multiplication."

Example 6
Multiply $(3x^2 - 2xy + 4y^2)(2x + 7y)$.

Solution

$$
\begin{array}{l}
3x^2 - 2xy + 4y^2 \\
\underline{\quad\quad 2x \ + 7y} \\
6x^3 - \ \ 4x^2y + \ \ 8xy^2 \\
\underline{\quad\quad + 21x^2y - 14xy^2 + 28y^3} \\
6x^3 + 17x^2y - \ \ 6xy^2 + 28y^3
\end{array}
$$

(Multiply by $2x$)
(Multiply by $7y$)
(Add)

Be sure to add only like terms.

Special products
Certain products will appear so often—in the next section, on factoring, and in later chapters—that they should be memorized.

■   **Square of a sum**

$$(p + q)^2 = p^2 + 2pq + q^2$$

Here, $p + q$ stands for any expression with two terms. You can check this formula by multiplying the product out.

$$(p + q)^2 = (p + q)(p + q) = p^2 + pq + pq + q^2 = p^2 + 2pq + q^2$$

Example 7

(a) $(x + 2)^2 = x^2 + 2(x)(2) + 2^2 = x^2 + 4x + 4$ (Replace p by x and q by 2)

(b) $(2x + 3y)^2 = (2x)^2 + 2(2x)(3y) + (3y)^2$ ($p = 2x$, $q = 3y$)
         $= 4x^2 + 12xy + 9y^2$

(c) $(x^2 + 2y^3)^2 = x^4 + 4x^2y^3 + 4y^6$ ($p = x^2$, $q = 2y^3$)

■ **Square of a difference**

$$(p - q)^2 = p^2 - 2pq + q^2$$

Check this formula by multiplying out $(p - q)(p - q)$.

Example 8

(a) $(x - \sqrt{3})^2 = x^2 - 2(x)(\sqrt{3}) + (\sqrt{3})^2$ $\qquad\qquad$ $(p = x, q = \sqrt{3})$

$\qquad\qquad = x^2 - 2\sqrt{3}x + 3$

(b) $(2x - 5y)^2 = (2x)^2 - 2(2x)(5y) + (5y)^2$ $\qquad$ $(p = 2x, q = 5y)$

$\qquad\qquad = 4x^2 - 20xy + 25y^2$

■ **Product of a sum and a difference**

$$(p + q)(p - q) = p^2 - q^2$$

Check this formula by multiplying

$$(p + q)(p - q) = p^2 + pq - pq - q^2 = p^2 - q^2$$

Example 9

(a) $(x + \sqrt{7})(x - \sqrt{7}) = x^2 - (\sqrt{7})^2$ $\qquad\qquad$ $(p = x, q = \sqrt{7})$

$\qquad\qquad = x^2 - 7$

(b) $(3x + 2y)(3x - 2y) = (3x)^2 - (2y)^2$ $\qquad\qquad$ $(p = 3x, q = 2y)$

$\qquad\qquad = 9x^2 - 4y^2$

(c) $(x^2 + y^3)(x^2 - y^3) = x^4 - y^6$

Division

To divide one term by another, divide the coefficients and the variables separately, and use the Properties of Exponents on the variables.

Example 10

(a) $\dfrac{8x^2y^5}{2xy^3} = \dfrac{8}{2} \cdot \dfrac{x^2}{x} \cdot \dfrac{y^5}{y^3} = 4xy^2$

(b) $\dfrac{2x^3y^8}{3x^4z^3} = \dfrac{2}{3} \cdot \dfrac{x^3}{x^4} \cdot \dfrac{y^8}{1} \cdot \dfrac{1}{z^3} = \dfrac{2y^8}{3xz^3}$ or $\dfrac{2}{3}x^{-1}y^8z^{-3}$

Both forms of the last answer are acceptable.

Division of expressions that contain more than one term will be explained in Chapter 4.

Review of basic ideas
Write out the instructions for finding the sum, difference, and product of algebraic expressions.

Write the formulas for the square of a sum, the square of a difference, and the product of a sum and difference.

The formula for the square of a sum may be put into words: The square of a sum of two terms is the square of the first term plus twice the product of the two terms plus the square of the second term. Write a similar sentence describing the other two formulas.

Exercises

Perform the indicated operations.

1. $(2x^2 + 3) + (-x^2 + x - 4)$
2. $(-x^3 + y) + (x^4 - y^2)$
3. $(2a + 4b - 3c) + (-a - 2b + c)$
4. $(u - v + w) + (2u + 3v - 4w)$
5. $(4x^2 - 3y + z) - (-x^2 + y - 2z)$
6. $(9y^2 + 2a) - (3y^2 + ay - 4)$
7. $(6p - 3q + r) - (-3p - 2q - 3r)$
8. $(2u - 5v) - (6v - 2u)$
9. $(\frac{1}{2}a - \frac{1}{3}b) - (\frac{1}{4}b + \frac{1}{3}a)$
10. $(\frac{3}{4}x^2y + \frac{2}{3}xy^2) - (xy^2 - x^2y)$
11. $(3x + 1)^2$
12. $(4a + b)^2$
13. $(\sqrt{7}u + 3v)^2$
14. $(9s + 6)^2$
15. $(3x - 1)^2$
16. $(4a - b)^2$
17. $(\sqrt{7}u - 3v)^2$
18. $(9s - 6)^2$
19. $(3x + 1)(3x - 1)$
20. $(4a + b)(4a - b)$
21. $(\sqrt{7}u + 3v)(\sqrt{7}u - 3v)$
22. $(9s + 6)(9s - 6)$
23. $(x + 1)^3$
24. $(u + v)^3$
    [Think of $(x + 1)^2(x + 1)$.]
25. $(2x - 3y)^3$
26. $(2x - 3)^3$
27. $(2x + 3)(x - 7)$
28. $(3x - 4)(2x + 5)$
29. $(\frac{1}{2}x + 5)(\frac{1}{2}x - 5)$
30. $(\frac{1}{3}u + \frac{1}{2})^2$

31. $(2x - y)(x^2 + 3xy - y^2)$
32. $(s - t)(5s^2 - 6st + t^2)$
33. $(x + 1)(x^2 - x + 1)$
34. $(x + 2)(x^2 - 2x + 4)$
35. $(3x - 4)(9x^2 + 12x + 16)$
36. $(a - 4c)(a^2 + 4ac + 16c^2)$
37. $(x + y - z)(2x - 3y + z)$
38. $(2x - 4y + 3z)(x + y + z)$
39. $(x^2 + xy - y^2)(2x^2 - 3xy + y^2)$
40. $(a^2 + b^2 + c^2)(a^2 - b^2 - c^2)$

41. $\dfrac{16x^3y^4}{8xy^5}$
42. $\dfrac{\sqrt{3}x^{-4}y^{-5}}{8x^4y^5}$

43. $\dfrac{3a^2b^{-3}c^4}{4a^{-3}b^2c}$
44. $\dfrac{14u^2v^7w^{-7}}{t^3}$

45. $\dfrac{(2r^2s^{-4}t^3)^2}{(3r^{-1}st^2)^3}$
46. $\dfrac{(\sqrt[3]{-3}x^2y^{-3})^3}{(\sqrt{8}x^{-1}z^4)^2}$

47. $\dfrac{(2x)^{-3}(3y)^{-2}}{x^{-4}y^{-5}}$
48. $\dfrac{(\sqrt{3}x)^2(\sqrt[3]{-5}y)^{-3}}{x^{-6}y^2}$

Find the value of each expression at the indicated replacements for *x*.*
49. $x^2 + 3x - 4$ at $x = 1$ and at $x = -4$
50. $x^2 - 2x - 7$ at $x = 1 + 2\sqrt{2}$ and at $x = 1 - 2\sqrt{2}$
51. $3x^2 + x - 1$ at $x = \frac{1}{6}(-1 + \sqrt{13})$ and at $x = \frac{1}{6}(-1 - \sqrt{13})$

1-3
Factoring

Factoring an expression means rewriting it as a product of expressions, each of which is called a **factor.** Factoring can simplify certain problems. Here is an illustration.

Find replacements for x that give the expression $x^2 + 6x + 5$ the value 0.

It could be rather difficult to solve this problem by simply trying out various replacements. It will be much easier if you notice that the expression can be factored as

$$x^2 + 6x + 5 = (x + 5)(x + 1)$$

You can check the factorization by multiplying the factors on the right-hand side. If the value of the original expression is to be 0, then this product must be 0; that is,

---

*If you work these exercises with a calculator, the answers to Exercises 50 and 51 will probably differ slightly from the answers you will get by hand. This is due to rounding-off errors made by the calculator. You may find it easier to work these exercises by hand.

$(x + 5)(x + 1) = 0$. Recall that if $ab = 0$, then $a = 0$ or $b = 0$ (see Multiplication by 0, in Section 1-1); therefore, $x + 5 = 0$ or $x + 1 = 0$. It follows that $x = -5$ or $x = -1$. Let us check these replacements: if $x = -5$, then $(-5)^2 + 6(-5) + 5 = 25 - 30 + 5 = 0$; and if $x = -1$, then $(-1)^2 + 6(-1) + 5 = 1 - 6 + 5 = 0$. Therefore,

$$x = -5 \text{ or } x = -1 \text{ are solutions of the problem.}$$

As you can see, factoring is a useful technique.

The expressions we shall factor in this section fall into various forms or patterns. Your skill in factoring will depend on your ability to recognize these patterns.

Common factors

The Distributive Property permits us to factor out **common factors.** For example, $2x^2$ is a common factor of $4x^3$ and $6x^2$, because $4x^3 = 2x^2 \cdot 2x$ and $6x^2 = 2x^2 \cdot 3$. Thus,

$$4x^3 + 6x^2 = 2x^2(2x + 3)$$

You can check your work (always a good idea) by multiplying out the factors on the right-hand side. Here are more examples of common factors. Check each one.

> **Example 1**
>
> (a) $3x^2 + 6x = 3x(x + 2)$
>
> (b) $9x^3y - 6x^2y^2 + 3xy^3 = 3xy(3x^2 - 2xy + y^2)$
>
> (c) $\frac{1}{2}t^5 - \frac{3}{4}t^3 + \frac{1}{6}t^2 = \frac{1}{2}t^2(t^3 - \frac{3}{2}t + \frac{1}{3})$
>
> (d) $(x + 2)(y + 4) - (x + 2)(y - 3) = (x + 2)[(y + 4) - (y - 3)]$
> $$= 7(x + 2)$$

Perfect squares

An expression is called a **perfect square** if it can be written as the square of another expression. For example, $x^2 + 6x + 9 = (x + 3)^2$; thus, $x^2 + 6x + 9$ is a perfect square. Notice that the first term is the square of x, the last term is the square of 3 and the middle term is twice the product of x and 3. Any expression that fits this pattern is a perfect square. In general,

$$p^2 + 2pq + q^2 = (p + q)^2$$

$$\text{and} \quad p^2 - 2pq + q^2 = (p - q)^2$$

You may recognize these as two of the special products discussed in Section 1-2. Check these factorizations and those in the examples below by multiplying out the factors to see whether they give back the original expressions.

Example 2
(a) $t^2 + 4t + 4$ is a perfect square because the first term is the square of t, the last term is the square of 2, and the middle term is twice the product of t and 2. So

$$t^2 + 4t + 4 = (t + 2)^2$$

(b) $4y^4 + 12y^2z^3 + 9z^6$ is a perfect square because the first term is the square of $2y^2$, the last term is the square of $3z^3$, and the middle term is twice the product of $2y^2$ and $3z^3$. So

$$4y^4 + 12y^2z^3 + 9z^6 = (2y^2 + 3z^3)^2$$

Example 3
(a) $u^2 - 8u + 16$ is a perfect square because the first term is the square of u, the last term is the square of -4, and the middle one is twice the product of u and -4. So

$$u^2 - 8u + 16 = (u - 4)^2$$

(b)   Multiply the factors to check that

$$s^2 - 2\sqrt{2}s + 2 = (s - \sqrt{2})^2$$

Difference of two squares
When the expression to be factored is the difference of two squares, simply write it as the product of the sum and the difference of their square roots. In symbols,

$$p^2 - q^2 = (p + q)(p - q)$$

This also is one of the special products discussed in Section 1-2. Check each factorization in Example 4 by multiplying the factors.

Example 4
(a)   To factor $x^2 - 4$, first rewrite it as the difference of two squares $x^2 - 2^2$. Then

$$x^2 - 4 = (x + 2)(x - 2)$$

(b)   Rewrite $4y^2 - \dfrac{1}{9}$ as $(2y)^2 - \left(\dfrac{1}{3}\right)^2$, so that

$$4y^2 - \frac{1}{9} = \left(2y + \frac{1}{3}\right)\left(2y - \frac{1}{3}\right)$$

(c)   Rewrite $s^4 - 16$ as $(s^2)^2 - 4^2$, and then

$$s^4 - 16 = (s^2 + 4)(s^2 - 4)$$
$$= (s^2 + 4)(s + 2)(s - 2)$$

General quadratics

An algebraic expression $ax^2 + bx + c$, in which x is a variable and a, b, and c are constants, is called a **quadratic.** Many of the expressions we have factored in this section are quadratic. The perfect squares $u^2 - 8u + 16$ and $s^2 - 2\sqrt{2}s + 2$ are quadratic. So are $3x^2 + 6x$ (the third constant is 0) and $x^2 - 4$ (the coefficient of the middle term is 0).

There are also many quadratics that cannot be factored by the methods we have used so far. In the following description of how some of them can be factored, let us assume that all constants are integers. We shall first deal separately with expressions in which the first coefficient is 1.

CASE I: $a = 1$.   We must find two integers m and n such that

$$x^2 + bx + c = (x + m)(x + n)$$

The product on the right is $x^2 + (m + n)x + mn$. Thus, if we can find m and n such that

$$m + n = b \quad \text{and} \quad mn = c$$

then $(x + m)(x + n)$ will equal $x^2 + bx + c$. Finding m and n is done strictly by trial and error. We guess two numbers and try them out.

Example 5

(a)   To factor $x^2 + 3x - 4$, look for integers m and n such that $m + n = 3$ and $mn = -4$. Take a guess. Because $mn = -4$, try $m = 2$ and $n = -2$. Does $m + n = 3$? No! Wrong guess, try again. How about $m = 4$ and $n = -1$? This works because $4 + (-1) = 3$ and $4 \cdot (-1) = -4$. Therefore,

$$x^2 + 3x - 4 = (x + 4)(x - 1)$$

Verify this by multiplying the factors.

(b)   Factor $x^2 - 8x + 12$. We search for m and n such that $m + n = -8$ and $mn = 12$. Take a guess. Because $mn = 12$, we could use the pairs 1, 12 or -1, -12 or 3, 4 or -3, -4 or 2, 6 or -2, -6. Because $m + n = -8$, we choose $m = -2$ and $n = -6$. Thus,

$$x^2 - 8x + 12 = (x - 2)(x - 6)$$

Verify this by multiplying out the right-hand side.

(c)   Sometimes there is no pair of integers that satisfies the requirements. To factor $x^2 + 2x + 7$, we would need two integers whose sum is 2 and whose product is 7. Because there is no such pair, we say that $x^2 + 2x + 7$ is *not factorable with integer coefficients.*

CASE II: $a \neq 1$.   Now we need four integers m, n, r, and s such that

$$ax^2 + bx + c = (rx + m)(sx + n)$$

The product on the right this time is $rsx^2 + (rn + sm)x + mn$, so m, n, r, and s must satisfy the equations

$$rs = a, \qquad rn + sm = b, \qquad \text{and} \quad mn = c$$

We must guess *four* numbers and try them out.

Example 6

(a)   To factor $3x^2 - 10x - 8$, we look for integers m, n, r, and s with

$$rs = 3, \qquad rn + sm = -10, \qquad \text{and} \quad mn = -8$$

Because $rs = 3$, try $r = 3$ and $s = 1$. Because $mn = -8$, let $m = 8$ and $n = -1$. Now check the middle term. Does $rn + sm = 3 \cdot (-1) + 1 \cdot 8 = -10$? No; try again. There is not much choice for r and s, because their product must be 3, so let's stick with $r = 3$ and $s = 1$. This time, try $m = 2$ and $n = -4$. Then $mn = -8$. Now check the middle term: does $rn + sm = 3 \cdot (-4) + 1 \cdot 2 = -10$? Yes; therefore,

$$3x^2 - 10x - 8 = (3x + 2)(x - 4)$$

Verify this by multiplying out the right-hand side.

(b)   Guess the four numbers needed to factor $6x^2 - 13x - 5$. Note that $rs = 6$ and $mn = -5$. Guess four numbers; then check to see whether the middle term $rn + sm = -13$. The answer is in the footnote* on page 28.

Sum and difference of cubes
If p and q are any algebraic expressions, then

$$p^3 + q^3 = (p + q)(p^2 - pq + q^2)$$

and

$$p^3 - q^3 = (p - q)(p^2 + pq + q^2)$$

Verify these formulas by multiplying out the right-hand side of each.

Example 7
(a) Think of $x^3 - 8$ as $x^3 - 2^3$; apply the second formula above, with $p = x$ and $q = 2$. Then

$$x^3 - 8 = (x - 2)(x^2 + 2x + 4)$$

(b) Think of $y^6 + 27x^3$ as $(y^2)^3 + (3x)^3$; here, $p = y^2$ and $q = 3x$. Apply the first formula above, to write

$$y^6 + 27x^3 = (y^2 + 3x)(y^4 - 3y^2x + 9x^2)$$

Review of basic ideas
Memorize these formulas for factoring perfect squares, the difference of squares, and the sum and the difference of cubes.

$$p^2 + 2pq + q^2 = (p + q)^2$$

$$p^2 - 2pq + q^2 = (p - q)^2$$

$$p^2 - q^2 = (p + q)(p - q)$$

$$p^3 + q^3 = (p + q)(p^2 - pq + q^2)$$

$$p^3 - q^3 = (p - q)(p^2 + pq + q^2)$$

To factor an expression of the form $ax^2 + bx + c$ (if it does not fit one of the special formulas), use the trial and error method. If $a = 1$, find two integers m and n with $m + n = b$ and $mn = c$. Then

$$x^2 + bx + c = (x + m)(x + n)$$

If $a \neq 1$, find four integers $m, n, r,$ and s with $rs = a, rn + sm = b,$ and $mn = c.$ Then

---

*6x^2 - 13x - 5 = (3x + 1)(2x - 5)$

$$ax^2 + bx + c = (rx + m)(sx + n)$$

If there are no such integers, we say that the expression is not factorable with integer coefficients.

Exercises

Factor the expressions in Exercises 1–51.

Common factors
1. $9x^2 + 3x$
2. $10y^3 - 5y^2$
3. $3t^4 - 9t^3 + 27t^2$
4. $6x^3 - 2x^2 + 10x$
5. $5x^3 - 10x^2 + x - 2$
6. $16t^6 - 8t^4 + 4t^2 - 2$

Perfect squares
7. $x^2 + 12x + 36$
8. $y^2 - 10y + 25$
9. $4x^2 + 12xy + 9y^2$
10. $4x^4 - 4x^2y + y^2$
11. $t^2 - 2\sqrt{3}t + 3$
12. $9s^2 + 6\sqrt{5}st + 5t^2$

Difference of squares
13. $x^2 - 25$
14. $4y^2 - 9t^2$
15. $(s - 3)^2 - 81$
16. $(x + 2)^2 - 121$
17. $\left(x + \dfrac{b}{2a}\right)^2 - \left(\dfrac{\sqrt{b^2 - 4ac}}{2a}\right)^2$
18. $9 - (u + 7)^2$

Sum and difference of cubes
19. $x^3 + 64$
20. $27t^6 - 8$
21. $u^9 - 125v^3$
22. $x^6 + 64y^3$
23. $(t + 1)^3 - 8$
24. $(u - 1)^3 + (v + 1)^3$

$x^2 + bx + c$ (find m and n)
25. $x^2 + 9x + 14$
26. $y^2 + 5zy - 24z^2$
27. $t^2 - t - 30$
28. $x^2 - 5x - 6$
29. $y^2 - 22zy + 57z^2$
30. $t^2 + 14t - 51$

$ax^2 + bx + c$ (find m, n, r, and s)
31. $3x^2 + x - 2$
32. $12x^2 + 7xy - 12y^2$
33. $8x^2 + 38x + 35$
34. $3x^2 + 32x + 20$
35. $-3x^2 + x + 2$
36. $-6x^2 + 14x - 4$

Mixed
37. $(x + 1)^2 - 9$
38. $x^2 - 16x + 64$
39. $x^2 - 16xy + 15y^2$
40. $t^6 - \frac{1}{9}$
41. $t^6 - \frac{1}{27}$
42. $t^6 - 64$
43. $5x^2 + 39x - 8$
44. $4y^2 + 12yz + 9z^2$
45. $s^2 - (t - 4)^2$
46. $u^2 + \frac{2}{3}u + \frac{1}{9}$
47. $x^2 - 8x + 15$
48. $t^3 + u^3$
49. $16x^4 - \frac{1}{16}$
50. $6x^2 + 29xy + 28y^2$
51. $9y^2 - 9y + 2$

☐   **Evaluation**

Factoring can be used to simplify complicated evaluations. For example, to evaluate $x^2 - 3x - 4$ at $x = 99$ directly, we would have to calculate the number $(99)^2 - 3(99) - 4$, a tedious chore. However, the calculation is much easier if the expression is factored first:

$$x^2 - 3x - 4 = (x + 1)(x - 4); \quad \text{therefore,}$$

$$(99)^2 - 3(99) - 4 = (99 + 1)(99 - 4)$$

$$= (100)(95)$$

$$= 9500$$

Use this method to evaluate the following expressions at the given values of the variable.

52. $x^2 + 7x + 12$ at $x = 96$

53. $9y^2 - 28y - 32$ at $y = 14$

54. $2t^2 + 17t + 21$ at $t = -1.5$

55. $64t^4 - 113t^2 + 49$ at $t = 7/8$

Solving equations

Factoring can be used to solve certain equations. For example, to solve $3x^2 - 10x - 8 = 0$, factor the left side to obtain

$$(3x + 2)(x - 4) = 0$$

The product of $3x + 2$ and $x - 4$ is zero only if one of them is zero. Thus,

$$3x + 2 = 0 \quad \text{or} \quad x - 4 = 0$$

$$\text{and} \quad x = -\frac{2}{3} \quad \text{or} \quad x = 4$$

Check these numbers as solutions by using them as replacements for x in the original equation

$$3\left(-\frac{2}{3}\right)^2 - 10\left(-\frac{2}{3}\right) - 8 = \frac{12}{9} + \frac{60}{9} - \frac{72}{9} = 0$$

$$\text{and} \quad 3(4)^2 - 10(4) - 8 = 48 - 40 - 8 = 0$$

Use this method to solve the following equations; check your answers.

56. $x^2 + 5x - 14 = 0$ **57.** $y^2 - 13y + 42 = 0$

58. $-2x^2 - x + 3 = 0$ **59.** $25u^2 - 9 = 0$

1-4
Rational Expressions

An algebraic expression that is the product of a real number and variables raised to nonnegative integer powers is called a **monomial.** The expressions $-2x^3$ and y^4z are monomials. The real number in the monomial y^4z is understood to be 1. Even constants can be thought of as monomials by considering the exponent of each variable to be 0. Thus, 5 is a monomial if we think of it as the product of 5 and x^0. A **polynomial** is a sum of monomials.

When an algebraic expression is written as one polynomial divided by another, it is called a **rational expression;** for example,

$$\frac{x^3}{x^2 + y^2}, \qquad \frac{x^2 + 3x - 4}{2x + 3}, \qquad \text{and} \qquad \frac{t^3 + 1}{t^2 - 4}$$

Such an expression is called rational because replacement of its variables by integers yields a rational number. Allowable replacements for the variables in a rational expression are any numbers (not just integers) for which the value of the denominator is not 0.

In the following description of operations with rational expressions, notice their similarity to operations with fractions.

Multiplication and division
To multiply two rational expressions, simply multiply their numerators and their denominators. To divide, invert the divisor and then multiply.

> ### *Example 1*
>
> (a) $\dfrac{x + 3}{2x - 4} \cdot \dfrac{x - 5}{x^2} = \dfrac{(x + 3)(x - 5)}{x^2(2x - 4)}$
>
> $\qquad\qquad\qquad = \dfrac{x^2 - 2x - 15}{2x^3 - 4x^2}$
>
> (b) $\dfrac{x + 3}{2x - 4} \div \dfrac{x - 5}{x^2} = \dfrac{x + 3}{2x - 4} \cdot \dfrac{x^2}{x - 5}$
>
> $\qquad\qquad\qquad = \dfrac{x^2(x + 3) \cdot}{(2x - 4)(x - 5)}$
>
> $\qquad\qquad\qquad = \dfrac{x^3 + 3x^2}{2x^2 - 14x + 20}$

Simplifying by cancellation

Simplifying a rational expression is like reducing a fraction to lowest terms: factor both numerator and denominator and then cancel common factors. Cancellation is easy to do properly if you understand the principles that justify it, namely,

(1)   The rule for multiplying fractions: $\dfrac{ac}{bc} = \dfrac{a}{b} \cdot \dfrac{c}{c}$.

(2)   Dividing any nonzero number by itself gives the answer 1.

(3)   Multiplying by 1 leaves a number unchanged.

Here is an illustration:

	Principle	*Example*
(1)	$\dfrac{ac}{bc} = \dfrac{a}{b} \cdot \dfrac{c}{c}$	$\dfrac{(x + 5)(x - 3)}{(x - 7)(x - 3)} = \dfrac{x + 5}{x - 7} \cdot \dfrac{x - 3}{x - 3}$
(2)	$\dfrac{c}{c} = 1$ if $c \neq 0$	$\dfrac{x - 3}{x - 3} = 1$ if $x \neq 3$
(3)	$\dfrac{a}{b} \cdot \dfrac{c}{c} = \dfrac{a}{b}$	$\dfrac{x + 5}{x - 7} \cdot \dfrac{x - 3}{x - 3} = \dfrac{x + 5}{x - 7}$

Therefore, we may cancel:

$$\frac{a\cancel{c}}{b\cancel{c}} = \frac{a}{b} \quad \text{if}\ c \neq 0, \quad \text{and} \quad \frac{(x + 5)(x \cancel{- 3})}{(x - 7)(x \cancel{- 3})} = \frac{x + 5}{x - 7} \quad \text{if}\ x \neq 3$$

Notice that the canceled expression was a common factor of the numerator and the denominator. You may cancel *only* factors.

Example 2

(a) $\dfrac{15x^2y^3}{9xy^2} = \dfrac{\cancel{3} \cdot 5 \cdot \cancel{x} \cdot x \cdot \cancel{y} \cdot \cancel{y} \cdot y}{\cancel{3} \cdot 3 \cdot \cancel{x} \cdot \cancel{y} \cdot \cancel{y}} = \dfrac{5xy}{3}$ *

---

*We should point out that the expressions $15x^2y^3/9xy^2$ and $5xy/3$ are not equal for all values of x and y. For example, when $x = 0$, the second expression has the value 0, but the first *isn't even defined.* The same is true for $y = 0$. However, the two expressions are equal for any other values of x and y. What is actually meant by writing

$$\frac{15x^2y^3}{9xy^2} = \frac{5xy}{3}$$

is that the "cross products" $(3)(15x^2y^3)$ and $(9xy^2)(5xy)$ are equal for all x and y.

(b) $\dfrac{x^2 + 7x + 10}{x^3 + x^2 - 2x} = \dfrac{(x + 5)(\cancel{x + 2})}{x(x - 1)(\cancel{x + 2})}$ (Factor; then cancel.)

$\qquad\qquad\qquad = \dfrac{x + 5}{x(x - 1)}$

The x in the numerator is not a factor, so it should not be canceled.

(c) $\dfrac{t^3 - 1}{2t^2 - t - 1} = \dfrac{(\cancel{t - 1})(t^2 + t + 1)}{(2t + 1)(\cancel{t - 1})}$ (Factor and cancel.)

$\qquad\qquad\quad = \dfrac{t^2 + t + 1}{2t + 1}$

Here is an application of simplifying by cancellation.

Example 3
Find the value of

$$\frac{x^2 - 2x - 3}{x^3 - 3x^2 + 2x} \cdot \frac{x^3 - x^2 - 2x}{x^2 + 2x + 1} \div \frac{x^2 + x - 12}{x + 4}$$

at $x = 6/5$.

Solution
To calculate this value by hand would be tedious; it would not be easy even with a calculator. Let us simplify the expression by factoring everything possible and canceling common factors. Remember to invert the last expression. Then

$$\frac{(\cancel{x - 3})(\cancel{x + 1})}{\cancel{x}(\cancel{x - 2})(x - 1)} \cdot \frac{\cancel{x}(\cancel{x - 2})(\cancel{x + 1})}{(\cancel{x + 1})(\cancel{x + 1})} \cdot \frac{(\cancel{x + 4})}{(\cancel{x + 4})(\cancel{x - 3})} = \frac{1}{x - 1}$$

Now replacing x by $6/5$ is simple:

$$\frac{1}{\dfrac{6}{5} - 1} = \frac{1}{\dfrac{1}{5}} = 5$$

The original expression has the value 5 at $x = 6/5$.

Addition and subtraction
The technique for adding or subtracting rational expressions is exactly the same as for fractions. To add or subtract, factor each denominator and find the least common

denominator. Then change each rational expression to an equivalent one with the common denominator, and add or subtract the new numerators.

Example 4

Add $\dfrac{3}{x^2 + 5x + 4} + \dfrac{2x - 1}{x^2 + 3x - 4}$

Solution
Factor the denominators:

$$x^2 + 5x + 4 = (x + 4)(x + 1) \quad \text{and} \quad x^2 + 3x - 4 = (x + 4)(x - 1)$$

The least common denominator is $(x + 4)(x + 1)(x - 1)$; it contains, *only once,* each factor that appears in the given denominators. Now change each rational expression to an equivalent one with this denominator:

$$\frac{3}{x^2 + 5x + 4} = \frac{3}{x^2 + 5x + 4} \cdot \frac{(x - 1)}{(x - 1)} = \frac{3(x - 1)}{(x + 4)(x + 1)(x - 1)}$$

$$\frac{2x - 1}{x^2 + 3x - 4} = \frac{2x - 1}{x^2 + 3x - 4} \cdot \frac{(x + 1)}{(x + 1)} = \frac{(2x - 1)(x + 1)}{(x + 4)(x - 1)(x + 1)}$$

Now add (LCD stands for the least common denominator):

$$\frac{3(x - 1)}{\text{LCD}} + \frac{(2x - 1)(x + 1)}{\text{LCD}} = \frac{(3x - 3) + (2x^2 + x - 1)}{\text{LCD}}$$

$$= \frac{2x^2 + 4x - 4}{\text{LCD}}$$

The final answer is

$$\frac{3}{x^2 + 5x + 4} + \frac{2x - 1}{x^2 + 3x - 4} = \frac{2x^2 + 4x - 4}{(x + 4)(x + 1)(x - 1)}$$

Usually, we shall not multiply out the denominator, because it is more useful in factored form if more computations are necessary.

Example 5

Simplify $\dfrac{3}{x^2 - 3x - 4} - \dfrac{x - 1}{x^2 - 8x + 16} - \dfrac{x}{x + 1}$

Solution
Factor the denominators and find the LCD.

$$(x^2 - 3x - 4) = (x - 4)(x + 1)$$

$$x^2 - 8x + 16 = (x - 4)^2$$

$$x + 1 \text{ cannot be factored}$$

$$\text{LCD} = (x - 4)^2(x + 1)$$

Notice that this LCD must contain $(x - 4)$ twice as a factor, because it appears twice in one of the given denominators. Now change each rational expression to an equivalent one with the LCD as the denominator:

$$\frac{3}{x^2 - 3x - 4} - \frac{x - 1}{x^2 - 8x + 16} - \frac{x}{x + 1}$$

$$= \frac{3(x - 4)}{\text{LCD}} - \frac{(x - 1)(x + 1)}{\text{LCD}} - \frac{x(x - 4)^2}{\text{LCD}}$$

$$= \frac{(3x - 12) - (x^2 - 1) - (x^3 - 8x^2 + 16x)}{\text{LCD}}$$

$$= \frac{3x - 12 - x^2 + 1 - x^3 + 8x^2 - 16x}{\text{LCD}}$$

$$= \frac{-x^3 + 7x^2 - 13x - 11}{(x - 4)^2(x + 1)}$$

Rationalizing
When the denominator of a rational expression contains a radical, computation is sometimes made easier if you rewrite the expression without a radical in the denominator. This is called **rationalizing the denominator.** Your knowledge of factoring will help you to do this.

Example 6
Rationalize the denominators of

(a) $\dfrac{3}{\sqrt{2}}$ and   (b) $\dfrac{2}{x - \sqrt{5}}$

Solution
(a)   Recall that $\sqrt{2} \cdot \sqrt{2} = 2$. Thus,

$$\frac{3}{\sqrt{2}} = \frac{3}{\sqrt{2}} \cdot \frac{\sqrt{2}}{\sqrt{2}} = \frac{3\sqrt{2}}{2}$$

The denominator no longer contains a radical.

(b) Recall that $(x - \sqrt{5})(x + \sqrt{5}) = x^2 - (\sqrt{5})^2 = x^2 - 5$. Therefore,

$$\frac{2}{x - \sqrt{5}} = \frac{2}{x - \sqrt{5}} \cdot \frac{x + \sqrt{5}}{x + \sqrt{5}} = \frac{2(x + \sqrt{5})}{x^2 - 5}$$

Sometimes you will need to rationalize the numerator.

Example 7

Rationalize the numerator of $\dfrac{\sqrt{3} - \sqrt{5}}{7}$.

Solution

$$\frac{\sqrt{3} - \sqrt{5}}{7} = \frac{\sqrt{3} - \sqrt{5}}{7} \cdot \frac{\sqrt{3} + \sqrt{5}}{\sqrt{3} + \sqrt{5}}$$

$$= \frac{(\sqrt{3})^2 - (\sqrt{5})^2}{7(\sqrt{3} + \sqrt{5})}$$

$$= \frac{-2}{7(\sqrt{3} + \sqrt{5})}$$

Exercises

Simplify the following rational expressions. State the allowable replacements before and after simplification.

1. $\dfrac{36x^2y}{12xy}$

2. $\dfrac{22x^3y^4z^2}{6x^3yz^7}$

3. $\dfrac{x^2 - 9}{x^2 + 5x - 24}$

4. $\dfrac{x^2 - 16}{x^2 - 10x - 56}$

5. $\dfrac{y^2 - 10y + 25}{y^2 - 5y}$

6. $\dfrac{3y^2 + 6y}{y^2 + 4y + 4}$

7. $\dfrac{2t^3 - 16}{t^2 + t - 6}$

8. $\dfrac{t^2 + t - 6}{t^3 + 27}$

Perform the indicated operations and simplify.

9. $\dfrac{x^2 - y^2}{x + y} \cdot \dfrac{3xy}{x - y}$

10. $\dfrac{x^2 - y^2}{x + y} \cdot \dfrac{x + y}{3xy}$

11. $\dfrac{x^2 + y^2}{x + y} \cdot \dfrac{3xy}{x + y}$

12. $\dfrac{x^2 - y^2}{x + y} \cdot \dfrac{3xy}{x + y}$

13. $\dfrac{3x^2 - 48}{x + 4} \div \dfrac{x}{x + 7}$

14. $\dfrac{x}{3x + 6} \div \dfrac{x}{9 + 3x}$

15. $\dfrac{5}{s + t} - \dfrac{3}{s - t}$

16. $\dfrac{8}{s + 2t} - \dfrac{9}{2s + t}$

17. $\dfrac{x}{x^2 + 8x + 16} - \dfrac{3x}{x^2 + 5x + 4}$

18. $\dfrac{2x}{x^2 - 13x + 12} - \dfrac{4x - 1}{x^2 - 24x + 144}$

19. $\dfrac{2y}{y^2 - y - 6} - \dfrac{y + 1}{y^2 + y - 2} - \dfrac{y - 1}{y^2 - 4y + 3}$

20. $\dfrac{t - 3}{2t^2 - 5t - 3} - \dfrac{t}{t^2 - 9} - \dfrac{1}{t + 3}$

21. $\left(\dfrac{1}{x} - \dfrac{1}{y}\right)\left(\dfrac{3}{x} - \dfrac{5}{y}\right)$

22. $\left(\dfrac{2}{x^2} - \dfrac{1}{x}\right)\left(\dfrac{3}{x} - \dfrac{1}{x^2}\right)$

23. $\left(x - \dfrac{1}{x}\right) \div \left(x + \dfrac{1}{x}\right)$

24. $\left(x^2 - \dfrac{1}{x}\right) \div \left(x - \dfrac{1}{x^2}\right)$

25. $\left(\dfrac{4}{3 + x} - \dfrac{5}{3 - x}\right) \div \left(\dfrac{8}{9 - x^2} - \dfrac{3}{x}\right)$

26. $\left(\dfrac{1}{x} + \dfrac{1}{y} + \dfrac{1}{z}\right) \div \left(\dfrac{1}{x} - \dfrac{1}{y} - \dfrac{1}{z}\right)$

Rationalize the denominators.

27. $\dfrac{5}{\sqrt{8}}$

28. $\dfrac{-3}{\sqrt{7}}$

29. $\dfrac{3x}{x + \sqrt{3}}$

30. $\dfrac{5x}{x + \sqrt{7}}$

31. $\dfrac{5}{\sqrt{3} + \sqrt{5}}$

32. $\dfrac{6}{\sqrt{10} - \sqrt{8}}$

Rationalize the numerators.

33. $\dfrac{5\sqrt{6} - 3\sqrt{5}}{2}$

34. $\dfrac{2\sqrt{x} + 3\sqrt{y}}{17}$

35. $\dfrac{\sqrt{x + h} - \sqrt{x}}{h}$

36. Find the value of the following expression at $x = -2.675$ (both with and without the use of a calculator).

$$\frac{x^2 - x - 6}{x^2 + 4x + 3} \cdot \frac{x^2 - x - 12}{x^2 - 7x + 12} \div \frac{x - 5}{2x^2 - 8x - 10}$$

■   From time to time you will be asked to try your hand at making up problems. You may be surprised to find that you can learn as much by making up exercises as you can by working them. It might be fun and also profitable to form a group with some of your classmates for exchanging problems that you have made up.

37.   Make up two problems similar to Exercise 36. Exchange them with someone in your group.

1-5
Radicals and Rational Exponents

Section 1-1 briefly described the notions of square roots and cube roots. A square root of x is a number whose square is x. Every positive real number has two square roots; negative numbers do not have square roots in the real number system. If x is positive, the symbol $\sqrt{x}$ denotes the positive, or principal, square root of x. The cube root of x is a number whose cube is x. Every real number has a unique cube root denoted by the symbol $\sqrt[3]{x}$. The symbols $\sqrt{}$ and $\sqrt[3]{}$ are called radicals.

It is easy to extend these notions to numbers larger than 3. For any positive integer n, let us say that an **nth root** of x is a number whose nth power is x. We must distinguish between n even and n odd. If n is even, every positive number has *two* nth roots—two square roots, two fourth roots, two sixth roots, and so on; negative numbers have *no* square roots, no fourth roots, and so on. When $x \geq 0$ and n is even, the expression $\sqrt[n]{x}$ will denote the nonnegative, or principal, nth root of x; the negative nth root will then be written $-\sqrt[n]{x}$.

If n is odd, every real number has a *unique* nth root—one cube root, one fifth root, one seventh root, and so on. When n is odd, $\sqrt[n]{x}$ will denote the unique nth root of x. Odd or even, the symbol $\sqrt[n]{}$ is called a radical.

■ n even: If $x \geq 0$, $\sqrt{x}$ or $\sqrt[n]{x}$ denotes the principal root.

  If $x < 0$, $\sqrt{x}$ and $\sqrt[n]{x}$ are not defined.

  n odd: If x is any real number, $\sqrt[n]{x}$ is the unique nth root of x.

Rational exponents

Exponents can simplify the writing of algebraic expressions, and their governing properties help to shorten computations. So far, we have used only integer exponents, but now we can extend the definition of exponents to include rational numbers. This extension will make exponents even more useful.

For $x \geq 0$, let us define $x^{\frac{1}{2}}$ to be the principal square root of x; that is, $x^{\frac{1}{2}} = \sqrt{x}$. This may seem peculiar to you, but it is actually very reasonable. For integer exponents m and n, we know that $(x^m)^n = x^{mn}$. If the same rule is to hold for rational exponents, then $(x^{\frac{1}{2}})^2 = x^{(\frac{1}{2})2} = x$. Thus, $x^{\frac{1}{2}}$ is a number whose square is x, so it must be a square root of x; we have chosen the principal square root. Similarly, $x^{\frac{1}{3}}$ must be the cube root of x because $(x^{\frac{1}{3}})^3 = x^{(\frac{1}{3})3} = x$. In general, if n is a positive integer, it is reasonable to define $x^{1/n}$ as the principal nth root of x. To complete the extension to all rational numbers, we can observe that $(m/n) = (1/n)m$ and then define $x^{m/n}$ as $(x^{1/n})^m$, which is the mth power of the nth root of x.

■   **Definition of $x^{m/n}$**

Suppose that $x \geq 0$, m and n are integers, and $n > 0$. Then

(a) $x^{1/n} = \sqrt[n]{x}$

(b) $x^{m/n} = (\sqrt[n]{x})^m = \sqrt[n]{x^m}$

Notice that this definition applies only when the base x is nonnegative. We must make this restriction on the definition of *fractional* exponents so that $x^{1/n} = \sqrt[n]{x}$ will make sense when n is even.*

Statement (b) follows from the equality $(x^{1/n})^m = (x^m)^{1/n}$. It says that the mth power of the nth root equals the nth root of the mth power.

Example 1

(a) $8^{\frac{2}{3}} = (8^{\frac{1}{3}})^2 = 2^2 = 4$

(b) $16^{\frac{3}{4}} = (16^{\frac{1}{4}})^3 = 2^3 = 8$

(c) $16^{\frac{-3}{4}} = \dfrac{1}{16^{\frac{3}{4}}} = \dfrac{1}{8}$

---

*Calculators with a power key y^x (or x^y) will not accept a negative number as a base. For example, enter -2 and try to cube it using the power key; the display will probably flash an error signal.

Example 2
Compute $\sqrt[5]{(32)^4}$.

Solution
This difficult computation can be simplified by writing $\sqrt[5]{(32)^4} = (\sqrt[5]{32})^4 = 2^4 = 16$.

Rational exponents, as we have defined them, have all the properties of integer exponents. These properties allow us to perform certain simplifying operations. For example, $\sqrt{50} = \sqrt{25 \cdot 2} = 5\sqrt{2}$; the justification for this is Property of Exponents (b):

$$\sqrt{xy} = (xy)^{\frac{1}{2}} = x^{\frac{1}{2}}y^{\frac{1}{2}} = \sqrt{x}\sqrt{y}$$

The examples below illustrate other ways of simplifying expressions by using rational exponents.

Example 3

(a) $\sqrt[3]{5}\,\sqrt{5} = (5^{\frac{1}{3}})(5^{\frac{1}{2}}) = 5^{\frac{1}{3}+\frac{1}{2}} = 5^{\frac{5}{6}} = \sqrt[6]{5^5} = \sqrt[6]{3125}$

(b) $\sqrt[6]{4} = 4^{\frac{1}{6}} = (4^{\frac{1}{2}})^{\frac{1}{3}} = \sqrt[3]{2}$

(c) $\sqrt[5]{\sqrt{x^3}} = (x^{\frac{3}{2}})^{\frac{1}{5}} = x^{\frac{3}{10}} = \sqrt[10]{x^3}$ [or $(\sqrt[10]{x})^3$]

(d) $\sqrt[8]{x^2} = x^{\frac{2}{8}} = x^{\frac{1}{4}} = \sqrt[4]{x}$

(e) $\sqrt{x^7} = x^{\frac{7}{2}} = x^{3+\frac{1}{2}} = x^3 x^{\frac{1}{2}} = x^3 \sqrt{x}$

(f) $\dfrac{\sqrt{y}\,\sqrt[3]{y^2}}{\sqrt[6]{y^5}} = y^{(\frac{1}{2}+\frac{2}{3}-\frac{5}{6})} = y^{\frac{2}{6}} = \sqrt[3]{y}$

Example 4
Simplify and convert to radical notation.

(a) $t^{\frac{1}{2}}t^{\frac{3}{5}} = t^{\frac{1}{2}+\frac{3}{5}} = t^{\frac{11}{10}} = \sqrt[10]{t^{11}}$

(b) $y^{\frac{5}{2}} = y^{2+\frac{1}{2}} = y^2 \sqrt{y}$

(c) $(s^{\frac{1}{4}})^{\frac{3}{2}} = s^{\frac{3}{8}} = \sqrt[8]{s^3}$

(d) $(x^2 y^3)^{\frac{1}{2}} = (x^2)^{\frac{1}{2}}(y^3)^{\frac{1}{2}} = xy\sqrt{y}$

Rational exponents can also be used to rationalize denominators.

Example 5

(a) $\dfrac{6}{\sqrt[3]{3}} = \dfrac{6}{3^{\frac{1}{3}}} \cdot \dfrac{3^{\frac{2}{3}}}{3^{\frac{2}{3}}} = \dfrac{6 \cdot 3^{\frac{2}{3}}}{3^{\frac{1}{3}+\frac{2}{3}}} = \dfrac{6\sqrt[3]{9}}{3} = 2\sqrt[3]{9}$

(b) $\dfrac{x}{\sqrt[5]{(x+1)^2}} = \dfrac{x}{(x+1)^{\frac{2}{5}}} \cdot \dfrac{(x+1)^{\frac{3}{5}}}{(x+1)^{\frac{3}{5}}} = \dfrac{x\sqrt[5]{(x+1)^3}}{x+1}$

Exercises

Compute the values of the following expressions without using a calculator.

1. $8^{-\frac{2}{3}}$ 2. $64^{\frac{5}{6}}$ 3. $4^{\frac{3}{2}}$ 4. $1^{\frac{1}{8}}$

5. $\sqrt[4]{81^3}$ 6. $\sqrt[5]{32^4}$ 7. $\sqrt[6]{27^2}$ 8. $\sqrt[10]{16^5}$

Find approximate values of the following. Use a calculator for $\sqrt{\ }$ and $\sqrt[3]{\ }$.

9. $\left(\dfrac{2}{3}\right)^{\frac{2}{3}}$ 10. $\left(\dfrac{3}{4}\right)^{\frac{-1}{3}}$ 11. $8^{\frac{1}{6}}$ 12. $27^{\frac{-1}{6}}$

Convert the radicals to rational exponents and simplify.

13. $\sqrt[4]{7}\sqrt[3]{7}$ 14. $\sqrt[10]{x^5}$ 15. $\sqrt[5]{\sqrt[4]{x^{10}}}$ 16. $\sqrt[4]{\sqrt[3]{x^5}}$

17. $\sqrt[6]{\sqrt[3]{x^{36}}}$ 18. $\sqrt[3]{x^9}$ 19. $\sqrt{50x^5}$ 20. $\sqrt[3]{54x^4}$

21. $\dfrac{\sqrt[3]{x}\sqrt[4]{x}}{\sqrt[5]{x}}$ 22. $\dfrac{\sqrt{x+1}\sqrt[4]{(x+1)^2}}{\sqrt[3]{x+1}}$

Simplify the expressions and rewrite them in radical form.

23. $x^{\frac{1}{4}}x^{\frac{3}{5}}$ 24. $(2y)^{\frac{1}{2}}(2y)^{\frac{1}{3}}$ 25. $t^{\frac{7}{3}}$

26. $(s^{\frac{2}{5}})^{\frac{1}{2}}$ 27. $(x^3y^4)^{\frac{1}{2}}$ 28. $(st)^{\frac{2}{3}}$

Decide whether the following equalities are true or false. (Rational exponents will help.)

29. $\sqrt{x}\sqrt{y} = \sqrt{xy}$ 30. $\sqrt{x}/\sqrt{y} = \sqrt{x/y}$

31. $\sqrt{x}\sqrt[3]{y} = \sqrt[5]{xy}$ 32. $\sqrt{x}\sqrt[3]{x} = \sqrt[5]{x}$

33. $\sqrt{x}\sqrt[3]{x} = \sqrt[6]{x^5}$ 34. $\sqrt[3]{x} = \sqrt[6]{x^2}$

35. $\sqrt{x} + \sqrt{y} = \sqrt{x+y}$ 36. $\sqrt{x}/\sqrt[3]{y} = \sqrt[6]{x/y}$

37. $\sqrt{x}\sqrt[3]{y} = \sqrt[6]{(xy)^5}$

Guess the value of x and check your answer. For example, $2^x = 1/8$; guess $x = -3$; does $2^{-3} = 1/8$? Yes.

38. $2^x = 8$ 39. $3^x = 1/9$ 40. $3^x = 81$

41. $16^x = 1/2$ 42. $4^x = 2$ 43. $(2/3)^x = 3/2$

44. $(2/3)^x = 1$ 45. $(1/9)^x = 1/3$ 46. $(1/4)^x = 2$

Rationalize the denominators.

47. $\dfrac{5}{\sqrt[6]{x^5}}$ 48. $\dfrac{3}{1 + \sqrt{5}}$ 49. $\dfrac{2x}{\sqrt[5]{(x + 1)^2}}$

50. $\dfrac{x + 1}{\sqrt[7]{x - 3}}$ 51. $\dfrac{-2}{\sqrt[3]{x} - \sqrt[3]{4}}$ 52. $\dfrac{h}{\sqrt[3]{x + h} - \sqrt[3]{x}}$.

1-6
Equations and Word Problems

Solving equations is one of the most useful applications of the methods and concepts you have learned so far. In this section, you will solve equations that contain polynomials, for example,

$$2x - 3 = 1, \qquad (t + 1)^2 - 2t = t^2 + 1, \qquad \text{and} \quad 3x + 2y = 6$$

The first is an equation in the variable x, the second is an equation in the variable t, and the third is an equation in the variables x and y.

When the variables are replaced by real numbers, the equations may yield true statements, or they may not. Consider the equation $2x - 3 = 1$. If x is replaced by 1, the result is a false statement, $2(1) - 3 = 1$; if x is replaced by 2, the result is a true statement, $2(2) - 3 = 1$. Any replacement that results in a true statement is called a **solution** or **root** of the equation. A solution of an equation with two variables, such as $3x + 2y = 6$, will be an ordered pair of numbers; the first is a replacement for x, the second for y. For example, the pair $(2, 0)$ is a solution, because $3(2) + 2(0) = 6$ is a true statement. On the other hand, $(1, 4)$ is not a solution, because $3(1) + 2(4) = 6$ is false. We shall explore solutions of this type in more detail in the next chapter.

To **solve** an equation means to find all possible solutions. If all allowable replacements for the variables are solutions, the equation is called an **identity.** The equation $(t + 1)^2 - 2t = t^2 + 1$ is an identity. To see that this is so, simplify the left-hand side:

$$(t + 1)^2 - 2t = t^2 + 2t + 1 - 2t = t^2 + 1$$

Because this is exactly the same as the right-hand side, every replacement of t is a solution. If the result of even one allowable replacement is a false statement, the equation is called **conditional.** For the present, we shall be concerned with solving only conditional equations.

There are three simple principles that can be used to solve a surprisingly large number of equations. Notice their similarity to the Replacement and Cancellation properties of real numbers, and to the properties of multiplication by 0.

■   Let p, q, and r represent algebraic expressions all with the same domain (see Section 1-2). Then

I. The equations $p = q$ and $p + r = q + r$ have all the same solutions. That is, you may add (or subtract) the same thing to (or from) both sides of an equation.

II. If no allowable replacements give r the value zero, then the equations $p = q$ and $pr = qr$ have all the same solutions. That is, you may multiply or divide both sides of an equation by the same nonzero expression.

III. If the number a is a solution of the equation $pq = 0$, then it is also a solution of either $p = 0$ or $q = 0$. Conversely, if a is a solution of either $p = 0$ or $q = 0$, it is also a solution of $pq = 0$.

The object is to use these principles to reduce the given equation to a simpler equation with the same solutions. This process is continued until all the solutions have been found. In the following examples, the Roman numerals in the justification of each step refer to the three principles above. Some of the examples use set notation to indicate the solutions; others do not. You may use either method.

Example 1
Solve the following equation.

$$2x + 4 = 5x + 1$$

$$2x = 5x + 1 - 4 \qquad \text{(I: subtract 4)}$$

$$2x - 5x = 1 - 4 \qquad \text{(I: subtract } 5x\text{)}$$

$$-3x = -3 \qquad \text{(Combine like terms.)}$$

$$x = 1 \qquad \text{(II: divide by } -3\text{)}$$

$$\text{Solution set} = \{1\}$$

Check in the original equation:

$$2(1) + 4 = 6 \text{ (left side)} \quad \text{and} \quad 5(1) + 1 = 6 \text{ (right side)}$$

Example 2

Solve $4(3t - 1) - 5 = 6 - 3(t + 12)$.

$$12t - 9 = -3t - 30 \qquad \text{(Multiply out; simplify.)}$$

$$15t = -21 \qquad \text{(I: add } 3t \text{ and } 9.)$$

$$\text{Solution:} \quad t = -\frac{21}{15} = -\frac{7}{5} \qquad \text{(II: divide by 15.)}$$

Check in the original equation:

$$\text{(left side)} \quad 4\left[3\left(-\frac{7}{5}\right) - 1\right] - 5 = 4\left(-\frac{26}{5}\right) - 5 = -\frac{129}{5}$$

$$\text{(right side)} \quad 6 - 3\left(-\frac{7}{5} + 12\right) = 6 - 3\left(\frac{53}{5}\right) = -\frac{129}{5}$$

Example 3

Solve $\dfrac{x}{2} + \dfrac{1}{3} = \dfrac{3x}{4} - \dfrac{2}{3}$.

It is usually best to "clear fractions" by multiplying both sides of the equation by the least common denominator. CAUTION: Be sure to multiply *each* term on *both* sides of the equation by the LCD.

$$\frac{x}{2} + \frac{1}{3} = \frac{3x}{4} - \frac{2}{3}$$

$$6x + 4 = 9x - 8 \qquad \begin{array}{l}\text{(II: Multiply by 12} \\ \text{to clear fractions.)}\end{array}$$

$$-3x = -12 \qquad \text{(I: Subtract } 9x \text{ and } 4.)$$

$$\text{Solution:} \quad x = 4 \qquad \text{(II: Divide by } -3.)$$

Check the solution: $\quad \dfrac{4}{2} + \dfrac{1}{3} = \dfrac{7}{3} \quad$ and $\quad \dfrac{3(4)}{4} - \dfrac{2}{3} = \dfrac{7}{3}$

Example 4

Solve $(2x + 3)(x - 4) = 0$.

$$2x + 3 = 0 \quad \text{or} \quad x - 4 = 0 \qquad \text{(III)}$$

$$x = -3/2 \quad \text{or} \quad x = 4$$

$$\text{Solution set} = \{-3/2, 4\}$$

Check each solution: $\left[2\left(-\dfrac{3}{2}\right)+3\right]\left(-\dfrac{3}{2}-4\right)=0\cdot\left(-\dfrac{11}{2}\right)=0$

$$(2\cdot4-3)(4-4)=5\cdot0=0$$

Example 5
Solve (a) $x^2-4x=5$ and (b) $2x^2-3=5x$. Use principle I to rewrite each equation with only 0 on the right. Then factor the left side and use principle III as in Example 4.

(a) $\qquad\qquad\qquad\qquad x^2-4x=5$

$\qquad\qquad\qquad x^2-4x-5=0$ $\qquad\qquad\qquad$ (I: Subtract 5.)

$\qquad\qquad\quad (x-5)(x+1)=0$ $\qquad\qquad\qquad$ (Factor.)

$\qquad\qquad$ Solution: $x=5$ or $x=-1$ $\qquad\qquad$ (III)

Check each solution: $(5)^2-4(5)=25-20=5$
$\qquad\qquad\qquad\qquad\qquad (-1)^2-4(-1)=1-(-4)=5$

(b) $\qquad\qquad\qquad\qquad 2x^2-3=5x$

$\qquad\qquad\qquad 2x^2-5x-3=0$ $\qquad\qquad\qquad$ (I: Subtract 5x.)

$\qquad\qquad\quad (2x+1)(x-3)=0$ $\qquad\qquad\qquad$ (Factor.)

$\qquad\qquad\quad x=-1/2$ or $x=3$ $\qquad\qquad\qquad$ (III)

$\qquad\qquad$ Solution set $=\{-1/2,3\}$ $\qquad\qquad\qquad$ (Check.)

In the next chapter, you will encounter equations in two variables, and you will sometimes have to solve for one variable in terms of the other. For example, you may be asked to solve the equation $3x+2y=6$ for y in terms of x. This means to treat x as though it were a constant, and then solve in the usual manner for y.

Example 6
(a)   Solve $3x+2y=6$ for y in terms of x.

$\qquad\qquad\qquad\qquad 3x+2y=6$

$\qquad\qquad\qquad\qquad 2y=6-3x$ $\qquad\qquad\qquad$ (I: Subtract 3x.)

$\qquad\qquad$ Solution: $y=3-\dfrac{3}{2}x$ $\qquad\qquad\qquad$ (II: Divide by 2.)

(b)   Solve $3v - u^2 + 4 = 0$ for v in terms of u.

$$3v - u^2 + 4 = 0$$

$$3v = u^2 - 4 \qquad\qquad \text{(I: add } u^2 - 4.\text{)}$$

Solution: $v = \dfrac{1}{3}u^2 - \dfrac{4}{3}$ $\qquad\qquad$ (II: divide by 3.)

Word problems
Every problem covered so far has been subject to systematic analysis. There were steps to follow, properties to use, or principles to apply. This is not the case with word problems. They represent applications of mathematics to real-life situations and, therefore, are as diverse as experience or imagination can make them. Nevertheless, the examples below do contain hints about how to approach various kinds of word problems. Although textbook problems are contrived and, consequently, some may seem silly and far removed from reality, they are good training for solving real problems.

Example 7
(Numbers) The product of two consecutive integers is 240. Find the integers.

Solution
(1)   *Translate the English into mathematical form.* KEY WORDS: Integer, consecutive, product, 240. ANALYSIS: If x is an integer, then $x + 1$ is the next integer. Thus, x and $x + 1$ is *Mathematics* for "two consecutive integers." Now translate:

$$\underbrace{\text{Their product}}_{x(x + 1)} \quad \overset{\displaystyle \text{is}}{=} \quad \overset{\displaystyle 240}{240}$$

The solutions of this equation will indicate the solutions of the problem.
(2)   *Solve the equation.*

$$x(x + 1) = 240$$

$$x^2 + x - 240 = 0$$

$$(x + 16)(x - 15) = 0$$

$$x = -16 \quad \text{or} \quad x = 15$$

Check
For $x = -16$, the numbers -16 and -15 are consecutive integers whose product is 240. Similarly for $x = 15$.
(3)   *Answer:* -16 and -15 *or* 15 and 16.

Example 8
(Percentage) Ten gallons of acid are added to 25 gallons of water. What percentage of the solution is acid?

Solution
(1)   *Translate the English into mathematical form.* KEY WORDS: 10, added, 25. ANALYSIS: There are 35 gallons of solution and 10 of them are acid. Therefore, the question is:

$$\underline{\text{What percentage}} \quad \text{of} \quad 35 \quad \text{is} \quad 10?$$
$$\quad\quad\uparrow \quad\quad\quad\quad \uparrow \quad \uparrow \quad \uparrow \quad \uparrow$$
$$\quad\quad x \quad\quad\quad\quad\quad\quad \cdot \quad 35 \quad = \quad 10$$

(2)   *Solve the equation.*

$$35x = 10$$
$$x = 10/35 \quad \text{(about .29)}$$

(3)   *Answer:* 29%.

Example 9
(Mixture) A 12-quart car radiator is full of a mixture that is 60% antifreeze. How much liquid should be drained and replaced with pure antifreeze to change the mixture in the radiator to 90% antifreeze?

Solution
(1)   *Translate English to mathematical form.* KEY WORDS: 12, 60%, drain mixture, add pure antifreeze, 90%. ANALYSIS: The number of quarts drained equals the number of quarts of pure antifreeze added; let x represent that number. Then $12 - x$ quarts of mixture are left after draining, and 60% of $12 - x$, or $.60(12 - x)$, is the number of quarts of antifreeze left after draining. Therefore, $.60(12 - x) + x$ is the number of quarts of antifreeze in the radiator after refilling it with pure antifreeze. This is to be 90% of 12 quarts, or $.90(12) = 10.8$ quarts. Therefore,

$$.60(12 - x) + x = 10.8$$

(2)   *Simplify this equation and solve it.*

$$7.2 + .4x = 10.8$$

$$x = 9$$

(3)   *Answer:* 9 quarts should be drained.

Example 10

(Area) A picture 9 inches wide and 12 inches high is put into a frame of uniform width. The picture and frame together have an area of 154 square inches. How wide is the frame?

Solution

(1)   *Translate into mathematical form.* In geometric problems *always* draw a diagram (see Figure 1-2). KEY WORDS: 9×12, uniform width, 154. ANALYSIS: Call the width of the frame x inches. According to the diagram, the outside dimensions of the frame are $9 + 2x$ and $12 + 2x$. It follows that

$$(9 + 2x)(12 + 2x) = 154$$

(2)   *Solve the equation.* Rewrite the equation with 0 on the right-hand side; then simplify and solve:

$$(9 + 2x)(12 + 2x) - 154 = 0$$

$$108 + 42x + 4x^2 - 154 = 0$$

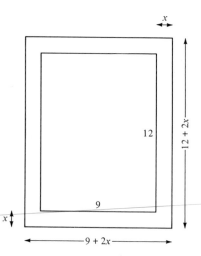

Figure 1-2
The picture and its frame in Example 10.

$$4x^2 + 42x - 46 = 0$$

$$(2x + 23)(2x - 2) = 0$$

The solution set is $\left\{ -\dfrac{23}{2}, 1 \right\}$, but only a positive number makes sense in this problem.

(3)   *Answer:* The frame is 1 inch wide.

Example 11

(Rate · Time = Distance) Airline schedules between San Francisco and Chicago are based on the assumption that the prevailing westerly winds will blow at a constant rate. The flight east, with a tailwind, takes $3\frac{1}{2}$ hours; the flight west, with a headwind, takes 4 hours. The jets have an air speed of 550 miles per hour. What is the speed of the wind?

Solution

(1)   *Translate.* KEY WORDS: tailwind, $3\frac{1}{2}$, headwind, 4, 550. ANALYSIS: Let w be the speed of the wind. Going east, the wind helps. The ground speed is $550 + w$, and the time in flight is $3\frac{1}{2}$ hours. Because distance = rate · time, $3.5(550 + w)$ is the distance traveled east. Going west, the wind hinders; it follows that the distance traveled is $4(550 - w)$. But, clearly, the distances are the same—going east or west. Therefore,

$$3.5(550 + w) = 4(550 - w)$$

Verify that $w = 36\frac{2}{3}$ miles per hour.

Exercises

Solve the following equations. Check each solution in the original equation.

1. $3x + 4 = -11$

2. $5x - 7 = 3$

3. $4y - 6 = -6y - 11$

4. $y + 22 = 8y - 15$

5. $4(x + 3) - 5 = -7(2x - 1)$

6. $-2(x - 1) + 4 = 6 - 3x$

7. $3(2t + 1) + 4 = 2 - (t + 3)$

8. $2(3 - 4) = 5 - (3t - 2)$

9. $6.5x + 3.9 = -2.6x - 4.1$

10. $2.1 - 3.6x = 2.8x + 3.2$

11. $\dfrac{u}{6} + \dfrac{2}{3} = u - 1$

12. $-\dfrac{1}{4} + \dfrac{u}{3} = -\dfrac{1}{2} - \dfrac{u}{4}$

13. $\frac{1}{2}(x + 1) = \frac{2}{3} - \frac{1}{4}(x - 3)$

14. $\frac{3}{4}(x - 3) = \frac{1}{3} - 2x$

15. $\dfrac{v - 3}{4} - \dfrac{1}{3} = \dfrac{1}{6} - \dfrac{2v + 1}{3}$

16. $\dfrac{3v + 4}{-2} - 1 = 5 - \dfrac{2v + 3}{3}$

17. $(2x - 1)(x + 4) = 0$ **18.** $(3x - 4)(x + 6) = 0$

19. $(x - \sqrt{2})(x + \sqrt{3}) = 0$ **20.** $(2x + \sqrt{5})(x - \frac{1}{2}) = 0$

21. $y^2 + 5y + 6 = 0$ **22.** $y^2 - 8y + 12 = 0$

23. $x^2 - 18 = 7x$ **24.** $x^2 + 20 = 9x$

Solve the following equations for y in terms of x.

25. $3y - 4x + 7 = 0$ **26.** $5x - 2y = -1$

27. $2(x + y) - 5 = 6y$ **28.** $\frac{1}{2}(x - 3y) = x - 1$

29. The sum of four consecutive integers is 90. Find the integers.

30. The sum of four consecutive *even* integers is 76. Find the integers. [HINT: An even integer may be written as $2x$.]

31. The product of two consecutive *odd* integers is 483. Find the integers.

32. If a 7% raise in yearly salary amounts to $500, what was the original salary?

33. If a solution is 22% acid, how much acid is there in 15 gallons of solution?

34. How many liters of water must be added to 5 liters of a 25% alkaline solution to make it a 15% solution?

35. One solution is 25% acid, and another is 40% acid. How much of each should be mixed to make 10 gallons of a 35% solution?

36. How many pounds of cashews that sell for $3.00 a pound should be mixed with 20 pounds of pecans that sell for $1.50 a pound to obtain a mixture that will sell for $2.50 a pound?

37. A plane makes a 3000-mile trip in 5 hours, but takes 6 hours to return. If the speed of the wind is constant, what is it? What is the speed of the plane in still air?

38. A motorist has driven 300 miles. If he had driven 10 miles per hour faster, he could have saved one hour. What was his average speed?

39. Find the dimensions of a rectangle whose perimeter is 36 inches and whose area is 56 square inches.

40. If an object is thrown straight up with a speed of 160 feet per second, after t seconds its height h (in feet) is $h = -16t^2 + 160t$. How long will it take for the object to hit the ground?

41. A border of uniform width is added to a rectangular lot whose dimensions are 20 feet and 40 feet. This addition triples the area of the lot. What is the width of the border?

42. Make up an equation whose solution set is $\{-1/2\}$. Make up one whose solution set is $\{0, 3\}$. Make up one with solution set $\{4, -1\}$.

43. Make up (and solve) a word problem of each type: number, percentage, mixture, area, and rate · time = distance.

Chapter 2

Functions

Functions and their graphs are the instruments by which mathematics is applied to the physical, social, and business sciences. Roughly speaking, a function sets up a relationship between two changing quantities, and the graph is a picture of that relationship. The graph can be used to obtain geometric information about the function. These ideas are described in Sections 2-1 through 2-4.

The last section in this chapter introduces the notion of the average rate of change, which is crucial in many applications of mathematics to real-life situations.

As you study this chapter and work the exercises, here are a couple of things to keep in mind: (1) Learn the definitions, terms, and notations used to describe functions and graphs. (2) Master the techniques of evaluating functions and sketching simple graphs.

2-1
Functions

Given two sets X and Y, a function on X to Y is a rule or correspondence that assigns a unique element of Y to each element of X. The sets X and Y may be any sets whatsoever.

For example, let X be the set of students in a math class who have just taken a midterm exam, and let $Y = \{A, B, C, D, F\}$. The rule by which the teacher assigns each student a letter grade is a function on X to Y. This example illustrates three important facts about functions:

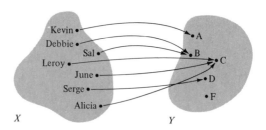

Figure 2-1
A picture of a function on X to Y, where X is the set of students in a math class and Y is the set of grades they can get on an exam.

(1) Each student is assigned only one grade; that is, each element of X is assigned one and only one element of Y.

(2) However, the same grade may be assigned to many different students; that is, the *same* element of Y may be assigned to many *different* elements of X.

(3) It may be that no one has failed the exam; that is, it is not necessary for every element of Y to be assigned to some element of X.

In this book, we shall be concerned with more practical applications of the function concept. For example, suppose an experiment is performed to observe how the number of bacteria in a culture changes with time. No food is added to the culture, and no waste products are removed. The experiment lasts 12 hours, and at the end of each hour, the bacteria are counted. Let X be the set of whole numbers from 1 to 12, and let Y be the set of all positive integers. The correspondence that assigns to each hour the number of bacteria present at that time is a function on X to Y. Again, notice that each element of X is assigned one and only one element of Y; the same element of Y may be assigned to many elements of X (for instance, if there is no growth for several hours); and not every element of Y need be assigned.

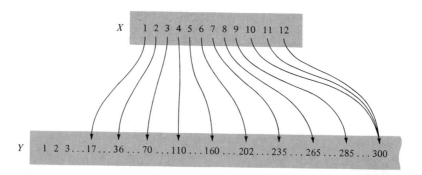

Figure 2-2
At the end of each hour, the bacteria are counted. The set X is the number of hours elapsed at each count. Y is the set of all whole numbers. Notice that the bacteria have stopped multiplying after the tenth hour.

■   **Definition**
Let X and Y be sets. A **function** on X to Y is a rule or correspondence which assigns to each element of X one and only one element of Y. The set X is called the **domain** of the function.

For the present, we shall consider only functions for which the sets X and Y are subsets of the real number system, which is denoted by $\mathbb{R}$. Such functions assign real numbers to real numbers.

Functions are often denoted by the letters f, g, h, F, and G. Let f be a function. If x is any number in its domain, then there is one and only one number that is assigned to x by the rule f. This number is denoted by $f(x)$, read "f of x," and is called the **value of f at x.** The set of *all* values of f is called the **range** of f.

■   The expression $f: X \rightarrow Y$ is read "the function f on X to Y". This means that f is a function, X is its domain, and Y contains its range. That is, for each x in X, $f(x)$ is an element of Y.

Each of the following examples introduces some property of functions. It is important that you remember the terms and use of symbols introduced here; they will be used throughout this book.

Example 1
The simplest of all functions is a **constant function:** it assigns the same number to all elements of its domain. For instance, if $f: \mathbb{R} \rightarrow \mathbb{R}$ is the constant function 5, then $f(x) = 5$ for *every* x in $\mathbb{R}$. Thus $f(3) = 5, f(-\sqrt{2}) = 5$, and $f(-1) = 5$. This shows that *a function may take the same value at many different elements in its domain.*

The range of f is the set $\{5\}$, which contains only one element.

Example 2
Let $f: \mathbb{R} \rightarrow \mathbb{R}$ be the rule that assigns each number to itself. In symbols, $f(x) = x$. This is called the **identity function.** Its values at various numbers are $f(3) = 3, f(-\sqrt{2}) = -\sqrt{2}, f(2 + t) = 2 + t$, and $f(y^2 + 3y) = y^2 + 3y$.

It does not matter whether the elements in a function's domain are written as specific real numbers (3 or $-\sqrt{2}$, for example) or as algebraic expressions ($2 + t$ or $y^2 + 3y$, for example). The important thing is the definition of the function: *the identity assigns each number to itself.* Even if a number is represented as $2 + t$, it is still true that $f(2 + t) = 2 + t$.

Furthermore, the letter f has no particular significance. The rule could have been called $G: \mathbb{R} \rightarrow \mathbb{R}$, with $G(x) = x$. Then $G(3) = 3, G(-\sqrt{2}) =$

$-\sqrt{2}$, $G(2 + t) = 2 + t$, and so on. Thus, it is the *rule* that counts, not the letter used to denote it, and not the letters used to represent elements of its domain. The range of the identity function is all of $\mathbb{R}$.

When you evaluate functions at numbers such as $x + h$ or $1/y^2$, which do not look like "ordinary" numbers, it may help to think this way: Let $f(x) = 3x - 1$. Then f of any number equals 3 times that number, minus 1. In symbols, $f(\ ) = 3(\ ) - 1$, and you are allowed to fill the parentheses with anything that makes sense, *provided the same thing appears in each pair of parentheses*. If $g(t) = t^2 + 2t + 1$, then g of any number is that number squared, plus 2 times that number, plus 1. In symbols, $g(\ ) = (\ )^2 + 2(\ ) + 1$; you are allowed to fill in the parentheses with anything that makes sense, *provided the same thing appears in each pair of parentheses*.

Example 3

Let $f(u) = u^2 + 5$. Find (a) $f(-2)$, (b) $f(1/x)$, (c) $f(\sqrt{u^2 + 1})$, (d) $f(x + h)$, and (e) $f(f(x))$.

Solution

Think of $f(\ ) = (\ )^2 + 5$ and boldly fill in the parentheses with the indicated expressions.

(a) $f(-2) = (-2)^2 + 5 = 9$

(b) $f(1/x) = (1/x)^2 + 5 = \dfrac{1}{x^2} + 5$

(c) $f(\sqrt{u^2 + 1}) = (\sqrt{u^2 + 1})^2 + 5 = u^2 + 6$

(d) $f(x + h) = (x + h)^2 + 5 = x^2 + 2xh + h^2 + 5$

(e) $f(f(x)) = (f(x))^2 + 5$

$\qquad\qquad = (x^2 + 5)^2 + 5 \qquad\qquad$ [Because $f(x) = x^2 + 5$.]

$\qquad\qquad = x^4 + 10x^2 + 30$

The range of this function f is the set of all real numbers that are greater than or equal to 5. This set can be represented in set notation as $\{t | t \geq 5\}$.

Example 4

It is standard practice to define functions by means of an equation whenever possible. If we say, "Consider the function $y = x^2 + 3x - 7$," we mean that there is a function, say F, defined by the rule $F(x) = x^2 + 3x - 7$. The equation tells us that $y = F(x)$; that is, y is *the value of F at x.* The letter x, which represents any element of the domain, is called the **independent variable.** The letter y, because it represents the value assigned to x by the function, is called the **dependent variable.** We say, in this case, that y *is a function of x.* The value of y at the number $x = 2$ is $y = F(2) = 2^2 + 3 \cdot 2 - 7 = 3$, its value at -1 is $y = F(-1) = (-1)^2 + 3(-1) - 7 = -9$, and its value at $2 + t$ is

$$y = F(2 + t) = (2 + t)^2 + 3(2 + t) - 7$$
$$= (4 + 4t + t^2) + (6 + 3t) - 7$$
$$= t^2 + 7t + 3$$

Notice that

$$y = x^2 + 3x - 7$$

$$u = v^2 + 3v - 7$$

$$F(t) = t^2 + 3t - 7$$

$$h(a) = a^2 + 3a - 7$$

all define the *same* function on $\mathbb{R}$ to $\mathbb{R}$; each assigns the number ( ) to the number ( )^2 + 3( ) − 7. THE PARTICULAR LETTERS USED HAVE NO SPECIAL MEANING. It is the sequence of instructions, "square the number, add three times the number, subtract seven," that determines the function.

In these examples the independent variables are represented by the letters $x, v, t,$ and a. In the first example, y is a function of x; in the second, u is a function of v; the last two examples do not specify a letter for the dependent variable.

The discussion in this example leads to the following definition.

■ **Definition**
Two functions f and g are **equal,** written $f = g$, if and only if they have the same domain X, and $f(x) = g(x)$ for *every* x in X.

Example 5
When a function is defined by an equation, the domain is understood to be the set of all allowable replacements of the independent variable. For example, if $w = \sqrt{s}$ is used to define w as a function of s, then the independent variable

cannot be negative. In this case, it is *automatically assumed* that $s \geq 0$. Again, if a function is defined as

$$z = \frac{t + 1}{t^2 - 1}$$

then the domain is assumed to exclude $t = 1$ and $t = -1$, because in those cases the denominator is 0.

■   If the domain of a function is not specified, it is automatically taken to be the set of allowable replacements of the independent variable.

Sometimes, functions are defined in "pieces." Extra care must be taken in evaluating such functions.

Example 6
Let

$$f(x) = \begin{cases} 3x - 7 & \text{if} \quad x \leq -1 \\ 0 & \text{if} \quad -1 < x < 2 \\ x + 2 & \text{if} \quad x \geq 2 \end{cases}$$

and find (a) $f(-3)$, (b) $f(1/2)$, and (c) $f(x^2 + 2)$.

Solution
Here the real line has been divided into three pieces, and f is defined differently on each one. To evaluate f at a number x, first determine which piece x belongs to, and use that particular part of the definition of f.
(a)   Because $-3 \leq -1$, use the first part of the definition:

$$f(-3) = 3(-3) - 7 = -16$$

(b)   For $f(\frac{1}{2})$, notice that $-1 < \frac{1}{2} < 2$, and use the second part of the definition. Here f is the constant 0, so $f(\frac{1}{2}) = 0$.
(c)   For $f(x^2 + 2)$, notice that $x^2 + 2 \geq 2$ for every x. Thus, the third part of the definition must be used, and $f(x^2 + 2) = (x^2 + 2) + 2 = x^2 + 4$.

Example 7
One function that is defined in pieces is so important that it is given a special name and a special symbol. It is called the **absolute value function** and is

denoted by $|\ \ |$; the expression $|x|$ is read "the absolute value of x." The definition of this function is

$$|x| = \begin{cases} x & \text{if } x \geq 0 \\ -x & \text{if } x < 0 \end{cases}$$

Evaluate $|3|$, $|-3|$, $|-x|$, and $|x^2|$.

Solution
Just as in Example 6, you must determine which part of the definition to use. Because $3 > 0$ and $-3 < 0$, the definition gives

$$|3| = 3 \quad \text{and} \quad |-3| = -(-3) = 3$$

What about $|-x|$? Your first impulse might be to write $|-x| = x$, but this could be wrong! For example, suppose that $x = -3$. Then $-x = 3$, and $|-x| = 3 = -x$. The best we can say is that $|-x| = x$ if x is positive or zero, and $|-x| = -x$ if x is negative.
    The last problem, however, is different: because $x^2 \geq 0$ for every x, we know that $|x^2| = x^2$.

Exercises

Evaluate the functions at the indicated numbers.
  1. $G: \mathbb{R} \rightarrow \mathbb{R}$ is the constant function -6; evaluate G at 6, -6, and $u + h$.
  2. $F: \mathbb{R} \rightarrow \mathbb{R}$ is the constant function $\sqrt{2}$; evaluate F at -1, x, and $x^2 + 1$.
  3. $f: \mathbb{R} \rightarrow \mathbb{R}$ is the absolute value function $|\ \ |$; evaluate f at -4, 4, and u^2.
  4. $g: \mathbb{R} \rightarrow \mathbb{R}$ is the absolute value function $|\ \ |$; evaluate g at $-\sqrt{2}$, $\sqrt{2}$, and $x^2 + 1$.

  5. $h(u) = 5u - 2$; find $h(-1)$, $h(1/5)$, $h\left(\dfrac{y+1}{10}\right)$, and $h(h(u))$.

  6. $f(x) = 3x - 7$; find $f(4)$, $f(\frac{1}{2})$, $f(y + \frac{7}{3})$, and $f(f(x))$.
  7. $g(t) = 4t + 2$; find $g(-2)$, $g(-\frac{1}{2})$, $g(t + h)$, and $g(g(t))$.
  8. Let $y = x^2 - 3x - 2$ define y as a function of x. Evaluate y when x equals -3, 3, 2, and $t + k$.
  9. Let $v = -u^2 + 4u + 3$ define v as a function of u. Evaluate v when u equals -1, 4, $\sqrt{3}$, and $z + 1$.
  10. Let $h(z) = 1/z$; find $h(1)$, $h(-3)$, $h(\frac{1}{2})$, and $h(h(x))$.
  11. Let $k(a) = 1/a$; find $k(-4)$, $k(-1/3)$, $k(t + h)$, and $k(k(b))$.

12.   Let $f(x) = 1/(x - 3)$; find $f(4)$, $f(\frac{1}{2})$, and $f(f(x))$.
13.   Let $g(t) = \sqrt{t + 1}$; find $g(8)$, $g(5/4)$, $g(-1)$, and $g(t^4 - 1)$.
14.   Let $h(u) = \sqrt{u^2 + 2}$; find $h(2)$, $h(0)$, and $h(t + 1)$.
15.   Let $s = t^3 - t^2 + t + 1$ define s as a function of t. Evaluate s when t equals 2, -2, and $1/u$.

Equations 16–25 define y as a function of x. For each equation, describe the domain of the function (refer to Example 5).

16. $y = x^2 + 2x - 17$ 17. $y = 3x^3 - 2x + 12$
18. $y = \sqrt{1 + x^2}$ 19. $y = \sqrt{3 + 2x^2}$
20. $y = \sqrt[3]{1 + x}$ 21. $y = \sqrt{1 + x}$
22. $y = \sqrt{1 - x^2}$ 23. $y = \sqrt{x^2 - 1}$

24. $y = \dfrac{x}{1 - x}$ 25. $y = \dfrac{x^2}{2 - x^2}$

26.   Sometimes it is easier to evaluate a function if factoring is performed first. For example, let us evaluate $y = x^2 + 4x + 4$ at $x = 98$.

STRAIGHTFORWARD METHOD: $y = (98)^2 + 4(98) + 4$

$$= 9604 + 392 + 4$$

$$= 10{,}000$$

FACTOR METHOD: $y = x^2 + 4x + 4 = (x + 2)^2$

$$= (98 + 2)^2$$

$$= (100)^2 = 10{,}000$$

Evaluate each of the following functions at the indicated number, first by the straightforward method and then by the factor method.
   (a) $y = x^2 - 2x + 1$; $x = 31$
   (b) $u = v^2 + 6v + 9$; $v = 5x - 3$
   (c) $s = t^2 - 1$; $t = 9{,}999$

27.   (Powers and exponentials) The functions $f(x) = x^2$, $g(t) = t^3$, and $h(u) = u^{2/3}$ are **power functions**: the exponents are fixed and the base is the variable. The functions $F(x) = 2^x$, $G(t) = 3^t$ and $H(u) = (2/3)^u$ are **exponential functions**: here the base is fixed and the exponent is the variable. These two types of functions are quite distinct. Evaluate and compare $f(5)$ and $F(5)$, $g(-4)$ and $G(-4)$, and $h(8)$ and $H(8)$.

28.   (Continuation of Exercise 27) Let f be the power function $f(x) = x^2$ and let F be the exponential function $F(x) = 2^x$. Now $f(100) = (100)^2 = 10{,}000$. Show that $F(100) = 2^{100}$ is a number greater than a 1 followed by 30 zeros! [HINT: $2^{10} > 10^3$.]

Exercises 29–31 concern inverses. These exercises are optional, and may be omitted without loss of continuity. Optional exercises in later sections will continue to explore the notion of inverse, which will be explained in detail in Chapter 5.

29. The equation $6y - x = 12$ defines y as a function of x (solve for y):

$$y = \frac{1}{6}x + 2 \tag{1}$$

It also defines x as a function of y (solve for x):

$$x = 6y - 12 \tag{2}$$

(a)   Let $x = 24$ and evaluate y in Equation (1). Now, use *that* value for y and evaluate x in Equation (2).

(b)   Let $x = t - 12$ and evaluate y in Equation (1). Now, use *that* value for y and evaluate x in Equation (2).

(c)   Look over the results in parts (a) and (b). Do you notice any similarity? If you do, suggest a general rule that you think may be true whenever an equation with two variables defines each variable as a function of the other. Can you prove your rule?

30. Let $f(x) = 2x - 3$ and $g(t) = t^2 + 4$. Find $f(g(-2))$. [HINT: First find $g(-2) = (-2)^2 + 4 = 8$ and then find $f(8)$.] Now do the same with

(a) $g(f(3))$ (b) $f(g(1))$ (c) $g(f(x))$ (d) $g(g(t))$ (e) $f(g(u + 1))$

31. (Combination of Exercises 29 and 30) Let $f(x) = 2x - 3$. If we set $y = f(x) = 2x - 3$ and solve for x, then $x = \frac{1}{2}y + \frac{3}{2}$. So let $g(y) = \frac{1}{2}y + \frac{3}{2}$. Evaluate

(a) $f(g(-3))$ (b) $g(f(14))$ (c) $f(g(0))$ (d) $g(f(-2))$

Now verify that for any x and y, we have $g(f(x)) = x$ and $f(g(y)) = y$. [Evaluate g at $f(x)$ and f at $g(y)$.]

Two functions related in this way are said to be **inverses** of each other.

Exercises 32–35 are referred to in Section 2-2.

32. Notice that $\sqrt{3^2} = |3|$ and $\sqrt{(-4)^2} = |-4|$. Show that $\sqrt{x^2} = |x|$ for all real numbers x. [HINT: First take $x \geq 0$, then take $x < 0$.]

33. Use the hint of Exercise 32 to show that $|x|^2 = x^2$ for all real numbers x.

34. ($|x| =$ the distance from x to 0) Use a ruler to draw a line. Label one point 0; choose a unit distance by labeling another point 1. Then carefully mark off the numbers -3, -2, $-1/2$, $3/4$, 2, and 3. Verify by actual measurement that the absolute value of each number equals its distance from 0.

35. ($|a - b| =$ the distance between a and b) Using the same line you drew for Exercise 34, verify by actual measurement that $|a - b|$ is the distance between a and

b, if a and b are replaced by any two of the numbers you have marked on the line.

In Section 2-2 we shall *define* the distance between real numbers a and b to be $|a - b|$.

■   36.   Make up a function and evaluate it at $x + h$.

37.   Make up a function whose domain is all of $\mathbb{R}$ except for the numbers -2 and 2.

38.   Make up a function whose domain is $\{x \mid -2 \leq x \leq 2\}$.

39.   (Inverses) Make up a pair of functions that are inverses of each other. (See Exercise 31.)

40.   Make up a function that is hard to evaluate at $x = 97$ by the straightforward method, but easy to evaluate after factoring (see Exercise 26).

2-2
The Cartesian Plane

Like the real numbers, functions have both geometric and algebraic properties. We can visualize these properties together, combining algebra and geometry, by using one of the outstanding inventions of the seventeenth century. It is called the **coordinate plane,** or the **Cartesian plane,** in honor of René Descartes (1596–1650).

Imagine two straight lines, one horizontal and the other vertical, dividing the plane into four **quadrants.** These are called the first, second, third, and fourth quadrants, sometimes labeled I, II, III, and IV as in Figure 2-3. The lines are called **axes,** and their point of intersection is called the **origin.** Each of the axes is considered to be a real number line, with the origin as the 0 point of each line; the positive direction is to the right on the horizontal axis and upward on the vertical axis. The axes are sometimes called the **coordinate axes;** they are labeled with letters x and y, or s and t, or any other pair of letters, depending on what variables are being used in any particular problem. Although which letters are used has no particular significance, the *order* in which they appear is important: the label for the horizontal axis always comes first. For example, Figure 2-3 shows an xy-plane and Figure 2-4 shows a uv-plane.

Look at the xy-plane in Figure 2-3. Each point P in the plane can be assigned a unique ordered pair of real numbers in the following way. Draw two straight lines through P, each parallel to one of the axes. The line parallel to the y-axis intersects the x-axis, say at the number a; the line parallel to the x-axis intersects the y-axis, say at the number b. Then P is assigned the ordered pair of real numbers (a, b). These numbers are called the **coordinates** of P: a is the **x-coordinate** and b is the **y-coordinate.** Notice that the x-coordinate always comes first; the order is important.

Conversely, *each ordered pair of real numbers (a, b) can be assigned a unique point P in the Cartesian plane.* Mark the number a on the x-axis and the number b

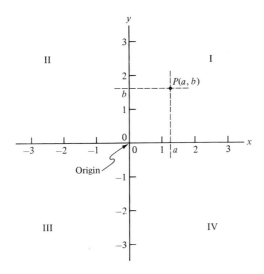

Figure 2-3
The Cartesian plane.

on the *y*-axis (again, the order is significant); through these numbers draw lines parallel to the axes. The point where these lines intersect is the point *P* corresponding to the ordered pair (a, b).

The preceding two paragraphs taken together establish a **one-to-one correspondence** between the points of a coordinate plane and the ordered pairs of real numbers: each point corresponds to exactly one ordered pair, and each ordered pair corresponds to exactly one point in the plane.

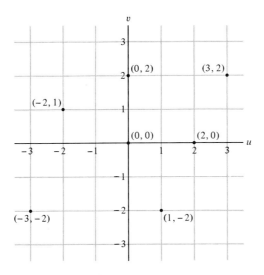

Figure 2-4
Plotting points in a Cartesian place.

"The point (a, b)" or "the point $P(a, b)$" means the point in the plane with coordinates (a, b). To **plot** a point (a, b) means to indicate the location of that point in the plane. In Figure 2-4 several points have been plotted. The usual practice is to make a dot and write its coordinates nearby. The origin has coordinates $(0, 0)$. Notice the difference that the order makes; for example, look at the points $(-2, 1)$ and $(1, -2)$.

A more exciting task than plotting random points is to plot points in the solution set of an equation or an inequality.

Example 1
Plot several points in the solution set of the equation $3x + 2y = 6$.

Solution
Section 1-6 briefly mentioned that any solution of this equation is an ordered pair of numbers (a, b). The first number is a replacement for x; the second, a replacement for y. For example, the pair $(2, 0)$ is a solution because $3 \cdot 2 + 2 \cdot 0 = 6$ is a true statement. The pair $(4, -3)$ is also a solution because $3 \cdot 4 + 2(-3) = 6$ is true. On the other hand, the point, $(-1, 2)$ is not a solution because $3(-1) + 2 \cdot 2 = 6$ is false. One way to find solutions is to make a **table of values,** like the one shown below. The first column of numbers represents the

x	2	4	1	0	$-\frac{1}{2}$
y	0	-3	$\frac{3}{2}$	3	$\frac{15}{4}$

ordered pair $(2, 0)$; the second column, the pair $(4, -3)$. Now let $x = 1$, and solve the resulting equation $3 \cdot 1 + 2y = 6$ for y; $y = \frac{3}{2}$. Thus, the pair $(1, \frac{3}{2})$ is a solution, and it appears in the third column of the table. In fact, *for any value of x, we can solve the equation for y to obtain a solution pair.* You should check to see that the last two columns in our table are solution pairs: when $x = 0, y = 3$; and when $x = -\frac{1}{2}, y = \frac{15}{4}$.

Now plot the points that correspond to the pairs in the table as in Figure 2-5. They all seem to lie on one straight line. In Chapter 3 we shall prove that the solution set is *exactly* that line; that is, all points on the line are solutions, and all points *not* on the line are *not* solutions. Notice, for example, that $(-1, 2)$ is not on the line.

It is usually impossible to draw an entire solution set. For instance, the solution set of $3x + 2y = 6$ is actually an entire line extending infinitely far in both directions. The best we can hope to do is to show a portion of the solution set. It should be a portion large enough to indicate what the rest of the set looks like.

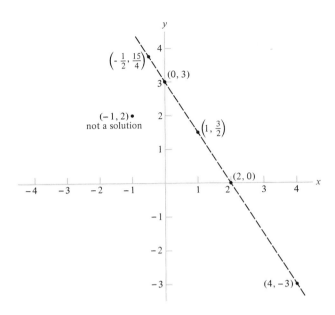

Figure 2-5
Points in the solution set of $3x + 2y = 6$ all lie on one straight line. See Example 1.

Example 2
In the xy-plane, indicate the set of all points (x, y) with

(a) $x = -2$ (b) $y = 3$ (c) $1 \leq x < 2$

Solution
(a)   In this case, the second coordinate is not specified, so it may be any number. Thus, $(-2, -1)$, $(-2, 5)$, and, in general, $(-2, y)$ all satisfy the condition that $x = -2$. Several such points are plotted in Figure 2-6A. They

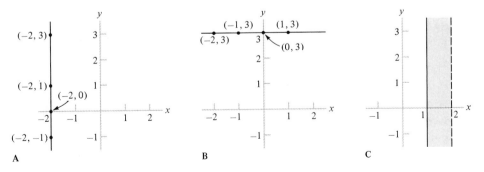

Figure 2-6
(A) The set of all points (x, y) with $x = -2$. (B) The set of all points (x, y) with $y = 3$.
(C) The set of all points (x, y) with $1 \leq x < 2$. See Example 2.

indicate that the solution set is the vertical line through the point $(-2, 0)$.
(b)   This case is similar to part (a), but now the first coordinate is not specified.
The points $(-2, 3)$, $(0, 3)$, $(1, 3)$ all satisfy the condition that $y = 3$. The points
in Figure 2-6B indicate a horizontal line through the point $(0, 3)$.
(c)   Now the first coordinate may vary between 1 and 2, whereas the second
coordinate may be any number. This solution set is not a line but rather a
vertical strip (see Figure 2-6C). The line $x = 2$ is broken to indicate that the
points on it are not included in the solution set (because $x < 2$).

We shall sometimes use set notation to indicate solution sets in the plane. For
example, $\{(x, y)|3x + 2y = 6\}$ is read "the set of all ordered pairs (x, y) such that
$3x + 2y = 6$." This   is   the   line   indicated   in   Figure   2-5.   The   expression
$\{(x, y)|x = -2\}$ is read "the set of all pairs (x, y) such that $x = -2$" and is the
vertical line in Figure 2-6A.

Example 3
Plot $\{(x, y)|y = 2x - 1\}$.

Solution
Make a table of values. Choose several different values for x, for example,
the numbers $-1, 0, 1$, and 2. Then compute the corresponding values of
$y = 2x - 1$. On a sheet of paper draw a coordinate plane and carefully plot
these points; they should all lie on one straight line. That line is the set
$\{(x, y)|y = 2x - 1\}$.

x	-1	0	1	2
y	-3	-1	1	3

Distance
The preceding discussion showed how algebraic equations and inequalities can be
interpreted geometrically. This interaction between algebra and geometry can also
work in the reverse direction. You will now see that the geometric notion of distance
can be thought of in algebraic terms.

If P_1 and P_2 are points in a plane, we denote the distance between them by the
symbol $d(P_1, P_2)$. The distance between two points does not depend on which point
you start from, so $d(P_1, P_2) = d(P_2, P_1)$.

First, let us define the distance between two points x_1 and x_2 on the real line as
$|x_2 - x_1|$. Because $|x_1 - x_2| = |x_2 - x_1|$, it is immaterial which point is taken first.
This definition will seem reasonable if you worked Exercise 35 in Section 2-1. Now
plot two points in the plane $P_1(x_1, y_1)$ and $P_2(x_2, y_1)$, with the same y-coordinate so

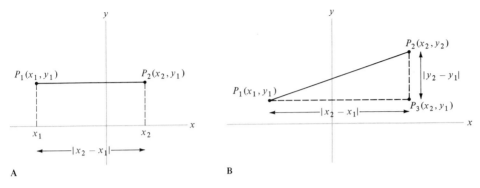

Figure 2-7
(A) The distance between two points that lie on a horizontal line is $d(P_1, P_2) = |x_2 - x_1|$.
(B) The distance between any two points in the xy-plane is

$$d(P_1, P_2) = \sqrt{(x_2 - x_1)^2 + (y_2 - y_1)^2}$$

the points lie on the horizontal line through $(0, y_1)$. As Figure 2-7A shows, $d(P_1, P_2) = |x_2 - x_1|$, the absolute value of the difference of the x-coordinates. In a similar way, you can show that the distance between points on a *vertical* line is the absolute value of the difference of their y-coordinates.

Now let $P_1(x_1, y_1)$ and $P_2(x_2, y_2)$ be any two points in the plane. Plot them. Draw a vertical line through P_2, and a horizontal line through P_1. These lines intersect at $P_3(x_2, y_1)$ (see Figure 2-7B). A right triangle is formed, with the line from P_1 to P_2 as the hypotenuse. The lengths of the sides are $|x_2 - x_1|$ and $|y_2 - y_1|$; the length of the hypotenuse is $d(P_1, P_2)$. Thus, by the Theorem of Pythagoras,

$$[d(P_1, P_2)]^2 = |x_2 - x_1|^2 + |y_2 - y_1|^2$$
$$= (x_2 - x_1)^2 + (y_2 - y_1)^2$$

The last line follows from the result of Exercise 33 in Section 2-1. Now take the square root of both sides of the equation. Because $d(P_1, P_2)$, being a length, is nonnegative,

$$\sqrt{[d(P_1, P_2)]^2} = d(P_1, P_2)$$

and we get the following result:

■ **Distance Formula**
   If $P_1(x_1, y_1)$ and $P_2(x_2, y_2)$ are any two points in the plane, then

$$d(P_1, P_2) = \sqrt{(x_2 - x_1)^2 + (y_2 - y_1)^2}$$

Although the argument used the particular triangle in Figure 2-7B, this result is valid for any two points.

Example 4

Find the distance between the points $P_1(-1, -3)$ and $P_2(4, 0)$.

Solution

Here, $x_1 = -1$, $y_1 = -3$, $x_2 = 4$, and $y_2 = 0$. Thus,

$$d(P_1, P_2) = \sqrt{(x_2 - x_1)^2 + (y_2 - y_1)^2}$$
$$= \sqrt{(4 + 1)^2 + (0 + 3)^2}$$
$$= \sqrt{34}$$

Let us also compute $d(P_2, P_1)$ to see that it makes no difference which point is chosen first:

$$d(P_2, P_1) = \sqrt{(x_1 - x_2)^2 + (y_1 - y_2)^2}$$
$$= \sqrt{(-1 - 4)^2 + (-3 - 0)^2}$$
$$= \sqrt{34}$$

Exercises

1.   Plot the following points: $(-3, 2)$, $(2, -3)$, $(-2, 3)$, $(3, 2)$, $(1, 0)$, and $(0, 1)$.

2.   Consider the equation $2u - v - 4 = 0$. Four of the eight pairs $(1, 0)$, $(2, 0)$, $(0, -4)$, $(3, 1)$, $(1/2, -3)$, $(0, 4)$, $(-2, 0)$, and $(3, 2)$ are solutions. The others are not. Test each pair, and plot the four solutions in the uv-plane. They should all lie on a straight line.

3.   Find four solutions to the equation $s + t - 2 = 0$ and plot them in the ts-plane. Are they collinear (lying on the same line)?

4.   Find four solutions of $3x - 2y + 1 = 0$ and plot them in the xy-plane. Are they collinear?

5.   Consider the equation $x^2 - y + 1 = 0$. Five of the eight pairs $(0, 1)$, $(-1, 1)$, $(1, 2)$, $(0, -1)$, $(-1, 2)$, $(2, 3)$, $(2, 5)$, and $(-2, 5)$ are solutions. The others are not. Test each pair and plot the five solutions in the xy-plane. They should not be collinear. Connect these points with a smooth curve. Such a curve is called a **parabola.**

6.   Follow the instructions in Exercise 5 for the equation $y = -2x^2 + 1$ and the pairs $(0, -1)$, $(1, -1)$, $(0, 1)$, $(-1, -1)$, $(2, 9)$, $(2, -7)$, $(-3, 19)$, and $(-2, -7)$.

Draw a uv-plane and show the following sets (as in Example 2).

7.	$u = 3$	8.	$u = -3$	9.	$|v| = 2$
10.	$v = 1$	11.	$u = 0$	12.	$v = 0$
13.	$|u| \le 1$	14.	$u \ge -2$	15.	$v > -1$

16. $|v| < 2$ 17. $1 < u \le 2$ 18. $-1 \le u < 2$
19. $-1 \le v < 0$ 20. $2 < v < 3$

Show the following sets in the xy-plane (as in Example 3).
21. $\{(x, y)|y = x\}$ 22. $\{(x, y)|y = -x\}$
23. $\{(x, y)|xy = 0\}$ 24. $\{(x, y)|xy \le 0\}$

Find the distance between each pair of points.
25. $(-3, 1)$ and $(4, 0)$ 26. $(4, -1)$ and $(0, 0)$
27. $(2, 5)$ and $(-1, -1)$ 28. $(0, 0)$ and $(-3, 4)$
29. $(1.7, 2.8)$ and $(-3.6, 4.1)$ 30. $(-1.03, 6.20)$ and $(0.07, -1.82)$

31.   A square plot of ground is located on a map on which coordinate axes have been drawn. The units are miles. Opposite vertices of the plot are at $(1, 1)$ and $(3, 3)$. How many square miles are in the plot? (Draw a picture.)

32.   Follow the instructions in Exercise 31, but suppose the opposite vertices are at $(-3, -1)$ and $(-6, -4)$.

33.   If $(1, 1)$, $(2, 3)$, and $(4, 3)$ are vertices of a parallelogram, what is the fourth?

34.   A **circle** may be defined as the set of points in the plane at the same given distance from a given point.
  (a) Check to make sure the following points are solutions of $x^2 + y^2 = 25$: $(3, 4)$, $(-3, 4)$, $(-3, -4)$, $(3, -4)$, $(5, 0)$, $(-5, 0)$, $(0, 5)$, $(0, -5)$, $(\sqrt{10}, \sqrt{15})$, $(-\sqrt{10}, \sqrt{15})$, $(\sqrt{10}, -\sqrt{15})$ and $(-\sqrt{10}, -\sqrt{15})$.
  (b) Now check to make sure that the distance from each of these points to the origin $(0, 0)$ is exactly 5 units.
  (c) Locate these points in the plane as best you can; how would you describe the curve they lie on?

35.   A map shows town A at the origin, town B at coordinates $(1, 3)$, and town C at $(2, -4)$. A cross-country race is to be run from A to B to C and back to A. If the coordinate units are kilometers, how long is the race?

36.   Use the results of Exercise 32 in Section 2-1 to show that

  (a) $|xy| = |x||y|$ and   (b) $|x/y| = |x|/|y|$.

Use the interpretation of $|x_1 - x_2|$ as the distance between x_1 and x_2 on the real line to solve the equations in Exercises 37–42. For example, to solve $|x + 4| = 2$, think of $|x + 4| = |x - (-4)|$ as the distance between x and -4. If $|x + 4| = 2$, then x must be 2 units to the left or to the right of -4. It follows that $x = -6$ or -2. CHECK: Does $|-6 + 4| = 2$ and $|-2 + 4| = 2$?

37. $|x - 3| = 4$ **38.** $|t - 4| = 2$ **39.** $|u + \sqrt{2}| = \frac{1}{2}$

40. $|t + \sqrt{3}| = \frac{1}{8}$ **41.** $|x + \frac{3}{4}| = \frac{1}{10}$ 42. $|y - \frac{1}{8}| = \frac{1}{100}$

2-3
Graphs of Functions

The Cartesian plane makes it possible to draw a picture of a function. This picture is called a graph, and it consists of all points (x, y) such that y is the value of the function at x.

■   **Definition**
The **graph** of the function f is the set of all points (x, y) with $y = f(x)$.

With this definition it is possible to look at any point (x, y) in the plane and decide whether it is on the graph of a function f. Simply determine whether the second coordinate, y, is f of the first coordinate, x. That is, does $y = f(x)$? If the answer is *yes*, then (x, y) is on the graph; if the answer is *no*, (x, y) is not on the graph.

To draw the graph of a function it is often useful to make a table of values. For example, let $f(x) = 3x - 5$. Assign various values to x and calculate the corresponding values of $f(x)$: if $x = 0$, $f(0) = -5$; if $x = -1$, $f(-1) = -8$, and so on. Now enter these values in a table. The table below shows x and $f(x)$ for $x = 0, \pm 1$, and ± 2. The points $(0, -5), (-1, -8), (1, -2), (-2, -11)$, and $(2, 1)$ are all on the graph of f.

x	0	-1	1	-2	2
$y = f(x)$	-5	-8	-2	-11	1

Example 1
Are the points $(0, -1), (2, -1), (-1, -4)$, and $(-2, 2)$ on the graph of $f(x) = 3x - 1$?

Solution
Make a table of values, giving x the values $0, 2, -1$, and -2; these are the first coordinates of the points in question. The table shows that $(0, -1)$ and $(-1, -4)$ are on the graph. Is $(2, -1)$ on the graph? The table shows that $f(2) = 5$, not -1; therefore, $(2, -1)$ is not on the graph. Neither is $(-2, 2)$.

x	0	2	-1	-2
$y = f(x)$	-1	5	-4	-7

Example 2
Graph the constant function $f(x) = 2$.

Solution
Make a table of values. For this function, it is easy: $f(x)$ is always 2. Plot several of the points and draw the graph shown in Figure 2-8A.

x	0	1	-1	2
$y = f(x)$	2	2	2	2

Example 3
Graph the identity function $G(t) = t$.

Solution
Make a table of values. Plot several points and draw the graph as in Figure 2-8B. *Remember this graph;* it will be used frequently.

t	0	1	-1	2
$s = G(t)$	0	1	-1	2

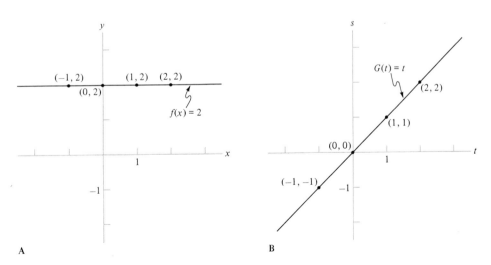

A   B

Figure 2-8
(A) The graph of a constant function is a horizontal line. (B) The graph of the identity function. See Examples 2 and 3.

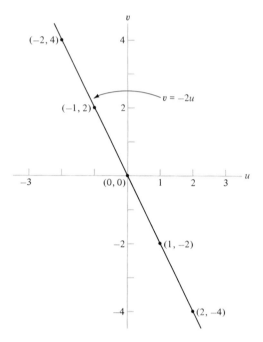

Figure 2-9
The graph of the equation $v = -2u$. See Example 4.

Often you will have to graph an equation. This simply means graphing the function defined by the equation.

Example 4
Graph the equation $v = -2u$.

Solution
This equation defines v as a function of u, namely, $f(u) = -2u$. The graph of the equation $v = -2u$ is the graph of this function f in a uv-plane. Fill in the missing entries in the table below. On a separate sheet of paper draw a uv-plane and carefully plot the points obtained from the table. They should all lie on a straight line; this line is the graph of $v = -2u$.* Compare your graph with Figure 2-9.

u	0	1	-1	2	-2
$v = -2u$	0	-2	2	-4	4

---

*At this point, you will simply have to believe the fact that the graph of such an equation is a line. This will be proved in Chapter 3.

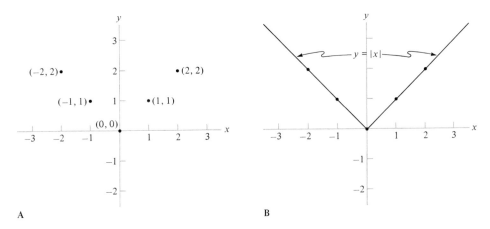

Figure 2-10
(A) Some points on the graph of $y = |x|$. (B) The graph of $y = |x|$. See Example 5.

Example 5
Sketch the graph of $y = |x|$.

Solution
This is the graph, in an xy-plane, of the absolute value function. Again, make a table of values and plot the points, as in Figure 2-10A. Notice that the second coordinates are never negative. Thus, no part of the graph can lie below the x-axis. The points in the first quadrant lie on a line through the origin; so do the points in the second quadrant. If you connect the points in each quadrant, the resulting graph is the V-shaped figure shown in Figure 2-10B.

x	-2	-1	0	1	2
$y = |x|$	2	1	0	1	2

Some graphs must be drawn in sections.

Example 6
Graph the function defined by

$$f(x) = \begin{cases} 1 \text{ if } x < -1 \\ |x| \text{ if } -1 \leq x \leq 1 \\ 1 \text{ if } x > 1 \end{cases}$$

Solution

The real line, which is the domain of f, is divided into three pieces and f is defined separately on each piece. It is the constant function 1 if x is to the left of -1 or to the right of 1; it is the absolute value function if x is in between. The graph of a constant function is a horizontal line (Example 2), and the graph of the absolute value function is V-shaped (Example 5). Putting all this together, you can draw the graph shown in Figure 2-11.

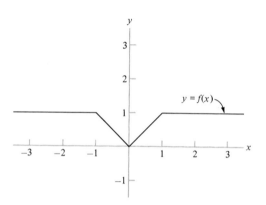

Figure 2-11
The graph of $y = f(x)$ defined in Example 6.

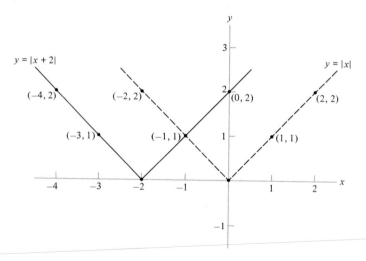

Figure 2-12
The graph of $y = |x + 2|$ is just the graph of $y = |x|$ shifted 2 units to the left. See Example 7.

Example 7
Graph the equation $y = |x + 2|$.

Solution
This function is similar to $y = |x|$. Compare the two functions by making a table of values for each. First choose several values for x and make a table for $y = |x|$. Then make a table for $y = |x + 2|$, but start with the y-row, using the same values for y that appeared in the first table. Notice the difference between the x-rows of the tables below: the point $(-2, 2)$ on the graph of $y = |x|$ corresponds to the point $(-4, 2)$ on the graph of $y = |x + 2|$; the point $(-1, 1)$ corresponds to the point $(-3, 1)$ and so on. It is as if each point on the graph of $y = |x|$ was moved horizontally two units to the left (see Figure 2-12). As a result, the graph of $y = |x + 2|$ can be obtained by shifting, or **translating,** the graph of $y = |x|$ two units to the left.

x	-2	-1	0	1	2
$y = |x|$	2	1	0	1	2

$$\updownarrow \quad \updownarrow \quad \updownarrow \quad \updownarrow \quad \updownarrow$$

x	-4	-3	-2	-1	0
$y = |x + 2|$	2	1	0	1	2

In Example 7, when a variable was replaced by the same variable plus 2, the graph of the original function was translated 2 units to the left. This is an example of the following general property of graphs:

■ **Translations**
Let $f: \mathbb{R} \to \mathbb{R}$ and let h and k be positive real numbers. Then the graph of $y = f(x)$ is translated
  (a) h units to the left to obtain the graph of $y = f(x + h)$;
  (b) h units to the right to obtain the graph of $y = f(x - h)$;
  (c) k units upward to obtain the graph of $y = f(x) + k$; and
  (d) k units downward to obtain the graph of $y = f(x) - k$.
These four types of translation are illustrated in Figure 2-13.

Example 8
Graph the following equations:

(a) $y = |x + 1|$ (b) $y = |x| + 1$ (c) $y = |x - 2| - 1$

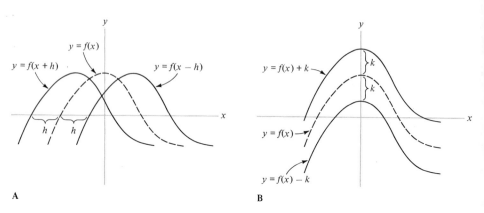

Figure 2-13
The four types of translation: (A) right and left translations; (B) up and down translations.

Solution

(a) $y = |x + 1|$. This graph is a translation, type (a), of the graph of the function $y = |x|$, with $h = 1$. The variable x is replaced by $x + 1$. This shifts the graph of $y = |x|$ one unit to the left. You know that the graph is V-shaped, so you need plot only a few points and then draw the graph as in Figure 2-14A.

x	-1	0	-2
$y = |x + 1|$	0	1	1

(b) $y = |x| + 1$. This is a translation of type (c), with $k = 1$. The graph of $y = |x|$ is translated one unit up. Plot a few points and draw the graph as in Figure 2-14B.

x	-1	0	1
$y = |x| + 1$	2	1	2

(c) $y = |x - 2| - 1$. This is a combination of translations of types (b) and (d), with $h = 2$ and $k = 1$. It shifts the absolute value graph two units to the right and one unit down. Make a table, plot a few points, and sketch the graph as in Figure 2-14C.

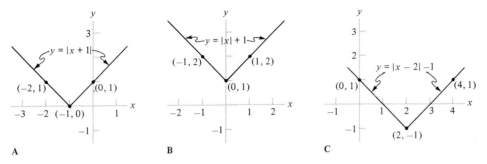

Figure 2-14
Three translations of the graph of $y = |x|$: (A) one unit to the left; (B) one unit up; (C) two units to the right and one unit down. See Example 8.

When the graph of a function is a translation of the graph of another function, the functions are called **translates** of each other.

Example 9
Graph the equation $s = t^2$ and the translates $s = (t - 1)^2$ and $s = t^2 + 1$.

Solution
Make a table of values for $s = t^2$. Notice that s takes the same value at t and at $-t$. The reason is that $t^2 = (-t)^2$. Plot these five points and connect them with a smooth curve as in Figure 2-15A. This curve is called a **parabola**; it will be described further in Chapter 3.

t	0	± 1	± 2
$s = t^2$	0	1	4

The graph of $s = (t - 1)^2$ is a translation of the graph of $s = t^2$ one unit to the right. Make a table of values using $t = 0, \pm 1, 2$, and 3. Plot the five points and sketch the graph (see Figure 2-15B).

t	0	-1	1	2	3
$s = (t - 1)^2$	1	4	0	1	4

To graph $s = t^2 + 1$, simply translate the graph of $s = t^2$ one unit up (see Figure 2-15C).

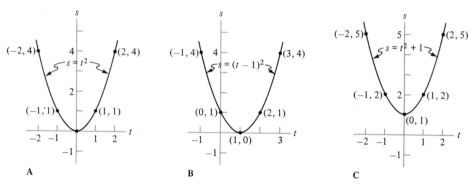

Figure 2-15
(A) The graph of $s = t^2$ (B) translated one unit to the right and (C) translated one unit up.
See Example 9.

Exercises

Learn to recognize translates. For example, $y = (x + 2)^2 + 3$ is a translate of $y = x^2$ two units to the left and three units up. Do the same for each of the following.

1. (a) $y = x - 2$ (b) $s = -t + 7$
2. (a) $y = |x + 1| - 3$ (b) $y = |x - 2| + 1$
3. (a) $s = (t - 3)^2 - 1$ (b) $v = (u + 1)^2 + (u + 1)$

In Exercises 4–8, decide whether the given points are on the graph of the given function.

4. $f(x) = -2x + 7$; $(0, 7)$ $(1, 9)$ $(1 + h, 5 - 2h)$
5. $g(t) = 3t - 2$; $(1, 2)$ $(0, -2)$ $(-1 + u, -5 + 3u)$
6. $h(u) = u^2 - 4$; $(2, 8)$ $(a + 2, a^2 + 4a)$ $(b, b^2 - 4)$
7. $k(w) = -w^2 + 1$; $(0, 2)$ $(1, 2)$ $(1 + v, 2v + v^2)$

8. $f(x) = \begin{cases} 3 \text{ if } x < -3 \\ |x| \text{ if } -3 \le x \le 3 \\ 3 \text{ if } x > 3 \end{cases}$

Are the points $(-7, 7)$, $(4, 3)$, and $(-2, 2)$ on the graph of f?

9.   If $(2, a)$ and $(-3, b)$ are on the graph of $f(x) = -3x + 2$, find a and b.
10. If $(-1, c)$ and $(2, d)$ are on the graph of $g(t) = t^2 + 1$, find c and d.
11. If $(a, 2)$ and $(b, -3)$ are on the graph of $f(x) = 7x + 1$, find a and b.
12. If $(c, 4)$ and $(d, -5)$ are on the graph of $g(t) = t^2 - 5$, find c and d. (There may be more than one answer.)

In Exercises 13–18, graph all three equations in the same plane. (The graphs are straight lines.) Notice the effect of changing the constants.

13. $y = \frac{1}{3}x$ $y = 2x$ $y = 3x$

14. $y = -\frac{1}{4}x$ $y = -2x$ $y = -4x$

15. $y = 3x - 1$ $y = 3x$ $y = 3x + 1$

16. $y = -4x - 1$ $y = -4x$ $y = -4x + 1$

17. $y = 3(x - 1)$ $y = 3x$ $y = 3(x + 1)$

18. $y = -4(x - 1)$ $y = -4x$ $y = -4(x + 1)$

Graph each pair of functions in the same plane. The graph of $-f$ is the **reflection** through the x-axis of the graph of f.

19. $y = x^2$ $y = -x^2$ 20. $y = x$ $y = -x$

21. $s = t^2 + 1$ $s = -t^2 - 1$ 22. $v = |u|$ $v = -|u|$

Graph the following equations.

23. $y = -3x + 4$ 24. $y = 2x - 7$

25. $v = u^2 - 1$ 26. $v = -u^2 + 3$

27. $s = |t + \frac{3}{2}|$ 28. $s = |t - \frac{1}{2}|$

29. $y = -(x - 2)^2 - 3$ 30. $y = (x + 2)^2 - 1$

31. $v = |u - \frac{1}{2}| - \frac{3}{4}$ 32. $v = |u - \frac{1}{8}| + \frac{1}{2}$

33. (Test your understanding of functions and graphs.)

(a) What kind of function does a horizontal line represent?

(b) Describe the type of function whose graph is a straight line through the origin.

(c) Write a function whose graph is a straight line inclined at an angle of $45°$ that passes through $(-1, 0)$.

(d) Write a function whose graph is V-shaped with its vertex at $(1, 2)$.

34. (Continuation of Exercise 33)

(a) Is a vertical line the graph of a function? If so, what kind? If not, explain why not.

(b) Look at the curves A and B in Figure 2-16. Could A be part of the graph of a function? Could B? Explain your answers.

(c) Make up a criterion (a sort of test) that could be used to decide whether a given curve is part of the graph of some function.

35. (Inverses) Let $f(x) = 2x - 1$ and $g(x) = \frac{1}{2}(x + 1)$. These functions are **inverses** of each other. (See Exercise 31 in Section 2-1.)

(a) Evaluate $f(g(-1))$, $g(f(5))$, $f(g(t))$, and $g(f(z + 7))$.

(b) If $f(3) = 5$, then $g(5) = $ _____; if $g(3) = 2$, then $f(2) = $ _____.

(c) If $f(x) = y$, then $g(y) = $ _____; if $g(t) = z$, then $f(z) = $ _____.

(d) Verify that the points $(-1, -3)$, $(0, -1)$, $(\frac{1}{2}, 0)$ and $(1, 1)$ are on the graph

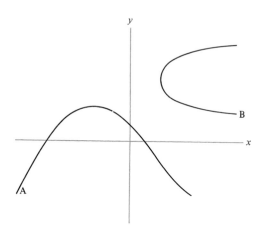

Figure 2-16
See Exercise 34.

of *f*. Now reverse the coordinates and verify that the points $(-3, -1)$, $(-1, 0)$, $(0, \frac{1}{2})$, and $(1, 1)$ are on the graph of *g*.

(e)   Explain why (x, y) is on the graph of *f* if and only if (y, x) is on the graph of *g*.

(f)   Finally, graph *f* and *g* in the same plane, and draw a dotted line representing the graph of the identity function $y = x$. Notice that the graphs of *f* and *g* are reflections of each other through the line $y = x$. *This is always true of inverses.*

2-4
More on Functions

The **greatest integer function**, written $f(x) = [x]$, assigns to each real number *x* the largest integer that is less than or equal to *x*. Thus, $[3] = 3$, $[-2] = -2$, $[5/2] = 2$ and $[-3/4] = -1$, and $[3/4] = 0$.

Example 1
Graph $f(x) = [x]$ and use the graph to evaluate $f(-1.5)$ and $f(22/5)$.

Solution
Between any two consecutive integers, the function is constant: its value is the smaller of the two integers. For instance, if $0 \le x < 1$, then $[x] = 0$; and if $-4 \le x < -3$, then $[x] = -4$. The graph is shown in Figure 2-17A. In each segment of the graph, the solid dot on the left indicates that the point on the left end is included; the open dot on the right indicates that the point on the right

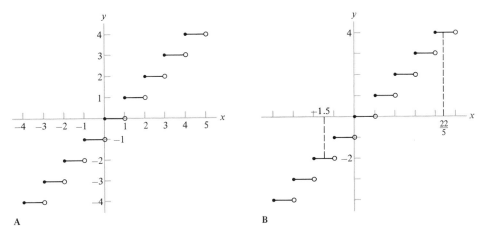

Figure 2-17
(A) The graph of the greatest integer function. (B) Using the graph to evaluate $[-1.5]$ and $[\frac{22}{5}]$. See Example 1.

end is *not* included. If both points were included, then this would not be the graph of a function, because over the point $x = 2$, for example, there would be *two* points, (2, 1) and (2, 2), on the graph. A true function has only one value at each number in its domain. Figure 2-17B shows how to use the graph to evaluate $[-1.5] = -2$ and $[22/5] = 4$. Of course, you can also find these values algebraically, without referring to the graph.

The greatest integer function is a **step function.** Its graph shows why this name is appropriate. Step functions are very common in real life, but it is usually the right end point of each segment that is included and the left end point that is omitted. For example, if a package weighs between 13 and 14 ounces, the postal rate is figured on 14 ounces. Similarly, parking-lot rates are often figured on the $\frac{1}{2}$ hour or any portion thereof. If you stay for $1\frac{1}{4}$ hours, the charge is for $1\frac{1}{2}$ hours.

Example 2
A taxi company charges \$1 for the first $\frac{1}{4}$ mile and 50¢ for every additional $\frac{1}{4}$ mile or portion thereof. Graph the fare against mileage and use the graph to compute the fare for trips of $\frac{5}{16}$ miles and $\frac{9}{8}$ miles.

Solution
Let the horizontal axis represent the mileage M and the vertical axis represent the fare F. If $0 < M \leq \frac{1}{4}$, the fare is \$1; if $\frac{1}{4} < M \leq \frac{1}{2}$, the fare is \$1.50; and so on. The graph is shown in Figure 2-18, which also indicates that the fare for $\frac{5}{16}$

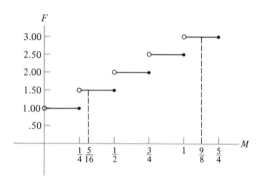

Figure 2-18
The graph of taxi fare against mileage is a step function. See Example 2.

miles is $1.50, and for $\frac{9}{8}$ miles is $3.00. Can you think up a function to calculate the fare without referring to the graph? The answer is the footnote * on page 82.

In Example 2, the fare was a function of mileage. Because mileage cannot be negative, the domain of this function is restricted: it is the set of nonnegative numbers. In applying mathematical functions to real-life problems, it is often necessary to restrict their domains.

Example 3
A projectile is fired straight up with a muzzle velocity of 160 feet per second. Its height, in feet above the ground, after t seconds is given by the function $h(t) = -16t^2 + 160t$. What is the domain of this function?

Solution
The function $y = -16x^2 + 160x$, which is the same function as $h(t)$, has an unrestricted domain. However, in this case the function makes sense only from the time the projectile is fired until it strikes the ground. At both those times, its height is zero. Therefore, set $-16t^2 + 160t = 0$ and solve for t.

$$0 = -16t^2 + 160t$$

$$= -16t(t - 10) \qquad \text{(Factor.)}$$

Thus, $-16t = 0$ or $t - 10 = 0$, and the solution set is $\{0, 10\}$. Time $t = 0$ is when the projectile was fired, so time $t = 10$ seconds must be when the projectile strikes the ground. It follows that the domain of t is the time interval $0 \leq t \leq 10$.

When you graph a function with a restricted domain, say X, you should consider only those points whose first coordinates are in X.

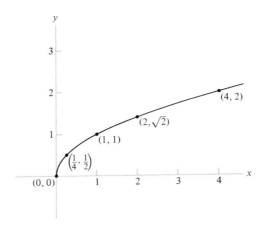

Figure 2-19
The graph of $y = \sqrt{x}$. See Example 4.

Example 4
Graph $y = \sqrt{x}$.

Solution
This function is defined only for $x \geq 0$. Make a table of values. The points $(0, 0)$, $(1, 1)$ and $(4, 2)$ are enough to show that the graph is curved, but to get a clearer picture of the graph, two more points are necessary. Now connect the five points with a smooth curve (see Figure 2-19). The graph lies entirely in the first quadrant because $x \geq 0$ and $y = \sqrt{x} \geq 0$.

x	0	1	4	1/4	2
$y = \sqrt{x}$	0	1	2	1/2	$\sqrt{2} \approx 1.4$

Example 5
Graph $y = x^2$ for $-1 \leq x < 2$.

Solution
The graph of $y = x^2$ is the parabola in Example 9 of Section 2-3. But now the domain has been restricted and, therefore, the graph must be restricted (see Figure 2-20). The open dot indicates that the point $(2, 4)$ is not included because the domain excludes $x = 2$.

So far, we have considered only functions of one independent variable. However, it is often necessary to deal with functions of more than one variable. For instance, such

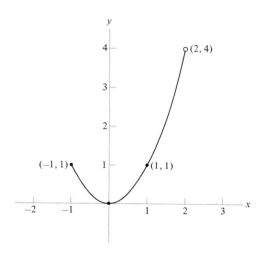

Figure 2-20
The graph of $y = x^2$ on the restricted domain $-1 \leq x < 2$. See Example 5.

a simple quantity as the area A of a triangle is a function of two variables, base b and height h. This function can be expressed in symbols as

$$A(b, h) = \tfrac{1}{2}bh$$

The expression on the left is read "A of b, h." The domain of this function consists of ordered pairs of positive numbers. It assigns to each such pair (b, h) one and only one number, namely, $\tfrac{1}{2}bh$.

Example 6
(a)   Evaluate $f(x, y) = x^2 + 3xy - y^2$ at the pairs $(0, 1)$, $(1, 0)$, and $(-2, 3)$.
(b)   Evaluate $g(b, d, a) = 3a - 4b + d$ at the triples $(0, 1, -2)$, and $(-5, -2, 0)$.

Solution
(a)   The order is important. Because the function reads "f of x, y," the value of x comes first in each pair. Thus,

$$f(0, 1) = 0^2 + 3(0)(1) - 1^2 = -1$$

$$f(1, 0) = 1^2 + 3(1)(0) - 0^2 = 1$$

*Taxi fare (see Example 2): $F = \begin{cases} 1.00 + .50([4M]) & \text{if } M \neq \dfrac{1}{4}, \dfrac{2}{4}, \dfrac{3}{4}, \ldots \\ 1.00 + .50([4M] - 1) & \text{if } M = \dfrac{1}{4}, \dfrac{2}{4}, \dfrac{3}{4}, \ldots \end{cases}$

$$f(-2, 3) = (-2)^2 + 3(-2)(3) - 3^2 = -23$$

(b)   The order in which the letters appear is important. This function reads "g of b, d, a" so in each triple, the value of b comes first, then the value of d, then a. Thus,

$$g(0, 1, -2) = 3(-2) - 4(0) + 1 = -5$$

$$g(-5, -2, 0) = 3(0) - 4(-5) - 2 = 18$$

Many useful quantities can be expressed as functions of one or more variables. The volume of a sphere is a function of the radius:

$$V_{sphere} = \frac{4}{3}\pi r^3 \qquad (r \geq 0)$$

The volume of a gas V is proportional to the temperature T and inversely proportional to the pressure P. Thus, it is a function of two variables, and

$$V_{gas} = \frac{c(T + 273.15)}{P} \qquad (c \text{ is a constant that is different for each gas,}$$

$$P > 0, \text{ and } T > -273.15°C^*)$$

The surface area S of a cylinder with radius r and height h is the sum of the areas of top and bottom (each is πr^2) and the area of the sides ($2\pi rh$). So S is a function of the two variables r and h:

$$S = 2\pi r^2 + 2\pi rh \qquad (r \geq 0, h \geq 0)$$

Example 7
A can manufacturer pays .05¢/cm² (.05 cents per square centimeter) for the material used for the top and bottom, and only .03¢/cm² for the side material. What is the cost of a can 10 cm high with a radius of 5 cm?

Solution
According to the formula in the paragraph just before this example, the cost C of any can is

$$C = (.05)2\pi r^2 + (.03)2\pi rh$$

---

* $-273.15°$ Celsius, or centigrade, is called **absolute zero**. It is believed to be the lowest temperature possible.

For this particular can, $r = 5$ and $h = 10$. Then

$$C = 2.5\pi + 3\pi \approx 17\text{¢}$$

The symbol $\approx$ means "approximately equal."

Exercises

Evaluate.

1. $[-5/3]$ **2.** $[\pi]$ **3.** $[-\pi]$ **4.** $[16.3]$

5. $[3x + 1]$ at $x = -\frac{2}{5}, \frac{3}{2}$, and $\sqrt{2} \approx 1.4$

6. $[4y - 3]$ at $y = -\frac{3}{2}, \frac{5}{6}$, and $\pi \approx 3.1$

7. $[t^2]$ at $t = -1, \frac{5}{2}$, and $-\sqrt{5}$

8. $[u^2 - \frac{1}{2}]$ at $u = 0, \sqrt{3}$, and -3.2

Graph the following functions.

9. $y = 3$ for $x > 0$

10. $y = -1$ for $1 < x < 2$

11. $y = 3x + 2$ for $-2 \leq x < 0$

12. $s = -2t + 3$ for $0 < t \leq 4$

13. $y = |x + 1|$ for $x < 0$

14. $y = |x| + 1$ for $x \geq 0$

15. $y = \sqrt{x + 1}$ (translate of $y = \sqrt{x}$)

16. $y = \sqrt{x} - 2$

17. $y = \sqrt{x - 1} + 1$

18. $v = u^2$ for $|u| < 2$

19. $v = (u + 1)^2$ for $|u - 1| < 2$

20. $v = u^2 - 1$ for $0 < u < 2$

21. $v = (u - 1)^2 + 1$ for $u > 0$

Evaluate.

22. $f(x, y) = 3x^2 - xy + y^2$ at $(-1, 0)$, $(0, 2)$, and $(-2, 2)$

23. $g(x, y, z) = xy + yz - xz$ at $(1, 1, 0)$, $(-2, 5, 1)$, and $(\frac{1}{2}, \frac{2}{3}, \frac{3}{4})$

24. $h(x, y) = 2[x]^2 - [3y + 1]$ at $(-1, 2)$, $(-\frac{5}{2}, \frac{4}{3})$, and $(0, 0)$

25. A taxi company charges 80¢ for the first $\frac{1}{8}$ mile and then 35¢ for each $\frac{1}{8}$ mile or portion thereof. What is the fare for a trip of 1 mile? $1\frac{1}{2}$ miles? Find a function that can be used to calculate the fare for any mileage.

26. To deliver a package, a delivery company charges $2.00 plus 30¢ for each $\frac{1}{2}$ kilometer or portion thereof. How much is the charge for a delivery of 3.1 kilometers? 15.8 kilometers? Find a function that can be used to calculate the charge for any distance. What is the domain of this function?

27. The material for the top and bottom of a can cost .013¢/cm², but the sides cost only .004¢/cm². Compute the cost of a can with radius 7 cm and height 10 cm.

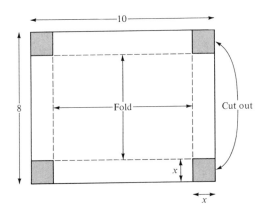

Figure 2-21
The piece of cardboard in Exercise 28.

28. A box without a top is to be made from an 8 × 10 rectangular piece of cardboard by cutting out a square from each corner and folding up the sides as indicated in Figure 2-21. What will be the volume of the box if the squares cut out are 1 × 1? 2 × 2? Find a function that will give the volume V if squares of side x are cut out. What is the domain of this function?

29. The outside dimensions of a picture frame are to be 25 × 30 inches. How much wood (in square inches) is needed if the frame is 3 inches wide? 5 inches wide? (Draw a picture). Find a function whose value at x is the amount of wood needed for a frame width of x inches. What is the domain of this function?

30. The electrical resistance R of a wire is proportional to its length L and inversely proportional to its diameter D. Thus,

$$R = c\frac{L}{D}$$

where c is a constant that depends on what material is used. If a certain wire 10 meters long and 1 centimeter in diameter has a resistance of 50 ohms, what resistance will a wire of the same material have if it is 25 meters long and 3 centimeters in diameter.

31. If two concentric circles (circles with the same center) have radii of r_1 and r_2, express the area of the ring between them as a function of r_1 and r_2.

32. (Part (c) may surprise you.)
(a)   The radius of a circle is r. If this radius is increased by h units, by how much is the circumference of the circle increased?
(b)   Suppose two balls have radii of 3 and 4 feet. What is the difference in the lengths of their equators?
(c)   Suppose a piece of string is wound once around the earth at the equator. A second piece of string is wound once around the earth at a height exactly one foot above the equator. How much longer is the second piece of string?

2-5
Average Rate of Change

By definition,

■   Speed is the rate of change of distance with respect to time.

Suppose that it takes two hours to drive from town A to town B, a distance of
100 miles. Then the **average speed** of the auto is

$$\frac{\text{distance}}{\text{time}} = \frac{100}{2} = 50 \text{ mi/hr}$$

This does not mean that the speedometer reads 50 throughout the trip. The speedometer reading indicates the speed *at that instant* rather than the *average* speed over
a time interval.

Suppose $s(t) = 25t^2$ is the distance, in miles, from A to the automobile at time t,
measured in hours from the time of departure. What is the speed when $t = 1$?

If h is any positive real number, we can compute the average speed during the
time interval from $t = 1$ to $t = 1 + h$. The change in the distance during that interval
is $s(1 + h) - s(1)$, and the change in time is h. Therefore, the average speed during
the interval is

$$\frac{\text{change in distance}}{\text{change in time}} = \frac{s(1 + h) - s(1)}{h}$$

Let us compute this average speed for several values of h, say $h = \frac{1}{2}, \frac{1}{10}, \frac{1}{100}, \frac{1}{1000}$.
The average speed during the half-hour period from $t = 1$ to $t = 3/2$ hours
($h = 1/2$) is

$$\frac{s(3/2) - s(1)}{1/2} = \frac{25(3/2)^2 - 25(1)^2}{1/2} = 62.5 \text{ mi/hr}$$

The average speed during the six-minute period from $t = 1$ to $t = 11/10$ hours
($h = 1/10$) is

$$\frac{s(11/10) - s(1)}{1/10} = \frac{25(11/10)^2 - 25(1)^2}{1/10} = 52.5 \text{ mi/hr}$$

For $h = 1/100$ and $1/1000$, the speeds are

$$\frac{s(101/100) - s(1)}{1/100} = 50.25 \text{ mi/hr} \quad \text{and} \quad \frac{s(1001/1000) - s(1)}{1/1000} = 50.025 \text{ mi/hr}$$

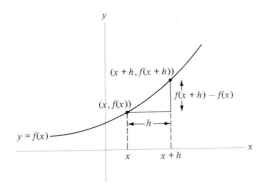

Figure 2-22
The average rate of change of f from x to $x + h$ is the change in f divided by the change in x. In symbols,

$$\text{a.r.c.}f(x, h) = \frac{f(x + h) - f(x)}{h}$$

As the average speeds are calculated over shorter and shorter time intervals, they get closer and closer to 50 mi/hr. Thus, it is reasonable to guess that the speedometer will read 50 when $t = 1$. We shall call the average speed during an interval the **average rate of change** of distance with respect to time; we shall call the actual speed at a single instant the **exact rate of change.**

The notions of average and exact rate of change can be applied to any function. Let $f: \mathbb{R} \to \mathbb{R}$ and let h be any nonzero number. Then $f(x + h) - f(x)$ represents the difference between the values of f at the points x and $x + h$, or the change in the value of f from x to $x + h$. If we now divide this change by h, we obtain the **average rate of change of f from x to $x + h$,** which we shall abbreviate a.r.c.$f(x, h)$. Thus,

$$\text{a.r.c.}f(x, h) = \frac{f(x + h) - f(x)}{h}$$

Figure 2-22 shows how the average rate of change can be interpreted geometrically.

Example 1
Let $f(x) = 3x - 7$; find a.r.c.$f(2, 3)$ and a.r.c.$f(-3, .1)$

Solution
To find a.r.c.$f(2, 3)$, set $x = 2$ and $h = 3$. Therefore,

$$\text{a.r.c.} f(2, 3) = \frac{f(2 + 3) - f(2)}{3}$$

$$= \frac{[3(2 + 3) - 7] - [3 \cdot 2 - 7]}{3}$$

$$= \frac{8 + 1}{3} = 3$$

To find a.r.c.$f(-3, .1)$, set $x = -3$ and $h = .1$. So

$$\text{a.c.r.} f(-3, .1) = \frac{f(-3 + .1) - f(-3)}{.1}$$

$$= \frac{[3(-3 + .1) - 7] - [3(-3) - 7]}{.1}$$

$$= \frac{-15.7 + 16}{.1} = 3$$

In Example 1, the average rate of change of f turned out to be the same from $x = 2$ to $x = 2 + 3$ and from $x = -3$ to $x = -3 + .1$. This should agree with your intuition, because the graph of $f(x) = 3x - 7$ is a straight line, and the rate of change of a straight line *should* be the same all along the line (see Figure 2-23).

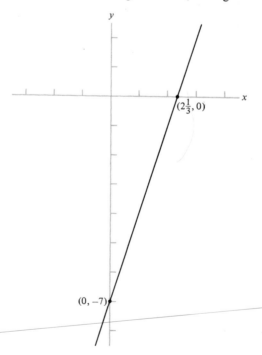

Figure 2-23
The graph of $f(x) = 3x - 7$ is a straight line. See Example 1.

Example 2
Let $f(x) = x^2 - 2x + 2$. First compute a.r.c.$f(x, h)$ for any x and h; then for $x = 1$ and $h = .5$; and finally for $x = 2$ and $h = .5$.

Solution
For any x and h,

$$\text{a.r.c.}f(x, h) = \frac{f(x + h) - f(x)}{h}$$

$$= \frac{[(x + h)^2 - 2(x + h) + 2] - [x^2 - 2x + 2]}{h}$$

$$= \frac{x^2 + 2xh + h^2 - 2x - 2h + 2 - x^2 + 2x - 2}{h}$$

$$= \frac{2xh + h^2 - 2h}{h}$$

$$= 2x - 2 + h$$

so a.r.c.$f(x, h) = 2x - 2 + h$ for *any* x and h. Now use this general formula to compute a.r.c.$f(x, h)$ when $x = 1$ and $h = .5$, and when $x = 2$ and $h = .5$.

$$\text{a.r.c.}f(1, .5) = 2 \cdot 1 - 2 + .5 = .5$$

$$\text{a.r.c.}f(2, .5) = 2 \cdot 2 - 2 + .5 = 2.5$$

Notice that, in the last example, the average rate of change is different for different intervals. The graph of this function f is not a straight line, so its values change more rapidly at some points than at others (see Figure 2-24).

The a.r.c.$f(x, h)$ is only an approximation to the exact rate of change of f at the point x. The smaller the value of h, the better the approximation. As we have seen, the rate of change of distance with respect to time is speed. The speedometer in an automobile gives the exact rate of change of distance with respect to time. By calculating the average rate of change, we can approximate the speedometer reading.

Example 3
An automobile is traveling so that its distance s miles from town at any time t hours is given by the function $s = 10t^2 - 3t$. Find the average speed during the second hour and during the third hour, and the speedometer reading at the end of the second hour.

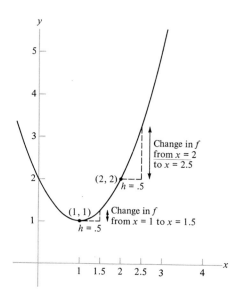

Figure 2-24
The graph of $f(x) = x^2 - 2x + 2$ is not a straight line, so its values change more rapidly at some points than at others. See Example 2.

Solution
First find the average rate of change of s for any t and h.

$$\text{a.r.c.}s(t, h) = \frac{s(t + h) - s(t)}{h}$$

$$= \frac{[10(t + h)^2 - 3(t + h)] - [10t^2 - 3t]}{h}$$

$$= \frac{10t^2 + 20th + 10h^2 - 3t - 3h - 10t^2 + 3t}{h}$$

$$= 20t - 3 + 10h$$

We can now use this formula to find the average rate of change for any particular t and h.
(a)   To find the average speed during the second hour, let $t = 1$ and $h = 1$. Then

$$\text{a.r.c.}s(1, 1) = 20(1) - 3 + 10(1)$$

$$= 27 \text{ mi/hr}$$

(b)   To find the average speed during the third hour, let $t = 2$ and $h = 1$. Then

$$\text{a.r.c.}s(2, 1) = 20(2) - 3 + 10(1)$$

$$= 47 \text{ mi/hr}$$

(c) To find the actual speedometer reading when $t = 2$, notice that $\text{a.r.c.}s(2, h) = 20(2) - 3 + 10h$ approximates the actual reading; the smaller h is, the better the approximation. As h gets close to 0, the number $20(2) - 3 + 10h$ gets close to 37. We can conclude that the speedometer reads 37 mi/hr at the end of 2 hours.

The average rate of change can also be applied to business problems. If the profit of a manufacturing company is a function of the number of units produced, then the exact rate of change of profit is called the **marginal profit.** It is the additional profit obtained by producing one more unit. We can calculate the average rate of change of the profit function to obtain an approximation to the marginal profit called the **average marginal profit.**

Example 4

The profit P in thousands of dollars obtained by manufacturing x thousand units of a certain product is given by the function $P(x) = -x^2 + 4x - 1$. At present the company is producing 1.5 thousand units. What is its profit? Management wants to increase production to 2 thousand units. Should they do it?

Solution

To find the present profit, simply evaluate P at $x = 1.5$. Thus,

$$P(1.5) = -(1.5)^2 + 4(1.5) - 1 = 2.75 \text{ thousand dollars}$$

To determine whether management should increase production, we find the average rate of change of profit P, that is, the average marginal profit:

$$\text{a.r.c.}P(x, h) = \frac{P(x + h) - P(x)}{h}$$

$$= \frac{[-(x + h)^2 + 4(x + h) - 1] - [-x^2 + 4x - 1]}{h}$$

$$= \frac{-x^2 - 2xh - h^2 + 4x + 4h - 1 + x^2 - 4x + 1}{h}$$

$$= -2x + 4 - h \text{ (thousand dollars/thousand units)}$$

To see what happens when production is increased from 1.5 to 2 thousand, let $x = 1.5$ and $h = .5$. Then a.r.c.$P(1.5, .5) = -2(1.5) + 4 - .5 = .5$ (thousand dollars/thousand units)

This means that the profit for the extra 500 (half a thousand) units is $250, or an average of $.50 per unit. The company's present profit on 1500 units is $2750, or almost $2 per unit. Management would be wise to maintain present production, especially if they can use their resources more profitably elsewhere.

The next example illustrates a useful application of rationalizing the numerator.

Example 5

Let $f(x) = \sqrt{x}$ $(x > 0)$. Calculate (a) a.r.c.$f(3, 2)$, (b) a.r.c.$f(4, 1)$, and (c) the exact rate of change at $x = 2$.

Solution

$$\text{a.r.c.}f(x, h) = \frac{f(x + h) - f(x)}{h}$$

$$= \frac{\sqrt{x + h} - \sqrt{x}}{h}$$

This formula gives

(a)   a.r.c.$f(3, 2) = \dfrac{\sqrt{5} - \sqrt{3}}{2}$ and

(b)   a.r.c.$f(4, -1) = \dfrac{\sqrt{3} - 2}{-1}$

(c)   To find the exact rate of change, we must let h get closer and closer to zero. In the expression $(\sqrt{x + h} - \sqrt{x})/h$, it is not at all clear what happens when h is small. However, if we rationalize the numerator, the result may be easier to predict.

$$\frac{\sqrt{x + h} - \sqrt{x}}{h} = \frac{\sqrt{x + h} - \sqrt{x}}{h} \cdot \frac{\sqrt{x + h} + \sqrt{x}}{\sqrt{x + h} + \sqrt{x}}$$

$$= \frac{x + h - x}{h(\sqrt{x + h} + \sqrt{x})}$$

$$= \frac{1}{\sqrt{x + h} + \sqrt{x}}$$

Now when h is close to 0, $\sqrt{x + h}$ is close to $\sqrt{x}$, so the sum $\sqrt{x + h} + \sqrt{x}$ is close to $2 \sqrt{x}$. We can thus conclude that the exact rate of change at any $x > 0$ is $1/2 \sqrt{x}$. The rate of change when $x = 2$ is, therefore, $1/2 \sqrt{2}$.

Exercises

1. Write out the definition of
    (a) function
    (b) identity function
    (c) coordinates of a point in a plane
    (d) absolute value of a real number
    (e) graph of a function
    (f) average rate of change of f from x to $x + h$
2. Explain the following terms and notations:
    (a) $f: X \to Y$
    (b) independent and dependent variable in an equation such as $s = g(t)$
    (c) the difference between power functions and exponential functions
    (d) translations of graphs
    (e) a.r.c.$f(x, h)$

Calculate the average rate of change of each of the following functions at the indicated values of the variable and h.

3. $f(x) = 4$; $(3, -2)$
4. $g(u) = 7$; $(2, 1)$
5. $s(t) = 3t + 1$; $(-2, 4)$
6. $F(y) = -5y + 4$; $(1, 4)$
7. $f(u) = -2u^2 + 3u + 4$; $(-1, -2)$
8. $g(y) = y^2 - 3y$; $(1, 3)$
9. $k(a) = a^3 - 2a^2 + a$; $(2, 2)$
10. $G(x) = 2x^3 - x + 2$; $(0, 1)$
11. $f(x) = \sqrt{x + 2}$; $(9, 5)$
12. $g(y) = \sqrt[3]{y + 1}$; $(0, 7)$

For each of the following functions, compute the average rate of change for any x and h.

13. $f(x) = 3$
14. $g(x) = 4$
15. $s(x) = -2x + 4$
16. $F(x) = 9x + 1$
17. $g(x) = 3x^2 - 5$
18. $G(x) = -x^2 + 2x - 3$
19. $k(x) = -2x^3 + x - 3$
20. $H(x) = x^3$
21. $f(x) = \sqrt{x - 4}$ $(x > 4)$
22. $g(x) = \sqrt{x + 3}$ $(x > -3)$

23. For each of the functions in Exercises 13, 15, 17, 19, and 21, find the exact rate of change at $x = 5$. (For Exercise 21, it will help to rationalize the numerator as in Example 5.)

24. Do the same with Exercises 14, 16, 18, 20, and 22.

25. Let $f(x) = \dfrac{1}{x}$. Then $f(x + h) - f(x) = \dfrac{1}{x + h} - \dfrac{1}{x}$.

Combine these fractions and show that a.r.c.$f(x, h) = -1/x(x + h)$. What is the exact rate of change of f at x?

26.   Use the procedure of Exercise 25 to show that if $f(x) = 1/\sqrt{x}$ for $x > 0$, then

$$a.r.c.f(x, h) = \frac{\sqrt{x} - \sqrt{x + h}}{h\sqrt{x + h}\sqrt{x}}$$

Now rationalize the numerator and show that the exact rate of change of f at x is

$$-\frac{1}{2x\sqrt{x}}$$

27.   Let $f(x) = 2^x$.   Use   the   Properties   of   Exponents   to   prove   that a.r.c.$f(x, h) = 2^x(2^h - 1)/h$. In this case, it is very difficult to predict what happens when h is small (but see Exercise 32).

28.   The height s, in feet above the earth, of a freely falling object (that is, it is acted on by gravity alone) is given as a function of time t, in seconds, by the equation

$$s = -16t^2 + v_0t + d_0$$

where v_0 is the initial velocity and d_0 is the initial height.

A baseball is dropped from a balloon 1000 feet above the earth (so the initial velocity $v_0 = 0$ and the initial height $d_0 = 1000$). Find the average rate of change of $s = -16t^2 + 1000$ during the first second (from $t = 0$ to $t = 1$) and during the third second (from $t = 2$ to $t = 3$). The average rate of change of height is the average velocity. The average velocities in this problem are negative, which indicates that the direction of motion is down. What is the exact velocity when $t = 4$?

29.   The profit P in thousands of dollars for x thousand units produced is $P(x) = 2x^3 - 27x^2 + 120x - 25$. Current production is 4 thousand units; management wants to increase it to 5 thousand units. What would you advise? (Refer to Example 4.) Suppose the current production were 6 thousand. Would you advise an increase?

30.   The volume V of a sphere is a function of the radius: $V = \frac{4}{3}\pi r^3$. A balloon is attached to a tank that pumps a constant amount of gas per minute into the balloon. As the radius increases from 6 to 9 inches, what is the average rate of increase in the volume of the balloon? Naturally, the balloon will increase in radius more slowly as time goes on. Does the notion of the a.r.c. help explain why this happens?

31.   (Inverses) In Exercise 31 of Section 2-1, the pair of functions $f(x) = 2x - 3$ and $g(y) = \frac{1}{2}y + \frac{3}{2}$ were shown to be inverses of each other. Here is another pair of

inverses. Let $F(x) = x^3 + 4$. Set $y = F(x) = x^3 + 4$ and solve for x, so that $x = \sqrt[3]{y - 4}$. Let $G(y) = \sqrt[3]{y - 4}$. Evaluate $F(G(-4))$ and $G(F(0))$. Show that $G(F(x)) = x$ and $F(G(y)) = y$ for all x and y. Thus, F and G are inverses.

32.   (This exercise requires a calculator with a power key.) Let $f(x) = 2^x$. In Exercise 27 you showed that

$$\text{a.r.c.} f(x, h) = 2^x \left(\frac{2^h - 1}{h} \right)$$

Evaluate the quotient $(2^h - 1)/h$ at $h = .1, .01,$ and $.001$. Now predict the exact rate of change of f at x. In particular, what is the rate of change at $x = 2$? (Round off your answer to three digits.)

Chapter 3

Linear and Quadratic Functions

In this chapter we shall explore the algebraic and geometric properties of linear and quadratic functions. Their graphs are, respectively, straight lines and parabolas.

Sections 3-1 and 3-2 deal with linear functions. Algebraically, they are of the form $f(x) = mx + b$; geometrically, their graphs are (nonvertical) straight lines. Section 3-3 concerns quadratic functions. They are of the form $f(x) = ax^2 + bx + c$, and their graphs are parabolas. An easy method of graphing parabolas by using translation (introduced in Chapter 2) is described. Section 3-4 discusses the important quadratic formula and its use in solving equations. Section 3-5 concerns linear and quadratic inequalities. An application of inequalities to straight-line motion completes this chapter.

Here are some things to concentrate on. (1) Writing an equation of a line subject to given conditions. (2) Sketching the graph of a parabola. (3) Recognizing the interplay between algebra and geometry: learn to use information about one aspect of a function to get information about the other.

3-1
Linear Functions

Any equation that can be put into the form

$$y = mx + b \tag{1}$$

is called a **linear equation.** Such an equation defines y as a **linear function** of x.

Graph of a linear function

Linear functions are called linear because their graphs are straight lines. The proof of this statement appears as an exercise at the end of this section. The graphs must be nonvertical, because a vertical line is not the graph of any function. (Why?)

To graph a linear function, simply locate two points on the graph and draw a straight line through them.

Example 1

Graph (a) $y = 3x - 2$ and   (b) $u + 3v + 3 = 0$

Solution

(a)   Locate *any* two solutions of the equation $y = 3x - 2$. For example, if $x = 0$, then $y = -2$; and if $x = 1$, then $y = 1$. Plot $(0, -2)$ and $(1, 1)$ and draw a straight line through them (Figure 3-1A).

(b)   The equation $u + 3v + 3 = 0$ can be put into the form of Equation (1) by solving for v (we are assuming that u is the independent variable). Thus,

$$v = -\frac{1}{3}u - 1$$

If $u = 0$, then $v = -1$; and if $u = 3$, then $v = -2$. Plot and graph (Figure 3-1B).

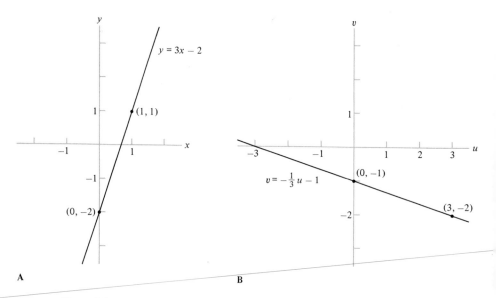

Figure 3-1

(A) The graph of $y = 3x - 2$. (B) The graph of $v = -\dfrac{1}{3}u - 1$. See Example 1.

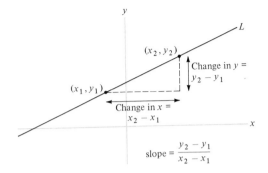

Figure 3-2
The slope of a line L in the xy-plane is the change in y divided by the change in x.

Slope of a line
Does a line tilt up or down? How steep is it? These geometric questions can be answered by using an algebraic concept, the slope of a line.

■ **Definition**
Let L be any nonvertical straight line, and let (x_1, y_1) and (x_2, y_2) be any two distinct points on L. The **slope** of L is the change in y (between the two points) divided by the change in x. In symbols,

$$\text{slope} = \frac{\text{change in } y}{\text{change in } x} = \frac{y_2 - y_1}{x_2 - x_1}$$

Figure 3-2 illustrates this definition. The order in which the points are chosen is not important, as the next example shows.

Example 2
If $(-3, 2)$ and $(4, -1)$ are points on a straight line, find the slope of the line.

Solution
Here, $x_1 = -3$, $y_1 = 2$, $x_2 = 4$, and $y_2 = -1$. According to the definition,

$$\text{slope} = \frac{y_2 - y_1}{x_2 - x_1} = \frac{-1 - 2}{4 - (-3)} = -\frac{3}{7}$$

Let us now see whether taking the points in reverse order changes the slope. This time let $x_1 = 4$, $y_1 = -1$, $x_2 = -3$, and $y_2 = 2$. Then

$$\text{slope} = \frac{y_2 - y_1}{x_2 - x_1} = \frac{2 - (-1)}{-3 - 4} = -\frac{3}{7}$$

There is an easy way to find the slope of a line if you know its equation.

■   Given an equation of a nonvertical line L, write it in the form

$$y = mx + b$$

Then m is the slope of L.

For example, the slope of the line $y = 3x - 2$ is 3. To find the slope of $u + 3v + 3 = 0$, rewrite it as $v = -\frac{1}{3}u - 1$; then its slope is $-\frac{1}{3}$.

The proof of the displayed statement is as follows: If (x_1, y_1) and (x_2, y_2) are any two distinct points on L, then

$$y_1 = mx_1 + b \quad \text{and} \quad y_2 = mx_2 + b$$

because the coordinates of the points must satisfy the equation of L. Subtract the first equation from the second:

$$y_2 - y_1 = (mx_2 + b) - (mx_1 + b)$$
$$= m(x_2 - x_1)$$

Because (x_1, y_1) and (x_2, y_2) are distinct points on a nonvertical line, $x_2 \neq x_1$ and $x_2 - x_1 \neq 0$. Thus, we may divide by $x_2 - x_1$:

$$m = \frac{y_2 - y_1}{x_2 - x_1}$$

By definition, this is the slope of L.

The sign of the slope has a geometric interpretation: it indicates how the line is inclined. In Figure 3-3A, the slope is positive and the line is inclined upward, that is, from lower left to upper right. This is described mathematically by saying that $y = mx + b$ is an **increasing function:** as the values of x increase, so do the values of y. In Figure 3-3C, the slope is negative and the line is inclined downward, that is, from upper left to lower right. In this case, we say that $y = mx + b$ is a **decreasing function:** as the values of x increase, the values of y decrease. In Figure 3-3B, the slope is zero, so the equation $y = mx + b$ reduces to $y = b$ and the graph is a horizontal line.

Let us verify these statements for the lines in Figure 3-1. In Figure 3-1A, $y = 3x - 2$; the slope is 3 and the line slants upward. As x increases, say from $x = 0$ to $x = 1$, so does y, from $y = -2$ to $y = 1$. In Figure 3-1B, $v = -\frac{1}{3}u - 1$; the slope is $-\frac{1}{3}$ and the line slants downward. As u increases, say from $u = 0$ to $u = 3$, the value of v decreases, from $v = -1$ to $v = -2$.

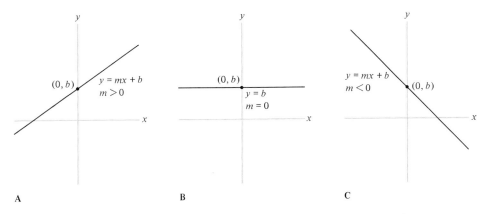

A   B   C

Figure 3-3
(A) A line with positive slope is the graph of an increasing function. (B) A line with 0 slope is the graph of a constant function. (C) A line with negative slope is the graph of a decreasing function.

■   Let $f(x) = mx + b$ and let L be its graph.

If $m > 0$, then L is inclined upward and f is increasing.

If $m = 0$, then L is horizontal and f is constant.

If $m < 0$, then L is inclined downward and f is decreasing.

The absolute value of the slope also has a geometric interpretation. A large absolute value indicates a steep slope—the change in y is great compared to the corresponding change in x. A small absolute value indicates a gentle slope—the change in y is small compared to the change in x (see Figure 3-4).

■   The absolute value of the slope measures steepness of inclination: the larger the value of $|m|$, the steeper the inclination of the line.

If $f(x) = mx + b$, and L is its graph, then the slope of L is the rate of change of f (see Exercise 37).

The slopes of parallel lines are related in a simple way. If the constant b is allowed to vary, the result is a set of lines $y = mx + b$ all with the same slope. As we observed in Section 2-3, each of these lines is just a translation of the line $y = mx$ up or down $|b|$ units. Thus, all the lines are parallel to each other. Conversely, if two lines are parallel, then a change in x will cause the same corresponding change in y on both lines. Therefore, *two lines are parallel if and only if they have the same slope* (see Figure 3-5).

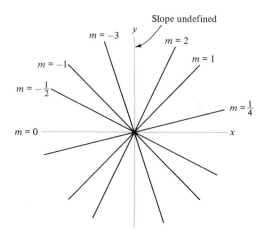

Figure 3-4
The absolute value of the slope indicates the steepness of the line. The larger the absolute value, the steeper the line.

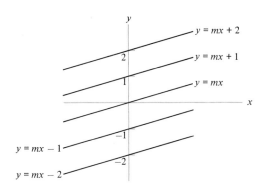

Figure 3-5
Lines are parallel if and only if they have the same slope.

The slopes of perpendicular lines also are related in a simple way. Figure 3-6 shows two perpendicular lines that intersect at the origin. Suppose that their equations are $y = mx$ and $y = m'x$. If you draw a vertical line through the point 1 on the x-axis, it will cross the two lines at $(1, m)$ and $(1, m')$. Three right triangles are formed; the two smaller ones are marked A and B, and the large one is composed of A and B together. Let us apply the Theorem of Pythagoras to these triangles:

$$m^2 + 1^2 = (\text{hypotenuse of A})^2$$

$$(m')^2 + 1^2 = (\text{hypotenuse of B})^2$$

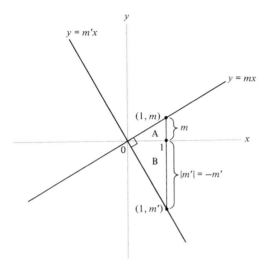

Figure 3-6
If two lines, $y = mx$ and $y = m'x$, are perpendicular, then $m = -1/m'$.

The hypotenuses of A and B are the legs of the big triangle, so

$$[m^2 + 1] + [(m')^2 + 1] = (m - m')^2$$
$$= m^2 - 2mm' + (m')^2$$

By combining like terms, we can rearrange this equation as

$$2 = -2mm'$$

Dividing by $-2m'$, we get

$$\frac{1}{-m'} = m$$

In words, the slopes of perpendicular lines are negative reciprocals of each other. Check this statement with Figure 3-1. The slopes are 3 and $-\frac{1}{3}$. Extend the line in part B until it crosses the line in part A. Notice that the two lines are perpendicular.

■   Slopes of parallel lines are equal.

Slopes of perpendicular lines are negative reciprocals of each other.

Equation of a line

If you know that two points (x_1, y_1) and (x_2, y_2) lie on a nonvertical line L, then the **two-point form**

$$y - y_1 = \frac{y_2 - y_1}{x_2 - x_1}(x - x_1)$$

is an equation whose graph is L.

If you know that the point (x_1, y_1) is on a line L whose slope is m, then the **point-slope form**

$$y - y_1 = m(x - x_1)$$

is an equation of L. You should memorize these equations; their proofs are exercises at the end of this section.

Example 3

Find an equation of the line through $(2, 1)$ and $(-4, 6)$. Is the line slanted upward?

Solution

Use the two-point form with $x_1 = 2$, $y_1 = 1$, $x_2 = -4$, and $y_2 = 6$.

$$y - 1 = \frac{6 - 1}{-4 - 2}(x - 2)$$

$$= -\frac{5}{6}x + \frac{10}{6}$$

In the form $y = mx + b$, this equation is

$$y = -\frac{5}{6}x + \frac{8}{3}$$

The slope is $-5/6$, so the line slants downward.

Example 4

Find an equation of the line through $(-1, 4)$ with slope 2. Where does the line cross the y-axis?

Solution

Use the point-slope form. The slope is 2 and the line passes through $(-1, 4)$, so let $x_1 = -1$ and $y_1 = 4$. Then

$$y - 4 = 2(x - (-1))$$

$$= 2x + 2$$

Thus, $y = 2x + 6$. The line crosses the y-axis at the point where $x = 0$. If $x = 0$, then $y = 6$, so the line crosses the y-axis at $(0, 6)$; the value of y at this point is called the **y-intercept.**

The information given in a textbook exercise or an exam question can be cleverly disguised, but don't be thrown off the track. Every problem calling for an equation of a nonvertical line can be solved by using either the two-point form or the point-slope form. Here are a few examples.

Example 5
Find an equation of the line through $(2, 4)$ that is parallel to the line $3x - 4y + 2 = 0$.

Solution
Solve for y to find the slope.

$$y = \frac{3}{4}x + \frac{1}{2}; \quad \text{slope} = \frac{3}{4}$$

Because the line you seek is parallel to this one, its slope is also $\frac{3}{4}$. Now use the point-slope form to obtain $y - 4 = \frac{3}{4}(x - 2)$, and simplify.

Example 6
Find an equation of the line that crosses the x-axis 3 units to the left of the origin and crosses the y-axis 4 units above the origin; that is, the x-intercept is -3 and its y-intercept is 4.

Solution
The x-intercept and the y-intercept yield two points, $(-3, 0)$ and $(0, 4)$, on the line. Use the two-point form to obtain

$$y - 0 = \frac{4 - 0}{0 - (-3)}(x - (-3))$$

and simplify.

Example 7

Find an equation of the line L_1 through $(-1, 3)$ that is perpendicular to the line L_2 through $(2, -7)$ and $(0, 5)$.

Solution

Find the slope of L_2 by using the two points given:

$$m = \frac{y_2 - y_1}{x_2 - x_1} = \frac{5 - (-7)}{0 - 2} = -6$$

Thus, the slope of the line L_1 is $\frac{1}{6}$. (Why?) Now use the point-slope form for L_1.

Exercises

Graph the following linear equations. The independent variables are $x, t,$ and u.

1. $y = -1$
2. $v = 2$
3. $y = 2x + 1$
4. $v = 4u + 2$
5. $s = -5t - 1$
6. $w = 6u - 1$
7. $y - \frac{4}{3}x + 2 = 0$
8. $y = \frac{8}{5}x + 1$
9. $v + \frac{1}{2}u = 1$
10. $v + \frac{1}{6}u = 3$
11. $3x - 4y - 6 = 0$
12. $4y - x + 5 = 0$
13. $1.5t + .3s = .9$
14. $6.4t - .8s = 1.6$

15. Compare slopes and decide which lines in Exercises 3, 5, 7, 9, 11, and 13 are parallel. Which are perpendicular? Look at the graphs to check your answers geometrically.

16. Do the same with Exercises 4, 6, 8, 10, 12, and 14.

In Exercises 17–26, find an equation of the line with the given properties. Compute the slope of each line and decide whether the linear function is increasing or decreasing.

17. Passes through $(-1, 2)$ and $(4, 1)$.
18. Passes through $(4, -7)$ and $(-2, 6)$.
19. Passes through $(-3, 2)$ with slope 5.
20. Passes through $(4, -1)$ with slope 0.
21. Passes through $(0, -3)$ and is parallel to $3y - 4x + 2 = 0$.
22. Passes through $(-2, 5)$ and is parallel to $x + y = 6$.
23. Passes through $(-4, 7)$ and is parallel to the line through $(0, 0)$ and $(5, 2)$.
24. Passes through $(2, 3)$ and is perpendicular to the line through $(-1, 3)$ and $(2, 2)$.
25. With x-intercept 2 and y-intercept -1.
26. With x-intercept -2 and y-intercept -4.

27. It is proved in every geometry course that "a line tangent to a circle is perpendicular to the radius at the point of tangency." Suppose there is a circle with center at the origin and radius 1.

(a) Find an equation of the line tangent to the circle at the point ($\sqrt{1/3}$, $\sqrt{2/3}$). (Draw a picture.)

(b) What is the slope of the line tangent to the circle at the point (0, 1)? How about the slope of the tangent line at the point (1, 0)?

28. (Inverses) We have already observed (Exercises 31 in Sections 2-1 and 2-5) that, if an equation can be used to define each of the variables as a function of the other, these functions are inverses.

(a) Show that a linear function $f(x) = mx + b$ has an inverse if and only if the slope m is not zero. [HINT: Set $y = mx + b$ and solve for x.]

(b) Suppose $f(x) = mx + b$ and $m \neq 0$. Let

$$g(x) = \frac{1}{m}x - \frac{b}{m}$$

and prove that f and g are inverses; in other words, show that $f(g(x)) = x = g(f(x))$.

(c) If f and g are linear functions and are inverses of each other, what can you say about the relationship of the slopes of their graphs?

29. (Continuation of Exercise 28) In an xy-plane, carefully plot the line $y = x$ as a dotted line. In the same plane, graph $f(x) = 3x - 4$ and its inverse. Notice that each graph is the reflection of the other through the line $y = x$. *This is always true of inverses.*

30. (Absolute value) Although the function $y = 3x + 1$ is linear, the function $y = |3x + 1|$ is not: its graph is not a straight line. To plot its graph, first plot the line $y = 3x + 1$. However, absolute value is never negative, so the part of the line below the x-axis must be reflected back above it. This is shown in Figure 3-7. (Another way to plot this equation is to factor out the 3, and consider $y = 3|x + \frac{1}{3}|$ as a translation of $y = 3|x|$ by $\frac{1}{3}$ unit to the left.) Now try your hand at graphing (a) $y = |2x - 1|$ and (b) $y = |-3x + 2|$.

31. The relationship between Fahrenheit (F) and Celsius (C) temperatures is linear. Given that $0°C = 32°F$ and $100°C = 212°F$, write F as a linear function of C. What is F when $C = 50$?

32. The sales S of a certain company are found to be a linear function of time t. If the sales the first year ($t = 1$) were $10,000, and the sales the fifth year ($t = 5$) were $30,000, can you predict the sales during the tenth year? What is the rate of increase of sales per year? Does this have anything to do with slope?

In Exercise 32, sales were a linear function of time. The rate of increase will be the same each year. If sales are not a linear function of time, the increase will change from year to year.

33. (Average rate of change) The sales (in thousands of dollars) of a certain company are a function of time: $S = t^2 + 3t$. What is the average rate of change of

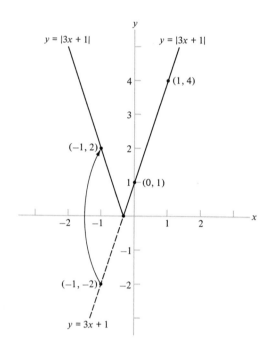

Figure 3-7
The line through $(1, 4)$ and $(-1, -2)$ is the graph of $y = 3x + 1$. The V-shaped graph is the graph of $y = |3x + 1|$. The left half of the V is the reflection above the x-axis of the part of $y = 3x + 1$ that is below the x-axis.

sales over the first five years (from $t = 0$ to $t = 5$)? What is the average rate of change over the next five years? What is the exact rate of change at the beginning of the sixth year?

In the text you were promised the proofs of three statements:

The graph of a linear function is a straight line.

If (x_1, y_1) and (x_2, y_2) are on a nonvertical line, then the two-point form is an equation of the line.

If a line has slope m and passes through (x_1, y_1), then the point-slope form is an equation of the line.

Here are the proofs:

34.   (The graph of a linear equation is a straight line.) We shall use the fact that three points P_1, P_2, P_3 are collinear if and only if the distance $d(P_1, P_2)$ plus the distance $d(P_2, P_3)$ equals the distance $d(P_1, P_3)$ (see Figure 3-8).

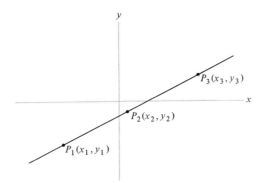

Figure 3-8
Three points P_1, P_2, and P_3 are collinear if and only if $d(P_1, P_2) + d(P_2, P_3) = d(P_1, P_3)$.
See Exercise 34.

Let $y = mx + b$ and let P_1, P_2, P_3 be any three distinct points whose coordinates satisfy the equation. Assume they are arranged as in Figure 3-8, with $x_1 < x_2 < x_3$. Justify each of the statements below to show that the three points are collinear.

(1) $y_1 = mx_1 + b$, $y_2 = mx_2 + b$ and $y_3 = mx_3 + b$

(2) $\quad\quad d(P_1, P_2) = \sqrt{(x_2 - x_1)^2 + (mx_2 - mx_1)^2}$

(3) $\quad\quad\quad\quad\quad = \sqrt{(x_2 - x_1)^2(m^2 + 1)}$ (Factor.)

(4) $\quad\quad\quad\quad\quad = (x_2 - x_1)\sqrt{m^2 + 1}$ (Careful! $\sqrt{t^2} = |t|$.)

(5) $\quad\quad d(P_2, P_3) = (x_3 - x_2)\sqrt{m^2 + 1}$

(6) Add: $(4) + (5) = (x_3 - x_1)\sqrt{m^2 + 1}$

(7) $\quad\quad\quad\quad\quad = d(P_1, P_3)$

(8) Therefore, P_1, P_2, and P_3 are collinear.

35. (Two-point form) Let (x_1, y_1) and (x_2, y_2) be distinct points on a nonvertical line. If the point (x, y) is also on that line, then its coordinates must satisfy the equation

$$y - y_1 = \frac{y_2 - y_1}{x_2 - x_1}(x - x_1)$$

Justify each of the steps in the following proof.
(1) If $x = x_1$, then $y = y_1$. (Why?) In this case, the equation is satisfied. It also holds if $x = x_2$. (Why?)
(2) If $x \neq x_1$ and $x \neq x_2$, then two similar triangles are formed, as in Figure 3-9. (If (x, y) lies between the two points or to the left of both of them, other triangles will be formed, but they will always be similar.)

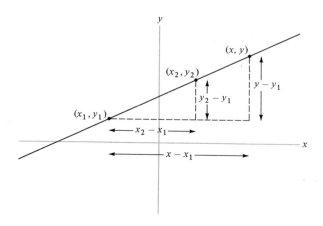

Figure 3-9
If (x_1, y_1), (x_2, y_2), and (x, y) are on the same line, then

$$\frac{y - y_1}{x - x_1} = \frac{y_2 - y_1}{x_2 - x_1}$$

See Exercise 35.

(3) $$\frac{y - y_1}{x - x_1} = \frac{y_2 - y_1}{x_2 - x_1}$$

(4)   The equation in (3) is equivalent to the two-point form.

36.   (Point-slope form) Let (x_1, y_1) be on a line whose slope is m. If (x, y) is also on the line, then its coordinates must satisfy the equation

$$y - y_1 = m(x - x_1)$$

Justify each of the steps in the following proof.
    (1)   The coordinates of (x_1, y_1) satisfy the equation.
    (2)   If (x, y) is a point on the line distinct from (x_1, y_1), then

$$m = \frac{y - y_1}{x - x_1}$$

    (3)   The equation in (2) is equivalent to the point-slope form.

37.   Let $f(x) = mx + b$. Show that a.r.c.$f(x, h) = m$ for all x and h. Thus, *the slope of a line is its rate of change.*

38. (Graphs)
    (a) Make up a function whose graph is a horizontal line through $(-17, 6)$; through $(5, 0)$.
    (b) Make up a function whose graph is a line inclined at an angle of $45°$ passing through $(0, -2)$; through $(-2, 0)$.
    (c) Make up a function whose graph is V-shaped with a vertex at $(3, 2)$; at $(-1, -1)$.
    (d) Same as (c), but the graph is Λ-shaped.
39. Make up some problems that call for an equation of a line; disguise the information carefully. Get a classmate to do the same, and exchange problems.
40. Find the slope of $3p + 2q - 12 = 0$. Did you solve for p in terms of q or vice versa? Are the answers different? Is there any relationship between the answers? On an exam, how would you know which answer is correct?

3-2
Systems of Linear Equations

Combining algebra and geometry enables us to represent the (algebraic) linear equation $y = mx + b$ as a (geometric) straight line. This line is the set of all points (x, y) in the plane that satisfy the equation.

Going one step further, suppose we have two such linear equations, each represented by a line. If the two lines have different slopes, they are not parallel, so they will intersect at a single point. The coordinates of this point must satisfy *both* equations at the same time. Thus, once more, from geometry we can draw an algebraic conclusion: a **system** of two linear equations with two variables will have a **simultaneous solution** if the equations do not represent two distinct parallel lines.

Example 1
Find the simultaneous solution of the system

$$3x - 2y = 4$$

$$-x + 5y = 3$$

by using graphs.

Solution
Carefully graph both equations in the same plane. The coordinates of the point at which the graphs intersect will be the simultaneous solution. According to

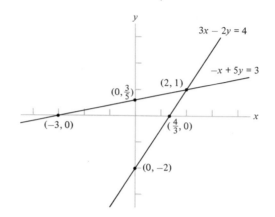

Figure 3-10
If the graphs of the two equations intersect, the coordinates of the point of intersection are a
simultaneous solution of both equations. See Example 1.

Figure 3-10, this point is (2, 1). Now check the result:

$$3(2) - 2(1) = 4 \quad \text{and} \quad -(2) + 5(1) = 3$$

so $x = 2$ and $y = 1$ is the simultaneous solution.

The graphic method of getting algebraic information has limitations. For one
thing, it is not very accurate. For instance, if the solution of a system were the pair
(1.0312, 4.1290), it would be pretty difficult to obtain these figures from a graph.
Thus, although the geometric approach, with its pictures, can aid understanding, we
need a more precise method of solving systems of equations. There are many such
methods: substitution and elimination are described below, and the method of
determinants is touched on in the exercises at the end of this section.*

Substitution is solving one equation for one of the variables in terms of the
others, and substituting this value into the remaining equations.

Example 2
Solve this system by substitution:

$$2x + y = 3$$

$$5x - 2y = 4$$

---

*These and other methods are explained in more detail in Appendix B.

Solution

Solve the first equation for y in terms of x. Thus, $y = 3 - 2x$. Now substitute this value for y in the second equation:

$$5x - 2(3 - 2x) = 4$$

$$5x - 6 + 4x = 4$$

$$9x = 10$$

$$x = \frac{10}{9}$$

Now replace x by $\frac{10}{9}$ in either equation to obtain a value for y. Using the first equation, we have $2(\frac{10}{9}) + y = 3$, so

$$y = 3 - \frac{20}{9}$$

$$= \frac{27}{9} - \frac{20}{9} = \frac{7}{9}$$

Thus, $x = \frac{10}{9}$ and $y = \frac{7}{9}$ is the simultaneous solution. Check this solution in each of the original equations:

$$2\left(\frac{10}{9}\right) + \frac{7}{9} = \frac{27}{9} = 3 \quad \text{and} \quad 5\left(\frac{10}{9}\right) - 2\left(\frac{7}{9}\right) = \frac{50}{9} - \frac{14}{9} = 4$$

In the method of **elimination,** the equations are multiplied by nonzero constants chosen so that the new equations can be added or subtracted to eliminate one or more of the variables.

Example 3

Solve by elimination:

$$(1) \quad 3x + y = -2$$

$$(2) \quad -2x - 3y = 13$$

Solution

Multiply Equation (1) by 3 to obtain the new system

$$(1') \quad 9x + 3y = -6$$

$$(2) \quad -2x - 3y = 13$$

Equations (1′) and (1) have all the same solutions, so the original system and the new system have the same simultaneous solution; they are called **equivalent systems.** Why did we multiply the first equation by the number 3? To eliminate one of the variables. Notice that if we now add Equations (1′) and (2), the y's will drop out; that is, we will eliminate the variable y. (We could have multiplied Equation (1) by 2 and Equation (2) by 3, obtaining the equivalent system

$$6x + 2y = -4$$

$$-6x - 9y = 39$$

Adding these equations would eliminate x. The elimination of y requires less computation and is, therefore, preferable.) Now add (1′) and (2) to obtain:

$$(3) \quad 7x = 7$$

If (x, y) is the simultaneous solution of the original system, then x must satisfy Equation (3); that is, $x = 1$.* Insert this value of x into one of the original equations to obtain the value of y. Using (1), we have

$$3(1) + y = -2$$

$$y = -5$$

Thus, $(1, -5)$ is the simultaneous solution. Check this solution in each of the original equations:

$$3(1) + (-5) = -2 \quad \text{and} \quad -2(1) - 3(-5) = 13$$

In the next example there are three equations with three unknowns. The simultaneous solution will be a triple (x, y, z). The procedure is exactly the same as with two equations and two unknowns: *Multiply any of the equations by a nonzero constant and combine the new equations to eliminate one or more variables.*

Example 4
Solve by elimination:

$$\begin{align}
(1) \quad & 3x + 2y + 5z = 8 \\
(2) \quad & -4x + y + 3z = 5 \\
(3) \quad & x + 4y + 2z = 0
\end{align}$$

---

*This statement is justified in Exercise 33 at the end of this section.

Solution
Look over the three equations and decide which variable to eliminate first; choose the one that will make the computations as easy as possible. In this case, y seems like a good choice. To eliminate y from Equations (1) and (2), multiply (2) by 2 and *subtract* it from (1) yielding the new equation (1′):

$$
\begin{array}{rlrl}
& (1) & 3x + 2y + 5z &= 8 \\
\text{subtract} & 2 \times (2) & -8x + 2y + 6z &= 10 \\
\hline
& (1') & 11x \quad\quad - z &= -2
\end{array}
$$

Now eliminate y from any other pair of equations, either (1) and (3) or (2) and (3); suppose we choose the latter:

$$
\begin{array}{rlrl}
& 4 \times (2) & -16x + 4y + 12z &= 20 \\
\text{subtract} & (3) & x + 4y + 2x &= 0 \\
\hline
& (2') & -17x \quad\quad + 10z &= 20
\end{array}
$$

Notice that the *same variable, y,* was eliminated *both* times. We now have a new system, (1′) and (2′), of two equations with just *two* unknowns. If (x, y, z) is a solution for the original system, then x and z must satisfy the new system

$$(1') \quad 11x - z = -2$$

$$(2') \quad -17x + 10z = 20$$

Multiply (1′) by 10 and add it to (2′) to obtain $93x = 0$; thus, $x = 0$. Inserting $x = 0$, into either (1′) or (2′) yields $z = 2$. Using these values for x and z in one of the original equations, say (1), we see that $y = -1$. Therefore, the triple $(0, -1, 2)$ is the simultaneous solution. Check this solution in each of the original equations:

$$3(0) + 2(-1) + 5(2) = 8, \quad\quad -4(0) + (-1) + 3(2) = 5$$

$$\text{and} \quad 0 + 4(-1) + 2(2) = 0$$

Simultaneous systems are often used to solve word problems.

Example 5
The sum of the digits of a two-digit number is 11. If the digits are reversed, the resulting number is 45 larger than the original number. Find the original number.

Solution
Let x be the tens digit and y be the units digit. The sum of the digits is 11 so

$$(1) \quad x + y = 11$$

The original number has the value $10x + y$; with the digits reversed, the value is $10y + x$. The difference $(10y + x) - (10x + y) = -9x + 9y$ equals 45. Thus,

$$(2) \quad -9x + 9y = 45$$

Now $9 \times$ (1) plus (2) yields the equation $18y = 144$; therefore, $y = 8$. It follows that $x = 3$, and the original number is 38. CHECK: $3 + 8 = 11$ and $83 - 38 = 45$.

Example 6

Two solutions are 20 and 50 percent sulfuric acid. How many cc (cubic centimeters) of each should be mixed to make 100 cc of 30 percent solution?

Solution

Let x and y be the number of cc of 20 and 50 percent solutions mixed. Then $x + y = 100$. We also know that

$$.20x = \text{amount of acid in first solution,}$$

$$.50y = \text{amount of acid in second solution, and}$$

$$.30(100) = 30 = \text{amount of acid in final solution.}$$

Because the amount of acid in the final solution is the same as the total amount in the first two solutions, we have $.20x + .50y = 30$, or, multiplying by 100 to get rid of the decimal points, $20x + 50y = 3000$. Thus, we have two equations with two unknowns:

$$(1) \quad x + \quad y = 100$$

$$(2) \quad 20x + 50y = 3000$$

Now, 20 times Equation (1) *minus* Equation (2) yields $-30y = -1000$, or $y = 33\frac{1}{3}$ cc; it follows that $x = 66\frac{2}{3}$ cc.

Example 7

At a constant airspeed, a pilot flew from Chicago to San Francisco against the wind in 4 hours; the return flight with the wind took only $3\frac{1}{2}$ hours. The distance from Chicago to San Francisco is 3000 kilometers. Find the airspeed of the plane and the speed of the wind.

Solution
Let v and w be the airspeed of the plane and the speed of the wind. Then $v - w$ and $v + w$ are the ground speeds of the plane in the two directions. Thus, $4(v - w) = 3000$ and $\frac{7}{2}(v + w) = 3000$. Multiplying through to eliminate fractions, we have

$$(1) \quad 4v - 4w = 3000$$

$$(2) \quad 7v + 7w = 6000$$

Now 7 × (1) plus 4 × (2) yields $56v = 45000$ or $v = \dfrac{45000}{56}$ kilometers (about 500 miles) per hour. As for the wind, $w = \dfrac{3000}{56}$ kilometers (about 30 miles) per hour.

Exercises

Solve graphically and check your answers.

1. $2x + 3y = 0$ **2.** $3x - 4y = 5$ **3.** $y = -2x + 3$
   $-x + 7y = 0$ $2x + y = -4$ $x = 3y - 2$

Solve by substitution and check your answers.

4. $t - 3s = 2$ **5.** $5x - y = -2$ **6.** $\dfrac{2}{3}u - \dfrac{1}{2}v = 2$
   $4t + 5s = -9$ $2x + 6y = 12$

   $\dfrac{1}{3}u + \dfrac{3}{4}v = \dfrac{1}{2}$

Solve by elimination and check your answers.

7. $2x - y = 1$ **8.** $3x + 2y = -1$ **9.** $12a - 5b = 9$
   $3x + 2y = 33$ $4x - 3y = -7$ $3a - 8b = -18$

10. $\dfrac{3}{2}t - 4s = 7$ **11.** $\dfrac{x}{2} + \dfrac{y}{3} = 8$ **12.** $\dfrac{3u}{2} - \dfrac{v}{3} = 5$

   $t + \dfrac{1}{2}s = \dfrac{3}{2}$ $\dfrac{2x}{3} + \dfrac{3y}{2} = 17$ $\dfrac{5u}{2} + \dfrac{2v}{3} = 12$

13. $2x + y - 3z = 7$ **14.** $a + 4b - c = 6$ **15.** $u + 3v + 4w = 14$
    $-x + 4y + z = 6$ $2a - b + c = 3$ $2u - 3v + 2w = 10$
    $3x + 2y + 7z = 0$ $3a + 2b + 3c = 16$ $3u - v + w = 9$

Use the method you think easiest and check your answers.

16. $\dfrac{3}{2}x + \dfrac{3}{4}y = 1$ 17. $3x + 4y = 5$
                                                                                   $3x + 4y = 7$

    $\dfrac{1}{10}x + \dfrac{3}{10}y = 4$

18. $3a + b + c = 1$ 19. $a + b - 2c = 0$
      $-2a - 4b + c = 1$ $2a - b - c = 0$
      $5a + 2b - c = -1$ $a + b + c = 3$

20.   (Determinants) Here is yet another method of solving simultaneous equations.
It can be applied to systems with any number of equations (see Appendix B).
      (a)   Solve the system of equations

$$(1) \quad a_1 x + b_1 y = c_1$$

$$(2) \quad a_2 x + b_2 y = c_2$$

as follows:

      (i) multiply (1) by b_2 and (2) by $-b_1$;
      (ii) add the new equations, eliminating y;
      (iii) show that $x = \dfrac{c_1 b_2 - c_2 b_1}{a_1 b_2 - a_2 b_1}$; and
      (iv) show that $y = \dfrac{a_1 c_2 - a_2 c_1}{a_1 b_2 - a_2 b_1}$.

      (b)   If four numbers a, b, c, and d are written in two rows

$$a \quad b$$
$$c \quad d$$

then their **determinant,** written

$$\begin{vmatrix} a & b \\ c & d \end{vmatrix}$$

is $ad - bc$. For example,

$$\begin{vmatrix} 2 & -1 \\ 4 & 3 \end{vmatrix} = 2 \cdot 3 - 4(-1) = 10$$

$$\begin{vmatrix} 0 & 2 \\ 1 & -3 \end{vmatrix} = 0(-3) - 1 \cdot 2 = -2$$

$$\begin{vmatrix} a_1 & b_1 \\ a_2 & b_2 \end{vmatrix} = a_1 b_2 - a_2 b_1$$

Thus, the numerators and denominators in steps (iii) and (iv) above can be written as determinants:

$$x = \frac{\begin{vmatrix} c_1 & b_1 \\ c_2 & b_2 \end{vmatrix}}{\begin{vmatrix} a_1 & b_1 \\ a_2 & b_2 \end{vmatrix}} \quad \text{and} \quad y = \frac{\begin{vmatrix} a_1 & c_1 \\ a_2 & c_2 \end{vmatrix}}{\begin{vmatrix} a_1 & b_1 \\ a_2 & b_2 \end{vmatrix}}$$

(c) **Cramer's Rule:** For any system of linear equations

$$a_1 x + b_1 y = c_1$$

$$a_2 x + b_2 y = c_2$$

if

$$\begin{vmatrix} a_1 & b_1 \\ a_2 & b_2 \end{vmatrix} \neq 0$$

there is a unique simultaneous solution given by

$$x = \frac{\begin{vmatrix} c_1 & b_1 \\ c_2 & b_2 \end{vmatrix}}{\begin{vmatrix} a_1 & b_1 \\ a_2 & b_2 \end{vmatrix}} \quad \text{and} \quad y = \frac{\begin{vmatrix} a_1 & c_1 \\ a_2 & c_2 \end{vmatrix}}{\begin{vmatrix} a_1 & b_1 \\ a_2 & b_2 \end{vmatrix}}$$

For example, let us solve the system

$$3x + 2y = 1$$

$$4x - 5y = -14$$

The denominator we need in order to use Cramer's Rule is

$$\begin{vmatrix} a_1 & b_1 \\ a_2 & b_2 \end{vmatrix} = \begin{vmatrix} 3 & 2 \\ 4 & -5 \end{vmatrix} = 3(-5) - 4 \cdot 2 = -23 \neq 0$$

Therefore, by Cramer's Rule,

$$x = \frac{\begin{vmatrix} c_1 & b_1 \\ c_2 & b_2 \end{vmatrix}}{-23} = \frac{\begin{vmatrix} 1 & 2 \\ -14 & -5 \end{vmatrix}}{-23} = \frac{(1)(-5) - (-14)(2)}{-23} = -1$$

$$y = \frac{\begin{vmatrix} a_1 & c_1 \\ a_2 & c_2 \end{vmatrix}}{-23} = \frac{\begin{vmatrix} 3 & 1 \\ 4 & -14 \end{vmatrix}}{-23} = \frac{(3)(-14) - (4)(1)}{-23} = 2$$

CHECK: $3(-1) + 2(2) = 1$ and $4(-1) - 5(2) = -14$.
(d)   Solve the systems in Exercises 1–8 above by using Cramer's Rule.

Solve these word problems by using systems of equations.

21.   Find values of m and b so that the line $y = mx + b$ passes through $(1, 3)$ and $(-2, 4)$. [HINT: Use the coordinates of the two points to obtain two equations. Solve for m and b.]

22.   Find values of a, b, and c so that the graph of $y = ax^2 + bx + c$ passes through the points $(-1, -2)$, $(1, 0)$, and $(2, 1)$.

23.   Show that if $mx + b = -3x + 6$ for all x, then $m = -3$ and $b = 6$. [HINT: Let $x = 1$ to obtain the equation $m + b = 3$; then set $x = 2$ to obtain $2m + b = 0$. Solve these two equations simultaneously. Actually, any two values of x will do; $x = 0$ and $x = 1$ makes things pretty easy.]

24.   Show that if $ax^2 + bx + c = 2x^2 - 3x - 4$ for all x, then $a = 2$, $b = -3$, and $c = -4$. [HINT: See the hint for Exercise 23. Choose three different values of x to obtain a system of three equations.]

25.   Find two numbers whose difference is 8, and the sum of twice the first and 3 times the second is 32.

26.   Find three numbers whose sum is 2/3, the difference of twice the first and three times the second is $-1/2$, and the third is the sum of the first two.

27.   The sum of the digits of a two-digit number is 8. If the digits are reversed, the resulting number is 18 larger than the original number. Find the original number.

28.   One alloy contains 20% copper, and another contains 35% copper. How much of each alloy should be melted and combined to produce 100 grams of a new alloy containing 30 percent copper?

29.   If it takes a man 3 hours to row 12 kilometers downstream and 5 hours to return, find the speed of the current and the man's rowing speed in still water.

30.   Fahrenheit and Celsius temperatures are linearly related; that is, there are constants a and b such that

$$F = aC + b$$

Find a and b if the freezing point of water is $32°F$ and $0°C$, and the boiling point of water is $212°F$ and $100°C$.

31. Two kilos of meat and three kilos of butter cost $6.50. A month later the prices of meat and butter have increased by 10% and 5%, respectively, and the same order now costs $7.00. What was the original cost of a kilo of each? (*Kilo* is short for kilogram.)

32. (Use three equations.) A collection of 30 coins consists of nickels, dimes, and quarters. The total amount of money is $3.25. If the numbers of nickels and dimes were reversed, the total amount would be $3.00. How many of each coin are there?

33. Suppose that the pair (p, q) is the simultaneous solution of the system

$$a_1 x + b_1 y = c_1$$

$$a_2 x + b_2 y = c_2$$

(a) Show that if $d \neq 0$, then $x = p$ and $y = q$ also satisfy the new equation $d a_1 x + d b_1 y = d c_1$.
(b) Show that $x = p$ and $y = q$ also satisfy $(a_1 + a_2)x + (b_1 + b_2)y = c_1 + c_2$, which is the sum of the two equations.
Parts (a) and (b) together justify the procedures used in solving systems of equations by elimination.

34. Make up a system of two equations with two unknowns; solve and check. Make up and solve a system of three equations with three unknowns. Did the answers come out messy? Try again; this time make up systems whose solutions are integers.

35. Make up word problems like Exercises 25–32. Exchange problems with a classmate.

3-3
Quadratic Functions

Any equation that can be put into the form

$$y = ax^2 + bx + c \qquad (a \neq 0)$$

is called a **quadratic equation.** Such an equation defines y as a **quadratic function** of x.

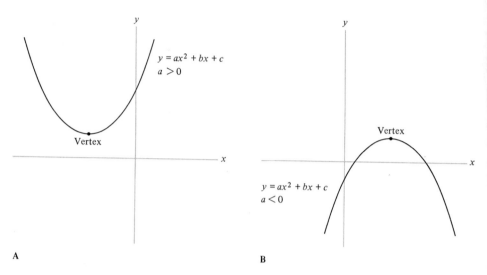

Figure 3-11
If $a \neq 0$, then the graph of $y = ax^2 + bx + c$ is a parabola. (A) If $a > 0$, then the parabola opens upward, and the vertex is the lowest point on the graph. (B) If $a < 0$, then the parabola opens downward, and the vertex is the highest point on the graph.

Graph of a quadratic function

The graph of any quadratic function is a curve called a **parabola.** Parabolas have the general shape of the curves in Figure 3-11. The point at which a parabola changes direction is called its **vertex.**

Example 1
Graph the function $y = x^2$.

Solution
This is a quadratic with $a = 1$, $b = 0$, and $c = 0$. It is the simplest kind of quadratic function. Make a table of values. Plot these points and connect them with a smooth curve as in Figure 3-12. This curve is a parabola: it opens upward, and the origin is its vertex.

x	0	1	-1	2	-2
$y = x^2$	0	1	1	4	4

Example 2
Graph the quadratics $y = 2x^2$ and $y = \frac{1}{2}x^2$, and compare them with the graph of $y = x^2$.

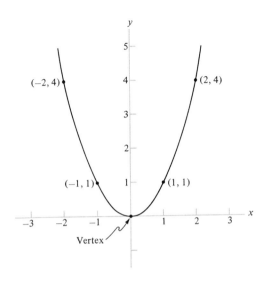

Figure 3-12
The graph of $y = x^2$ is a parabola. See Example 1.

Solution
Make a table of values for each of the functions. Plot these points and sketch the curves as in Figure 3-13. Each parabola opens upward and its vertex is at the origin. The graph of $y = 2x^2$ is steeper than the graph of $y = x^2$; the graph of $y = \frac{1}{2}x^2$ is flatter. In general, the graph of $y = ax^2$ opens *upward* if $a > 0$; its vertex is at the origin; it is *steeper* than $y = x^2$ if $a > 1$, and *flatter* if $a < 1$.

x	0	± 1	± 2
$y = x^2$	0	1	4

x	0	± 1	± 2
$y = \frac{1}{2}x^2$	0	1/2	2

x	0	± 1	± 2
$y = 2x^2$	0	2	8

The equation $y = (x - 2)^2 + 1$ is a quadratic; multiplied out, it is $y = x^2 - 4x + 5$. The similar equation $y = 2(x + 1)^2 - 1 = 2x^2 + 4x + 1$ is also a quadratic. The graphs of these functions are parabolas, but their vertices are not at the origin.

Example 3
Graph (a) $y = (x - 2)^2 + 1$ and (b) $y = 2(x + 1)^2 - 1$.

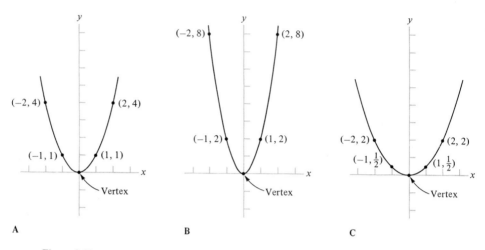

Figure 3-13
(A) The graph of $y = x^2$. (B) The graph of $y = 2x^2$ (C) The graph of $y = \frac{1}{2}x^2$. See Example 2.

Solution
You should recognize these graphs as translations: the first is a translation of $y = x^2$ two units to the right and one unit up; the second translates $y = 2x^2$ one unit to the left and one unit down.

(a) $y = (x - 2)^2 + 1$. If $y = x^2$ is shifted two units to the right and one unit up, its vertex will be at the point $(2, 1)$. Plot one point to the left of the vertex (let $x = 1$) and one point to the right (let $x = 3$). If $x = 1$, then $y = (1 - 2)^2 + 1 = 2$. If $x = 3$, then $y = (3 - 2)^2 + 1 = 2$. Plot the vertex $(2, 1)$ and the points $(1, 2)$ and $(3, 2)$. It is also a good idea to set $x = 0$ to find the y-intercept, $y = (0 - 2)^2 + 1 = 5$. Now connect these points with a parabola as in Figure 3-14.

(b) $y = 2(x + 1)^2 - 1$. Now it is $y = 2x^2$ that is shifted: one unit to the left and one unit down. It follows that the vertex is $(-1, -1)$. Again, determine a point to the left of the vertex (let $x = -2$) and to the right (let $x = 0$). If $x = -2$, then $y = 2(-2 + 1)^2 - 1 = 1$. If $x = 0$, then $y = 2(0 + 1)^2 - 1 = 1$. Plot the vertex $(-1, -1)$ and the points $(-2, 1)$ and $(0, 1)$. The y-intercept is 1. Now connect these points with a parabola as in Figure 3-15.

In the equations graphed so far, the coefficient of the squared term was positive; the parabolas opened upward. If this coefficient is negative, the parabola will open downward (see Figure 3-11B).

Example 4
Graph (a) $y = -x^2$ and (b) $y = -\frac{1}{2}(x - 1)^2 + 2$.

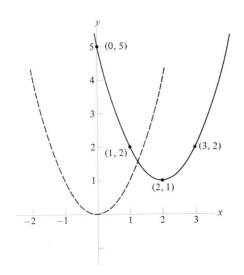

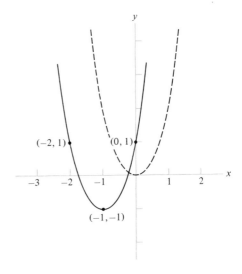

Figure 3-14
The graph of $y = (x - 2)^2 + 1$ (solid curve) is a translation of the graph of $y = x^2$ (dashed curve). See Example 3(a).

Figure 3-15
The graph of $y = 2(x + 1)^2 - 1$ (solid curve) is a translation of the graph of $y = 2x^2$ (dashed curve). See Example 3(b).

Solution
(a)   Make a table of values.

x	0	± 1	± 2
$y = -x^2$	0	-1	-4

Plot these points and join them with a parabola as in Figure 3-16.
(b)   This graph is a translation of $y = -\frac{1}{2}x^2$ one unit to the right and two units up. Thus, the vertex is the point $(1, 2)$. Now find a point on each side of the vertex.   If $x = 0$,   then $y = -\frac{1}{2}(0 - 1)^2 + 2 = \frac{3}{2}$.   If $x = 2$,   then $y = -\frac{1}{2}(2 - 1)^2 + 2 = \frac{3}{2}$. Plot these points and sketch the curve as in Figure 3-17.

The preceding examples show how a quadratic equation can be graphed easily if it can be written in the form $y = a(x - h)^2 + k$: locate the vertex at (h, k); plot a point on either side of this vertex, and plot the y-intercept; connect these points with a parabola. Can every quadratic equation be written in that form? Yes!

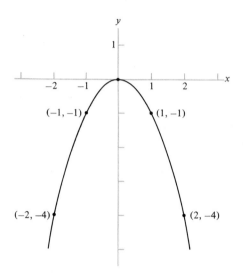

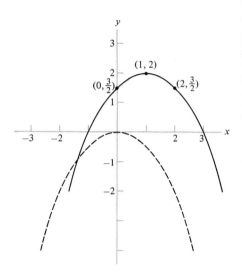

Figure 3-16
The graph of $y = -x^2$ is a parabola that opens downward. See Example 4(a).

Figure 3-17
The graph of $y = -\frac{1}{2}(x - 1)^2 + 2$ (solid curve) is a translation of the graph of $y = -\frac{1}{2}x^2$ (dashed curve). See Example 4(b).

Completing the square

Adding a constant to a quadratic expression $x^2 + bx$ in order to make it into a perfect square is called **completing the square**. The constant that is added must be $(b/2)^2$, that is, the square of one half of the coefficient of the linear term. This is because in the formula for a perfect square $(x + r)^2 = x^2 + 2rx + r^2$, the third term is the square of one-half of the coefficients of x. Here are some examples:

$$x^2 + 4x; \text{ add } (4/2)^2 = 4 \text{ to get } x^2 + 4x + 4 = (x + 2)^2$$

$$t^2 - 6t; \text{ add } (-6/2)^2 = 9 \text{ to get } t^2 - 6t + 9 = (t - 3)^2$$

$$u^2 - 5u; \text{ add } (-5/2)^2 = 25/4 \text{ to get } u^2 - 5u + \tfrac{25}{4} = (u - \tfrac{5}{2})^2$$

The next examples show how to use this method to rewrite any quadratic $y = ax^2 + bx + c$ in the new form

$$y = a(x - h)^2 + k \tag{1}$$

This locates the vertex at (h, k) and makes it easy to sketch the graph.

Example 5

Complete the square, locate the vertex, and sketch the graph of (a) $y = x^2 - 2x + 3$ and (b) $s = -t^2 - 3t + 1$.

Solution

(a)   Forget about the constant 3 for a moment. We must add $(-2/2)^2 = 1$ to $x^2 - 2x$ to make it into a perfect square. But adding the constant 1 changes the original function, *unless* we also subtract 1. Thus,

$$y = x^2 - 2x + 3$$

$$= (x^2 - 2x + 1 - 1) + 3 \qquad \text{(Leaves original function}$$

$$= (x^2 - 2x + 1) - 1 + 3 \qquad \text{unchanged)}$$

$$= (x - 1)^2 + 2$$

This is in the form (1) above, with $a = 1$, $h = 1$, and $k = 2$. It follows that the vertex is at $(1, 2)$; the graph is shown in Figure 3-18A.

(b) $s = -t^2 - 3t + 1$. In this function, the coefficient of the squared term is negative. This calls for a slightly different approach. Think of $-t^2 - 3t$ as $-(t^2 + 3t)$ and add $(\frac{3}{2})^2 = \frac{9}{4}$ *inside the parentheses* to make $t^2 + 3t$ into a perfect square. To leave the original function unchanged, we must also subtract $\frac{9}{4}$. Therefore,

$$s = -t^2 - 3t + 1$$

$$= -(t^2 + 3t + \tfrac{9}{4} - \tfrac{9}{4}) + 1 \qquad \text{(Leaves original function}$$

$$= -(t^2 + 3t + \tfrac{9}{4}) + \tfrac{9}{4} + 1 \qquad \text{unchanged)}$$

$$= -(t + \tfrac{3}{2})^2 + \tfrac{13}{4} \qquad (+\tfrac{9}{4}, \textit{not} -\tfrac{9}{4}; \text{ why?})$$

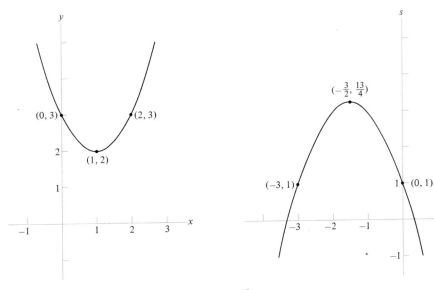

A
B

Figure 3-18
(A) The graph of $y = x^2 - 2x + 3 = (x - 1)^2 + 2$. (B) The graph of $s = -t^2 - 3t + 1 = -(t + \frac{3}{2})^2 + \frac{13}{4}$. See Example 5.

This is in the form (1) with $a = -1$, $h = -3/2$, and $k = 13/4$. The graph is shown in Figure 3-18B.

Example 6

Graph the equations (a) $y = 2x^2 + 4x + 3$ and (b) $v = -\frac{1}{2}u^2 - u + 2$.

Solution

(a)   Forget about the constant 3 for a moment and think of $2x^2 + 4x$ as $2(x^2 + 2x)$. We must add 1 *inside the parentheses* to make $x^2 + 2x$ into a perfect square. Notice that the parentheses are preceded by a 2:

$$y = 2x^2 + 4x + 3$$
$$= 2(x^2 + 2x + 1 - 1) + 3$$
$$= 2(x^2 + 2x + 1) - 2 + 3 \qquad \text{(Subtract 2, } not \text{ 1; why?)}$$
$$= 2(x + 1)^2 + 1$$

This is form (1) with $a = 2$, $h = -1$, and $k = 1$. The graph is shown in Figure 3-19A.

(b) $v = -\frac{1}{2}u^2 - u + 2$. Pay special attention to the negative sign and the constant that precede the parentheses:

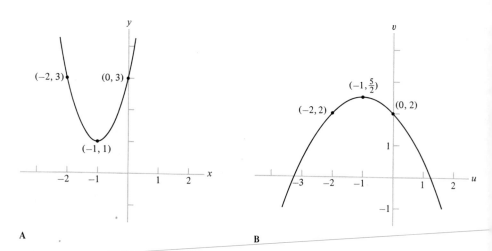

A   B

Figure 3-19

(A) The graph of $y = 2x^2 + 4x + 3 = 2(x + 1)^2 + 1$. (B) The graph of $v = -\frac{1}{2}u^2 - u + 2 = -\frac{1}{2}(u + 1)^2 + \frac{5}{2}$. See Example 6.

$$v = -\tfrac{1}{2}u^2 - u + 2$$
$$= -\tfrac{1}{2}(u^2 + 2u + 1 - 1) + 2$$
$$= -\tfrac{1}{2}(u^2 + 2u + 1) + \tfrac{1}{2} + 2$$
$$= -\tfrac{1}{2}(u + 1)^2 + \tfrac{5}{2}$$

Therefore, $a = -\tfrac{1}{2}$, $h = -1$ and $k = \tfrac{5}{2}$. The graph is shown in Figure 3-19B.

■   To graph $y = ax^2 + bx + c$ $(a \neq 0)$:
(1)   Rewrite it as $y = a(x - h)^2 + k$ by completing the square.
(2)   Locate the vertex at (h, k).
(3)   Find the y-intercept and plot a point on each side of the vertex; draw the parabola.

Maximum and minimum values
Locating the vertex is a crucial step in graphing a parabola. The coordinates of the vertex can also be used to obtain important information about maximum and minimum values. A glance at the preceding figures will convince you that if a parabola opens upward, then the second coordinate of the vertex is the smallest value that the function takes; this is called the minimum value of the function. If a parabola opens downward, then the second coordinate of the vertex is the largest value that the function takes; this is called the maximum value of the function.

■   **Definition**
Let $f: X \to Y$. The number M is the **maximum value** of f if
(1)   there is some x in X for which $f(x) = M$ and
(2) $f(t) \leq M$ for all t in X.

A number m is the **minimum value** of f if
(1) $f(x) = m$ for some x in X and
(2) $f(t) \geq m$ for all t in X.

Linear functions that are not constant have neither maximum nor minimum values. For instance, the value of the linear function $f(x) = 2x - 7$ gets larger and larger without bound as the value of x increases without bound; thus, the function has no maximum value. In a similar way, you can show that it has no minimum value. However, *every* quadratic function has either a maximum or a minimum value. For example, look at Figure 3-19A. The vertex is at $(-1, 1)$. The graph shows that 1 is the smallest value taken by y. Thus, 1 is the minimum value of the function $y = 2x^2 + 4x + 3$, which takes this value at $x = -1$. Now look at Figure 3-19B. The vertex is at $(-1, \frac{5}{2})$, so $\frac{5}{2}$ is the largest value taken by v. Thus, $\frac{5}{2}$ is the maximum value of $v = -\frac{1}{2}u^2 - u + 2$, which takes this value at $u = -1$.

■   To find the maximum or minimum value of a quadratic function $y = ax^2 + bx + c$ $(a \neq 0)$:
(1)   Write it as $y = a(x - h)^2 + k$ by completing the square.
(2)   If $a > 0$, then k is the minimum value. If $a < 0$, then k is the maximum value.
(3)   The function takes this value at $x = h$.

Example 7

A man has 100 feet of fencing to enclose a rectangular garden. What dimensions will make the largest possible garden?

Solution

First, draw a rectangle and label one side x. Then the opposite side must also have length x. Because the total length of fencing is 100 feet, each of the other two sides must have length

$$\frac{100 - 2x}{2} = 50 - x$$

For each possible length x, the area of the garden is given by the function $A(x) = x(50 - x) = 50x - x^2$; this is the function that we want to maximize. With careful thought about minus signs, complete the square:

$$A(x) = 50x - x^2$$
$$= -(x^2 - 50x + 625) + 625$$
$$= -(x - 25)^2 + 625.$$

So the maximum area is 625 square feet, when $x = 25$ feet. This makes the garden a square.

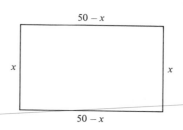

Figure 3-20
The garden in Example 7.

Example 8

A publisher estimates that the cost per book, C, if x thousand copies are printed is given by the equation $C = x^2 - 16x + 76$. How many should she print to minimize her unit cost? (Textbook examples and exercises are always somewhat contrived. They must be kept simple in order to illustrate a single topic. If you actually worked for a publisher, you could very well have the task of deciding how many copies of a book to print, but it is unlikely that you would be handed a nice function like the one above. Indeed, the real problem would probably be to *find* a cost function that took into account the expenses of that particular publisher and the costs of producing that particular book.)

Solution

Notice that some money must be spent even if no books are produced (that is, if $x = 0$). This is because of fixed costs (overhead, salaries, and so on) and prepress costs (design, layout, typesetting, and so on). To find the minimum value of the cost function, complete the square:

$$C = x^2 - 16x + 76$$
$$= (x^2 - 16x + 64) + 12$$
$$= (x - 8)^2 + 12$$

Thus, the minimum cost, $12 per book, is the cost if 8 thousand copies are produced.

Unlike a straight line, which is either horizontal, increasing everywhere, or decreasing everywhere, a parabola is increasing in some parts and decreasing in others (see Figure 3-21).

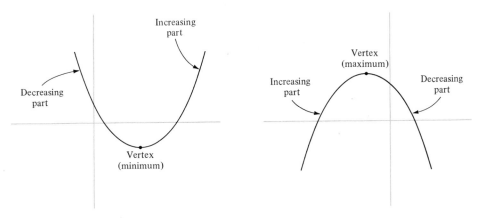

Figure 3-21
A parabola increases in some parts and decreases in others.

Exercises

Write the following quadratics in the form $y = a(x - h)^2 + k$, locate the vertex, find the y-intercept, plot one point on each side of the vertex, and sketch the graph.

1. $y = -x^2 + 1$ 2. $s = -(t - 1)^2$ 3. $v = u^2 - 2$

4. $y = 3x^2 - 1$ 5. $s = -(t + 2)^2 + 2$ 6. $v = -u^2 + 1$

7. $z = y^2 - 2y + 1$ 8. $w = 3z^2 - 3z - 2$ 9. $y = -4 + 6x - 3x^2$

10. For each function in Exercises 1–9 find the set of points where it is increasing and decreasing. For example, let $s = -(t + 2)^2 + 2$. The graph is shown in Figure 3-22; it shows that the function is increasing for $t < -2$ and decreasing for $t > -2$.

Graph the following quadratic functions:

11. $f(u) = -2u^2$ 12. $x(t) = (t - 1)^2$ 13. $y(t) = (t + 1)^2 - 2$

14. $s = 4t^2$ 15. $v = u^2 + 6u + 8$ 16. $w = 2(z + 1)^2 + 1$

17. $y = -3 + 2t - t^2$ 18. $x = 2 - 3t - t^2$ 19. $y = -x^2 + x - 2$

20. Find the maximum or minimum value of each function in Exercises 11–19, and the point at which it occurs.

☐   **21.** (Average rate of change and increase or decrease) The sign of the rate of change indicates whether a function is increasing or decreasing. A positive rate of change

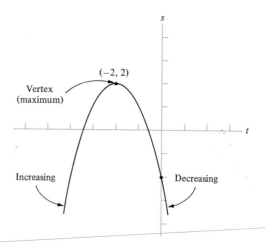

Figure 3-22
The function $s = -(t + 2)^2 + 2$ is increasing for $t < -2$, and decreasing for $t > -2$. See Exercise 10.

means the function is increasing. A negative rate of change means the function is decreasing. Test these statements with $f(x) = x^2 + 2x - 3$ by performing the following steps:

(a)   Graph f and note where it is increasing and decreasing.

(b)   Recall that a.r.c.$f(x, h) = \dfrac{f(x + h) - f(x)}{h}$. Verify that in this case

a.r.c.$f(x, h) = 2x + 2 + h$

(c)   Let h approach 0, and find the exact rate of change at these points: $x = -3, -2, 2,$ and 3.

(d)   Do the positive and negative values of the rate of change correspond to the increasing and decreasing parts of f?

(e)   When $x = -1$, the rate of change is zero. The number -1 is also the first coordinate of the vertex. This is always true: *The value of x that makes the rate of change 0 is the x-coordinate of the vertex.*

22.   (Average rate of change and steepness). The size of the rate of change indicates the steepness of a curve. The larger the absolute value of the rate of change, the steeper the curve. Compute and compare the exact rates of change of $p(x) = 4x^2$, $q(x) = x^2$, and $r(x) = \frac{1}{4}x^2$.

23.   A projectile is fired into the air so that its height h feet above the ground at any time t seconds is given by $h(t) = -16t^2 + 160t$.

(a)   Draw a graph of its height (see Figure 3-23 for an idea of how to set up).

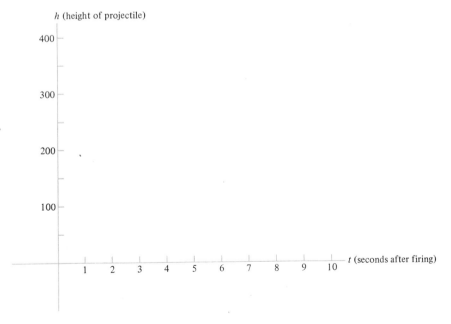

Figure 3-23
Graph the function $h(t) = -16t^2 + 160t$. See Exercise 23.

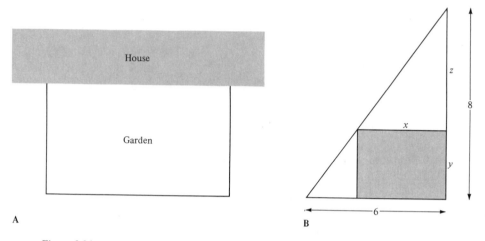

Figure 3-24
(A) The house and garden in Exercise 25. (B) The rectangle and right triangle in Exercise 27.

    (b)   What is the maximum height and when will it be reached?
    (c)   How do you interpret physically the increasing and decreasing parts of this function?
    (d)   When will the projectile hit the ground?
24.   The sum of two positive integers is 11, and the difference of their squares is 55. Find the numbers.
25.   A rectangular garden is to be fenced with 100 feet of fencing. The wall of a house will be one side of the garden, so that fencing is needed on only three sides (see Figure 3-24A). What is the largest garden possible?
26.   A company estimates that its profit P, in thousands of dollars, is given by the function $P(x) = -x^2 + 20x + 100$, where x represents thousands of dollars spent on advertising. How much would you advise them to spend on advertising?
27.   What are the dimensions of the rectangle with the largest area that can be inscribed in a right triangle whose legs are 6 feet and 8 feet long? [HINT: See Figure 3-24B. Use similar triangles to write $x/6 = z/8$, and solve for z. Then $y = 8 - z$.]
28.   A farmer has 240 feet of fencing to enclose one of the shaded areas shown in Figure 3-25. No fencing is required along the river. Which shape, a rectangular or a right triangle, gives him the maximum enclosed area?
29.   If the price of an apple is 10¢, a merchant can sell 400 of them. He finds that, for each penny increase in price, he sells 10 fewer apples. How much should he charge to maximize his sales?

■   Although $y = ax^2 + bx + c$ is a quadratic, the function $y = |ax^2 + bx + c|$ is not necessarily a quadratic: its graph may not be a parabola. Graph the following

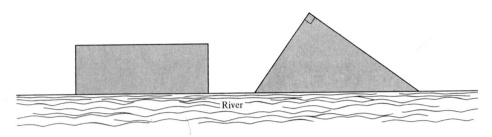

Figure 3-25
Each plot of land is surrounded by 240 feet of fence, but there is no fence along the river.
See Exercise 28.

equations. If you would like a hint, consult Exercise 30 in Section 3-1.

30. $y = |x^2 - 1|$ **31.** $y = |x^2 + 2x - 1|$ **32.** $y = |-x^2 + 4x - 3|$

33. Under what conditions will the graph of $y = |ax^2 + bx + c|$ be a parabola?

34. Every time $ax^2 + bx + c$ is to be expressed as $a(x - h)^2 + k$, must we go through the process of completing the square? Or is there some formula relating a, b, and c to h and k that will work in every case?

3-4
Quadratic Equations

In this section, we shall explore methods of solving quadratic equations, for example,

$$x^2 - 4x + 4 = 1 \qquad 3t^2 = 2 - 5t \qquad u = -2u^2 + 1$$

Every equation can be rewritten as an equivalent equation (same set of solutions) with only 0 on the right. For example, the equations above can be rewritten as

$$x^2 - 4x + 3 = 0 \qquad 3t^2 + 5t - 2 = 0 \qquad 2u^2 + u - 1 = 0$$

Each equation can be used to define a function:

$$f(x) = x^2 - 4x + 3 \qquad g(t) = 3t^2 + 5t - 2 \qquad h(u) = 2u^2 + u - 1$$

The solution set for each equation is the set of numbers at which the corresponding function takes the value 0.

■ **Definition**
A number r is a **zero** of the function f if $f(r) = 0$. The number r is also called a **root** of the equation $f(x) = 0$.

Thus, the problem of finding the solutions of an equation can be transformed into the problem of finding the zeros of a function.

Example 1
Solve these quadratic equations:

(a) $x^2 - 4x + 4 = 1$ (b) $3t^2 = 2 - 5t$ (c) $u = -2u^2 + 1$

Solution
(a)   Rewrite the equation as $x^2 - 4x + 3 = 0$, define $f(x) = x^2 - 4x + 3$, and find the zeros of f. Now $f(x)$ can be factored as $f(x) = (x - 3)(x - 1)$. If this product is to be 0, then $x - 3 = 0$ or $x - 1 = 0$. Thus, $x = 3$ and $x = 1$ are the zeros of f.

Check
$f(3) = 3^2 - 4(3) + 3 = 0$ and $f(1) = (1)^2 - 4(1) + 3 = 0$
Therefore, $x = 3$ and $x = 1$ are the solutions of Equation (a):
$$(3)^2 - 4(3) + 4 = 1 \text{ and } (1)^2 - 4(1) + 4 = 1$$

(b)   Rewrite $3t^2 = 2 - 5t$ as $3t^2 + 5t - 2 = 0$, define $g(t) = 3t^2 + 5t - 2$, and find the zeros of g. Because $g(t)$ can be easily factored as $g(t) = (3t - 1)(t + 2)$, it follows that $t = 1/3$ and $t = -2$ are the zeros of g and the solutions of Equation (b). Check by substituting each solution into the original equation:

$$t = 1/3: \quad 3(1/3)^2 = 1/3 \quad \text{and} \quad 2 - 5(1/3) = 1/3$$

$$t = -2: \quad 3(-2)^2 = 12 \quad \text{and} \quad 2 - 5(-2) = 12$$

(c)   Rewrite $u = -2u^2 + 1$ as $2u^2 + u - 1 = 0$ and find the zeros of $h(u) = 2u^2 + u - 1$. This function is not easily factored; so we must find another method:
(1)   Factor out the coefficient of u^2:

$$h(u) = 2u^2 + u - 1 = 2(u^2 + \tfrac{1}{2}u - \tfrac{1}{2})$$

(2)   Complete the square *inside the parentheses:*

$$h(u) = 2(u^2 + \tfrac{1}{2}u + \tfrac{1}{16} - \tfrac{1}{16} - \tfrac{1}{2})$$
$$= 2[(u + \tfrac{1}{4})^2 - \tfrac{9}{16}]$$

(3)   Now factor $(u + \frac{1}{4})^2 - \frac{9}{16}$ as the difference of two squares:

$$h(u) = 2[(u + \tfrac{1}{4}) + \tfrac{3}{4}][(u + \tfrac{1}{4}) - \tfrac{3}{4}]$$
$$= 2(u + 1)(u - \tfrac{1}{2})$$

(4)   Read off the zeros: $u = -1$ and $u = \frac{1}{2}$; these are the solutions of the equation $u = -2u^2 + 1$.

Check

$$u = -1: \quad -1 = -2(-1)^2 + 1$$

$$u = \tfrac{1}{2}: \quad \tfrac{1}{2} = -2(\tfrac{1}{2})^2 + 1$$

Example 1 illustrates that, once the quadratic is factored, the zeros can be read off immediately. However, Equation (c) was not easy to factor, so some preliminary work had to be done. Now we shall develop a formula that will do the preliminary work automatically. The development of the formula mimics what was done in part (c) of Example 1.

Let $f(x) = ax^2 + bx + c$ $(a \neq 0)$, and find the zeros of f.

(1) Factor out a.

$$f(x) = ax^2 + bx + c = a\left(x^2 + \frac{b}{a}x + \frac{c}{a}\right)$$

(2 and 3) Complete the square, and factor as the difference of two squares within the parentheses:

$$f(x) = a\left(x^2 + \frac{b}{a}x + \frac{b^2}{4a^2} - \frac{b^2}{4a^2} + \frac{c}{a}\right)$$

$$= a\left[\left(x + \frac{b}{2a}\right)^2 - \frac{b^2 - 4ac}{4a^2}\right]$$

$$= a\left[\left(x + \frac{b}{2a}\right)^2 - \left(\frac{\sqrt{b^2 - 4ac}}{2a}\right)^2\right]$$

$$= a\left(x + \frac{b + \sqrt{b^2 - 4ac}}{2a}\right)\left(x + \frac{b - \sqrt{b^2 - 4ac}}{2a}\right)$$

(4) Read off the zeros:

$$x = \frac{-b - \sqrt{b^2 - 4ac}}{2a} \quad \text{and} \quad x = \frac{-b + \sqrt{b^2 - 4ac}}{2a}$$

■ This is the **quadratic formula:**

$$x = \frac{-b \pm \sqrt{b^2 - 4ac}}{2a}$$

The roots of $ax^2 + bx + c = 0$ (or the zeros of $f(x) = ax^2 + bx + c$) are gotten by adding or subtracting the square root of b^2 minus $4ac$ to (from) minus b, and dividing the result by $2a$.

The expression $b^2 - 4ac$ is called the **discriminant.**

Example 2
Solve these equations:

(a) $x^2 - 4x + 4 = 0$ (b) $3t^2 = t + 5$ (c) $u = 2u^2 + 1$

Solution
(a)   The left side of this equation is a perfect square, $(x - 2)^2$. Thus, there is only one solution, $x = 2$. (Check.) Notice that the quadratic formula yields the same answer. Here, $a = 1$, $b = -4$, and $c = 4$. Therefore,

$$x = \frac{-(-4) \pm \sqrt{(-4)^2 - 4(1)(4)}}{2(1)}$$

$$= \frac{4 \pm 0}{2} = 2$$

(b) $3t^2 = t + 5$. In order to use the quadratic formula, you must rewrite the equation as $3t^2 - t - 5 = 0$; thus, $a = 3$, $b = -1$, and $c = -5$. The solutions are

$$t = \frac{-(-1) \pm \sqrt{(-1)^2 - 4(3)(-5)}}{2(3)}$$

$$= \frac{1 \pm \sqrt{61}}{6}$$

(c) $u = 2u^2 + 1$. Again, you must write the equation in the proper form, which is $-2u^2 + u - 1 = 0$; thus, $a = -2$, $b = 1$, and $c = -1$. The solutions are

$$u = \frac{-1 \pm \sqrt{(1)^2 - 4(-2)(-1)}}{2(-2)}$$

$$= \frac{-1 \pm \sqrt{-7}}{-4}$$

Because $\sqrt{-7}$ is not a real number, *there are no real-number solutions* of this equation. The solution set for this equation is the empty set (written $\emptyset$).

Example 2 illustrates the three possibilities for quadratic equations:

■   If the discriminant is 0, there is one solution.

If the discriminant is positive, there are two solutions.

If the discriminant is negative, there are no real-number solutions.

Geometrically, the zeros of a function are those points where the graph crosses the x-axis. (see Figure 3-26).

Summary
To solve a quadratic equation, write it in the form $ax^2 + bx + c = 0$. The roots of this equation are given by the quadratic formula:

$$x = \frac{-b \pm \sqrt{b^2 - 4ac}}{2a}$$

The expression $b^2 - 4ac$ is called the discriminant. There will be one, two, or no real-number solutions depending on whether the discriminant is zero, positive, or negative.

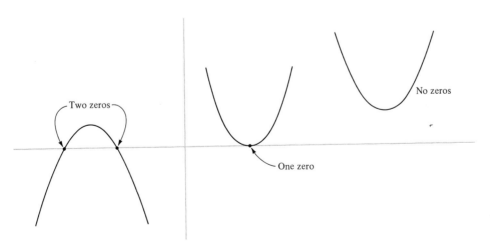

Figure 3-26
A quadratic function, whose graph is a parabola, can have one zero, two zeros, or no zeros.

Exercises

Solve the following equations. Try to factor first; if that is not easy, use the quadratic formula. If there are no real-number solutions, say so.

1. $x^2 + 2x + 1 = 0$ 2. $x^2 - 4x + 4 = 0$
3. $t^2 = -2t - 2$ 4. $3t = -t^2 + 5$
5. $y^2 + 3 = 3y + 1$ 6. $y^2 + 8y = 2y - 5$
7. $4u^2 + 5u = 2u + 1$ 8. $5u^2 - 3 = 2u + 4$
9. $x^2 + 4 = 0$ 10. $x^2 - 10 = 0$
11. $-2t^2 + 1 = t$ 12. $3t^2 + 4 = 2t$
13. $y^2 + 2y + 15 = 50$ 14. $2y^2 - y = 20$
15. $-\frac{2}{3}u^2 + \frac{1}{2}u + \frac{1}{4} = 0$ 16. $-\frac{1}{2}u^2 + 3u - \frac{1}{8} = 0$
17. $1.2x^2 = 2.4x$ 18. $3.6x^2 = 7.2x$
19. $4.2t^2 + 1.1t + 1.6 = 0$ 20. $1.4t^2 - 2.5t = .5$

21. A particle is traveling through space. Its distance s, measured in meters from a fixed reference point p_0, at time t, measured in seconds, is given by the formula $s = t^2 + 2t + 15$.
    (a)   How far from p_0 is it at the start (that is, when $t = 0$)?
    (b)   How far does it travel during the third second?
    (c)   At what time will it be 50 meters from p_0? [HINT: Look at Exercise 13.]

22. A ball is thrown upward with a speed of 64 feet per second from a cliff 80 feet above the ground. Its path will cause it to land on the ground at the base of the cliff. Its height h (in feet) above the base of the cliff at any time t (in seconds) is given by $h = -16t^2 + 64t + 80$.
    (a)   How high will the ball be after 1 second?
    (b)   After 3 seconds?
    (c)   Do your answers to (a) and (b) seem incompatible?
    (d)   At what time will the ball hit the ground?

23. (Continuation of Exercise 22) What is the maximum height that the ball will reach?

24. A ball is dropped from a balloon 1600 feet above the ground. Its distance above the ground t seconds after it was dropped is $f(t) = -16t^2 + 1600$ feet.
    (a)   How far does it fall during the first second?
    (b)   During the third second?
    (c)   The fifth second?
    (d)   Do your answers to (a), (b), and (c) seem incompatible?
    (e)   When will the ball hit the ground?

25. (Continuation of Exercise 24) The rate of change of distance with respect to time is velocity. Thus, the rate of change of f at time t is the velocity of the ball at time t. Find the a.r.c. $f(t, h)$, and then find the exact rate of change at t. How fast is the ball falling after 2 seconds? 5 seconds? When it hits the ground?

26. A company manufactures expensive, hand-painted dinner plates. If they make x plates, their profit is $P = .01x^2 - .48x - 1$ dollars. If they only make a few plates, they will lose money because of their fixed costs. For example, if they only make 5 plates, they will *lose* \$3.15, because $P = .25 - 2.40 - 1 = -3.15$. What is the number of plates they must produce to break even?

27. (Continuation of Exercise 26) What is their marginal profit when they are making 50 plates? (See page 91 for the definition of marginal profit.)

28. (Sum and product of roots) According to the quadratic formula, the roots of $ax^2 + bx + c = 0$ are

$$r_1 = \frac{-b + \sqrt{b^2 - 4ac}}{2a} \quad \text{and} \quad r_2 = \frac{-b - \sqrt{b^2 - 4ac}}{2a}$$

(a) Show that $r_1 + r_2 = -\dfrac{b}{a}$ and $r_1 r_2 = \dfrac{c}{a}$.

(b) Find b and c if $f(x) = x^2 + bx + c$ and its zeros are -2 and 3; $1 + \sqrt{3}$ and $1 - \sqrt{3}$; $\dfrac{-1 + \sqrt{2}}{6}$ and $\dfrac{-1 - \sqrt{2}}{6}$.

(c) Let $f(x) = 2x^2 - 2x + c$. Can its zeros be equal? If so, find c.

29. (Zeros and factors)

(a) If r_1 and r_2 are zeros of $f(x) = ax^2 + bx + c$, show that f can be factored as $f(x) = a(x - r_1)(x - r_2)$. [HINT: Multiply out $a(x - r_1)(x - r_2)$ and use Exercise 28(a).]

(b) Factor $f(x) = 2x^2 + 3x - 1$ and $g(t) = 1 + t - t^2$.

30. Use the quadratic formula to show that, if a and c have opposite signs, then $ax^2 + bx + c = 0$ has two real roots.

The following equations are not quadratic, but can you think of a method for solving them?

31. $x^4 - 16 = 0$ **32.** $x^4 - 5x^2 + 4 = 0$

33. $x^4 + 2x^2 - 1 = 0$ **34.** $10x^6 - x^3 - 1 = 0$

3-5
Linear and Quadratic Inequalities

Like equations, inequalities can be rewritten as equivalent inequalities (same solution set) with 0 on the right. For example,

$$-2x - 4 < 3 \quad \text{and} \quad x^2 + 2 \geq 2x + 5$$

can be rewritten as

$$-2x - 7 < 0 \quad \text{and} \quad x^2 - 2x - 3 \geq 0$$

Therefore, it is enough to learn how to solve inequalities with 0 on the right. Let us first consider linear inequalities.

Example 1
Solve the inequality $-2x - 7 < 0$ and graph the solution set on the real line.

Solution
Proceed as though you were solving an equation, but remember that inequalities are reversed when each side is multiplied or divided by the same negative number:

$$-2x - 7 < 0$$

$$-2x < 7 \qquad \text{(Add 7.)}$$

$$x > -7/2 \qquad \text{(Divide by } -2; \text{ reverse inequality.)}$$

The solution set is $\{x \mid x > -7/2\}$. This is read, "The set of all x such that $x > -7/2$." The graph is shown in Figure 3-27A. The open circle on the left indicates that the point $x = -7/2$ is not in the solution set.

Example 2
Solve $3 + 2x \leq 5$ and graph the solution set.

Solution

$$3 + 2x \leq 5$$

$$2x \leq 2 \qquad \text{(Subtract 3)}$$

$$x \leq 1 \qquad \text{(Divide by 2; same inequality)}$$

The solution set is $\{x \mid x \leq 1\}$, which is read "the set of all x such that x is less than or equal to 1." The graph of the solution set is shown in Figure 3-27B. The solid dot on the right indicates that the point $x = 1$ is in the solution set.

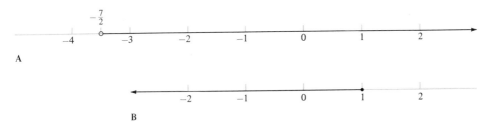

A

B

Figure 3-27
(A) The solution set of $-2x - 7 < 0$. Example 1. (B) The solution set of $3 + 2x \leq 5$.
See Example 2.

■   To solve a linear inequality, proceed as though it were a linear equation, but remember that inequalities are reversed when each side is multiplied or divided by the same negative number.

Like linear inequalities, quadratic inequalities can be solved algebraically, as though they were equations. For example, to solve $x^2 - 2x - 3 > 0$, factor the left side to obtain $(x - 3)(x + 1) > 0$. Now determine where each factor is positive, negative, and zero, and remember that a product of two factors is positive when both of them have the same sign. The solution is the set of all numbers x such that both factors are positive or both are negative.

Rather than employ this method, let us take a geometric approach that uses our knowledge of parabolas. Notice that, if a parabola opens upward, the values of y are negative between the zeros and positive outside of those zeros; if it opens downward, then the values of y are positive between the zeros and negative outside (see Figure 3-28).

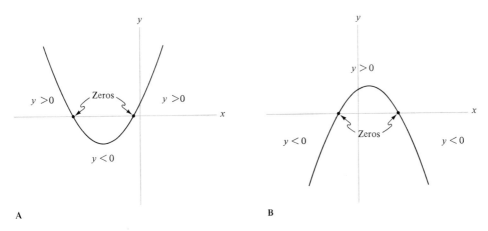

A   B

Figure 3-28
(A) If a parabola opens upward, the values of y are negative between the zeros and positive outside the zeros. (B) If a parabola opens downward, the values of y are positive between the zeros and negative outside them.

A

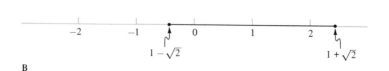

B

Figure 3-29

(A) The solution set of $x^2 - 2x - 3 > 0$ is $\{x|x < -1\} \cup \{x|x > 3\}$. The open circles indicate two points that are not in the solution set. See Example 3. (B) The solution set of $-x^2 + 2x + 1 \geq 0$ is $\{x|1 - \sqrt{2} \leq x \leq 1 + \sqrt{2}\}$. The solid dots indicate that these points are in the solution set. See Example 4.

Example 3

Solve $x^2 - 2x - 3 > 0$ and graph the solution set.

Solution

Let $y = x^2 - 2x - 3$; then the solutions of the inequality are the points x for which $y > 0$. The graph of $y = x^2 - 2x - 3$ is a parabola and it opens upward. (Why?) According to our observations, $y > 0$ *outside* of the zeros. To find the zeros, factor:

$$x^2 - 2x - 3 = (x + 1)(x - 3)$$

so the zeros are $x = -1$ and $x = 3$. It follows that $y > 0$ if $x < -1$ or $x > 3$; these are the solutions of the original inequality. The solution set is graphed in Figure 3-29A. In set notation, this set is written $\{x|x < -1\} \cup \{x|x > 3\}$. The symbol $\cup$ is read "union." This solution set is the union of two sets; in other words, any number in *either* set is a solution.

Example 4

Solve $-x^2 + 2x + 1 \geq 0$ and graph the solution set.

Solution

Let $y = -x^2 + 2x + 1$; the solutions of the inequality are the numbers x for which $y \geq 0$. The graph of $y = -x^2 + 2x + 1$ is a parabola that opens downward, so $y > 0$ *between* the zeros. The factors are not easy to spot, so use the quadratic formula to find the zeros:

$$x = \frac{-2 \pm \sqrt{2^2 - 4(-1)(1)}}{-2} = \frac{-2 \pm \sqrt{8}}{-2} = 1 \pm \sqrt{2}$$

It follows that $y \geq 0$ if $1 - \sqrt{2} \leq x \leq 1 + \sqrt{2}$. The solution set is $\{x \mid 1 - \sqrt{2} \leq x \leq 1 + \sqrt{2}\}$, and the graph is shown in Figure 3-29B.

■ To solve a quadratic inequality $ax^2 + bx + c < 0$, set $y = ax^2 + bx + c$. The solutions of the inequality are the numbers x for which $y < 0$. Locate the zeros of $ax^2 + bx + c$; the solutions will be the numbers between or outside the zeros, depending on whether the graph of $y = ax^2 + bx + c$ opens upward or downward. Variations of this procedure will solve inequalities $\leq$, $>$, and $\geq$.

The next two examples illustrate the use of inequalities to describe straight-line motion.

Example 5
A particle is moving in a straight line; its velocity, in feet per second, at any time t is given by the function $v(t) = 3t - 6$, $t \geq 0$. Describe its motion; that is, give a complete account of the particle's direction and speed.

Solution
Trace the particle's motion on a horizontal line. Suppose that a negative velocity means movement to the left, and positive velocity indicates movement to the right. Thus, the initial velocity (when $t = 0$) is $v(0) = -6$; this means that at the starting point the particle is moving to the *left* with a speed of 6 ft/sec. At 3 seconds, the velocity is $v(3) = 3$, which means that the particle is now moving to the *right* with a speed of 3 ft/sec.

To describe its motion completely, you must know when $v(t) = 3t - 6$ is positive, negative, and zero. Notice $3t - 6 = 0$ when $t = 2$. Thus, $v(2) = 0$, which means that the particle is momentarily at rest at $t = 2$. Furthermore, $3t - 6$ is negative for t less than 2, and positive for t greater than 2.

The particle's motion can be described as follows: It starts out moving to the left with speed 6 ft/sec ($v(0) = -6$). It is slowing down, and it comes to rest in 2 seconds ($v(2) = 0$), after which it reverses direction ($v(t) > 0$ if $t > 2$) and moves toward the right with increasing speed. The motion of the particle is pictured in Figure 3-30.

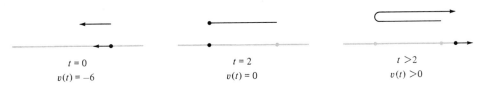

Figure 3-30
The motion of the particle in Example 5.

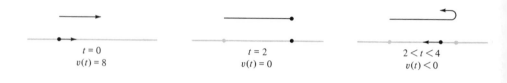

Figure 3-31
The motion of the object in Example 6.

Example 6
An object is moving in a straight line; its velocity, in feet per second, at time t is $v(t) = t^2 - 6t + 8$, for $t \geq 0$. Describe its motion.

Solution
Proceed as in Example 5. Find where the velocity is positive, negative, and zero. The zeros of $v(t)$ are $t = 2$ and $t = 4$. Therefore,

$$\text{the velocity is} \begin{cases} \text{positive if } 0 \leq t < 2 \text{ or } t > 4 \\ \text{negative if } 2 < t < 4 \\ 0 \text{ if } t = 2 \text{ or } t = 4 \end{cases}$$

The object starts out moving to the right with speed 8 ft/sec ($v(0) = 8$). It slows down and comes to rest in 2 seconds ($v(2) = 0$), and then moves to the left ($v(t) < 0$ for $2 < t < 4$) until it again comes to rest, after 4 seconds ($v(4) = 0$). Now it moves to the right with ever-increasing speed. The motion is pictured in Figure 3-31.

Exercises

Solve the following inequalities and graph their solution sets. If there are no real-number solutions, say so.

1. $\dfrac{x - 17}{-2} < 9$

2. $6 - \dfrac{1}{2}x > 7$

3. $3y + 2 \geq 11 + 6y$ **4.** $8 - y \leq 9 + y$

5. $-\frac{2}{3}t + \frac{1}{4} > \frac{1}{2}t$ **6.** $-\frac{5t + 1}{-3} < -4$

7. $x - (3x + 2) \leq 1$ **8.** $3(x - 2) \geq 6 + x$

9. $-4(2 - y) + 1 \geq 5y$ **10.** $9(-3 - y) < -8y - 25$

11. $x^2 - 16 > 0$ **12.** $9 - x^2 \leq 0$

13. $t^2 < -t + 6$ **14.** $-t^2 > -t - 6$

15. $6u - 4 \geq 2u^2$ **16.** $3u + 1 \leq u^2$

17. $x^2 + x - 1 \leq 0$ **18.** $x^2 - x - 1 \leq 0$

19. $-2y^2 + 2y - 1 > 0$ **20.** $3y^2 + 1 < 0$

An inequality such as $-2 \leq -3x + 4 \leq 1$ is just a shorthand notation for two inequalities: $-2 \leq -3x + 4$ *and* $-3x + 4 \leq 1$. They can be solved simultaneously as follows:

$$-2 \leq -3x + 4 \leq 1$$

$$-6 \leq -3x \leq -3 \qquad\qquad \text{(Subtract 4.)}$$

$$2 \geq x \geq 1 \qquad\qquad \begin{array}{l}\text{(Divide by } -3;\\ \text{reverse inequalities.)}\end{array}$$

The solution set, therefore, is $\{x | 1 \leq x \leq 2\}$. Use this method to solve the following inequalities, and graph their solution sets.

21. $5 \leq 2x + 1 \leq 9$ **22.** $3 \leq x + 7 \leq 5$

23. $-\frac{1}{2} \leq -3x - 2 \leq \frac{1}{2}$ **24.** $-\frac{1}{4} \leq 2x - 1 \leq \frac{1}{4}$

25. $-.1 \leq 3x - 6 \leq .1$ **26.** $-.1 \leq -x + 1 \leq .1$

27. $-.01 \leq 3x - 6 \leq .01$ **28.** $-.01 \leq -x + 1 \leq .01$

29. $-4 \leq -2(4 - x) \leq 0$ **30.** $-2 \leq -3(x + 1) - 2 \leq 2$

To solve inequalities that include absolute values, think of absolute value as distance. Thus, $|x - 3| < \frac{1}{2}$ means that the distance from x to 3 is less than $\frac{1}{2}$, so x could be any number between $2\frac{1}{2}$ and $3\frac{1}{2}$. The solution set is therefore $\{x | 5/2 < x < 7/2\}$. Similarly, $|x + 7| > 1$ means that the distance from x to -7 is greater than 1, so x could be any number less than -8 or bigger than -6. The solution set is the union $\{x | x < -8\} \cup \{x | x > -6\}$. Solve the following inequalities and graph their solution sets.

31. $|x - 1| < \frac{1}{2}$ **32.** $|x + 1| < \frac{1}{3}$

33. $|y + 6| > 2$ **34.** $|y - 5| > 1$

35. $|t - 3| > 2$ **36.** $|t - 2| > 3$

37. $|3x - 6| < .3$ **38.** $|2x - 8| < .2$

39. $|5x - 10| < \frac{1}{2}$ **40.** $|3x - 1| < 1$

☐ Describe the straight-line motion of particles with the following velocity functions.

41. $v(t) = 30 - 6t$ 42. $v(t) = \tfrac{1}{2}t - 4$

43. $v(t) = t^2 - 4t + 3$ 44. $v(t) = -2 + 5t - 3t^2$

45. Sam has to pick up his boss in a town 50 miles away. He leaves his office at 2 P.M. and wants to arrive within 10 minutes (either before or after) of 3 P.M. What is the range of Sam's possible average driving speeds?

■ 46. (Zeros and rate of change)

    (a) Let $f(x) = mx + b$ with positive slope; that is, $m > 0$. If r is the zero of f, is $f(x)$ positive or negative to the right of r? (Think geometrically—draw a picture.)

    (b) Let f be a quadratic function with zeros r_1 and r_2. Suppose $r_1 < r_2$. If the rate of change of f at r_1 is positive, is $f(x)$ positive or negative between r_1 and r_2? (Think geometrically.)

47. Make up and solve inequality problems of the following types:

    (a) $ax + b < 0$ (b) $ax^2 + bx + c > 0$

    (c) $c \leq ax + b \leq d$ (d) $|ax + b| < c$

    (e) $d \leq ax^2 + bx + c \leq e$ (f) $|ax^2 + bx + c| < d$

Types (e) and (f) should be quite a challenge.

Chapter 4

Polynomials

This chapter concerns a wide class of functions called polynomials. In polynomial functions that are linear or quadratic, the exponents of the independent variable can be only 1 or 2, but other polynomials admit any nonnegative integer exponents; for example, $f(x) = 3x^4 - 5x^3 + x^2$ and $g(t) = -t^5 + t - 4$.

Chapter 3 dealt with the algebraic and geometric properties of linear and quadratic functions. Those principles and applications will be extended in this chapter to include all polynomials. This extension will require the new methods that are developed in Sections 4-3 and 4-4, following preliminary material in Sections 4-1 and 4-2. The geometric aspects of polynomials are discussed in Section 4-5, including procedures for plotting points, locating zeros, and sketching curves. Finally, Section 4-6 deals with quotients of polynomials, which are called rational functions.

As you study the text and work through the exercises, pay close attention to these topics: (1) the Division Algorithm and the technique of synthetic division—both are presented in Section 4-2, and much of what is discussed in later sections depends on them; (2) the connection between zeros and factors of polynomial functions.

Notice how the simple ideas introduced in the early sections lead to a rather sophisticated procedure for solving polynomial equations.

4-1
Algebraic Operations with Polynomials

Linear and quadratic expressions belong to a large class of expressions called polynomials. Here are some *non*linear, *non*quadratic polynomials:

$$x^3 + 2x^2 - 3x + 4 \qquad y^5 - \frac{1}{3} \qquad z^4 - z^2 + \sqrt{2}$$

Notice that the constants are all real numbers and the exponents are nonnegative integers. The word *polynomial* is used to mean both this kind of algebraic expression and the function whose value is given by the expression.

■ **Definition**
A polynomial in one variable is any function of the form

$$f(x) = a_n x^n + a_{n-1} x^{n-1} + \cdots + a_1 x + a_0$$

where $a_n, a_{n-1}, \cdots, a_0$ are real numbers, n is a nonnegative integer, and x is the independent variable.

The function is often written as a polynomial expression alone, instead of as a complete equation. Not every expression represents a polynomial function. For instance,

$$2\sqrt{x} + \sqrt[3]{x} \quad \text{and} \quad 4t^{-5} + 2t^{-3}$$

are not polynomials, because the exponents are not nonnegative integers.

Coefficients
In the polynomial $a_n x^n + a_{n-1} x^{n-1} + \cdots + a_1 x + a_0$, the a's are called **coefficients:** a_n is the coefficient of x^n, a_{n-1} the coefficient of x^{n-1}, and so on. The last term, a_0, is also called the **constant term.**

Example 1
(a)   In the polynomial $y^3 + 0y^2 - y - 5$, the numbers 1, 0, -1, and -5 are the coefficients; 1 is the coefficient of y^3 (when no number appears, the coefficient is assumed to be 1), 0 the coefficient of y^2, -1 the coefficient of y, and the constant term is -5.
(b)   The terms with zero coefficients are usually omitted. Thus,

$$3y^3 + 0y^2 - 2y - 5 \quad \text{is written} \quad 3y^3 - 2y - 5$$

and $-2t^5 + 0t^4 - t^3 + 0t^2 + 0t + 1$ is written $-2t^5 - t^3 + 1$. Conversely, in the polynomial $x^4 - 2x + 1$, the coefficients are 1, 0, 0, -2, and 1; in $5x^4 + x^2$, the coefficients are 5, 0, 1, 0, and 0. The missing terms have zero coefficients.

Degree of a polynomial
The largest power of the independent variable with a nonzero coefficient is the **degree** of the polynomial. This nonzero coefficient is called the **leading coefficient.**

Example 2

$$x^4 + 3x^2 - 2 \text{ has degree 4 and leading coefficient } 1$$

$$-t^5 + 1 \text{ has degree 5 and leading coefficient } -1$$

$$3u^3 \text{ has degree 3 and leading coefficient } 3$$

Some care must be taken if the terms are not in descending order of power.

$$2 - x + x^3 \text{ has degree 3, leading coefficient } = 1$$

$$v - 2v^5 \text{ has degree 5, leading coefficient } = -2$$

■   By convention, the zero polynomial has no degree; all other constant polynomials have degree 0. Thus, $f(x) = 0$ has no degree, but $g(t) = 5$ has degree 0.

The domain of a polynomial function is $\mathbb{R}$, the set of all real numbers. Therefore, two polynomials are equal if and only if they have the same value at each real number x.

■   If two polynomials are equal, then all corresponding coefficients must be equal.

Although we shall not prove this statement here, we can make use of it.

Example 3
Given the identity

$$(x + 6)(x - 4) = ax^3 + bx^2 + cx + d$$

find a, b, c, and d.

Solution
Recall that an equation is an identity if it is a true statement for all allowable replacements of the independent variable (Section 1-6). For polynomials, this means replacement by *any* real number.

Simplify the left side of the equation to get

$$x^2 + 2x - 24 = ax^3 + bx^2 + cx + d$$

for all x. Thus, corresponding coefficients must be equal, and it follows that $a = 0$, $b = 1$, $c = 2$, and $d = -24$.

Polynomials in two variables

The polynomials discussed so far have contained only one independent variable. The function

$$f(x, y) = 3x^2 + 2xy - 4y^2$$

read "f of x, y," is a polynomial in *two* variables. Notice that the constants are real numbers and the exponents are nonnegative integers. This function assigns to each ordered pair of numbers a and b the unique number $f(a, b)$. To find that number, simply replace the x's and y's by a and b. For instance, to find $f(1, 2)$, replace x by 1 and y by 2:

$$f(1, 2) = 3 \cdot 1^2 + 2 \cdot 1 \cdot 2 - 4 \cdot 2^2 = -9$$

To find $f(0, -1)$, replace x by 0 and y by -1:

$$f(0, -1) = 3 \cdot 0^2 + 2 \cdot 0 \cdot (-1) - 4 \cdot (-1)^2 = -4$$

If $g(u, v) = u^2 - 2uv^2 + v^3$, then

$$g(2, 1) = 2^2 - 2 \cdot 2 \cdot 1^2 + 1^3 = 1$$

$$g(\sqrt{2}, 0) = (\sqrt{2})^2 - 2 \cdot (\sqrt{2}) \cdot 0^2 + 0^3 = 2$$

There are many common functions of two variables. The *area* of a triangle or rectangle is a function of the *base* and the *height, voltage* depends on *current* and *resistance,* and *profit* is a function of *sales* and *cost.*

The *average rate of change* of a function $f(x)$ over an interval is also a function of two variables, x and h. That is, it depends on the values of both x *and* h:

$$\text{a.r.c.}f(x, h) = \frac{f(x + h) - f(x)}{h}$$

Example 4

Let $g(t) = t^3 - 4t + 2$. Find a.r.c.$g(t, h)$ for $t = 4$ and $h = 1, .1,$ and $.01$.

Solution

First find a.r.c.$g(t, h)$ for any t and h:

$$\text{a.r.c.}g(t, h) = \frac{g(t + h) - g(t)}{h}$$

$$= \frac{[(t + h)^3 - 4(t + h) + 2] - [t^3 - 4t + 2]}{h}$$

$$= \frac{(t^3 + 3t^2h + 3th^2 + h^3 - 4t - 4h + 2) - (t^3 - 4t + 2)}{h}.$$

$$= 3t^2 + 3th + h^2 - 4$$

Now use this general formula to find

$$\text{a.r.c.}g(4, 1) = 3 \cdot 4^2 + 3 \cdot 4 \cdot 1 + 1^2 - 4 = 57$$

$$\text{a.r.c.}g(4, .1) = 3 \cdot 4^2 + 3 \cdot 4 \cdot \frac{1}{10} + \frac{1}{10^2} - 4 = 45.21$$

$$\text{a.r.c.}g(4, .01) = 3 \cdot 4^2 + 3 \cdot 4 \cdot \frac{1}{100} + \frac{1}{100^2} - 4 = 44.1201$$

The *exact* rate of change at $t = 4$ is 44.

The derived polynomial

If $f(x) = a_n x^n + a_{n-1} x^{n-1} + \cdots + a_1 x + a_0$, then the **derived polynomial** of $f(x)$ is a new polynomial $f'(x)$ defined by

$$f'(x) = n \cdot a_n x^{n-1} + (n - 1)a_{n-1} x^{n-2} + \cdots + a_1$$

The expression $f'(x)$ is read "f prime of x."

Example 5

(a) If $f(x) = 7x^4 - 3x^3 + 5x^2 - 4x + 2$, then

$$f'(x) = 4 \cdot 7x^{4-1} + 3(-3)x^{3-1} + 2 \cdot 5x^{2-1} - 4$$

$$= 28x^3 - 9x^2 + 10x - 4$$

(b) If $g(x) = 3x^2 - 4$, then $g'(x) = 6x$.

(c) If $h(x) = 5$, then $h'(x) = 0$.

(d) If $F(t) = -\sqrt{2}t^4 - \pi t^3 + \sqrt{3}t - 1$,
then $F'(t) = -4\sqrt{2}t^3 - 3\pi t^2 + \sqrt{3}$.

(e) If $G(u) = \frac{1}{2}u^5 - \frac{3}{4}u^4 + \frac{1}{4}u^3$, then $G'(u) = \frac{5}{2}u^4 - 3u^3 + \frac{3}{4}u^2$.

Exercises with derived polynomials will appear throughout this chapter. They are good practice in manipulating polynomials. However, all such exercises are clearly marked and they may be omitted without loss of continuity.

The arithmetic operations of addition, subtraction, multiplication, and division can be applied to polynomials. Operations with polynomials have the properties that were described for all algebraic expressions in Section 1-2. If $f(x)$ and $g(x)$ are polynomials, their sum, difference, product, and quotient are denoted by $f + g, f - g, fg$, and f/g. This notation can be used to simplify complicated formulas.

Example 6
Let $f(x) = x^3 + x^2 - 4$ and $g(x) = 2x^2 + 3x$. To find their *sum,* add like terms:

$$(f + g)(x) = (x^3 + x^2 - 4) + (2x^2 + 3x) = x^3 + 3x^2 + 3x - 4$$

To find their *difference,* change the appropriate signs and add:

$$(f - g)(x) = (x^3 + x^2 - 4) - (2x^2 + 3x) = x^3 - x^2 - 3x - 4$$

To find their *product,* multiply each term of f by each term of g and add like terms:

$$(fg)(x) = (x^3 + x^2 - 4)(2x^2 + 3x) = 2x^5 + 2x^4 - 8x^2 + 3x^4 + 3x^3 - 12x$$
$$= 2x^5 + 5x^4 + 3x^3 - 8x^2 - 12x$$

or use "long multiplication":

$$
\begin{array}{lr}
x^3 + \ x^2 - 4 & \\
2x^2 + 3x & \\
\hline
2x^5 + 2x^4 \qquad\quad - 8x^2 & \text{(Multiply by } 2x^2.) \\
+ 3x^4 + 3x^3 \qquad\quad - 12x & \text{(Multiply by } 3x.) \\
\hline
Product:\quad 2x^5 + 5x^4 + 3x^3 - 8x^2 - 12x & \text{(Add like terms.)}
\end{array}
$$

The *division* of polynomials will be explained in Section 4-2.

The derived polynomial of a sum or a difference is simply the sum or the difference of the derived polynomials; however, the derived polynomial of a product does not have such a simple formula. As in the next example, we shall sometimes refer to the derived polynomial simply as the **prime.**

Example 7
Let $f(x) = x^3 + x^2 - 4$ and $g(x) = 2x^2 + 3x$, as in Example 6. Show that (a) $(f + g)' = f' + g'$ and (b) $(fg)' = fg' + gf'$.

Solution
(a)   *The prime of a sum is the sum of the primes.* In symbols, $(f + g)' = f' + g'$.

   (1)   Find $f + g$: $(f + g)(x) = x^3 + 3x^2 + 3x - 4$
                                                                  (From Example 6)

   (2)   Find $(f + g)'$: $(f + g)'(x) = 3x^2 + 6x + 3$
                                                                  (Definition of prime)

   (3)   Find f' and g': $f'(x) = 3x^2 + 2x$; $g'(x) = 4x + 3$
                                                                  (Definition of prime)

   (4)   Find $f' + g'$: $(f' + g')(x) = 3x^2 + 6x + 3$ (From (3))

   (5)   Compare (2) and (4).

(b)   *The prime of a product of two polynomials is the first polynomial times the prime of the second, plus the second polynomial times the prime of the first.* In symbols, $(fg)' = fg' + gf'$.

   (1)   Find fg: $fg(x) = 2x^5 + 5x^4 + 3x^3 - 8x^2 - 12x$ (Example 6)

   (2)   Find $(fg)'$: $(fg)'(x) = 10x^4 + 20x^3 + 9x^2 - 16x - 12$
                                                                  (Definition of prime)

   (3)   Find f' and g': $f'(x) = 3x^2 + 2x$; $g'(x) = 4x + 3$
                                                                  (Definition of prime)

   (4)   Find fg': $(fg')(x) = (x^3 + x^2 - 4)(4x + 3)$

$$= 4x^4 + 4x^3 - 16x + 3x^3 + 3x^2 - 12$$

$$= 4x^4 + 7x^3 + 3x^2 - 16x - 12$$

   (5)   Find gf': $(gf')(x) = (2x^2 + 3x)(3x^2 + 2x)$

$$= 6x^4 + 13x^3 + 6x^2$$

(6)   Add(4)and(5) $(fg' + gf')(x) = 10x^4 + 20x^3 + 9x^2 - 16x - 12$

(7)   Compare (2) and (6).

Exercises

Perform the indicated operations.
1. $(x^5 + 3x^4 - 2x^2 + 1) + (2x^3 + x^2 - 4)$
2. $(t^3 - 2t^2 + t) + (-t^3 + 2t^2 - t)$
3. $(-\frac{1}{2}y^7 + \frac{2}{3}y^5 - y^2 + 1) + (\frac{3}{4}y^7 - y^4 - 1)$
4. $(\frac{1}{2}u^2 + 1) + (\frac{1}{4}u^2 - 1)$
5. $(x^4 - 3x^2 + 2) - (-2x^4 + x + 1)$ 6. $(t^3 - t^2 + 3) - (2t^3 - t^2 - 3)$
7. $(y^2 + y + 1)(y - 3)$ 8. $(u^3 - u + 2)(u^5 + 2)$
9. $(x^3 + x^2 - 2x + 7)(x^2 - x + 1)$ 10. $(t^2 - t + 1)(t^3 + t^2 - t)$

Exercises 11–20 refer to the following polynomials. Exercises 15–19 concern derived polynomials.

$$f(x) = 2x^3 + 3x^2 - 2x \qquad\qquad F(x) = x^5 + x^3$$

$$g(x) = x^4 - 2x + 1 \qquad\qquad G(x) = -2x^3 + 2$$

$$h(x) = x^4 + 0x^3 + 0x^2 - 2x + 1 \qquad H(x) = 4$$

11.   What is the degree of each polynomial?
12.   What are the coefficients of each polynomial?
13.   Are any pairs of these polynomials equal?
14.   Find at least one zero (see Section 3-4) of f, F, and G.
15.   Find the derived polynomial of each of the six polynomials listed above.
16.   Show that $(f + g)' = f' + g'$
17.   Show that $(F - G)' = F' - G'$
18.   Show that $(FG)' = FG' + GF'$
19.   Show that $(GH)' = GH' + HG'$
20.   Find a.r.c.$f(x, h)$ and a.r.c.$g(x, h)$. Find the exact rate of change of f and g at $x = -2$. Are f and g increasing or decreasing near $x = -2$?

Given the identities below, find the constants $a, b, c, d, e,$ and f (see Example 3).
21. $2u - 3u^2 + 1 = au^3 - bu + c + du^2$
22. $t^3 - 1 = at^4 + bt^3 + ct^2 + dt + e$
23. $(x - 1)(x^2 + 2x + 1) = ax^4 - bx^3 + cx^2 - dx + e$

24. $(y^2 + y^3)(y - y^2) = ay^5 + by^4 + cy^3 + dy^2 + ey + f$

25.   Let $f(x, y) = 4x^2 - 3xy + y^2$ and $g(x, y) = x^2 + y^2$. Evaluate $f(-1, 1), f(0, 2), f(\sqrt{2}, \sqrt{2}), g(3, 4), g(0, 0)$, and $g(1/\sqrt{2}, 1/\sqrt{2})$.

26.   There are polynomials in three variables. Let $f(x, y, z) = x^2 + y^2 - z^2 + xy - yz + xz$. Evaluate $f(1, 0, -1)$ and $f(-1, 2, 1)$.

27.   Write the volume V of a cylinder as a polynomial in two variables, radius r and height h.

28.   Write the surface area S of a cylinder as a polynomial in the same two variables, r and h, defined in Exercise 27.

29.   Write the volume V of a rectangular prism as a polynomial in three variables, length l, width w, and height h.

30.   Write the surface area S of a rectangular prism as a polynomial in the same three variables, l, w, and h, defined in Exercise 29.

4-2
The Division Algorithm and Synthetic Division

Given any two integers m and n, with $n \neq 0$, it is possible to divide m by n. Usually, there is a remainder. For example, to divide 35 by 8 you could think "8 goes into 35 four times, plus a remainder of 3," and write

$$\frac{35}{8} = 4 + \frac{3}{8} \quad \text{or, equivalently,}$$

$$35 = 4 \cdot 8 + 3$$

This illustrates a general rule for dividing whole numbers.

■   **Division Algorithm for whole numbers***
  If m and n are any two whole numbers, and $n \neq 0$, then there are whole numbers q and r such that

$$m = q \cdot n + r$$

  and $r < n$. The number q is called the **quotient**, and r is called the **remainder.**

---

*Remember that whole numbers are *non*negative integers.

Notice that the remainder r must be less than the divisor n. In dividing 35 by 8, it was easy to find the quotient $q = 4$ and remainder $r = 3$. If the problem were more complicated, say 1,706,357 divided by 3,291, you would use long division.

Given any two polynomials $f(x)$ and $g(x)$, with $g(x) \neq 0$, it is possible to divide f by g. Usually, there is a remainder. For example, to divide $4x^2 + x$ by $2x^2$ you could think (with some practice) "$2x^2$ goes into $4x^2 + x$ two times, plus a remainder of x," and write

$$\frac{4x^2 + x}{2x^2} = 2 + \frac{x}{2x^2} \quad \text{or, equivalently,}$$

$$4x^2 + x = 2 \cdot 2x^2 + x$$

This illustrates a general rule for dividing polynomials.

■   **Division Algorithm for polynomials**
If $f(x)$ and $g(x)$ are any two polynomials, and $g(x) \neq 0$, then there are polynomials $q(x)$ and $r(x)$ such that

$$f(x) = q(x)g(x) + r(x)$$

and either $r(x) = 0$ or the degree of $r(x)$ is less than the degree of $g(x)$. The polynomial $q(x)$ is called the **quotient,** and $r(x)$ is called the **remainder.**

Notice that the *degree* of the remainder $r(x)$ must be less than the *degree* of the divisor $g(x)$. This is a consequence of the division method explained in Example 1 below. In dividing $4x^2 + x$ by $2x^2$, it was easy to find the quotient $q(x) = 2$ and the remainder $r(x) = x$. If the problem were more complicated, say $6x^4 - 3x^3 + x^2 - 6x + 1$ divided by $2x^2 + 3x - 7$, you would use **long division.**

Example 1
Divide $6x^4 - 3x^3 + x^2 - 6x + 1$ by $2x^2 + 3x - 7$.

Solution
Follow the rules for long division of numbers. Write

$$2x^2 + 3x - 7 \overline{)6x^4 - 3x^3 + x^2 - 6x + 1}$$

Divide the first term of the divisor into the first term of the dividend: $6x^4/2x^2 = 3x^2$. Write this result over the division line and multiply it by the entire divisor: $3x^2(2x^2 + 3x - 7) = 6x^4 + 9x^3 - 21x^2$. Write this result under the dividend and subtract. So far, we have

$$3x^2$$
$$2x^2 + 3x - 7 \overline{)6x^4 - 3x^3 + x^2 - 6x + 1}$$
$$6x^4 + 9x^3 - 21x^2 \longleftarrow \text{—————— To subtract, change}$$
$$ - 12x^3 + 22x^2 \text{the signs and add}$$

Now bring down the next term of the dividend, $-6x$, to form the new dividend $-12x^3 + 22x^2 - 6x$ and start all over again. Repeat these steps until the new dividend has a degree that is less than the degree of the divisor. The final tableau will look like this:

$$3x^2 - 6x + 20$$
$$2x^2 + 3x - 7 \overline{)6x^4 - 3x^3 + x^2 - 6x + 1}$$
$$6x^4 + 9x^3 - 21x^2$$
$$\overline{}$$
$$- 12x^3 + 22x^2 - 6x$$
$$- 12x^3 - 18x^2 + 42x$$
$$\overline{}$$
$$40x^2 - 48x + 1$$
$$40x^2 + 60x - 140$$
$$\overline{}$$
$$- 108x + 141$$

Thus, $q(x) = 3x^2 - 6x + 20$ is the quotient, and the last new dividend, $r(x) = -108x + 141$, is the remainder:

$$\frac{6x^4 - 3x^3 + x^2 - 6x + 1}{2x^2 + 3x - 7} = 3x^2 - 6x + 20 + \frac{-108 + 141}{2x^2 + 3x - 7}$$

or, in terms of the Division Algorithm,

$$6x^4 - 3x^3 + x^2 - 6x + 1 = (3x^2 - 6x + 20)(2x^2 + 3x - 7)$$
$$+ (-108x + 141)$$

All long division problems follow the same sequence of steps: (1) divide, (2) multiply, (3) subtract, and (4) "bring down" to form a new dividend. This is repeated until either the new dividend is 0 or its degree is less than the degree of divisor.

There are two additional rules to remember about long division. First, the powers of the terms in both the dividend and the divisor must be in increasing or decreasing order. The usual practice is to write them both in decreasing order. For example, to divide $3x^3 - 4x^5 - 8 - x$ by $-3 + x$, rewrite them as $-4x^5 + 3x^3 - x - 8$ and $x - 3$. Second, if some powers of the dividend are missing, be sure to leave space or write them with 0 coefficients, so that you subtract only like terms.

Example 2
Divide $3x^3 - 4x^5 - 8 - x$ by $-3 + x$.

Solution

Rewrite the polynomials in decreasing order. Think of the dividend as $-4x^5 + 0 \cdot x^4 + 3x^3 + 0 \cdot x^2 - x - 8$ and either write it like that or leave blank spaces for the zero terms.

$$
\begin{array}{r}
-4x^4 - 12x^3 - 33x^2 - 99x - 298 \\
x - 3 \overline{) -4x^5 \qquad + 3x^3 \qquad - x - 8} \\
\underline{-4x^5 + 12x^4} \\
-12x^4 + 3x^3 \\
\underline{-12x^4 + 36x^3} \\
-33x^3 \\
\underline{-33x^3 + 99x^2} \\
-99x^2 - x \\
\underline{-99x^2 + 297x} \\
-298x - 8 \\
\underline{-298x + 894} \\
-902
\end{array}
$$

Thus,

$$-4x^5 + 3x^3 - x - 8 = (-4x^4 - 12x^3 - 33x^2 - 99x - 298)(x - 3) - 902$$

Divisors of the form $x - c$ occur so frequently that a shortcut method called **synthetic division** has been developed especially for problems with these divisors. The division in Example 2 can be performed in this way. First, eliminate all the variables and write only the coefficients. Be sure to use 0 to represent missing terms. Because the coefficient of x in the divisor is always 1, you may omit it also. Compare this simplified version to Example 2.

$$
\begin{array}{r}
-4 - 12 - 33 - 99 - 298 \\
-3 \overline{) -4 \quad 0 \quad 3 \quad 0 \quad -1 \quad -8} \\
-4 + 12 \\
-12 + 3 \\
-12 + 36 \\
-33 \\
-33 + 99 \\
-99 - 1 \\
-99 + 297 \\
-298 - 8 \\
-298 + 894 \\
-902
\end{array}
$$

The circled numbers simply repeat the numbers directly above them, which, in turn, are identical to the coefficients in the quotient. There is no need to write these numbers three times. Eliminating the circled numbers and the quotient, above the line, yields a further reduction. You can now write the whole division problem in greatly condensed form:

$$\begin{array}{r|rrrrrr}
-3 & -4 & 0 & 3 & 0 & -1 & -8 \\
& & 12 & 36 & 99 & 297 & 894 \\
\hline
& -4 & -12 & -33 & -99 & -298 & -902
\end{array} \longleftarrow \text{Subtract}$$

Because it is easier to add than subtract, change the divisor, -3 to 3 (this will change the signs in the second row of numbers). The final tableau for using synthetic division to divide $-4x^5 + 3x^3 - x - 8$ by $x - 3$ is

$$\begin{array}{r|rrrrrr}
3 & -4 & 0 & 3 & 0 & -1 & -8 \\
& & -12 & -36 & -99 & -297 & -894 \\
\hline
& -4 & -12 & -33 & -99 & -298 & -902
\end{array} \longleftarrow \text{Add}$$

from which we may read off the answer obtained in Example 2 above;

$$q(x) = -4x^4 - 12x^3 - 33x^2 - 99x - 298 \quad \text{and} \quad r(x) = -902$$

WARNING: *Synthetic division works only when the divisor is of the form $x - c$.*

Example 3
Use synthetic division to divide $3x^4 - 4x^2 + x - 1$ by $x + 2$.

Solution
Write

$$\begin{array}{r|rrrrr}
-2 & 3 & 0 & -4 & 1 & -1 \\
& & & & & \\
\hline
& 3 & & & &
\end{array}$$

Notice that the constant 2 has been changed to -2. If you were dividing by $x - 2$, then you would use 2. Write the first coefficient of the dividend, 3, below the line. Multiply it by -2 and add the result to the 0:

$$\begin{array}{r|rrrrr}
-2 & 3 & 0 & -4 & 1 & 1 \\
& & -6 & & & \\
\hline
& 3 & -6 & & &
\end{array}$$

Now multiply -6 by -2 and add the result to -4:

$$\begin{array}{r|rrrrr} -2 & 3 & 0 & -4 & 1 & -1 \\ & & -6 & 12 & & \\ \hline & 3 & -6 & 8 & & \end{array}$$

Add the product of 8 and -2 to 1, and so on. The final tableau looks like this

$$\begin{array}{r|rrrrr} -2 & 3 & 0 & -4 & 1 & -1 \\ & & -6 & 12 & -16 & 30 \\ \hline & 3 & -6 & 8 & -15 & 29 \end{array}$$

The result can be read from the bottom row: The degree of the dividend is 4, so the quotient must begin with an x^3 term. Therefore, the quotient is $q(x) = 3x^3 - 6x^2 + 8x - 15$, and the remainder is $r(x) = 29$.

Example 4
Divide $x^5 - 4x^2 + 5$ by $x - 3$.

Solution
Write

$$\begin{array}{r|rrrrrr} 3 & 1 & 0 & 0 & -4 & 0 & 5 \\ & & & & & & \\ \hline & 1 & & & & & \end{array}$$

Now multiply 1 by 3 and add, step by step, as indicated:

$$\begin{array}{r|rrrrrr} 3 & 1 & 0 & 0 & -4 & 0 & 5 \\ & & 3 & 9 & 27 & 69 & 207 \\ \hline & 1 & 3 & 9 & 23 & 69 & 212 \end{array}$$

The dividend has degree 5, so the quotient begins with x^4. The answer is $q(x) = x^4 + 3x^3 + 9x^2 + 23x + 69$ with remainder 212.

Exercises

Divide.

1. $(x^4 + 3x^2 - 1) \div x^2$ 2. $(x^5 - 2x^4 + x - 1) \div x^3$
3. $(6y^4 - 3y^2 + y - 2) \div (y^2 + 1)$ 4. $(3y^5 + y^3 - y^2) \div (y^3 - 1)$

5. $(t^5 - 1) \div (t^3 + t^2)$ **6.** $(t^4 + t^2 + 1) \div (t^2 - t)$
7. $(6m^6 + 10m^4 - 3m^3 + 3m^2 - 5m + 5) \div (3m^2 + 5)$
8. $(4m^5 - m^3 + m - 1) \div (-3m^2 + m - 4)$

Use synthetic division.
  9. $(9x^2 - 3x + 4) \div (x - 2)$ **10.** $(3x^3 + 1) \div (x - 4)$
11. $(3t^5 - t^3 + t) \div (t + 1)$ **12.** $(-2t^4 + t^2 + 1) \div (t + 7)$
13. $(8m^3 - m^2 + 3m + 2) \div (m + \frac{1}{2})$ **14.** $(6m^2 - 4m + 1) \div (m - \frac{1}{4})$
15. $(r^5 - 1) \div (r - 1)$ **16.** $(r^6 - 1) \div (r + 1)$

Exercises 17–26 refer to the following six polynomials. These exercises concern the
derived polynomial, or prime, defined in Section 4-1.

$$f(t) = 3t^4 - 4t^2 + t \qquad F(t) = t^5 - 1$$

$$g(t) = -2t^4 + 3t^2 - t \qquad G(t) = t - 1$$

$$h(t) = t^3 - 1 \qquad H(t) = t^7 - t^4 + t^3 - 1$$

17. Show that $(f + g)' = f' + g'$.
18. Show that $(f - g)' = f' - g'$.
19. Show that $(fh)' = fh' + hf'$.

*If one polynomial is divided by another, the prime of the result is the denominator times
the prime of the numerator, minus the numerator times the prime of the denominator, all
divided by the square of the denominator. In symbols, for any polynomials $f(x)$ and
$g(x) \neq 0$,*

$$(f/g)' = \frac{gf' - fg'}{g^2} \tag{1}$$

20. Compute F/G (use your answer to Exercise 15), $(F/G)'$, GF', FG', and
$G^2 = GG$. Then show that formula (1) holds.
21. Verify formula (1) for f/G.   **22.** Verify formula (1) for H/G.
23. Verify formula (1) for H/h.   **24.** Verify formula (1) for g/G.
25. Divide H by F and write $H(x) = q(x) F(x) + r(x)$. Find $(qF + r)'$ by using the
sum and product rules for primes. Verify that your answer equals H'.
26. Follow the instructions in Exercise 25 for F and h.

27. (Zeros and factors) If a number a is a zero of the polynomial $f(x)$, then $(x - a)$
is a factor of $f(x)$. This statement will be proved in Section 4-3. Show that it is true for

(a) $f(x) = x^3 - 3x^2 + 2x - 6;$ $a = 3$
(b) $f(x) = 4x^5 - x^3 + 3x + 6;$ $a = -1$

by verifying that $f(a) = 0$; then use synthetic division to show that $f(x)/(x - a)$ has a zero remainder, which proves that $(x - a)$ is a factor of f.

28.   (Zeros and solutions) Find a solution of each equation:

(a) $t^3 + 10 = 3t^2 - 2t + 4$ (b) $3y + 8 = 2 + y^3 - 4y^5$

[HINT: Rewrite the equations with 0 on the right. Then look at Exercise 27.]

29.   ("Primes" and graphs) The derived polynomial, or prime, of a linear polynomial $f(x) = mx + b$ is $f'(x) = m$, a constant equal to the slope of the line. Hence, *the function f is increasing or decreasing according to whether $f'(x)$ is positive or negative.* This statement is also true of parabolas. Verify it for

(a) $f(x) = x^2 + 2$ and   (b) $f(x) = -x^2 + 2x + 3$

by following these three steps: (1) Graph each parabola and note where it is increasing and decreasing. (2) Find $f'(x)$; it will be linear. Determine where the linear polynomial $f'(x)$ is positive, negative, and zero. (3) Show that, where $f'(x)$ is positive, the parabola is increasing; where $f'(x)$ is negative, the parabola is decreasing; the zero of $f'(x)$ is the x-coordinate of the vertex. Thus, *the simple algebraic manipulation of finding the derived polynomial can yield a great deal of geometric information.*

4-3
Zeros of a Polynomial

In Section 3-4, a *zero* of a function f was defined as any number a for which $f(a) = 0$. It is also called a *root* of the equation $f(x) = 0$. Zeros and roots are useful tools in factoring and solving equations.

■   **Factor Theorem**
Let $f(x)$ be a polynomial. Then a is a zero of f if and only if $x - a$ is a factor of $f(x)$.

Proof
To prove this statement we must show two things: (1) If $f(a) = 0$, then $f(x)$ can be written as a product $q(x)(x - a)$, where $q(x)$ is a polynomial; and, conversely, (2) if $f(x) = q(x)(x - a)$, then $f(a) = 0$. Statement (2) is easy to prove: if $f(x) = q(x)$ $(x - a)$, then $f(a) = q(a)(a - a) = 0$.

The validity of (1) depends on the Division Algorithm. We know there is a quotient $q(x)$ and a remainder $r(x)$ such that $f(x) = q(x)(x - a) + r(x)$. Because the remainder must be 0 or of smaller degree than $x - a$, it follows that $r(x)$ is some constant; call it c. Therefore,

$$f(x) = q(x)(x - a) + c$$

Now c is fixed. In fact, substituting a for x in this equation yields $f(a) = c$. If $f(a) = 0$, then $c = 0$ and the equation reads $f(x) = q(x)(x - a)$, which is exactly statement (1) above.

Application of this theorem can turn a difficult factoring problem into a simple chore.

Example 1
Let $f(x) = x^3 + 2x^2 - 13x + 10$. Show that 2 is a zero, and use that fact to factor $f(x)$ completely. Find two more zeros of f.

Solution
Showing that 2 is a zero is simple:

$$f(2) = 2^3 + 2 \cdot 2^2 - 13 \cdot 2 + 10 = 0$$

From the Factor Theorem, you know that $x - 2$ must be a factor. Use synthetic division to divide $f(x)$ by $x - 2$:

$$
\begin{array}{r|rrrr}
2 & 1 & 2 & -13 & 10 \\
  &   & 2 & 8 & -10 \\
\hline
  & 1 & 4 & -5 & 0
\end{array}
$$

Thus, $f(x) = (x^2 + 4x - 5)(x - 2)$. Now factor $x^2 + 4x - 5$, either by sight factoring or by the quadratic formula. Thus,

$$f(x) = (x + 5)(x - 1)(x - 2)$$

and it follows that -5, 1, and 2 are zeros of the function f; that is, $f(-5) = 0$, $f(1) = 0$, and $f(2) = 0$. (Check!)

Now suppose that a and b are distinct zeros of a polynomial $f(x)$. The Factor Theorem says that $f(x) = q(x)(x - a)$ for some polynomial $q(x)$. Because b is also a zero of f,

$$0 = f(b) = q(b)(b - a)$$

Because $b - a \neq 0$, $q(b)$ must be zero. What we have just proved is that

■ If a and b are distinct zeros of $f(x)$, and $f(x) = q(x)(x - a)$, then b must be a zero of $q(x)$.

Example 2

Use the fact that $\frac{1}{2}$ and -1 are zeros of

$$f(x) = x^4 + \tfrac{1}{2}x^3 - \tfrac{5}{2}x^2 - x + 1$$

to factor $f(x)$. Find two more zeros of $f(x)$.

Solution

Because $\frac{1}{2}$ is a zero of f, $x - \frac{1}{2}$ is a factor of f. Use synthetic division

$$
\begin{array}{r|rrrrr}
\frac{1}{2} & 1 & \frac{1}{2} & -\frac{5}{2} & -1 & 1 \\
            &   & \frac{1}{2} & \frac{1}{2} & -1 & -1 \\
\hline
            & 1 & 1 & -2 & -2 & 0
\end{array}
$$

to get $f(x) = (x^3 + x^2 - 2x - 2)(x - \frac{1}{2})$. Because -1 is given as a zero of f, it follows from the statement just before this example that -1 is also a zero of $x^3 + x^2 - 2x - 2$. Again use synthetic division

$$
\begin{array}{r|rrrr}
-1 & 1 & 1 & -2 & -2 \\
   &   & -1 & 0 & 2 \\
\hline
   & 1 & 0 & -2 & 0
\end{array}
$$

to get $x^3 + x^2 - 2x - 2 = (x^2 - 2)(x + 1)$. So far, then,

$$f(x) = (x^2 - 2)(x + 1)(x - \tfrac{1}{2})$$

The first factor can be rewritten as $(x + \sqrt{2})(x - \sqrt{2})$; therefore,

$$f(x) = (x + \sqrt{2})(x - \sqrt{2})(x + 1)(x - \tfrac{1}{2})$$

Thus, four zeros of f are $\pm\sqrt{2}$, -1, and $\frac{1}{2}$.

It may happen that a polynomial cannot be factored completely into linear factors $x - a$.

Example 3

Use the fact that $\frac{1}{2}$ and -1 are zeros of

$$f(x) = x^4 + \tfrac{1}{2}x^3 + \tfrac{3}{2}x^2 + x - 1$$

to factor $f(x)$.

Solution
Because $\tfrac{1}{2}$ is a zero of f, by the Factor Theorem, $x - \tfrac{1}{2}$ must be a factor. Use synthetic division

$$
\begin{array}{r|rrrrr}
\tfrac{1}{2} & 1 & \tfrac{1}{2} & \tfrac{3}{2} & 1 & -1 \\
 & & \tfrac{1}{2} & \tfrac{1}{2} & 1 & 1 \\
\hline
 & 1 & 1 & 2 & 2 & 0
\end{array}
$$

to get $f(x) = (x^3 + x^2 + 2x + 2)(x - \tfrac{1}{2})$. You also know that -1 is a zero of f. As in Example 2, it follows that -1 must be a zero of $x^3 + x^2 + 2x + 2$. Divide this polynomial by $x + 1$

$$
\begin{array}{r|rrrr}
-1 & 1 & 1 & 2 & 2 \\
 & & -1 & 0 & -2 \\
\hline
 & 1 & 0 & 2 & 0
\end{array}
$$

to get $x^3 + x^2 + 2x + 2 = (x^2 + 2)(x + 1)$. So far, then,

$$f(x) = (x^2 + 2)(x + 1)(x - \tfrac{1}{2})$$

Because the first factor cannot be factored further, this is as far as you can go.

As we have just seen, zeros play an important role in factoring a polynomial. Zeros are also the key to solving polynomial equations (see Section 4-4 and Exercises 26–28 at the end of this section), and knowing their location is an aid in graphing (see Section 4-5). Evidently, finding the zeros of a polynomial is a worthwhile skill.

For polynomials of degree one and two, that is, for linear and quadratic polynomials, the zeros are easy to locate. If $f(x) = mx + b$ and $m \neq 0$, then $-b/m$ is the only zero of f. If $f(x) = ax^2 + bx + c$ and $a \neq 0$, the zeros are given by the quadratic formula:

$$\frac{-b \pm \sqrt{b^2 - 4ac}}{2a}$$

There will be two, one, or no real-number zeros depending on whether the discriminant $b^2 - 4ac$ is positive, zero, or negative. For polynomials of degree three or more, unfortunately, we have no such neat package to work with, but there are some facts and procedures that will help to find or estimate the zeros.

First of all, there is a limit to the number of zeros a polynomial can have. If c_1, $c_2, \ldots, c_n$ are zeros of f, then $x - c_1, x - c_2, \ldots, x - c_n$ are factors of $f(x)$, by the

Factor Theorem. This means that $f(x)$ is a product of these (and perhaps other) factors. Because this product contains an x^n term, the degree of $f(x)$ must be at least n. Conversely, if the degree of $f(x)$ is n, then $f(x)$ can have no more than n linear factors, and no more than n zeros.

■ **Maximum Zeros Theorem**
A polynomial of degree n has at most n zeros.

In the real number system, a polynomial of degree n can have less than n linear factors and less than n zeros (see Example 3). In Chapter 9, you will learn about the complex numbers; in the complex number system, each polynomial of degree n has exactly n linear factors and n zeros. In the meantime, however, references to the zeros of a polynomial will mean only the real-number zeros.
  Another useful property of zeros is the following rule:

■ **Descartes' Rule of Signs**
Let $f(x)$ be a polynomial written in descending order of powers.
(a)   If j is the number of changes of sign of the coefficients of $f(x)$, then the number of positive zeros of f is $j - 2p$, for some nonnegative integer p.
(b)   If k is the number of changes of sign of the coefficients of $f(-x)$, then the number of negative zeros of f is $k - 2q$, for some nonnegative integer q.

Example 4
Find the number of positive and negative zeros of

(a) $f(x) = x^3 + 2x^2 - 13x + 10$

(b) $h(x) = x^4 + \frac{1}{2}x^3 - \frac{5}{2}x^2 - x + 1$

(c) $g(x) = x^4 + \frac{1}{2}x^3 + \frac{3}{2}x^2 + x - 1$

Solution
(a)   Count the changes in sign:

$$f(x) = x^3 + 2x^2 - 13x + 10 \qquad f(-x) = (-x)^3 + 2(-x)^2 - 13(-x) + 10$$
$$\qquad\qquad\quad 1 \qquad 2 \qquad\qquad\qquad = -x^3 + 2x^2 + 13x + 10$$
$$\qquad\qquad\qquad\qquad\qquad\qquad\qquad\qquad\qquad 1$$

There are two changes of sign in $f(x)$. Thus, there are either 2 positive zeros (if $p = 0$ in the formula) or no positive zeros (if $p = 1$). There is one change in

$f(-x)$ so there must be one negative zero ($q = 0$). In Example 1, the zeros of this polynomial $f(x)$ were found to be 2, 1, and -5.

(b)   Count the changes in sign:

$$h(x) = x^4 + \tfrac{1}{2}x^3 - \tfrac{5}{2}x^2 - x + 1 \qquad h(-x) = x^4 - \tfrac{1}{2}x^3 - \tfrac{5}{2}x^2 + x + 1$$

Thus, h may have two positive zeros or none, and it may have two negative zeros or none. Example 2 showed that this polynomial has two positive and two negative zeros.

(c)   Count the changes in sign:

$$g(x) = x^4 + \tfrac{1}{2}x^3 + \tfrac{3}{2}x^2 + x - 1 \qquad g(-x) = x^4 - \tfrac{1}{2}x^3 + \tfrac{3}{2}x^2 - x - 1$$

Thus, g must have one positive zero and either three or one negative zeros. In Example 3, this polynomial had one positive and one negative zero.

Exercises

In Exercises 1–16, the indicated numbers are zeros of the given polynomials. Factor each polynomial and find its zeros.

1. $f(x) = x^3 + 6x^2 + 3x - 10;\ a = -2$
2. $g(t) = t^3 - 3t + 2;\ a = 1$
3. $h(u) = u^3 - u^2 - 4u - 6;\ a = 3$
4. $f(x) = x^3 - 5x^2 + 3x + 4;\ a = 4$
5. $g(t) = 2t^3 - 3t^2 - 17t + 30;\ a = \tfrac{3}{2}$
6. $h(u) = 2u^3 + 9u^2 - 4u - 4;\ a = -\tfrac{1}{2}$
7. $f(x) = x^4 + 3x^3 - 30x^2 - 6x + 56;\ a = \sqrt{2},\ b = -\sqrt{2}$
8. $g(t) = t^4 - 12t^2 + 32;\ a = \sqrt{8},\ b = -\sqrt{8}$
9. $h(u) = 2u^4 + 2u^3 + u^2 + u;\ a = 0,\ b = -1$
10. $f(x) = x^4 + x^3 - 2x^2 - 2x;\ a = \sqrt{2},\ b = 0$
11. $g(t) = t^4 - \tfrac{7}{12}t^2 + \tfrac{1}{12};\ a = \tfrac{1}{2},\ b = -\tfrac{1}{2}$
12. $h(u) = u^4 - \tfrac{25}{144}u^2 + \tfrac{1}{144};\ a = \tfrac{1}{3},\ b = -\tfrac{1}{4}$
13. $f(x) = x^5 - 3x^4 - 16x + 48;\ a = 3$
14. $g(t) = t^5 + t^4 - 16t - 16;\ a = -1$
15. $h(u) = u^5 - u^4 - 5u^3 + 5u^2 + 6u - 6;\ a = 1,\ b = \sqrt{3},\ c = -\sqrt{3}$
16. $f(x) = x^5 + x^4 - 12x^3 - 12x^2 + 32x + 32;\ a = -1,\ b = \sqrt{8},\ c = -\sqrt{8}$

Use Descartes' Rule of Signs to determine how many positive and negative zeros the following functions may have. Then compare with the actual number of zeros found in Exercises 1–16.

17. $f(x) = x^3 + 6x^2 + 3x - 10$ (Compare with 1)

18. $h(u) = u^3 - u^2 - 4u - 6$ (Compare with 3)

19. $g(t) = 2t^3 - 3t^2 - 17t + 30$ (Compare with 5)

20. $f(x) = x^4 + 3x^3 - 30x^2 - 6x + 56$ (Compare with 7)

21. $h(u) = 2u^4 + 2u^3 + u^2 + u$ (Compare with 9)

22. $h(u) = u^5 - u^4 - 5u^3 + 5u^2 - 6u - 6$ (Compare with 15)

23.   (a)   Is there a real number x whose cube exceeds it by 1? [HINT: Write the polynomial $p(x) = x^3 - x - 1$ and use Descartes' Rule to see if there are any zeros.]

    (b)   Is it true that for every positive integer n, there is a real number whose nth power exceeds it by 1?

24.   (Continuation of Exercise 23)

    (a)   Is there a real number that exceeds its square by 1?

    (b)   Is there a real number that exceeds its cube by 1?

    (c)   Formulate conditions on the positive integer n for the polynomial $p(x) = x - x^n - 1$ to have a real zero.

25.   Show that, if $f(x)$ and $g(x)$ are both polynomials of degree n and $f(x) = g(x)$ at $n + 1$ distinct values of x, then $f(x) = g(x)$ for *every* value of x. [HINT: Consider the polynomial $f - g$. What is its degree? How many zeros will it have? Now look at the Maximum Zeros Theorem.]

(Equation solving) Solve the following equations. [HINT: Rewrite each equation with only 0 on the right. Then use the results of Exercises 1, 5 and 7.]

26. $x^3 + 6x^2 = 10 - 3x$

27. $2t^3 + 30 = 3t^2 + 17t$

28. $x^4 + 3x^3 = 30x^2 + 6x - 56$

29.   (Anticipation of the Remainder Theorem) Use synthetic division to divide $f(x) = x^3 - 2x + x - 4$ by

     (a) $x - 2$ (b) $x + 1$ (c) $x - \frac{1}{2}$

and then verify that the remainders are $f(2)$, $f(-1)$, and $f(\frac{1}{2})$, respectively.

30.   (Zeros of f') Let $f(x) = x^3 + 6x^2 + 3x - 10$ (as in Exercise 1). Find $f'(x)$ and verify that *the zeros of f' lie at or between the zeros of f.* This is always true.

31.   Follow the instructions in Exercise 30 for the polynomial in Exercise 5.

32.   Make up a polynomial of degree 3 that has three zeros. Make up another with only one zero. Can you make up one with no zeros?

33.   Make up a polynomial of degree 4 that has four zeros. Make up another with no zeros.

34.   Make up a polynomial (a quadratic will do) with two changes of sign and two positive zeros. Make up another with two changes of sign and *no* positive zeros.

35.   The polynomial $x^2 - 2x + 1$ has two changes of sign, but the quadratic formula shows only one positive zero. Does this contradict Descartes' Rule?

4-4
Zeros and Equations

Most of the polynomials we shall deal with have integer coefficients. For these polynomials, the next theorem describes a way to rule out all but a few rational numbers that can be zeros. We shall not prove it.

■ **Rational Zero Theorem**
   If $f(x) = a_n x^n + \cdots + a_1 x + a_0$ *has integer coefficients and the fraction* p/q
   (reduced to lowest terms) *is a zero of* f, *then* p *is a factor of* a_0 *and* q *is a factor*
   of a_n.

   Example 1
   Find all rational zeros of $g(t) = 2t^3 + 5t^2 - 11t + 4$.

   Solution
   According to the Rational Zero Theorem, if p/q is a zero, then p divides 4 and q divides 2. The possibilities are $p = \pm 1, \pm 2, \pm 4$ and $q = \pm 1, \pm 2$. Thus, if g has a rational zero p/q, it must come from the list

   $$\pm 1, \ \pm \tfrac{1}{2}, \ \pm 2, \ \pm 4$$

   It is possible that none of these is a zero, but there are two ways to check each one. Either evaluate $g(p/q)$ or divide $g(t)$ by $t - \dfrac{p}{q}$ (see the Factor Theorem, p. 164). There are advantages to using the second method.
       To check $+1$, divide by $t - 1$.

   $$
   \begin{array}{r|rrrr}
   1 & 2 & 5 & -11 & 4 \\
     &   & 2 & 7 & -4 \\
   \hline
     & 2 & 7 & -4 & 0
   \end{array}
   $$

Because the remainder is 0, we know that $t - 1$ is a factor and therefore 1 is a zero (Factor Theorem). The advantage of this method is that the quotient is obtained automatically. Now we know that $g(t) = (2t^2 + 7t - 4)(t - 1)$, and we can use the quadratic formula on $2t^2 + 7t - 4$.

$$t = \frac{-7 \pm \sqrt{7^2 - 4(2)(-4)}}{2(2)} = \frac{1}{2} \quad \text{or} \quad -4$$

It follows that $1, \frac{1}{2}$, and -4 are rational zeros of g. If the quadratic had had two irrational zeros, then we would know that 1 was the only rational zero of g. The reason is that $g(t)$ is of degree 3 and, therefore, can have at most 3 zeros (Maximum Zeros Theorem, p. 168).

The graph of a polynomial is a smooth curve, with no gaps. If $(x_1, f(x_1))$ and $(x_2, f(x_2))$ lie on opposite sides of the x-axis, then somewhere between x_1 and x_2 the curve must cross the axis. The point where it crosses is a zero of f (see Figure 4-1).

■   **Intermediate-Value Theorem**
If $f(x)$ is a polynomial and $f(x_1)$ and $f(x_2)$ have opposite signs, then there is a zero of f between x_1 and x_2.

This theorem can be used to approximate zeros to any desired accuracy. For example, if $f(2) > 0$ and $f(3) < 0$, then there is a zero between 2 and 3. Next, try $f(2.5)$; if it is positive, then the zero is between 2.5 and 3, but if it is negative, then the zero is

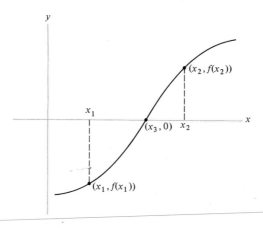

Figure 4-1
The graph of a polynomial $f(x)$ is a smooth curve, with no gaps. If $f(x_1) < 0$ and $f(x_2) > 0$, then the graph crosses the x-axis at some point x_3 between x_1 and x_2.

between 2 and 2.5. Continue with $f(2.75)$, or $f(2.25)$, as the case may be, and so on until the desired accuracy is reached. In the next two examples, we shall be content to locate zeros between consecutive integers.

Example 2
Approximate the location of the zeros of

$$h(u) = u^4 + u^3 - 6u^2 - 5u + 5$$

between consecutive integers.

Solution
Make a table of values and watch for changes in sign. Start with $u = 0$ and work in both directions until the values of $h(u)$ get very large in size.

u	-3	-2	-1	0	1	2	3
$h(u)$	20	-1	4	5	-4	-5	44

Sign changes

Thus, one zero lies between -3 and -2, another between -2 and -1, another between 0 and 1, and the last between 2 and 3. Because $h(u)$ has degree 4, these are all the zeros.

Making the table of values in Example 2 was tedious. When $u = -3$, for example, the calculation was $h(-3) = (-3)^4 + (-3)^3 - 6(-3)^2 - 5(-3) + 5$. There should be a better way to compute this—and there is.

■ **Remainder Theorem**
When a polynomial $f(x)$ is divided by $x - c$, the remainder is $f(c)$.

Proof
Write $f(x) = q(x)(x - c) + r(x)$. Because the degree of the divisor $x - c$ is 1, it follows that $r(x)$ is a constant, call it r. Now evaluate f at c to obtain

$$f(c) = q(c)(c - c) + r = r$$

which is what we wanted to prove.

Now compute $h(-3)$, if $h(u) = u^4 + u^3 - 6u^2 - 5u + 5$, by dividing $h(u)$ by $u - (-3)$. Use synthetic division:

$$
\begin{array}{r|rrrrr}
-3 & 1 & 1 & -6 & -5 & 5 \\
   &   & -3 & 6 & 0 & 15 \\
\hline
   & 1 & -2 & 0 & -5 & 20 \\
\end{array}
$$

The remainder is 20; thus, by the Remainder Theorem, $h(-3) = 20$. This technique is extremely useful.

Example 3
Approximate the location of the zeros of

$$ f(x) = x^4 - 6x^3 + 8x^2 + 2x - 1 $$

between consecutive integers.

Solution
Construct the following table:

Coefficients of $f(x)$

	1	−6	8	2	−1	
−2	1	−8	24	−46	91	$= f(-2)$
−1	1	−7	15	−13	12	$= f(-1)$
0	1	−6	8	2	−1	$= f(0)$
1	1	−5	3	5	4	$= f(1)$
2	1	−4	0	2	3	$= f(2)$
3	1	−3	−1	−1	−4	$= f(3)$
4	1	−2	0	2	7	$= f(4)$

Values of c (left column label)

Sign changes

The top row consists of the coefficients of $f(x)$; the left column consists of values of c in the divisor $x - c$; each of the lower rows is the result of the synthetic division of $f(x)$ by $x - c$, with the calculations performed mentally. For example, in the row that begins with −2, bring down the 1, multiply by −2, add the result to -6, and write in -8. Next, multiply -8 by -2, add the result to 8, and write in 24. Continue until the remainder of 91 is reached; then $f(-2) = 91$, by the Remainder Theorem.

This table shows clearly that there are zeros between -1 and 0, between 0 and 1, between 2 and 3, and between 3 and 4. There is no need to look further, because $f(x)$ has degree 4 and, therefore, has at most four zeros.

Solving equations

One of the main objectives of algebra is to solve polynomial equations. The facts about zeros gathered in this and the preceding section are tools that can be used to solve such equations.

Every polynomial equation can be rewritten as an equivalent equation (same solution set) with only 0 on the right and a polynomial $f(x)$ on the left. Then the roots of $f(x) = 0$, or the zeros of f, are the solutions of the original equation. The degree of $f(x)$ indicates the largest number of zeros to expect. The Factor Theorem relates zeros and factors of the form $x - c$. Descartes' Rule of Signs aids in discovering the number of positive and negative zeros. A table of values can approximate the location of zeros. The Rational Zero Theorem can eliminate all but a few rational numbers. The other zeros are irrational and can be approximated to any degree of accuracy by using the Intermediate-Value Theorem.

The next two examples show how to tie all this information together.

Example 4
Find the solutions of the equation

$$2x^4 - \frac{4}{3}x^3 + \frac{2}{3} = \frac{25}{6}x^2 - \frac{5}{6}x$$

Solution
(1) *Rewrite the equation* as

$$2x^4 - \frac{4}{3}x^3 - \frac{25}{6}x^2 + \frac{5}{6}x + \frac{2}{3} = 0$$

It will simplify computations if you clear fractions. Multiply both sides of the equation by 6 to obtain

$$12x^4 - 8x^3 - 25x^2 + 5x + 4 = 0$$

Multiplying both sides by a nonzero number will not change the solution set. Thus, the *zeros* of $f(x) = 12x^4 - 8x^3 - 25x^2 + 5x + 4$ are the *solutions* we seek.

(2)   *Use Descartes' Rule of Signs:*

$$f(x) = 12x^4 - 8x^3 - 25x^2 + 5x + 4$$

$$\underbrace{\qquad}_{1} \qquad \underbrace{\qquad}_{2}$$

$$f(-x) = 12x^4 + 8x^3 - 25x^2 - 5x + 4$$

$$\underbrace{\qquad}_{1} \qquad \underbrace{\qquad}_{2}$$

Thus, there are either two positive zeros or none, and the same for negative zeros.

(3)   *Make a table of values.* Start with 0 and work in both directions:

	12	-8	-25	5	4	
-3						
-2	12	-32	39	-73	150	
-1	12	-20	-5	10	-6	
0	12	-8	-25	5	4	Sign changes
1	12	4	-21	-16	-12	
2	12	16	7	19	42	
3						

There is no need to go further in either direction. The table already shows two positive zeros a_1 and a_2 and two negative zeros a_3 and a_4. Descartes' Rule says that there are no more than these. Furthermore,

$$1 < a_1 < 2, \quad 0 < a_2 < 1, \quad -1 < a_3 < 0 \quad \text{and} \quad -2 < a_4 < -1$$

(4)   *Find rational zeros.* If p/q is a zero, then p divides 4 and q divides 12. The possibilities for p/q, then, are

$$\pm 1, \pm 1/12, \pm 1/6, \pm 1/4, \pm 1/3, \pm 1/2, \pm 2/3, \pm 4/3, \pm 2, \pm 4$$

The information in step (3) rules out ± 1, ± 2, and ± 4. All the others are possible zeros, and you should check each one of them. You will find that $1/2$ and $-1/3$ are the only rational zeros of f.

(5)   *Locate all zeros.* Using the information in step (4) and the Factor Theorem

in Section 4-3, you can factor $f(x)$ as

$$f(x) = (12x^2 - 6x - 24)\left(x + \frac{1}{3}\right)\left(x - \frac{1}{2}\right)$$

$$= 6(2x^2 - x - 4)\left(x + \frac{1}{3}\right)\left(x - \frac{1}{2}\right)$$

The zeros of $2x^2 - x - 4$ can be obtained by the quadratic formula

$$\frac{1 \pm \sqrt{33}}{4}$$

Conclusion

The solutions of the equation $2x^4 - \frac{4}{3}x^3 + \frac{2}{3} = \frac{25}{6}x^2 - \frac{5}{6}x$ are $-\frac{1}{3}, \frac{1}{2}$, $\frac{1 + \sqrt{33}}{4}$, and $\frac{1 - \sqrt{33}}{4}$.

Example 5
Find the solutions of the equation

$$8x^5 + 2 = 16x^3 + x^2$$

Find as many exact solutions as possible, and approximate the others.

Solution
(1) *Rewrite the equation* with 0 on the right

$$8x^5 - 16x^3 - x^2 + 2 = 0$$

A number is a solution of the original equation if and only if it is a zero of $f(x) = 8x^5 - 16x^3 - x^2 + 2$
(2) *Use Descartes' Rule of Signs:*

$$f(x) = \underbrace{8x^5 - 16x^3}_{1} \underbrace{- x^2 + 2}_{2} \qquad f(-x) = \underbrace{-8x^5 + 16x^3}_{1} \underbrace{{} - x^2}_{2} \underbrace{{} + 2}_{3}$$

Thus, there are either two positive zeros or none, and either three negative zeros or one.

(3)   *Make a table of values.* Start with 0 and work in both directions:

	8	0	−16	−1	0	2
−3						
−2	8	−16	16	−33	66	−130
−1	8	−8	−8	7	−7	9
0	8	0	−16	−1	0	2
1	8	8	−8	−9	−9	−7
2	8	16	16	31	62	126
3						

Sign changes

There is no need to check additional positive values. There are already two changes of sign locating two positive zeros, which is the most there can be according to Descartes' Rule. On the negative side, we stopped at −2 because the value −130 is so large. (As a matter of fact, $f(-3) = -1519$.)

The table shows two positive zeros a_1 and a_2, with $0 < a_1 < 1$ and $1 < a_2 < 2$, and one negative zero a_3, with $-2 < a_3 < -1$. There may be two other negative zeros.

(4)   *Rational roots.* If p/q is a root, then p divides 2 and q divides 8. The possibilities for p/q are

$$\pm 1, \pm 1/8, \pm 1/4, \pm 1/2, \pm 2$$

The information in step (3) rules out all but $\pm 1/8$, $\pm 1/4$, and $\pm 1/2$. Check these values:

$$
\begin{array}{r|rrrrrr}
\tfrac{1}{8} & 8 & 0 & -16 & -1 & 0 & 2 \\
 & & 1 & \tfrac{1}{8} & -\tfrac{127}{64} & -\tfrac{191}{512} & \\
\hline
 & 8 & 1 & -\tfrac{127}{8} & -\tfrac{191}{64} & -\tfrac{191}{512} & \text{not zero}
\end{array}
$$

$$
\begin{array}{r|rrrrrr}
\tfrac{1}{4} & 8 & 0 & -16 & -1 & 0 & 2 \\
 & & 2 & \tfrac{1}{2} & -\tfrac{31}{8} & -\tfrac{39}{32} & -\tfrac{39}{128} \\
\hline
 & 8 & 2 & -\tfrac{31}{2} & -\tfrac{39}{8} & -\tfrac{39}{32} & \text{not zero}
\end{array}
$$

$$
\begin{array}{r|rrrrrr}
\tfrac{1}{2} & 8 & 0 & -16 & -1 & 0 & 2 \\
 & & 4 & 2 & -7 & -4 & -2 \\
\hline
 & 8 & 4 & -14 & -8 & -4 & 0
\end{array}
$$

Thus, $1/8$ and $1/4$ are not zeros, but $1/2$ is. Similar calculations show that $-1/8$, $-1/4$, and $-1/2$ are not zeros. All other zeros of f must be irrational.

(5)   *Locate all zeros.* The third synthetic division in step (4) yields

$$f(x) = q(x)(x - \tfrac{1}{2})$$

where $q(x) = 8x^4 + 4x^3 - 14x^2 - 8x - 4$. Any zero of q is also a zero of f. However, in contrast to Example 4, it is not easy to solve or factor this $q(x)$. The best we can do is use the information from step (3) above to approximate the remaining zeros of f.

Conclusion

The equation $8x^5 + 2 = 16x^3 + x^2$ has at least three solutions a_1, a_2, and a_3: $a_1 = \tfrac{1}{2}$; a_2 and a_3 are irrational, with $1 < a_2 < 2$ and $-2 < a_3 < -1$.

Making a table of values to locate changes of sign is not always feasible. For example, suppose that the solutions of $f(x)$ are all very large. What is needed in such cases is a high-speed computer.

Review of basic ideas

The steps in solving a polynomial equation are

(1)   Rewrite the equation in the form $f(x) = 0$.
(2)   Use Descartes' Rule of Signs on $f(x)$.
(3)   Make a table of values.
(4)   Find the rational zeros.
(5)   Locate all zeros.

Review in your mind how each step is taken, what information is obtained, and how it is used in succeeding steps.

Exercises

Solve the following linear equations.

1. $3x - \tfrac{1}{2} = \tfrac{4}{5}$

2. $\tfrac{2}{3} - 4x = 2$

3. $\sqrt{3} - \sqrt{2}x = \sqrt{6}$

4. $4.2x - 1.7 = 3.9$

Solve the following quadratics either by sight factoring or by the quadratic formula.

5. $x^2 + 6x = 27$

6. $t^2 + 15 = 8t$

7. $6u^2 + 5u = 4$

8. $13y + 6 = 5y^2$

9. $v^2 - 6 = 4v$

10. $w^2 - w = 5$

Use the methods you learned in this section to solve the following polynomial equations.

11. $x^3 + 6x^2 = 10 - 3x$

12. $t^3 + 2 = 3t$

13. $u^3 = u^2 + 4u + 6$

14. $x^3 + 3x = 5x^2 - 4$

15. $2t^3 - 3t^2 = 17t - 30$

16. $2u^3 + 11u^2 = 4u + 4$

17. $x^4 + 3x^3 + 56 = 30x^2 + 6x$

18. $t^4 - 12t^2 = -32$

19. $t^4 + \frac{7}{4}t^2 + \frac{3}{4} = 2t^3 + 2t$

20. $\frac{1}{4}u^4 + \frac{1}{6}u^2 = \frac{1}{12}u + \frac{1}{3}$

21. $y^4 + 48 = 3y^3 + 16$

22. $v^4 + v^3 = 16v + 16$

23. $\frac{1}{9}u^5 - \frac{2}{3}u^3 + \frac{2}{9}u^2 = u + \frac{2}{3}$

24. $\frac{2}{3}x^5 + \frac{1}{3} = \frac{1}{3}x^4 + \frac{2}{3}x$

25. $t^5 - 8t^3 = 8 - t^2$

26. $t^5 - 8t^2 = 8 - t^3$

27. $2v^6 + 3v^4 - 7v = 0$

28. $v^5 - 3v^2 + 4v = 0$

29. $x^6 + x^4 = 16(x^2 + 1)$

30. $x^6 = 7x^3 + 8$

31.   Use the Rational Zero Theorem to prove that $\sqrt{2}$ is not rational. [HINT: Show that $f(x) = x^2 - 2$ has no rational zeros.]

32.   (Continuation of Exercise 31) Show that, if n is a positive integer and it is not a perfect square, then $\sqrt{n}$ is irrational.

33.   (Anticipation of the behavior of $f(x)$ for large $|x|$.) Let $f(x) = 8x^5 - 16x^3 - x^2 + 2$, which is the polynomial in Example 5. Factor out $8x^5$:

$$f(x) = 8x^5\left(1 - \frac{2}{x^2} - \frac{1}{8x^3} + \frac{1}{4x^5}\right)$$

(a)   Show that $f(3) \approx 8(3)^5(.78)$ and $f(-3) \approx 8(-3)^5(.78)$.
(b)   Show that $f(10) \approx 8(10)^5(.98)$ and $f(-10) \approx 8(-10)^5(.98)$.
When $|x|$ is very large, the expression in parentheses is very close to 1, and therefore $f(x) \approx 8x^5$.

34.   You have learned to solve polynomial equations with integer and fractional coefficients. How would you solve the following two equations?
(a) $1.7x^3 - 2.4x^2 + .3x - .5 = 0$
(b) $\sqrt{2}x^3 - 4\sqrt{8}x^2 + 3\sqrt{18}x - \sqrt{32} = 0$

4-5
Graphs of Polynomials

To graph a linear function, locate two points and draw the straight line through them. To graph a quadratic, write it in the form $y = a(x - h)^2 + k$, locate the vertex at

(h, k) and a couple of other points, and draw the parabola. Graphing polynomials of degree greater than 2 is not as simple. However, there are methods for drawing rough sketches of their graphs.

Let us begin with the **cubic** $y = x^3$. The only zero is $x = 0$. The table of values for positive x shows that, when x is small, then x^3 is even smaller.

x	1/10	1/3	1/2	1	2	3	4
$y = x^3$	1/1000	1/27	1/8	1	8	27	64

This means the curve is rather flat near 0. For $x > 1$, on the other hand, the value of x^3 gets large very quickly, so the curve is steep (see Figure 4-2A). If (x, y) is on the graph, so is $(-x, -y)$, because $f(-x) = (-x)^3 = -x^3 = -y$. It follows that the graph of $y = x^3$ for negative x is just the reflection through the origin of the graph for positive x (see Figure 4-2B).

The procedure for graphing $y = x^4$ is much the same. The only difference is that $(-x)^4 = x^4$, so that the graph for negative x is a reflection through the y-axis of the graph for positive x (see Figure 4-3). For $x < 1$, the value of x^4 is even smaller than x^3, so $y = x^4$ is even flatter near zero than $y = x^3$. For $x > 1$, x^4 is greater than x^3, so its curve is steeper than $y = x^3$. Figure 4-4 compares the graphs of $y = x^2$, $y = x^3$, and $y = x^4$ for nonnegative x. Notice the different scales on the axes.

The graphs of $y = x^5$, $y = x^7$, . . . (all odd exponents) are all similar to the

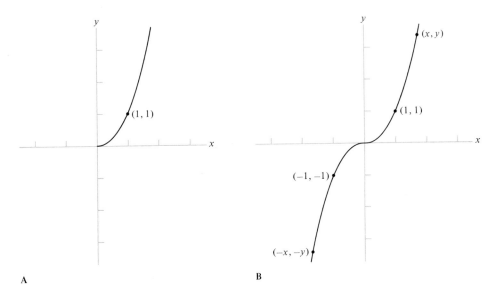

A   B

Figure 4-2
(A) The graph of $y = x^3$ for $x > 0$. The graph is fairly flat when x is near 0; it is rather steep for $x > 1$. (B) The graph of $y = x^3$ for all x. If a point (x, y) is on the graph, so is $(-x, -y)$.

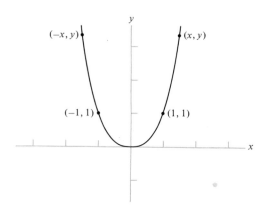

Figure 4-3
The graph of $y = x^4$. If the point (x, y) is on the graph, so is $(-x, y)$.

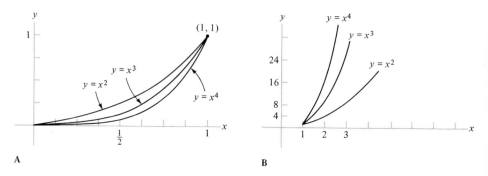

A

B

Figure 4-4
The graphs of $y = x^2$, $y = x^3$, and $y = x^4$ when (A) $0 \leq x \leq 1$ and (B) $x \geq 1$. Notice the different scales on the axes.

graph of $y = x^3$. The graphs of $y = x^6, y = x^8, \ldots$ (all even exponents) are all similar to $y = x^2$ and $y = x^4$. As the exponent increases, the curve becomes flatter near the origin and steeper for $|x| > 1$. The only zero of $y = x^n$ is $x = 0$; if n is odd, the curve actually crosses the x-axis, but if n is even, it merely touches the axis.

With this information, the principle of translation makes it possible to graph a whole new collection of functions.

Example 1
Graph

(a) $y = 4(x - 2)^3 - 1$ (b) $s = -(t + 1)^5 + 2$ (c) $v = -5u^6 + 1$

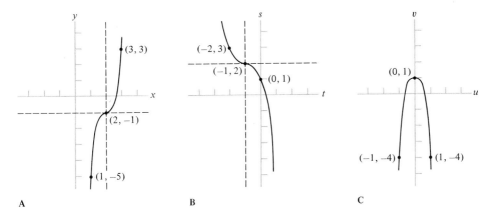

Figure 4-5
(A) The graph of $y = 4(x - 2)^3 - 1$. (B) The graph of $s = -(t + 1)^5 + 2$. (C) The graph
of $v = -5u^6 + 1$. See Example 1.

Solution

(a)   Plot a few points that are easy to calculate: $(3, 3)$, $(2, -1)$, and $(1, -5)$.
Now picture in your mind the graph of $y = x^3$. Then stretch the y values by a
factor of 4 and shift that curve 2 units to the right and 1 unit down. The
resulting curve is the graph of $y = 4(x - 2)^3 - 1$ (see Figure 4-5A).
(b)   Plot points easy to compute: $(-2, 3)$, $(-1, 2)$, and $(0, 1)$. The graph of
$s = t^5$ is similar to $s = t^3$, but the negative sign reverses the roles of the positive
and negative parts. Now translate 1 unit to the left and 2 units up to obtain the
curve in Figure 4-5B.
(c)   Plot the points $(-1, -4)$, $(0, 1)$, and $(1, -4)$. The graph of $v = -5u^6 + 1$
is similar to $v = u^6$ but the negative sign makes it open downward, and it is
translated up 1 unit (see Figure 4-5C).

If all polynomials of higher degree could be written in the form $a(x - h)^n + k$,
this section on graphs would now be complete. Unfortunately, this is not the case.
However, it is still possible to sketch these curves, by the following method:

(1)   Plot as many points as feasible.
(2)   Locate zeros.
(3)   Determine the behavior of the function for large $|x|$.
(4)   Sketch the graph.

What does it mean to determine the behavior of a function for large $|x|$? If $f(x) = a_n x^n + a_{n-1} x^{n-1} + \cdots + a_0$, then

$$f(x) = x^n \left(a_n + \frac{a_{n-1}}{x} + \cdots + \frac{a_0}{x^n} \right)$$

If $|x|$ is very large, the value of the expression in parentheses is very close to a_n, which is called the leading coefficient. Therefore,

■   If $f(x) = a_n x^n + \cdots + a_0$, then $f(x) \approx a_n x^n$ when $|x|$ is large.

An immediate consequence is the important fact that *every polynomial of odd degree has at least one zero*. This is so because, if n is odd, then $a_n x^n$ and $a_n(-x)^n$ have opposite signs. It follows that f takes both positive and negative values and must, therefore, have at least one zero.

Example 2
Graph $f(x) = x^3 + 2x^2 - 3x - 5$.

Solution
(1)   *Plot some points.* The easiest method is to use synthetic division and the Remainder Theorem to construct a table of values of f, as in Section 4-4.

Coefficients of f

	1	2	−3	−5	Plot
−4	1	−2	5	−25	(−4, −25)
−3	1	−1	0	−5	(−3, −5)
−2	1	0	−3	1	(−2, 1)
−1	1	1	−4	−1	(−1, −1)
0	1	2	−3	−5	(0, −5)
1	1	3	0	−5	(1, −5)
2	1	4	5	5	(2, 5)
3	1	5	12	31	(3, 31)

Values of x

(2)   *Locate zeros.* Descartes' Rule of Signs indicates that there is one positive zero, and two negative zeros or none. The Intermediate-Value Theorem applied to this table shows that the zeros are located between −3 and −2, between −2 and −1, and between 1 and 2.

(3) *Behavior of the function for large $|x|$*. Because $f(x) \approx x^3$, the graph rises very steeply for large $|x|$.

(4) *Sketch the graph.* The graph of $f(x)$ is shown in Figure 4-6. Notice the axes have different scales. Also notice where the function is increasing and decreasing.

Example 3
Graph $g(t) = 4t^4 - 21t^2 + 10t$.

Solution
(1) *Plot some points:*

Coefficients of g

	4	0	−21	10	0	Plot
−3	4	−12	15	−35	105	(−3, 105)
−2	4	−8	−5	20	−40	(−2, −40)
−1	4	−4	−17	27	−27	(−1, −27)
0	4	0	−21	10	0	(0, 0)
1	4	4	−17	−7	−7	(1, −7)
2	4	8	−5	0	0	(2, 0)
3	4	12	15	55	165	(3, 165)

(Values of t label the left side of the table.)

(2) *Locate zeros.* Zeros lie between −3 and −2, at $t = 0$, between 0 and 1, and at $t = 2$.

(3) For large $|t|$, $g(t) \approx 4t^4$. Thus, for large positive or negative values of t, $g(t)$ is positive. For large negative values of t, $g(t)$ falls very steeply; for large positive values, it rises steeply.

(4) Sketch the graph as in Figure 4-7. Notice where the function is increasing and decreasing. Also notice the different scales.

Polynomials of odd degree must have at least one zero and take every value. Thus, they have no maximum or minimum value. Cubic polynomials (degree 3) may have one, two, or three distinct zeros (see Figure 4-8). On the other hand, polynomials of even degree can possibly have no real zeros; they always have either a maximum or minimum, but not both (see Figure 4-9).

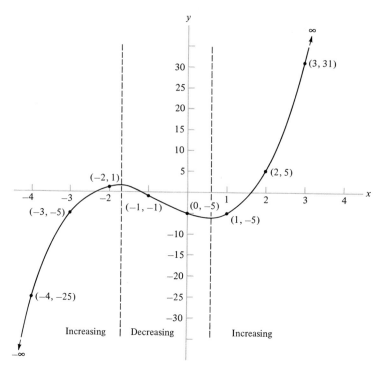

Figure 4-6

The graph of $f(x) = x^3 + 2x^2 - 3x - 5$. See Example 2.

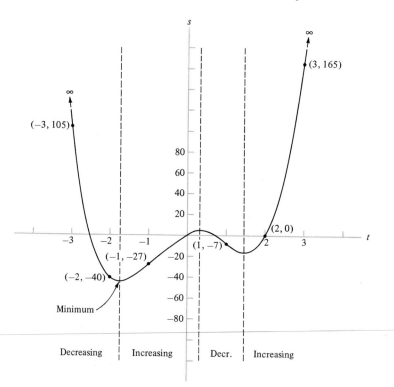

Figure 4-7

The graph of $g(t) = 4t^4 - 21t^2 + 10t$. See Example 3.

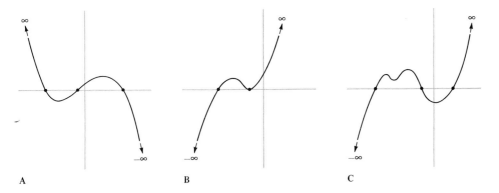

Figure 4-8
Graphs of polynomials of odd degree. (A) A cubic with three zeros and a negative leading coefficient. (B) A cubic with two distinct zeros and a positive leading coefficient. (C) A polynomial of degree 5 with three zeros and a positive leading coefficient.

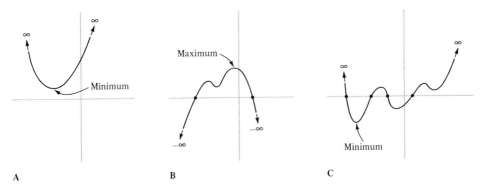

Figure 4-9
Graphs of polynomials of even degree. (A) Degree 4, no zeros, positive leading coefficient. (B) Degree 4, two zeros, negative leading coefficient. (C) Degree 6, four zeros, positive leading coefficient.

Review of Basic Ideas

Review the four steps to follow when graphing polynomials of degree 3 or more:

(1) Plot some points.
(2) Locate zeros.
(3) Determine the behavior of the function for large $|x|$.
(4) Sketch the curve.

Exercises

Graph these linear equations. Are the functions increasing or decreasing?

1. $y = 3x - \frac{1}{2}$ 2. $s = 4t - \frac{2}{3}$
3. $v = -\frac{1}{2}u + 4$ 4. $w = -\frac{1}{4}z + 1$

Graph these quadratic equations. Note where the functions are increasing and decreasing. Also note a minimum or a maximum.

5. $y = x^2 + 6x + 8$ 6. $s = t^2 - 8t + 15$
7. $v = -6u^2 + 12u - 4$ 8. $w = 5z^2 - 13z - 6$

Graph the following equations.

9. $y = 3x^3$ 10. $s = -3t^3$
11. $v = -2t^4$ 12. $w = 2z^4$
13. $y = -3(x - 2)^3$ 14. $s = (t + 4)^3 + 1$
15. $v = 5(u + 3)^4 - 4$ 16. $w = -2(z - 1)^4 + 3$
17. $y = x^3 + 3x^2 - 6$ 18. $s = t^3 - 3t + 1$
19. $v = u^3 + 4u^2 - 3u - 12$ 20. $w = z^3 - 3z^2 + 3$
21. $y = 2x^3 - 3x^2 + 1$ 22. $s = 6t^3 + 11t^2 - t - 6$
23. $v = -u^3 + 4u^2 + 3u - 8$ 24. $w = z^3 + 6z^2 - z - 14$
25. $y = x^4 - 2x^2 - 8$ 26. $s = t^4 + t^3 - 2$
27. $v = -u^4 - 2u^3 + 3u^2 + 3u + 5$ 28. $w = -u^4 + u^2 - 4$
29. $y = x^5 - 5x + 2$ 30. $s = 2t^5 + 3t^3 + 7$

☐   31.   (Increasing functions, decreasing functions, and "prime") Let $f(x) = x^3 + 3x^2 - 6$. This is the polynomial in Exercise 17. Compute $f'(x)$ and find where $f'(x) > 0, f'(x) = 0$, and $f'(x) < 0$, using the methods of Section 3-5. Look at the graph you drew for Exercise 17. Verify that, where $f'(x) > 0$, the function f is increasing; where $f'(x) < 0$, the function f is decreasing; where $f'(x) = 0$ is exactly where f changes from increasing to decreasing or vice versa.

The property of $f'(x)$ discussed in this exercise is very similar to the property of the *rate of change* discussed in Exercise 21 in Section 3-3. You will discover the reason for this similarity in Exercise 41 in Section 4-6.

32.   (Similar to Exercise 31) Let $f(u) = u^3 + 4u^2 - 3u - 12$. Compute $f'(u)$ and use the procedure of Exercise 31 to predict where f is increasing and decreasing. Compare your prediction with the graph of $v = f(u)$ that you drew for Exercise 19.

33.   (Increasing or decreasing sales) The sales S of a company are given as a function of time t by $S = t^3 - 3t^2 + 7$. At the end of the first year ($t = 1$), are the sales increasing or decreasing? When would be a good time to buy stock in this company?

34. (When to buy an automobile) If the price P of an automobile varies with the model year t according to the function $P(t) = \frac{3}{2}t^2 - 5940t + 4627$, which model year would be the best buy?

35. (Supply and demand) If the supply and demand of a certain commodity are given by $S(t) = 2t^3 + t^2 - 3t + 1$ and $D(t) = t^3 - 2t^2 + t + 43$, when will supply equal demand?

36. Let

$$f(x) = .000000001x^4 - 1,000,000,000x^3 - 1,000,000,000x^2$$
$$- 1,000,000,000x - 1,000,000,000$$

Will $f(x)$ ever be positive? Does f have a maximum? A minimum?

37. (Inverses) Let $f(x) = x^3$. Set $y = x^3$ and solve for x. Thus, $x = \sqrt[3]{y}$. Now set $g(y) = \sqrt[3]{y}$ and show that $f(g(y)) = y$ and $g(f(x)) = x$ for all x and y. This means that f and g are inverses. The graphs of inverses are reflections of each other through the line $y = x$. Use this fact to sketch the graph of $s = \sqrt[3]{t}$.

Two zeros between consecutive integers

38. Let $f(x) = 6x^3 - x^2 - 5x + 2$. According to Descartes' Rule, there are either two positive zeros or none. Find $f(0), f(1), f(2),$ and $f(3)$. It may seem from these values that there are no positive zeros. Now find $f(\frac{1}{2})$ and $f(\frac{2}{3})$. Graph f to see what is happening geometrically.

39. (Continuation of Exercise 38) Graph

(a) $y = 8x^3 - 2x^2 + 15x + 25$ (b) $y = -9x^3 - 9x^2 + 34x + 40$

and watch out for two zeros between consecutive integers.

4-6
Rational Functions

The result of dividing one polynomial function by another is called a **rational function**. For example, if $f(x) = 3x^2 - 2x + 4$ and $g(x) = x^2 - 4$, then

$$R(x) = \frac{f(x)}{g(x)} = \frac{3x^2 - 2x + 4}{x^2 - 4}$$

is a rational function. It is defined for all values of x except those that make the denominator zero.

Rational functions can be treated like rational numbers. We can add, subtract, multiply, divide, and simplify them, using the same rules as for numbers. To add or subtract rational functions, change each to an equivalent function with a common denominator; then add or subtract the numerators.

Example 1

Perform the indicated operation and simplify:

$$\frac{2x}{x^2 + 2x - 3} - \frac{4x + 1}{x^2 + 4x + 3}$$

Solution

Factor both denominators and find a least common denominator.

$$x^2 + 2x - 3 = (x + 3)(x - 1)$$

$$x^2 + 4x + 3 = (x + 3)(x + 1)$$

The least common denominator (abbreviated LCD) is $(x + 3)(x - 1)(x + 1)$. Thus,

$$\frac{2x}{(x + 3)(x - 1)} - \frac{4x + 1}{(x + 3)(x + 1)} = \frac{2x(x + 1)}{\text{LCD}} - \frac{(4x + 1)(x - 1)}{\text{LCD}}$$

$$= \frac{(2x^2 + 2x) - (4x^2 - 3x - 1)}{\text{LCD}}$$

$$= \frac{-2x^2 + 5x + 1}{\text{LCD}}$$

In the second line, notice that the minus sign acts on the whole term $4x^2 - 3x - 1$. The use of parentheses as shown here will lessen the chance of arithmetic errors.

To multiply, simply multiply the numerators and denominators separately. To divide, invert the divisor and multiply.

Example 2

Divide and simplify:

$$\frac{x^2 + 5x + 6}{x^2 - 4} \div \frac{x^2 + 6x + 9}{x + 5} = \frac{x^2 + 5x + 6}{x^2 - 4} \cdot \frac{x + 5}{x^2 + 6x + 9}$$

Now factor where possible and cancel common factors

$$\frac{(x^2 + 5x + 6)(x + 5)}{(x^2 - 4)(x^2 + 6x + 9)} = \frac{\cancel{(x+3)}\cancel{(x+2)}(x + 5)}{\cancel{(x+2)}(x - 2)\cancel{(x+3)}(x + 3)}$$

$$= \frac{x + 5}{(x - 2)(x + 3)}$$

It is often helpful to simplify a rational expression before attempting to evaluate it.

Example 3
Let

$$R(x) = \frac{x^2 - x - 2}{x^2 - x - 12} \cdot \frac{x^2 + 5x + 6}{x^2 - 4} \div \frac{x}{x^2 - 4x}$$

Calculate $R(1.369)$.

Solution
You are supposed to replace x by 1.369 and calculate the result. Before you get out your calculator, let us simplify the expression—you may not even need a calculator. Factoring, we have

$$R(x) = \frac{(x + 1)(x - 2)}{(x - 4)(x + 3)} \cdot \frac{(x + 3)(x + 2)}{(x + 2)(x - 2)} \cdot \frac{x(x - 4)}{x}$$

$$= \frac{(x + 1)\cancel{(x-2)}\cancel{(x+3)}\cancel{(x+2)}\cancel{(x)}\cancel{(x-4)}}{\cancel{(x-4)}\cancel{(x+3)}\cancel{(x+2)}\cancel{(x-2)}\cancel{(x)}}$$

$$= x + 1$$

Therefore, $R(1.369) = 1.369 + 1 = 2.369$.

The remainder of this section is about graphs of rational functions.

Example 4
Graph $y = 1/x$.

Solution
First consider only nonnegative values of x. The function is not defined at $x = 0$; as x gets larger, $y = 1/x$ gets closer to zero; when x is close to zero, $1/x$ is very large.

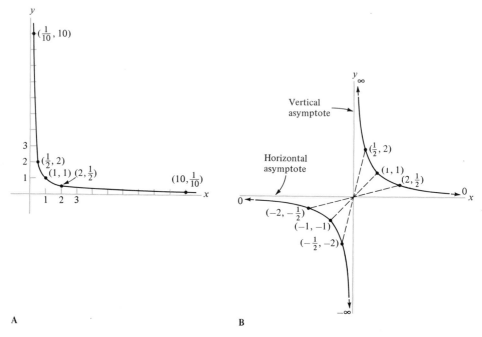

Figure 4-10
(A) The graph of $y = 1/x$ for $1/10 < x < 10$. (B) The function $y = 1/x$ is defined for all x except $x = 0$. The graph of this function for $x < 0$ can be obtained from the graph for $x > 0$ by reflecting it through the origin. See Example 4.

x	1/10	1/2	1	2	10
$y = 1/x$	10	2	1	1/2	1/10

Plot the points and sketch the curve shown in Figure 4-10A. The part of the graph corresponding to negative values of x is now obtained automatically by reflection *through the origin,* because if (x, y) satisfies the equation $y = 1/x$, then $(-x, -y)$ does too (see Figure 4-10B).

Example 5
Graph $y = 1/x^2$.

Solution
For $x \geq 0$, this function is quite similar to $y = 1/x$. However, its graph for negative x is a reflection *through the y-axis* of the graph for positive x. This follows from the fact that $1/x^2 = 1/(-x)^2$. A table of values shows that $1/x^2$

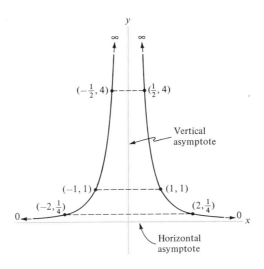

Figure 4-11
The graph of $y = 1/x^2$. The graph for $x < 0$ is the reflection through the y-axis of the graph
for $x > 0$. See Example 5.

approaches 0 and ∞ much faster than $1/x$ does. The graph of $y = 1/x^2$ is
shown in Figure 4-11.

x	$\pm 1/10$	$\pm 1/2$	± 1	± 2	± 10
$y = 1/x^2$	100	4	1	1/4	1/100

The axes played a special role in the two preceding examples. For the graphs of
$y = 1/x$ and $y = 1/x^2$, the axes are **asymptotes** (see Figure 4-10 and 4-11). In general,
if the values of $|f(x)|$ increase without bound as x gets close to some real number b,
then the vertical line through the point b on the x-axis is a **vertical asymptote** of the
graph of f. For example, as x gets close to 0, the values of $|1/x|$ and $|1/x^2|$ get very
large. Therefore, the vertical line through 0 (that is, the y-axis) is a vertical asymptote
of each of the curves $y = 1/x$ and $y = 1/x^2$. *Most rational functions will have vertical
asymptotes at points where the denominator takes the value 0.*
   On the other hand, if the value of $f(x)$ approaches some real number c as $|x|$
gets very large, then the horizontal line through c on the y-axis is a **horizontal
asymptote** of the graph of f. The x-axis is a horizontal asymptote of $y = 1/x$ and
$y = 1/x^2$, because each of these functions takes values close to 0 as $|x|$ gets large. Not
all rational functions have asymptotes.
   The technique of translation and information about asymptotes can be used to
graph a wide variety of rational functions. As you will see, when a graph is translated,
its asymptotes are also translated in the same way.

Example 6

Graph   (a) $y = \dfrac{2x}{x-1}$ and   (b) $s = \dfrac{-3}{t^2 + 4t + 4}$

Solution

(a) $y = 2x/(x-1)$ may not look like a translation of $y = 1/x$, but dividing $2x$ by $x - 1$ yields

$$\frac{2x}{x-1} = 2 + \frac{2}{x-1}$$

Thus, $y = 1/x$ is translated one unit to the right (x is replaced by $x - 1$), stretched by a factor of 2, and moved two units up. The asymptotes are also translated one unit to the right and two units up. Plot a few points and draw the curve as in Figure 4-12A.

(b)   Rewrite the denominator as a square:

$$s = \frac{-3}{t^2 + 4t + 4} = \frac{-3}{(t+2)^2}$$

This translates $s = 1/t^2$ two units to the left, stretches it by a factor of 3, and turns it upside down (the minus sign makes the values negative). The asymptotes are also translated two units to the left. Plot a few points and graph as in Figure 4-12B.

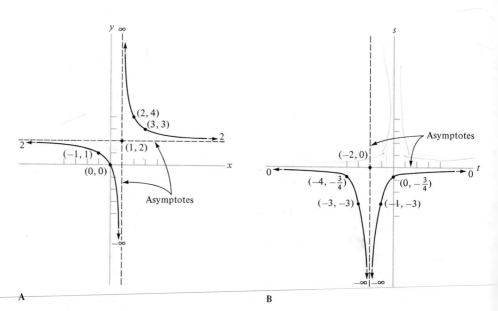

Figure 4-12

(A) The graph of $y = 2x/(x-1)$. (B) The graph of $s = -3/(t^2 + 4t + 4)$. See Example 6.

Certain rational functions are used frequently in physics. Newton's Law of Universal Gravitation states that the gravitational attraction of two bodies is inversely proportional to the square of the distance between them. In symbols,

$$F(x) = k/x^2$$

where x is the distance, k is some constant, and F is the force of attraction. The same function of distance (with a different value of k) will give the attraction beween two magnets or two electrically charged objects.

Example 7
The attraction between two magnets 2 units apart is 4 units of force. One magnet is held fixed and the other is moved in a straight line away from the first. (a) What is the force when $x = 3$ and when $x = 5$? (b) What is the average rate of change of force as the second magnet is moved from 3 to 5 units away?

Solution
(a)   Use the given information to find the constant k for this particular problem. Because $4 = F(2) = k/2^2$, it follows that $k = 16$ and

$$F(x) = 16/x^2$$

Thus, $F(3) = 16/9$ and $F(5) = 16/25$.
(b)   The average rate of change of F from x to $x + h$ is

$$\text{a.r.c.} F(x, h) = \frac{\dfrac{16}{(x + h)^2} - \dfrac{16}{x^2}}{h}$$

$$= \frac{16x^2 - 16(x^2 + 2xh + h^2)}{hx^2(x + h)^2}$$

$$= \frac{-32x - 16h}{x^2(x + h)^2}$$

This general formula yields a.r.c.$F(3, 2) = -128/225$. The minus sign indicates that the force is decreasing.

Exercises

Perform the indicated operations and simplify.

1. $\dfrac{3x - 1}{x} + \dfrac{x + 1}{2x}$

2. $\dfrac{x + 1}{x} - \dfrac{3x}{x - 1}$

3. $t - \dfrac{1}{t}$

4. $2 + \dfrac{s+1}{s-1}$

5. $\dfrac{y-5}{y} - \dfrac{y-2}{y+3}$

6. $\dfrac{u}{u+1} + \dfrac{u+1}{u-1}$

7. $5 - x + \dfrac{x}{x+1}$

8. $y - 3 - \dfrac{y+1}{y-3}$

9. $\dfrac{x}{x+3} + \dfrac{4}{x^2+5x+6}$

10. $\dfrac{t}{t-4} - \dfrac{2}{t^2-8t+16}$

11. $\dfrac{2u}{u^2-2u-8} - \dfrac{u+1}{u^2-8u+16}$

12. $\dfrac{5y}{y^2-3y-4} + \dfrac{1}{y^2-16}$

13. $\dfrac{x^2-25}{x^2-x-2} \cdot \dfrac{x^2-1}{x^2-6x+5}$

14. $\dfrac{z^2-3z-4}{z^2+2z+1} \cdot \dfrac{z^2-1}{z^2-5z+4}$

15. $\dfrac{t^3-1}{t^2+2t+1} \cdot \dfrac{t+1}{t^2+t-2}$

16. $\dfrac{1}{x^2-4} \cdot \dfrac{x^2+4x+4}{x-2}$

17. $\dfrac{x^2+4xy+4y^2}{x+y} \div \dfrac{x^2+xy-2y^2}{x^2-y^2}$

18. $\dfrac{s^4-1}{(s+1)^2} \div \dfrac{s^2+1}{s+1}$

19. $\dfrac{3/x-5/x^2}{x^2-1} \div \dfrac{x}{x+1}$

20. $x \div \dfrac{x-1}{1-1/x^2}$

21. Find $R(3.2491)$ if $R(t) = \dfrac{t^2-1}{t^3+1} \cdot \dfrac{t^2-t+1}{t+2} \div \dfrac{t-1}{3t+6}$

22. Find $Q(\frac{7}{3})$ if $Q(y) = \dfrac{y+1}{y^2-2y-3} \cdot \dfrac{y^2+2y-15}{y^2-4} \div \dfrac{(y+5)^2}{y^2+7y+10}$

Graph the following functions (as in Example 6).

23. $y = \dfrac{1}{x-2}$

24. $s = \dfrac{1}{t+1}$

25. $v = \dfrac{-1}{u+2}$

26. $s = \dfrac{-3}{t-4}$

27. $y = \dfrac{3x-2}{x-1}$

28. $s = \dfrac{t+3}{t+1}$

29. $v = \dfrac{-u+3}{2u+4}$

30. $y = \dfrac{-x-2}{x+1}$

31. $y = \dfrac{2}{(x-3)^2}$

32. $v = \dfrac{4}{(u+1)^2}$

33. $y = \dfrac{x^2-4x+2}{x^2-4x+4}$

34. $s = \dfrac{t^2+2t-3}{t^2+2t+2}$

☐ **35.** The attraction between two magnets 7 units is apart is 2 units of force. One magnet is fixed and the other is moved in a straight line towards the first. (a) What is the force when the magnets are 5 and 2 units apart? (b) What is the average rate of change of force as the second magnet is moved from 5 units to 2 units away from the first? Is the force increasing or decreasing?

36. (Average rate of change) Let $f(x) = 1/x$. Show that

$$\text{a.r.c.} f(x, h) = \frac{-1}{x(x + h)}$$

What is the exact rate of change?

37. (Continuation of Exercise 36) The distance s (in feet) from a fixed point to a moving object at time t (in seconds) is given by the formula $s = 1/(t + 1)$.
    (a)   What is the average velocity of the object from $t = 7$ to $t = 9$?
    (b)   What is the exact velocity when $t = 7$?
    (c)   Is it moving towards or away from the fixed point?
    (d)   Will it ever reach the point?

38. The material and labor needed to manufacture a certain item cost $2.13. The company has fixed costs of $60,000 per year. What is the cost to the company *per item* if they produce x items a year?

39. (Inverses) Let $f(x) = 1/x$. Show that f is its own inverse. That is, show that $f(f(x)) = x$ for all $x \neq 0$.

40. (Primes) The formula for the prime of a quotient is

$$(f/g)' = \frac{gf' - fg'}{g^2}$$

Show that (a) $(1/x)' = -1/x^2$ and (b) $(1/x^2)' = -2/x^3$. In general, what is $(1/x^n)'$?

41. (Average rate of change and primes) You may have noticed a certain similarity between a.r.c.$f(x, h)$ and $f'(x)$. As h tends to 0, a.r.c.$f(x, h)$ tends to the exact rate of change. It turns out that *the exact rate of change of f at x is $f'(x)$*. For example, let $f(x) = x^2 - 3x + 4$. Then

$$\text{a.r.c.} f(x, h) = \frac{f(x + h) - f(x)}{h}$$

$$= \frac{[(x + h)^2 - 3(x + h) + 4] - [x^2 - 3x + 4]}{h}$$

$$= \frac{x^2 + 2xh + h^2 - 3x - 3h + 4 - x^2 + 3x - 4}{h}$$

$$= 2x - 3 + h$$

As h tends to zero, a.r.c.$f(x, h)$ tends to $2x - 3$, which is $f'(x)$.

Show that this is also true of the following functions.

(a) $f(x) = 3x + 1$ (b) $f(x) = x^2 + 4x - 1$

(c) $f(x) = 1 - 2z - 3x^2$ (d) $f(x) = x^3 - 2x + 4$

(e) $f(x) = 1/x$ (f) $f(x) = 1/x^2$

Chapter 5

Exponential and Logarithmic Functions

Because exponential and logarithmic functions are inverses of each other, Section 5-1 deals with the general topic of inverses. In Section 5-2, exponential functions are defined by equations of the form $y = b^x$. They are either increasing or decreasing functions, depending on the value of b. It then follows that an exponential function will always have an inverse; this inverse is called a logarithmic function. The properties of logarithmic functions are taken up in Section 5-3.

Section 5-4 (optional) introduces logarithm tables and their use in simplifying computations. Applications to such problems as compound interest, population growth, and radioactive decay are described in Section 5-5.

5-1
Inverses

Let $f(x) = 2x - 3$ and $g(x) = (x + 3)/2$. The instructions for f are "multiply by 2 and subtract 3." The instructions for g are "add 3 and divide by 2." *The instructions for g are opposite to those of f and performed in the reverse order.* For any x,

$$g(f(x)) = g(2x - 3) = \frac{(2x - 3) + 3}{2} = x$$

and

$$f(g(x)) = f\left(\frac{x + 3}{2}\right) = 2\left(\frac{x + 3}{2}\right) - 3 = x$$

You might say that each function cancels out what the other one does. If you start with x and find $f(x)$, then g of that number will take you back to x. Likewise, if you find $g(x)$, then f of that number is x. These functions are inverses of each other.

The concept of inverse is basic to an understanding of exponential and logarithmic functions. It also plays an important role in trigonometry and in calculus.

■   **Definition**

Let f and g be functions such that the range of f is the domain of g and the range of g is the domain of f. If

$$g(f(x)) = x \qquad \text{(for all } x \text{ in the domain of } f)$$

and

$$f(g(x)) = x \qquad \text{(for all } x \text{ in the domain of } g)$$

then g is called the **inverse** of f and is denoted by the symbol f^{-1}, read "f inverse."

Evidently, the functions f and f^{-1} are closely related. The range of f is the domain of f^{-1} and the range of f^{-1} is the domain of f. The function f^{-1} cancels out what f does, and vice versa. The instructions for f^{-1} are opposite to those for f, and they are performed in the reverse order. Most important: $f^{-1}(f(x)) = x$ and $f(f^{-1}(x)) = x$, as long as x is an element in the proper domain.

Example 1

Suppose f and f^{-1} are defined for all real numbers.

(a) $f^{-1}(f(17)) = 17$ and $f(f^{-1}(-\sqrt{2})) = -\sqrt{2}$.

(b)   If $f(3) = 5$, then $f^{-1}(5) = 3$. If $f^{-1}(\pi) = -13$, then $f(-13) = \pi$.

(c)   If $y = f(x)$, then $x = f^{-1}(y)$. This is true because, if $y = f(x)$, then $f^{-1}(y) = f^{-1}(f(x)) = x$.

Part (c) of Example 1 is important because it tells us that

■   if (x, y) is on the graph of f, then (y, x) is on the graph of f^{-1}.

If (x, y) is on the graph of f, it follows that $y = f(x)$. But Example (c) says that, in this

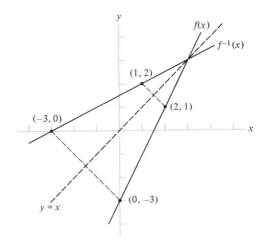

Figure 5-1
The graphs of $f(x) = 2x - 3$ and $f^{-1}(x) = (x + 3)/2$ are reflections of each other through the line $y = x$. See Example 2.

case, $x = f^{-1}(y)$, which means that (y, x) is on the graph of f^{-1}. The point (y, x) is a reflection, through the line $y = x$, of the point (x, y) (see Figure 5-1), so it follows that

■   the graph of f^{-1} is the reflection of the graph of f through the line $y = x$.

Example 2
Consider the functions $f(x) = 2x - 3$ and $g(x) = (x + 3)/2$, with which this section began. We know that g is the inverse of f; that is, $g = f^{-1}$. The graphs of f and f^{-1} are shown in Figure 5-1. Notice that they are reflections of each other through the line $y = x$.

Now suppose that only a function f is given. How do we find its inverse? One method is to set $y = f(x)$, and then solve that equation for x in terms of y. That will tell us what we must do to y, which is $f(x)$, in order to get back to x. Returning to our first example, $f(x) = 2x - 3$, set $y = 2x - 3$ and solve for x:

$$y = 2x - 3$$

$$y + 3 = 2x$$

$$x = \frac{y + 3}{2}$$

The last equation defines the inverse function $f^{-1}(y) = \dfrac{y+3}{2}$.

Example 3

Let $F(x) = x^3 + 4$. Find its inverse, check your answer, and then graph F and F^{-1} in the same plane.

Solution

Set $y = F(x)$ and solve for x.

$$y = x^3 + 4$$

$$x^3 = y - 4$$

$$x = \sqrt[3]{y - 4}$$

Thus, $F^{-1}(y) = \sqrt[3]{y - 4}$ is the inverse of F.

Check

$$F^{-1}(F(x)) = F^{-1}(x^3 + 4) = \sqrt[3]{(x^3 + 4) - 4} = \sqrt[3]{x^3} = x$$

$$F(F^{-1}(y)) = F(\sqrt[3]{y - 4}) = (\sqrt[3]{y - 4})^3 + 4 = (y - 4) + 4 = y$$

For graphing purposes, replace y by x in the definition of F^{-1}, so that the independent variable will be represented by the horizontal axis. Thus, $F^{-1}(x) = \sqrt[3]{x - 4}$. Although you have not yet graphed the cube root function, you can graph $x^3 + 4$ and then reflect through the line $y = x$, because $x^3 + 4$ and $\sqrt[3]{x - 4}$ are inverses (see Figure 5-2). As their graphs show, both F and F^{-1} are increasing functions. In general, *if a function is increasing, then its inverse is also increasing.*

The method for finding an inverse described in Example 3 results in a function with y as the independent variable. For graphing purposes, however, we usually want x to be the independent variable. One way to achieve this is to interchange x and y *at the start,* and then solve for y.

Example 4

Find the inverses of (a) $f(x) = -\tfrac{1}{4}x + 3$ and (b) $F(x) = \sqrt[3]{2 - 3x}$. Check each answer.

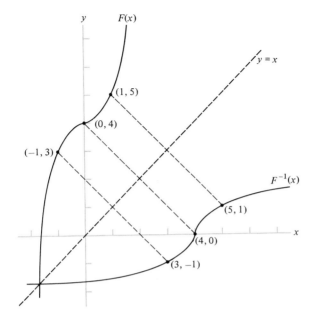

Figure 5-2
The graphs of $F(x) = x^3 + 4$ and $F^{-1}(x) = \sqrt[3]{x - 4}$ are reflections of each other through the line $y = x$. Both are increasing functions. See Example 3.

Solution
(a) Set $y = -\frac{1}{4}x + 3$; then interchange x and y to obtain $x = -\frac{1}{4}y + 3$. Solve for y:

$$x = -\tfrac{1}{4}y + 3$$

$$-\tfrac{1}{4}y = x - 3$$

$$y = -4(x - 3)$$

Thus, $f^{-1}(x) = -4(x - 3)$.

Check

$$f^{-1}(f(x)) = f^{-1}(-\tfrac{1}{4}x + 3) = -4[(-\tfrac{1}{4}x + 3) - 3] = x$$

$$f(f^{-1}(x)) = f(-4(x - 3)) = -\tfrac{1}{4}[-4(x - 3)] + 3 = x$$

(b) Set $y = \sqrt[3]{2 - 3x}$; then interchange x and y to obtain $x = \sqrt[3]{2 - 3y}$.

Solve for y:

$$x = \sqrt[3]{2 - 3y}$$

$$x^3 = 2 - 3y$$

$$y = \frac{x^3 - 2}{-3}$$

Thus, $F^{-1}(x) = \dfrac{x^3 - 2}{-3}$.

Check

$$F^{-1}(F(x)) = F^{-1}(\sqrt[3]{2 - 3x}) = \frac{(\sqrt[3]{2 - 3x})^3 - 2}{-3} = x$$

$$F(F^{-1}(x)) = F\left(\frac{x^3 - 2}{-3}\right) = \sqrt[3]{2 - 3\left(\frac{x^3 - 2}{-3}\right)} = x$$

Not every function has an inverse. For example, if $f(x) = x^2$, then $f(2) = 4$ *and* $f(-2) = 4$. If there were an inverse, what would be the value of $f^{-1}(4)$? If f^{-1} is a function, its value at 4 cannot be *both* 2 and -2. The trouble here is that f takes the same value at two distinct points in its domain. Functions with inverses cannot do that.

A function that takes distinct values at distinct points of its domain is called a **one-to-one** function. Figure 5-3 shows that, in the graph of a one-to-one function, every horizontal line meets the graph in *at most* one point.

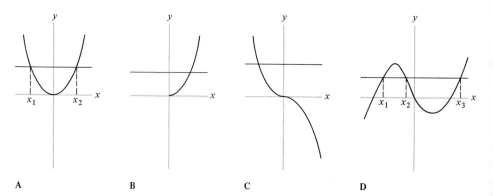

A   B   C   D

Figure 5-3
If there is a horizontal line that crosses the graph of a function at more than one point, the function is not one-to-one. (A) The function $y = x^2$. The horizontal line crosses the graph at two points, so this function takes the same value at those points; it is not one-to-one. (B) The function $y = x^2$ for $x \geq 0$; this function is one-to-one. (C) The function $y = -x^3$ is one-to-one. (D) The function $y = x^3 - x^2 - 6x$. The horizontal line crosses the graph at three points, so the function is not one-to-one.

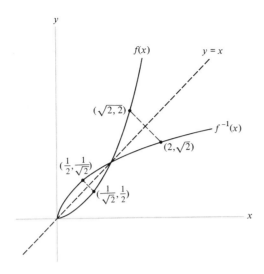

Figure 5-4
The function $f(x) = x^2$ for $x \geq 0$ has an inverse, $f^{-1}(x) = \sqrt{x}$ for $x \geq 0$. The graphs of
these functions are reflections of each other through the line $y = x$. See Example 5.

■   If a function is always increasing or always decreasing, as in graphs B and C,
    then it is one-to-one and it has an inverse.

In the other graphs, the functions are not one-to-one and do not have inverses.

Example 5
Let $f(x) = x^2$ for $x \geq 0$. Find f^{-1}, if it exists, and draw its graph.

Solution
Recall that $f(x) = x^2$ with unrestricted domain does not have an inverse. But
Figure 5-3B shows that the function under consideration here, $f(x) = x^2$ for
$x \geq 0$, is one-to-one; therefore, it does have an inverse, namely, $f^{-1}(x) = \sqrt{x}$
for $x \geq 0$. Notice that f and f^{-1} are both increasing (Figure 5-4).

Example 5 shows that

■   if a function is restricted to that part of its domain on which it is one-to-one,
    then the restricted function has an inverse.

Review of basic ideas
Review these important facts about inverses.

The instructions for f^{-1} are opposite to those for f and performed in the reverse order.

The functions f and f^{-1} "cancel" each other out; that is, if we start with x and find $f(x)$, then f^{-1} of that number brings us back to x. In symbols, $f^{-1}(f(x)) = x$. Similarly, $f(f^{-1}(x)) = x$.

The graph of f^{-1} is the reflection of the graph of f through the line $y = x$.

An always increasing or always decreasing function is one-to-one and, therefore, has an inverse.

To find the inverse of f, set $y = f(x)$. Then interchange x and y and solve for y.

Exercises

Find the inverse of each of the following functions. Check your results by graphing both f and f^{-1} in the same plane. (Exercise 9 is similar to Example 5. Exercise 21 is similar to Examples 3 and 4.)

1. $f(x) = x$
2. $f(x) = 3x$
3. $f(x) = x - 1$
4. $f(x) = x + 2$
5. $f(x) = \frac{1}{2}x + 2$
6. $f(x) = 2x - 1$
7. $f(x) = -\frac{3}{2}x + 1$
8. $f(x) = -\frac{1}{4}x + 2$
9. $f(x) = x^2; \quad x \le 0$
10. $f(x) = -x^2; \quad x \le 0$
11. $f(x) = -4x^2; \quad x \ge 0$
12. $f(x) = 3x^2; \quad x \ge 0$
13. $f(x) = x^2 - 4; \quad x \ge 0$
14. $f(x) = -x^2 + 2; \quad x \ge 0$
15. $f(x) = (x - 2)^2; \quad x \ge 2$
16. $f(x) = (x - 4)^2; \quad x \ge 4$
17. $f(x) = (x + 4)^2; \quad x \le -4$
18. $f(x) = (x + 2)^2; \quad x \le -2$
19. $f(x) = (x - 6)^2 - 1; \quad x \le 6$
20. $f(x) = (x - 4)^2 + 1; \quad x \ge 4$
21. $f(x) = x^3 - 1$
22. $f(x) = -x^3 + 1$
23. $f(x) = 1 - x^3;$
24. $f(x) = 5 - x^3$
25. $f(x) = (x - 1)^3 + 2$
26. $f(x) = (x + 2)^3 - 1$

27, 28, and **29.** The following are graphs of one-to-one functions with indicated domains. Sketch the graph of the inverse of each function, and find its domain and range.

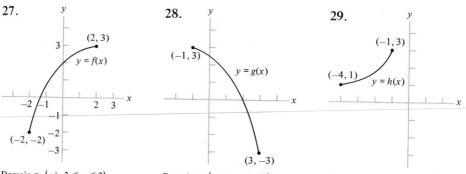

27.

(2, 3)

$y = f(x)$

(−2, −2)

Domain = $\{x | -2 \le x \le 2\}$

28.

(−1, 3)

$y = g(x)$

(3, −3)

Domain = $\{x | -1 \le x \le 3\}$

29.

(−1, 3)

(−4, 1)

$y = h(x)$

Domain = $\{x | -4 \le x \le -1\}$

30. and **31.** In the next few sections we shall be working with exponential and logarithmic functions. The inverse of an exponential function is a logarithmic function (and vice versa). The graphs below show two exponential functions with domain ℝ. Sketch the logarithmic function (the inverse) corresponding to each, and find its domain and range.

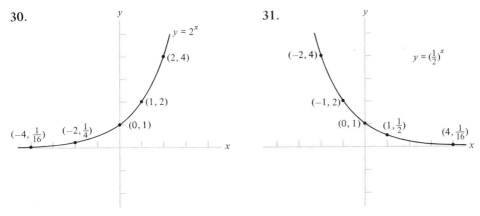

30.   **31.**

32. If L is the inverse of the function $y = 2^x$ in Exercise 30, find $L(\frac{1}{16})$, $L(1)$, and $L(4)$. Compute $L(2^3)$ and $2^{L(4)}$.

33. If L is the inverse of the function $y = (\frac{1}{2})^x$ in Exercise 31, find $L(\frac{1}{2})$, $L(1)$, and $L(2)$. Compute $(\frac{1}{2})^{L(4)}$.

5-2
Exponential Functions

We are so accustomed to the casual use of large numbers that we can easily lose our perspective. The federal budget is about 400 *billion* dollars, the Gross National Product is more than a *trillion* dollars, and the distance between stars is measured in *light years.** In order to bring these figures into proper perspective, consider these two facts: The average life span in this country is just a bit more than 2 billion *seconds.* Most of you reading this book have probably lived *less than 750 million seconds!*

Positive powers get large very quickly: the power function x^2 evaluated at $x = 100$ is $(100)^2 = 10{,}000$. However, this number is rather insignificant compared to the value of the exponential function 2^x at $x = 100$. The value of 2^{100} is greater than a 1 followed by 30 zeros! The proof is simple: $2^{10} > 10^3$, so it follows that

$$2^{100} = (2^{10})^{10} > (10^3)^{10} = 10^{30}$$

---

*A light-year is the distance that light travels in a year. Light moves at a speed of about 300,000 kilometers per second; thus, a light-year is about 9,460,800,000,000 kilometers. Proxima Centauri, the star closest to our solar system, is 4.28 light-years away. That is about 40,492,000,000,000 kilometers!

The properties of exponents were explored in detail in Sections 1-1 and 1-5. You may recall that there is some trouble with fractional exponents when the base is negative. It suits our purpose here to eliminate this difficulty by considering only positive bases. Here is a list of the properties of exponents.

■   **Basic Properties of Exponents**
    Suppose $a > 0$ and $b > 0$, and n and m are integers.

(a) $b^n b^m = b^{n+m}$ (b) $a^n b^n = (ab)^n$
(c) $b^n / b^m = b^{n-m}$ (d) $a^n / b^n = (a/b)^n$
(e) $(b^n)^m = b^{nm}$ (f) $b^0 = 1$
(g) $b^{-n} = 1/b^n = (1/b)^n$ (h) $\sqrt[n]{b^m} = b^{m/n} = (\sqrt[n]{b})^m$

Thus, if the base b is positive, the function $f(x) = b^x$ is defined for all rational x. Naturally, it is desirable to enlarge the domain to include all real numbers. But how should $b^{\sqrt{2}}$ and b^π be defined? A detailed discussion of irrational exponents properly belongs to a calculus course. What we shall do here is to assume that this can be done in a natural way—a way which that makes the graph of the exponential function a smooth curve. Therefore, let us assume that, given any positive number b, there is a rule that assigns to each real number x a positive number b^x. This rule is called the **exponential function with base b,** and it is denoted by $\exp_b$.* Thus

■ $$\exp_b : \mathbb{R} \to \mathbb{R}^+$$

    where $\mathbb{R}^+$ denotes the positive real numbers and

$$\exp_b(x) = b^x$$

The rules of exponents have their counterparts for $\exp_b$. For instance,

$b^n b^m = b^{n+m}$ translates to $\exp_b(x)\exp_b(y) = \exp_b(x + y)$.

$b^0 = 1$ translates to $\exp_b(0) = 1$.

$b^{-n} = 1/b^n = (1/b)^n$ translates to $\exp_b(-x) = \dfrac{1}{\exp_b(x)} = \exp_{1/b}(x)$.

and so on.

Now let $b = 2$ and make a table of values to plot the graph of $y = 2^x$. The curve, shown in Figure 5-5, indicates that for $x > 0$ the exponential rises very steeply,

---

*For the first time, we have used more than one letter to denote a function. Here, exp is an abbreviation for *exponential*. We shall use similar notation later, for logarithmic and trigonometric functions.

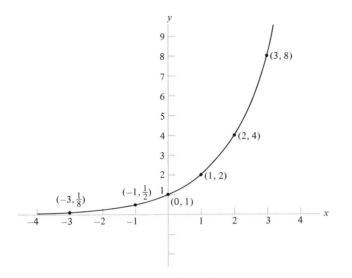

x	$y = 2^x$
-3	$\frac{1}{8}$
-2	$\frac{1}{4}$
-1	$\frac{1}{2}$
0	1
$\frac{1}{2}$	$\sqrt{2} \approx 1.4$
1	2
2	4
3	8

Figure 5-5
The graph of $y = \exp_2(x) = 2^x$.

whereas for $x < 0$ it approaches 0 and is quite flat. The negative x-axis is an asymptote. This is true for any base $b > 1$. The curves get steeper as b increases, as Figure 5-6 shows. On the other hand, the graphs for $0 < b < 1$ are reflections through the y-axis of the graphs of $b > 1$; when $x > 0$, the curve begins to flatten out, and the positive x-axis is an asymptote. This is shown in Figure 5-7.

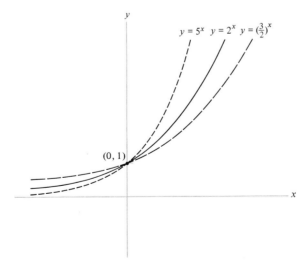

Figure 5-6
The graphs of $y = b^x$ get steeper as b gets larger.

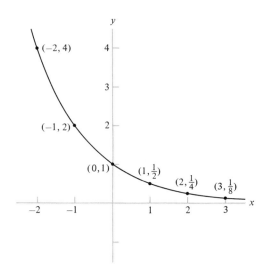

Figure 5-7
The graph of $y = (\frac{1}{2})^x$.

The base $b = 2$ was used above in the graphs of $y = exp_b(x)$ because powers of 2 are easy to calculate and plot. Although the powers of 10 are even easier to compute, the values get so large so fast that they would be inconvenient to graph ($2^3 = 8$, whereas $10^3 = 1000$). Oddly enough, the base that is used in many applications, especially in calculus, is the irrational number 2.71828. . . . (It is surprises like this that help make mathematics so interesting.) This number is always designated by the letter e. If your hand calculator has an exponent key, it will probably be labeled e^x. The graph of $y = e^x$ (see Figure 5-8) resembles the other exponential graphs.

The average rate of change of an exponential function is

$$\text{a.r.c.exp}_b(x, h) = \frac{b^{x+h} - b^x}{h}$$

$$= \frac{b^x b^h - b^x}{h}$$

$$= b^x \left(\frac{b^h - 1}{h} \right)$$

Suppose $b > 1$. The first factor, b^x, is always positive. The second factor, which is a quotient, is also positive: if $h > 0$, then $b^h > 1$, so both numerator and denominator are positive; if $h < 0$, then $b^h < 1$, so both numerator and denominator are negative. Thus, when $b > 1$, the a.r.c.exp$_b(x, h)$ is positive for any h; this means the function is always increasing. For $b < 1$, however, the a.r.c. is negative; the first factor, b^x, is still positive, but now the quotient is always negative (Why?), so the function is always decreasing. It follows, therefore, that exp$_b$ is either *always increasing* (if $b > 1$) or *always decreasing* (if $b < 1$). This means that exp$_b$ is one-to-one as long as $b \neq 1$.

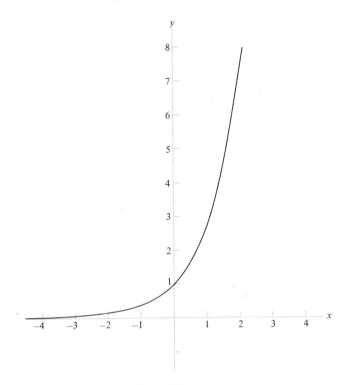

Figure 5-8
The graph of $y = e^x$.

Two important conclusions can be drawn from this fact. First,

$$b^x = b^y \text{ if and only if } x = y$$

Second, $\exp_b$ has an inverse. The graph of any inverse is the reflection through the line $y = x$. The graph of the inverse of a function $\exp_b$ is shown in Figure 5-9. It is called a *logarithmic function,* and it is the subject of the next two sections.

Exponential functions appear naturally in many ways, especially when an event repeats itself periodically; for example, the payment of compound interest. Suppose that P dollars are invested at i percent compounded quarterly, as in many savings accounts. The rate per compounding period, then, is $\left(\frac{1}{4}\right)i$ percent. At the end of first quarter, the interest paid is $P \cdot \frac{i}{4}$ so the total amount A in the account is

$$P + P \cdot \frac{i}{4} = P\left(1 + \frac{i}{4}\right)$$

At the end of the second period, the interest paid is $\left[P\left(1 + \frac{i}{4}\right)\right]\left(\frac{i}{4}\right)$, and now the

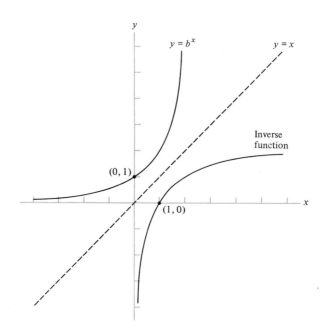

Figure 5-9
A function $y = b^x$ $(b > 1)$ and its inverse.

total amount is

$$A = P\left(1 + \frac{i}{4}\right) + P\left(1 + \frac{i}{4}\right)\left(\frac{i}{4}\right)$$

$$= P\left(1 + \frac{i}{4}\right)^2 \qquad \left[\text{Factor out } P\left(1 + \frac{i}{4}\right).\right]$$

Similar calculations will show that, at the end of the third period, $A = P\left(1 + \frac{i}{4}\right)^3$. In general, the function $A(n) = P\left(1 + \frac{i}{4}\right)^n$ gives the total amount in the account after n periods.

Example 1
If \$1000 is invested at 6% compounded semiannually, write a formula for the total amount accumulated after t years.

Solution
The semiannual rate is 3% = .03; according to the preceding discussion,

$$A(t) = 1000(1.03)^{2t} \qquad \qquad \text{(Why } 2t?\text{)}$$

Example 2
The population of a strain of bacteria growing in a laboratory is found to double in size every 3 hours. If a culture starts with Q bacteria, write a formula for the population P as a function of t hours after the start.

Solution
When $t = 3$, there will be $2Q$ bacteria; when $t = 6$, there will be $2(2Q) = 2^2Q$ bacteria; in general, at any time t there will be $Q2^{t/3}$ bacteria. So

$$P(t) = Q2^{t/3}$$

Notice that $P(300) = Q2^{100}$; that is how many bacteria will grow in just 300 hours! Remember, 2^{100} is larger than a 1 followed by 30 zeros.

Exercises

Calculate the following numbers.
1. $\exp_2(3)$ 2. $\exp_3(-2)$ 3. $\exp_{100}(0)$
4. $\exp_{1/10}(1)$ 5. $\exp_{1/10}(-3)$ 6. $\exp_3(3)$

Find y if the graph of $\exp_2$ contains the given point.
7. $(3, y)$ 8. $(-2, y)$ 9. $(-\frac{1}{2}, y)$
10. $(0, y)$ 11. $(1, y)$ 12. $(x + h, y)$

Find x if the graph of $\exp_3$ contains the given point.
13. $(x, 1/9)$ 14. $(x, 27)$ 15. $(x, \sqrt[4]{3})$
16. $(x, 1)$ 17. $(x, 3)$ 18. $(x, 9 \cdot 3^h)$

REMARK: The answers to Exercises 13–18 are values of the inverse of $\exp_3$, which is called the *logarithm with base* 3.

Find the base b if the graph of $\exp_b$ contains the given point.
19. $(3, 8)$ 20. $(-2, \frac{1}{100})$ 21. $(1, \pi)$
22. $(-3, 8)$ 23. $(2 + h, 49 \cdot 7^h)$ 24. $(0, 1)$

Sketch the graph of each function.
25. $y = \exp_3(x)$ 26. $s = \exp_{1/3}(t)$ 27. $v = \exp_2(u + 2)$
28. $f(x) = 3^{(x-1)} - 2$ 29. $g(t) = 3 \cdot 2^t$ 30. $h(u) = (\frac{1}{2})^{u+1}$

Because $\exp_b$ is always increasing (if $b > 1$) or always decreasing (if $b < 1$), there are no maximum or minimum values unless the domain is restricted. Find the maximum and minimum of each of the following two functions restricted to the indicated domains.

31. $f(x) = 3^x$; $-2 \leq x \leq 3$ **32.** $g(t) = (\frac{1}{4})^t$; $-1 \leq t \leq 2$

33. Make a table of values and sketch the graph of $y = 2^{-x^2}$. This is similar to the *normal distribution curve* that is used in statistics. Does $y = 2^{-x^2}$ have a maximum? A minimum? Does it have an inverse?

34. Suppose it is known that $(1.05)^{50} > 10$. If Columbus had deposited one dollar five hundred years ago in a bank that paid 5% interest compounded annually, about how much would it be worth today?

35. The **half-life** of a radioactive material is the time it takes for one half of it to decay. The half-life of a certain radioactive isotope is 2 years; thus, if Q kilos is the amount present now, then $Q/2$ kilos will be the amount present two years from now.

    (a)   If Q kilos is the amount present now, write a function whose value is the amount t years from now.

    (b)   How much will be left after 8 years?

    (c)   Will the amount present ever be 0?

36. (a)   Using the graph of $y = e^x$ in Figure 5-8, estimate the values of e^2, $\sqrt{e}$, and $1/e$.

    (b)   Use the graph of $y = 2^x$ in Figure 5-5 to estimate the value of x if $2^x = 5$, $2^x \approx 1.4$, and $2^x = \frac{1}{3}$.

37. Evaluate the following. Do your answers support the conclusion in the text, that the average rate of change of $\exp_b(x)$ is positive for $b > 1$ and negative for $b < 1$?

    (a)   a.r.c.$\exp_2(3, -1)$ (b)   a.r.c.$\exp_{1/4}(2, \frac{1}{2})$

    (c)   a.r.c.$\exp_8(-2, \frac{1}{3})$ (d)   a.r.c.$\exp_{1/16}(-1, \frac{1}{4})$

38. In Example 2, the size of a population P of a strain of bacteria after t hours was found to be $P(t) = Q2^{t/3}$. Show that

$$\text{a.r.c.}P(t, h) = Q2^{t/3}\left(\frac{2^{h/3} - 1}{h}\right)$$

Calculate a.r.c.$P(t, h)$ for (a) (3, 6), (b) (30, 6), and (c) (300, 6). You will see that the average rate of increase during 6 hours rises as the population grows: *the larger the population, the faster it grows.*

5-3
Logarithmic Functions

Exponential functions can be used to analyze growth and decay. For example, starting with an amount Q_0 of a certain radioactive material, the amount $Q(t)$ present after t years is given by an exponential formula

$$Q(t) = Q_0 b^{kt}$$

where k and b are constants that are different for each radioactive material.

Suppose the present amount Q is known and you want to know how long it took for the material to decay from the initial amount Q_0 to the present amount Q. Fortunately, the exponential has an inverse; by evaluating this inverse at Q, it is possible to solve for the time t. This is the method employed, for example, in dating archeological artifacts by measuring their content of carbon-14, which is radioactive. The amount of carbon-14 in living plants is known; if the amount of carbon-14 in a wooden object is determined, the age of the object can be calculated. This method and other applications of exponential functions will be explained in Section 5-5.

The inverse of the $\exp_b$ function is called the **logarithm base b** and is denoted by $\log_b$.

■ $\log_b x = y$ if any only if $b^y = x$

The expression $\log_b x$ is read "log base b of x." To find $\log_4 16$, for example, ask yourself, "What power of 4 equals 16?" The answer is 2; therefore, $\log_4 16 = 2$. In other words, because $4^2 = 16$, the value of the function $\log_4$ at the number 16 is 2. Thus,

$$\log_4 16 = 2 \quad \text{is equivalent to} \quad 4^2 = 16$$

similarly,

$$\log_3 81 = 4 \quad \text{is equivalent to} \quad 3^4 = 81$$

$$\text{and} \quad \log_9 3 = \frac{1}{2} \quad \text{is equivalent to} \quad 9^{\frac{1}{2}} = 3$$

Given any two of the three numbers y, b, and x in the equation $\log_b x = y$, it is possible to solve for the third.

Example 1
(a) $\log_2 x = 3$; solve for x.   (b) $\log_b (\frac{1}{27}) = 3$; solve for b.   (c) $\log_9 3 = y$; solve for y.

Solution
(a) By the definition of logarithm,

$$\log_2 x = 3 \quad \text{if and only if} \quad 2^3 = x$$

so $x = 8$.

(b)　By definition,

$$\log_b(\tfrac{1}{27}) = 3 \quad \text{if and only if} \quad b^3 = \tfrac{1}{27}$$

"Guess" $b = \tfrac{1}{3}$ and check: $(\tfrac{1}{3})^3 = \tfrac{1}{27}$.

(c)　Again, by definition,

$$\log_9 3 = y \quad \text{if and only if} \quad 9^y = 3.$$

Again, "guess" $y = \tfrac{1}{2}$ and check: $9^{\frac{1}{2}} = \sqrt{9} = 3$.

As inverses of exponential functions, logarithm functions inherit many properties:

(1)　The graph of $\log_b$ is the reflection of $\exp_b$ through the line $y = x$ (see Figure 5-10).

(2)　The function $\log_b$ is increasing if $b > 1$ and decreasing if $b < 1$.

(3)　$\log_b x = \log_b y$ if and only if $x = y$.

(4)　For $0 < x < 1$ and $b > 1$, the graph of $\log_b$ is very steep; for $x > 1$, it increases without bound but is rather flat (in contrast to the graph of $\exp_b$.)

(5)　Because $\exp_b : \mathbb{R} \to \mathbb{R}^+$, it follows that $\log_b : \mathbb{R}^+ \to \mathbb{R}$. That is, the domain of $\log_b$ is the *positive* real numbers (see p. 208).

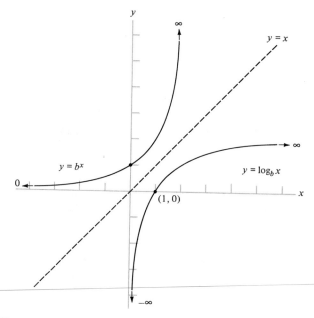

Figure 5-10
The graph of $y = \log_b x$ is the reflection of the graph of $y = \exp_b x$ through the line $y = x$.

As you might expect, the algebraic properties of logarithms are merely rewordings of the Basic Properties of Exponents discussed in Section 5-2.

■   **Basic Properties of Logarithms**
    If $b > 0$ and $b \neq 1$, then

(a) $\log_b xy = \log_b x + \log_b y$ (x and y positive)

(b) $\log_b x^y = y \log_b x$ (x positive)

(c) $\log_b \dfrac{x}{y} = \log_b x - \log_b y$ (x and y positive)

(d) $\log_b 1 = 0$ and $\log_b b = 1$

Proof of Logarithm Property (a)
Let $u = \log_b x$; then $x = b^u$, by the definition of $\log_b$. Similarly, if we let $v = \log_b y$, then $y = b^v$. Thus,

$$xy = b^u b^v = b^{u+v}$$

Therefore, the value of $\log_b$ at the number xy is $u + v$. In other words,

$$\log_b xy = u + v$$
$$= \log_b x + \log_b y$$

which is what we wanted to prove.

You should prove the remaining properties as an exercise. These properties can be used to solve a wide assortment of problems.

Example 2
Given that $\log_{10} 2 \approx .3010$ and $\log_{10} 3 \approx .4771$, find

(a) $\log_{10} 6$ (b) $\log_{10} 32$ (c) $\log_{10} \sqrt{27}$ (d) $\log_{10}(\tfrac{2}{3})$

Solution

(a) $\log_{10} 6 = \log_{10} 2 \cdot 3 = \log_{10} 2 + \log_{10} 3$ (Logarithm Property (a))
$$\approx .3010 + .4771$$
$$= .7781$$

Thus, $10^{.7781} \approx 6.$*

(b) $\log_{10} 32 = \log_{10} 2^5 = 5 \log_{10} 2$ (Logarithm Property (b))

$\approx 5(.3010)$

$= 1.5050$

Thus, $10^{1.5050} \approx 32.$

(c) $\log_{10} \sqrt{27} = \log_{10} 3^{(\frac{3}{2})} = \frac{3}{2} \log_{10} 3$

$\approx \frac{3}{2}(.4771)$

$\approx .7156$

Thus, $10^{.7156} \approx \sqrt{27}.$

(d) $\log_{10}(\frac{2}{3}) = \log_{10} 2 - \log_{10} 3$ (Logarithm Property (c))

$\approx .3010 - .4771$

$= -.1761$

Thus, $10^{-.1761} \approx \frac{2}{3}.$

The base 10 is used so often that the notation has been simplified. Henceforth,

■ $\log_{10} x$ will be written simply as $\log x$.

Example 3
Given that $\log 2 \approx .3010$, find $\log 5$.

Solution
Because $\log 10 = 1$ (Logarithm Property (d)),

$$1 = \log 10 = \log 5 \cdot 2 = \log 5 + \log 2$$

$$\approx \log 5 + .3010$$

Therefore, $\log 5 \approx 1 - .3010 = .6990.$

---

*If your calculator has a power key, you can check this statement.

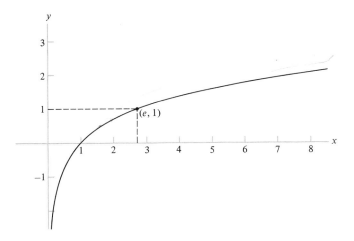

Figure 5-11
The graph of $y = \ln x = \log_e x$.

The values given for log 2 and log 3 in Example 2 are correct to four places; they may be found in Table 1 at the back of this book by following the instructions given in the next section. The most common logarithm base used in arithmetic computations is 10. Log base 10 is called the **common logarithm;** in this book, it is written simply as log x, omitting the base number 10. In calculus, however, the base $e = 2.71828$. . . is used almost exclusively. This number arises quite naturally in many applications; for that reason log base e is called the **natural logarithm** and is usually written as ln x (see Figure 5-11). A calculator that does logarithms will have a *log* key, a *ln* key, or both.

Exercises

Find the value of x.

1. $\log_4 x = 2$ 2. $\log_5 x = 3$ 3. $\log_{1/2} x = 5$
4. $\log_9 x = \frac{1}{2}$ 5. $\log_{16} x = -\frac{1}{2}$ 6. $\log x = 4 \text{(base 10)}$

Find the value of b.

7. $\log_b 4 = 2$ 8. $\log_b 81 = 2$ 9. $\log_b 81 = -2$
10. $\log_b 8 = -\frac{1}{3}$ 11. $\log_b \frac{1}{27} = 3$ 12. $\log_b \frac{1}{4} = 2$

Find the value of y.

13. $\log_{1/3} 81 = y$ 14. $\log_3 27 = y$ 15. $\log_2 \frac{1}{32} = y$
16. $\log_4 \frac{1}{16} = y$ 17. $\log 1 = y$ 18. $\log 10 = y$

Given that $\log 3 \approx .4771$ and $\log 5 \approx .6990$, find the following.

19. $\log 15$ 20. $\log \frac{1}{9}$ 21. $\log \frac{3}{5}$

22. $\log \frac{1}{25}$ 23. $\log 225$ 24. $\log 2$

25. Use the graph of $y = \ln x$ in Figure 5-11 to estimate $\ln 2$ and $\ln \frac{1}{2}$.

26. Use the graph in Figure 5-11 to estimate x if $\ln x = 2$ and $\ln x = -1$.

Sketch the graphs of the following functions.

27. $y = \log x$

28. $y = \log(x - 1)$ (Use translation.)

29. $y = \log 10x$ (Use Logarithm Property (a) and translation.)

30. $y = \log x^2$ (Use Logarithm Property (b).)

31. $y = \log \dfrac{x + 2}{100}$ (Use Logarithm Property (c) and translation.)

32. (a) If $\log_b x = 2$, then $\log_{1/b} x = ?$

(b) If $\log_b x = 2$, then $\log_b(1/x) = ?$

33. (Continuation of Exercise 32) Both parts of Exercise 32 are examples of the general formula

$$\log_{1/b} x = \log_b(1/x) \quad \text{for all } x > 0$$

Prove this formula by justifying each of the following steps.

(1) Let $y = \log_{1/b} x$; then $(1/b)^y = x$

(2) $b^y = 1/x$

(3) $y = \log_b (1/x)$

(4) Therefore, $\log_{1/b} x = \log_b (1/x)$

34. Another relationship of logarithms, which can be considered a fifth Basic Property is

$$\log_a x = \frac{\log_b x}{\log_b a}$$

where a, b, and x are all positive and neither a nor b is 1. This formula gives a method for transferring bases.

(a) Let $b = 10$ in the formula above, and use the log values given in Exercises 19–24 above to find $\log_3 5$.

(b) Prove the Basic Property above by justifying each of the following statements.

(1) Let $y = \log_a x$; then $a^y = x$

(2) $\log_b a^y = \log_b x$

(3) $y \log_b a = \log_b x$

(4) $\log_b a \neq 0$

(5)   Therefore, $\log_a x = \dfrac{\log_b x}{\log_b a}$

35.   (Anticipation of using scientific notation) Given that $\log 2 \approx .3010$, find the log of

(a) .02   (b) .2   (c) 20   (d) 200   (e) 2×10^n

where n is any integer. [HINT: Write .02 as 2×10^{-2}, .2 as 2×10^{-1}, and so on. Then use Logarithm Property (a).]

36.   Show that

$$\text{a.r.c.}\log_b(x, h) = \log_b\left(\frac{x + h}{x}\right)^{1/h}$$

[HINT: Work with the right side using the Basic Properties.]

37.   Prove the Logarithm Properties (b)–(d).

5-4
Computations with
Logarithms (optional)

Logarithms were once used extensively to simplify complicated computations. Then the use of slide rules and, more recently, hand calculators almost eliminated the use of logarithms for this purpose. However, both slide rules and calculators use logarithms to perform the operations of multiplication, division, and extraction of roots. Because our numeration system is a decimal system, it is the common logarithm (log base 10) that is used for computation.

Any positive number x can be expressed as a product

$$x = p \cdot 10^n \quad \text{with } 1 \leq p < 10, \ n \text{ an integer}$$

When x is written as such a product, we say that x is expressed in **scientific notation**. For example,

$$237 = 2.37 \times 10^2 \quad \text{and} \quad .0051 = 5.1 \times 10^{-3}$$

The integer exponent of 10 simply indicates how many places to move the decimal point to the right (if it is positive) or left (if negative). Thus, if we know the common logarithm of every number between 1 and 10, we can compute the logarithm of *any* positive number.

■   To find the logarithm of any positive number x, simply express x in scientific notation, and then

$$\log x = \log (p \cdot 10^n) = \log p + \log 10^n \qquad \text{(Logarithm Property (a))}$$

$$= \log p + n \log 10 \qquad \text{(Logarithm Property (b))}$$

$$= \log p + n \qquad \text{(log } 10 = 1)$$

Table 1 at the end of this book lists the common logarithms of all three-digit numbers from 1 to 10 (in jumps of .01). This is a four-place table; that is, the logarithms are given correct to four decimal places. The left-hand column contains the first two digits of the number p, and the third digit is at the top of the table. To find log 3.64, for example, look down the left column to 3.6 and then across to the column headed by 4. The entry .5611 is the logarithm of 3.64 correct to four places (see Figure 5-12). Now flip back to Table 1 and verify that

$$\log 7.09 \approx .8506 \quad \text{and} \quad \log 1.11 \approx .0453.$$

There are tables of logarithms with thousands of entries correct to six and more decimal places, but our small table is accurate enough for our purposes. When you study calculus, you will learn how the entries in such tables are computed.

Example 1
Use Table 1 to find (a) log 132 and (b) log .00452.

Solution
(a)   Write $132 = 1.32 \times 10^2$ and then

$$\log 132 = \log 1.32 + 2$$
$$\approx .1206 + 2 \qquad \text{(From Table 1)}$$
$$= 2.1206$$

Thus, $10^{2.1206} \approx 132$.

(b)   Write $.00452 = 4.52 \times 10^{-3}$ and then

$$\log .00452 = \log 4.52 + (-3)$$
$$\approx .6551 - 3 \qquad \text{(From Table 1)}$$
$$= -2.3449$$

Thus, $10^{-2.3449} \approx .00452$.

	0	1	2	3	4	5	6	7	8	9
3.0	.4771	.4786	.4800	.4814	.4829	.4843	.4857	.4871	.4886	.4900
3.1	.4914	.4928	.4942	.4955	.4969	.4983	.4997	.5011	.5024	.5038
3.2	.5051	.5065	.5079	.5092	.5105	.5119	.5132	.5145	.5159	.5172
3.3	.5185	.5198	.5211	.5224	.5237	.5250	.5263	.5276	.5289	.5307
3.4	.5315	.5328	.5340	.5353	.5366	.5378	.5391	.5403	.5416	.5428
3.5	.5441	.5453	.5465	.5478	.5490	.5502	.5514	.5527	.5539	.5551
3.6	.5563	.5575	.5587	.5599	.5611	.5623	.5635	.5647	.5658	.5670
3.7	.5682	.5694	.5705	.5717	.5729	.5740	.5752	.5763	.5775	.5786
3.8	.5798	.5809	.5821	.5832	.5843	.5855	.5866	.5877	.5888	.5899
3.9	.5911	.5922	.5933	.5944	.5955	.5966	.5977	.5988	.5999	.6010

Figure 5-12
Part of Table 1, "Common Logarithms of Numbers between 1 and 10," at the end of this book.

As we have seen, the logarithm of any positive number $x = p \cdot 10^n$ consists of two parts:

$$\log x = \log p + n$$

Log p is a decimal with $0 \le \log p < 1$ (because $1 \le p < 10$) and n is an integer. The decimal, *which must be nonnegative*, is called the **mantissa,** and the integer part, which may be positive, negative, or zero, is called the **characteristic** of $\log x$.

Antilogarithms

Finding the logarithm of a number x is only half the story. Equally important for computational work is the reverse operation, determining the **antilogarithm.** That is, given $\log x$, find the number x. The mantissa of $\log x$ is an entry in the body of Table 1 and the characteristic moves the decimal point.

Example 2

Given (a) $\log x = .9722$, (b) $\log y = 3.6243$, and (c) $\log z = -1.4191$, find $x, y,$ and z.

Solutions

(a)   Write $.9722 = .9722 + 0$; thus, the mantissa is $.9722$ and the characteristic is 0. You must find the number between 1 and 10 whose log is $.9722$, and then move the decimal 0 places. Look in the body of Table 1 (see Figure 5-13) to find the entry $.9722$; it is in the column headed by 8 and in the row labeled 9.3 on the extreme left. Therefore, $.9722$ is the log of 9.38; it follows that $x \approx 9.38$.

(b)   Write 3.6243 as $.6243 + 3$; thus, the mantissa is $.6243$ and the characteristic

	0	1	2	3	4	5	6	7	8	9
9.0	.9542	.9547	.9552	.9557	.9562	.9566	.9571	.9576	.9581	.9586
9.1	.9590	.9595	.9600	.9605	.9609	.9614	.9619	.9624	.9628	.9633
9.2	.9638	.9643	.9647	.9652	.9657	.9661	.9666	.9671	.9675	.9680
9.3	.9685	.9689	.9694	.9699	.9703	.9708	.9713	.9717	.9722	.9727
9.4	.9731	.9736	.9741	.9745	.9750	.9754	.9759	.9763	.9768	.9773
9.5	.9777	.9782	.9786	.9791	.9795	.9800	.9805	.9809	.9814	.9818
9.6	.9823	.9827	.9832	.9836	.9841	.9845	.9850	.9854	.9859	.9863
9.7	.9868	.9872	.9877	.9881	.9886	.9890	.9894	.9899	.9903	.9908
9.8	.9912	.9917	.9921	.9926	.9930	.9934	.9939	.9943	.9948	.9952
9.9	.9956	.9961	.9965	.9969	.9974	.9978	.9983	.9987	.9991	.9996

Figure 5-13
Part of Table 1, at the end of this book. See Example 2.

is 3. Find the number whose log is .6243 and move the decimal point three places to the right. Again, look for .6243 in the body of the table. It is in the row labeled 4.2 and the column headed by 1 (check this). Therefore, .6243 is the log of 4.21. Move the decimal point 3 places to get $y \approx 4,210$.

(c)   *Caution:* Although $\log z = -1.4191$, the mantissa is *not* .4191 and the characteristic is *not* -1, because you cannot write -1.4191 as $.4191 - 1$. To find the mantissa and characteristic of a negative logarithm, rewrite it as a difference of two numbers: the first number must be between 0 and 1; the second must be an integer.

$$-1.4191 = .5809 - 2 \qquad \text{(Add and subtract 2.)}$$

Then the mantissa is .5809 and the characteristic is -2. Now proceed as before: .5809 is the log of 3.81 and the decimal point must be moved two places to the left, so $z \approx .0381$.

Example 3
Find the antilogarithm of (a) -2.0487 and (b) $-.3420$.

Solution
(a)   Add and subtract 3 to rewrite -2.0487 as

$$-2.0487 = .9513 - 3$$

so the mantissa is .9513 and the characteristic is -3. Proceed as in Example 2(c) to find the antilogarithm, .00894.
(b)   This time, add and subtract 1, and then

$$-.3420 = .6580 - 1$$

It follows that .455 is the number whose log is $-.3420$.

Now suppose that you must find the logarithm of a four-digit number (for example, 3.167) or that you must find a number whose mantissa is .8465. Neither of these will be found in Table 1. The simplest solution is to **round off**; that is, use the table entry nearest to the given number. For example, if a problem requires the logarithm of 3.167, use the log of 3.17. If you must find a number whose mantissa is .8465, locate the number in the table whose log is closest to .8465. Table 1 contains the entries .8463 $=$ log 7.02 and .8470 $=$ log 7.03; use the former because it is closer to .8465. If the mantissa happens to fall precisely halfway between two entries, use the antilogarithm whose last digit is even. For example, in Figure 5-13, .9564 is halfway between .9562 and .9566. In this case, choose 9.04 as the antilogarithm rather than 9.05.

Although rounding off is the simplest method of estimation, it is also the least accurate. A more accurate method, *linear interpolation*, is described in Exercises 37 and 38 at the end of this section.

At last you are ready to use logarithms for computation. The next example shows how.

Example 4

Compute (a) $\dfrac{(3.12)^3(.4678)^2}{9821}$ and (b) $\sqrt[5]{(28.9)^3}$

Solution

Let $x = \dfrac{(3.12)^3(.4678)^2}{9821}$. Use the Basic Properties of Logarithms and round off to write

$\log x = 3 \log 3.12 + 2 \log .4678 - \log 9821$

$\approx 3 \log 3.12 + 2 \log(4.68 \times 10^{-1}) - \log(9.82 \times 10^3)$ (Round off.)

$\approx 3(.4942) + 2(.6702 - 1) - (.9921 + 3)$ (From Table 1)

$= 1.4826 - .6596 - 3.9921$

$= -3.1691$

Now that you know log x, you can find x as in the preceding examples. Write -3.1691 as .8309 $- 4$; the mantissa is .8309 and the characteristic is -4. Find the antilogarithm in Table 1 (you will have to round off), $x \approx .000678$.

(b)   Let $y = \sqrt[5]{(28.9)^3}$. First write it with fractional exponents: $y = (28.9)^{3/5}$.

Then

$$\log y = \frac{3}{5}\log 28.9$$

$$\approx \frac{3}{5}(.4609 + 1)$$

$$= \frac{(3)(1.4609)}{5} \approx .8765$$

Thus, $y \approx 7.52$.

Exercises

Use Table 1 to find the logarithms of the following numbers. Round off, if necessary.

1. 29.6	**2.** .0296	**3.** .00296	**4.** 2960
5. 1450	**6.** 14,500	**7.** 1045	**8.** 10,450
9. 346.3	**10.** 28.32	**11.** 5588	**12.** 9627

Use Table 1 to find the antilogarithms of the following numbers. Round off, if necessary.

13. 2.9299	**14.** 3.5527	**15.** -2.9299	**16.** -3.5527
17. 0	**18.** 4	**19.** $-.9312$	**20.** $-.8614$
21. $.3556 - 4$	**22.** $.1031 - 2$	**23.** $-.3566 + 4$	**24.** $-.1031 + 2$

Use logarithms to compute the following numbers. Round off, if necessary.

25. $\dfrac{(3.27)^3(.0628)^4}{591}$ **26.** $(261)^4(5.67)^{-3}$

27. $(2.831)^{-7.8}$ **28.** $(6.016)^{3.6}$

29. $\sqrt[4]{(7566)^3}$ **30.** $\sqrt[5]{(38.64)^2}$

31. $\sqrt{\dfrac{(4.31)(6.76)^3}{(82)(1.09)^5}}$ **32.** $\sqrt[3]{\dfrac{(.0023)(4.12)^2}{5283}}$

Use the formula in Exercise 34 of Section 5-3 to compute the following logarithms (round off e to 2.72).

33. $\log_5 497$ **34.** $\log_{14} 196$ **35.** $\log_e 14$ **36.** $\log_e .87$

Linear interpolation

37. (Logarithms) To find the logarithm of a number with more than three digits, assume that if the number x is p/q of the way between y and z, then $\log x$ will be p/q of the way between $\log y$ and $\log z$.

Example
Find the logarithm of 5.693. Because 5.693 is $\frac{3}{10}$ of the way between 5.69 and 5.70, assume that log 5.693 is $\frac{3}{10}$ of the way between log 5.69 and log 5.70.

$$\log 5.70 \approx .7559$$

$$\log 5.69 \approx .7551$$

The difference is .0008, and $\frac{3}{10}$ of this is .00024, which rounds off to .0002. Therefore,

$$\log 5.693 \approx \log 5.69 + .0002$$

$$\approx .7553$$

Example
Find the log of 32,175. Now 32,175 is $\frac{75}{100} = \frac{3}{4}$ of the way between 32,100 and 32,200. Assume that log 32,175 is $\frac{3}{4}$ of the way between the logs of these two numbers:

$$\log 32,200 \approx .5079 + 4$$

$$\log 32,100 \approx .5065 + 4$$

The difference is .0014, and $\frac{3}{4}$ of this is .00105, which rounds off to .0011. Therefore,

$$\log 32,175 \approx \log 32,100 + .0011$$

$$\approx .5076 + 4$$

Use linear interpolation and Table 1 to find

(a) log .1234   (b) log 1.001   (c) log 1.0001

38.   (Antilogarithms) Interpolation can be used, just as in finding logarithms.

Example
Find the antilogarithm of .8764. The number .8764 lies $\frac{2}{6}$, or $\frac{1}{3}$, of the way between .8762 and .8768, which are in Table 1. The antilogarithms of .8762 and .8768 are 7.52 and 7.53. Therefore, assume that the antilogarithm of .8764 lies $\frac{1}{3}$ of the way between 7.52 and 7.53. It follows that the number we seek is 7.523.

Example

Suppose $\log x \approx .0135$. Looking in Table 1, see that

$$\log 1.04 \approx .0170$$

$$\log 1.03 \approx .0128$$

Thus, .0135 is

$$\frac{.0135 - .0128}{.0170 - .0128} = \frac{.0007}{.0042} = \frac{1}{6}$$

of the way between the two numbers. Therefore, x must be $\frac{1}{6}$ of the way between 1.03 and 1.04. In other words, x is approximately 1.032.

Use linear interpolation to find the antilogarithms of

(a) 3.0149   (b) -1.9267 (c) $8.6213 - 10$

5-5
Applications of Exponentials and Logarithms

Mathematics is often used to describe the results of scientific experiments. This is true not only for the physical sciences, but, especially in recent years, for the social and behavioral sciences as well. The data collected in experiments are used to establish a relationship between appropriate variables. These relationships are usually expressed as equations, which quite often contain exponents and logarithms.

   Not too many years ago, logarithms were used to simplify complicated computations. The examples below show how this was done. However, slide rules and hand calculators have made this use of logarithms unnecessary. Nevertheless, as you will discover, logarithmic functions are still used to great advantage.

Example 1

The **period** of a pendulum is the time it takes for it to make one complete swing. Physicists have observed that the period P (in seconds) is related to the length L (in feet) by the equation

$$P = 2\pi \sqrt{\frac{L}{g}} \qquad (g \text{ is the gravitational constant})$$

Use the approximations $\pi \approx 3.14$ and $g \approx 32.2$ to compute the period of a pendulum 3 feet long.

Solution
Use logarithms (or a calculator) to compute $2\pi \sqrt{3/32.2}$.

$$P \approx 2(3.14)(3/32.2)^{1/2}$$

$$\log P \approx \log 2 + \log 3.14 + \tfrac{1}{2}\log 3 - \tfrac{1}{2}\log 32.2$$

$$\approx .3010 + .4969 + .2386 - .7540 \qquad \text{(From Table 1)}$$

$$= .2837$$

Now find the antilogarithm, which is $P \approx 1.92$ seconds.

The next example shows how to solve equations that contain exponents or logarithms. We shall lean heavily on the fact that $\exp_b$ and $\log_b$ are inverses of each other. This technique can then be put to use in applications.

Example 2
Solve for x in the equations (a) $\log_4 x = 3 + \log_4 6$ and (b) $2^{x+1} = 3^x$.

Solution
(a) This is a "log" equation, so use exponents to solve for x. Take $\exp_4$ of both sides of the equation:

$$\exp_4(\log_4 x) = \exp_4(3 + \log_4 6)$$

Now $\exp_4(\log_4 x) = x$(Why?) so

$$x = \exp_4(3 + \log_4 6) = (\exp_4 3) \times \exp_4(\log_4 6) \qquad \text{(Property of Exponents (a))}$$

$$= (64)(6) \qquad\qquad\qquad\qquad (4^3 = 64)$$

$$= 384$$

NOTE: There is another way to think about this: Because $\log_4 x = 3 + \log_4 6$, then $4^{\log_4 x} = 4^{3+\log_4 6}$. The left side is x and the right side is $(4^3)(4^{\log_4 6}) = 384$. Use whichever way is easier for you.
(b) This is an exponential equation, so use logarithms to solve for x. Take the log of both sides:

$$\log 2^{x+1} = \log 3^x$$

The left side is $(x + 1)\log 2$ (Why?) and the right side is $x \log 3$. Therefore,

$$(x + 1)(.3010) \approx x(.4771) \qquad \text{(From Table 1)}$$

$$x + 1 \approx \frac{.4771}{.3010}x$$

$$\approx 1.59x$$

Solving $x + 1 \approx 1.59x$ yields $x \approx 1/.59 \approx 1.69$

Example 3

Laboratory technicians observe that the population P (in thousands) of a bacteria culture is related to time t (in hours) by the equation

$$P = P_0 e^{.3t} \qquad (P_0 \text{ is the initial population.})$$

How long will it take for the population to triple?

Solution

You want to know the value of t when $P = 3P_0$. That is, what is t when $P = 3P_0$? Write

$$3P_0 = P_0 e^{.3t}$$

Divide by P_0 to get

$$3 = e^{.3t}$$

Take the log of both sides to obtain $\log 3 = .3t(\log e)$ or

$$t = \frac{\log 3}{.3 \log e}$$

$$\approx 3.66 \text{ hours} \qquad\qquad (\log e \approx .4343)$$

In the next two examples, you will have to first solve an equation and then compute a value.

Example 4 (Learning model)

Experiments with certain groups of students show that their average score S when they are tested on a particular topic is related to the time t (in days) after the topic was covered in class by

$$S = 80 - c \log(t + 1)$$

where c is a constant that depends on the class. If the average score was 75 after 9 days, what will the average score be after 20 days?

Solution
First use the given information to solve for c. If $S = 75$ when $t = 9$, then

$$75 = 80 - c \log(9 + 1)$$
$$= 80 - c \qquad\qquad (\log 10 = 1)$$

so $c = 5$ for this particular class. After 20 days the average score will be

$$S = 80 - 5 \log 21$$
$$\approx 80 - 5(1.3222) \qquad\qquad \text{(From Table 1)}$$
$$\approx 73 \qquad\qquad \text{(Round off.)}$$

Example 5 (Radioactive decay)
The half-life of a certain radioactive substance is 30 years. That is, after 30 years, one half of the original amount will have decomposed. The amount Q present at any time t (in years) is given by

$$Q = Q_0 e^{-kt}$$

where Q_0 is the original amount and k is a constant that depends on the material. If you start with 4 kilos of this material, how much will be left after 10 years?

Solution
The first step is to find the constant k. Starting with $Q_0 = 4$ kilos, you know that, after 30 years, one half will have decomposed, so $Q = 2$ when $t = 30$. Thus,

$$2 = 4e^{-k(30)}$$

Take the log of both sides:

$$\log 2 = \log 4 - 30k \log e \qquad\qquad (\log e \approx .4343)$$

It follows that $k \approx .023$. Therefore, the formula now reads

$$Q \approx 4e^{-.023t}$$

Evaluate this expression at $t = 10$. Use logarithms or a calculator.

$$\log Q = \log 4 - (.023)(10)\log e$$
$$\approx .6021 - .23(.4343)$$
$$\approx .5022$$

Find the antilogarithm to get $Q \approx 3.18$ kilos left after 10 years.

Exercises

The volume V of a sphere of radius r is $V = \frac{4}{3}\pi r^3$. Find the volume of a sphere if
1. $r = 42.6$ inches   **2.** $r = 39.1$ inches

The volume V of a right circular cone of height h and base radius r is $V = \frac{1}{3}\pi r^2 h$. Find the volume if
3. $r = 92.8$ in. and $h = 13.7$ in.   **4.** $r = 16.9$ in. and $h = 31.8$ in.

The period P of a pendulum of length L is given by $P \approx 2\pi\sqrt{L/32.2}$. Find the period if
5. $L = 26.9$ feet   **6.** $L = 98.4$ feet

The pressure p, in pounds per cubic feet, of a certain amount of gas contained in a volume v is given by $pv^{3.4} = 800$. Find p if
7. $v = 17.8$ cubic feet   **8.** $v = 23.1$ cubic feet

Find v if
9. $p = 38.1$ pounds/cu. ft   **10.** $p = 16.8$ pounds/cu. ft

Solve the following equations for x. Consider all other letters to be constants.
11. $3^x = 10$ **12.** $4^{x^2} = 20$
13. $3^{6x-1} = 32$ **14.** $2^{3-2x} = 4$
15. $I = \dfrac{1}{R}(1 - e^{-Rx})$ **16.** $Q = Q_0 e^{-kx}$
17. $\log x = 9 + \log 8$ **18.** $3\log x = 2\log 21 - 6$
19. $S = Q - R\log(x + 1)$ **20.** $\log Q = R\log(3x - 1)$

☐   (Compound interest) If P dollars are invested at an annual interest rate r, then Pr is the interest earned in one year, and the investment will increase to $P + Pr = P(1 + r)$ dollars at the end of the first year. The interest earned in the second year is therefore $P(1 + r)r$ and the accumulated amount at the end of the second year is $P(1 + r) + P(1 + r)r = P(1 + r)(1 + r) = P(1 + r)^2$. At the end of the third year, there will be $P(1 + r)^3$ dollars. In general, at the end of n years, the accumulated amount A will be

$$A = P(1 + r)^n$$

Most banks quote yearly rates, but pay interest quarterly, monthly, or even daily. If the yearly rate r is compounded quarterly, the formula above must be adjusted. The amount accumulated after n years is now

$$A = P\left(1 + \frac{r}{4}\right)^{4n}$$

because the rate per quarter is $r/4$ and it is compounded 4 times a year. Similar adjustments must be made for monthly and daily compounding.

21.   If $1000 is invested at an annual rate of 8% ($=.08$) compounded quarterly (quarterly rate is .02), how much will be accumulated after 10 years?

22.   Mr. Abramowitz wishes to accumulate $40,000 in 15 years to pay for his daughter's education. He can invest his money at 8% compounded quarterly. How much should he invest now in order to accomplish his goal?

23.   If $1000 is invested at 6% compounded monthly, how long will it take to double?

24.   Time deposits in a bank can earn $7\frac{1}{2}$% annual interest. At this rate, how long will it take to double your money if the interest is compounded (a) yearly, (b) monthly, and (c) daily (use 365 days/year). Banks advertise that, when it is compounded daily, a time deposit at $7\frac{1}{2}$% annual interest doubles in less than 9 years. Are they correct?

25.   Suppose one dollar is invested for one year at 100%. If the interest is compounded n times a year, then the accumulated amount after one year is

$$A = \left(1 + \frac{1}{n}\right)^n$$

It may seem that, if interest were compounded often enough in one year (that is, if n is very large), then A would grow without bound. You may be surprised to learn that this is false. On the contrary, for very large n, the number $\left(1 + \frac{1}{n}\right)^n$ is very close to the number $e \approx 2.718$. Compute $\left(1 + \frac{1}{n}\right)^n$ for $n = 1$, $n = 10$, $n = 100$, and $n = 1000$.

26.   (Atmospheric pressure) The atmospheric pressure at a fixed temperature is given by the equation

$$P = P_0 e^{-kh}$$

where P_0 is the pressure at sea level, k is a constant, and h is the height above sea level. If the pressure at 18,000 feet is one half the pressure at sea level, find the pressure at 10,000 feet.

27. (Population growth) Suppose that the size P of a population is given by the equation

$$P = P_0 e^{kt} \qquad (t \text{ in years})$$

where P_0 is the population when $t = 0$, and k is a constant. In 1960, the population of the United States was 202 million, and in 1970 it was 208 million. Estimate the population in the year 2000. [Let $t = 0$ represent the year 1960.]

28. (Radioactive decay) The half-life of carbon-14 is 5740 years. If a sample of carbon-14 weighs 100 grams now, how much will be left after 1000 years? The amount of carbon-14 found in ancient objects is used to date them.

29. (Electrical circuits) The current I in a certain electrical circuit is given by

$$I = \frac{1}{R}(1 - e^{-Rt})$$

where R is the resistance in ohms, and t is time in seconds. If $R = 1000$, find I when $t = 30$.

30. (Learning model) If the students in Example 4 scored an average of 72 after 5 days, what would be their average after 10 days?

Chapter 6

Trigonometric Functions

From *Webster's New World Dictionary* (Second College Edition):

> **trig · o · nom · e · try** . . . . [Gr. *trigōnon,* triangle (see TRIGON) + *-metria,* measurement (see -METRY)] the branch of mathematics that deals with the ratios between sides of a right triangle . . . the relations between these ratios, and the application of these facts in finding the unknown sides or angles of any triangle, as in surveying, navigation, engineering, etc.

Mathematicians have enlarged the scope of trigonometry so much that the above definition and the applications it lists give a very restricted idea of trigonometry and its uses. Trigonometry plays an important role in such subjects as harmonic motion (vibrating strings), the theory of relativity, and quantum mechanics. In order to apply trigonometry to these and other subjects, it is necessary to free it from the restricting concept of "ratios between sides of a right triangle." Thus, we shall begin by considering angles and functions of angles.

Section 6-1 deals with angles; it introduces a unit of measurement called the radian and compares it with the more familiar unit of angular measurement, the degree. Of the six trigonometric functions, the sine and cosine are the most important. Their basic definitions, properties, and graphs are discussed in Sections 6-2, 6-3, and 6-4. The other four trigonometric functions can be defined easily in terms of the sine and cosine; this is done in Section 6-5.

The important topics in this chapter are the sine and cosine functions. Learn everything you can about them and you will be well on your way towards mastering trigonometry. Notice the heavy reliance on diagrams in this chapter. It often happens that a quick sketch can help you recall a needed property, so get into the habit of using pictures to help solve problems.

6-1
Angles in Standard Position

An **angle** is a plane figure formed by two line segments with a common end point. If A and B are points on the segments L_1 and L_2, as shown in Figure 6-1, the angle can be written $< AOB$. Sometimes, if it is more convenient, the angle is labeled with a single letter. The angle in Figure 6-1A is labeled θ (the Greek letter *theta*).

Now draw a coordinate plane and position the angle θ as shown in Figure 6-1B. The line segment (L_1 in the figure) that lies on the positive x-axis is called the **initial side.** The point O coincides with the origin and is called the **vertex.** The segment L_2 is called the **terminal side.** An angle whose initial side is on the positive x-axis is said to be in **standard position.** When the terminal side lies in one of the four quadrants, we say the *angle is in that quadrant.*

You can think of an angle as being generated by rotating the initial side about the origin until it coincides with the terminal side. If the initial side is rotated in a counterclockwise direction, the angle is **positive;** if it is rotated clockwise, the angle is **negative.** There is no restriction on the number of complete revolutions, in either direction, that the initial side may make before it coincides with the terminal side. Thus, many different angles can have the same initial and terminal sides (see Figure 6-2).

In order to express the size of an angle it is necessary to have some unit of measurement. The one that most people are familiar with is the **degree,** written °. One complete rotation is 360°.

Example 1
Draw angles of 30°, $-135°$, $-330°$, and 585° in standard position. What quadrants are they in?

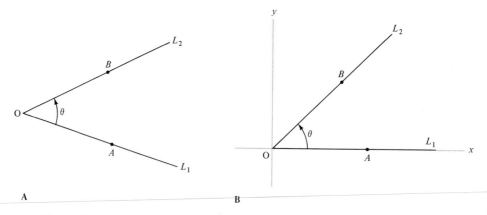

Figure 6-1
(A) The angle AOB or θ. (B) The angle θ in standard position. L_1 is the initial side, L_2 is the terminal side, and O is the vertex. This angle is in quadrant I.

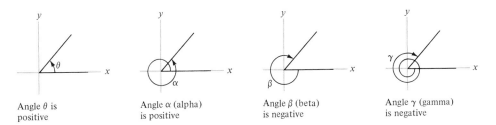

Figure 6-2
All of these angles have the same initial side and the same terminal side.

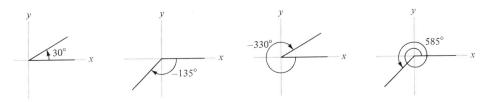

Figure 6-3
The angles of Example 1.

Solution
If you do not have a protractor, make a rough guess (see Figure 6-3). Notice that 30° and −330° have the same terminal side; both angles are in the first quadrant. Similarly, −135° and 585° have the same terminal side (585° is one revolution plus 225°); both angles lie in the third quadrant.

There is another unit of angular measurement, the radian, which is more suitable for calculus and scientific work.

■ **Definition**
An angle at the center of a circle of radius r measures **one radian** if it subtends an arc of length r on the circumference (see Figure 6-4).

One reason radian measure is useful is that, like metric measure, it simplifies computations. For instance, in a circle of radius 1, a central angle of 1 degree subtends an arc of length $\dfrac{2\pi}{360} = \dfrac{\pi}{180}$, whereas a central angle of 1 radian subtends an arc of length 1. We shall use both types of measurement, but mostly radians.

Because the whole circumference of a circle has length $2\pi r$, it follows that there are 2π radians in a complete revolution. Thus, 2π radians equals 360° (see Figure 6-5).

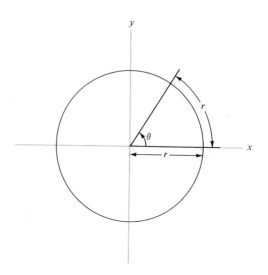

Figure 6-4
The radius of this circle is r. If the angle θ subtends an arc of length r on the circumference, then θ measures 1 radian.

■ 2π radians $= 360°$

   $1 \text{ radian} = \left(\dfrac{180}{\pi}\right)^{\circ}$

   $\phantom{1 \text{ radian}} \approx 57.296°$

   $1° = \dfrac{\pi}{180} \text{ radians}$

   $ \approx .017 \text{ radians}$

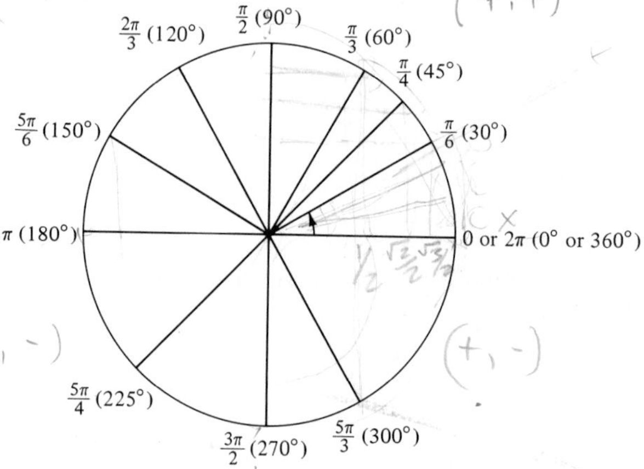

Figure 6-5
Some angles in standard position measured both in degrees and in radians.

Example 2
(a) Convert 30° and −60° to radians

(b) Convert $\dfrac{\pi}{4}$ radians and $\dfrac{-9\pi}{4}$ radians to degrees

(c) Draw each of the angles in (a) and (b).

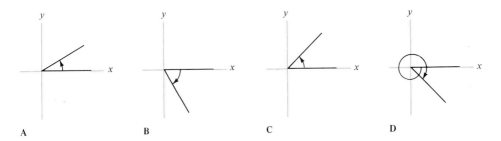

A   B   C   D

Figure 6-6
The angles in Example 2: (A) 30°, or $\pi/6$ radians; (B) $-60°$, or $-\pi/3$ radians; (C) 45°, or $\pi/4$ radians; (D) $-405°$, or $-9\pi/4$ radians.

Solution

(a)   To convert degrees to radians, multiply by $\frac{\pi}{180}$.

$$30° = 30\left(\frac{\pi}{180}\right) = \frac{\pi}{6}\text{ radians;}\qquad -60° = -60\left(\frac{\pi}{180}\right) = -\frac{\pi}{3}\text{ radians}$$

(b)   To convert radians to degrees, multiply by $\frac{180}{\pi}$.

$$\frac{\pi}{4}\text{ radians} = \left(\frac{\pi}{4}\right)\left(\frac{180}{\pi}\right) = 45°;\qquad -\frac{9\pi}{4}\text{ radians} = \left(-\frac{9\pi}{4}\right)\left(\frac{180}{\pi}\right) = -405°$$

(c)   Sketch the angles as shown in Figure 6-6.

Example 3
The radius of an automobile wheel, including the tire, is 30 centimeters. How many revolutions per second does it make when the auto is traveling 50 kilometers per hour?

Solution
There are 100 centimeters in one meter, and 1000 meters in one kilometer. Also, there are 3600 seconds in one hour. Therefore,

$$50\text{ km/hr} = 50 \times 1000 \times 100/3600$$

$$\approx 139\text{ cm/sec}$$

Furthermore, the circumference of the tire is

$$2\pi r = 2\pi 30$$

$$\approx 188\text{ cm}$$

This is the distance that the auto travels with each revolution of the wheel. Therefore, the wheel makes $139/188 \approx .74$ revolutions per second.

Angular speed is the angle of rotation per unit of time. In this example, the wheel makes .74 revolutions per second. The wheel turns through an angle of 2π radians with each revolution. Therefore, the angular speed of the wheel is

$$(.74)(2\pi) \approx 4.65 \text{ radians/sec}$$

Two special ratios

Suppose that θ is an angle in standard position and that $A(x_1, y_1)$ and $B(x_2, y_2)$ are points on its terminal side. Draw vertical lines through A and B. Figure 6-7 shows that two similar triangles are formed; AOC and BOD. Now,

$$\text{length of side } OA \text{ is } \sqrt{x_1^2 + y_1^2}$$

$$\text{length of side } OB \text{ is } \sqrt{x_2^2 + y_2^2}$$

because those are the distances from the origin to the points A and B. The other sides have the lengths indicated in the figure. Because the two triangles are similar, *the ratios of corresponding sides are equal.* Thus,

$$\frac{y_1}{\sqrt{x_1^2 + y_1^2}} = \frac{y_2}{\sqrt{x_2^2 + y_2^2}} \quad \text{and} \quad \frac{x_1}{\sqrt{x_1^2 + y_1^2}} = \frac{x_2}{\sqrt{x_2^2 + y_2^2}}$$

These results can be summed up in the following way.

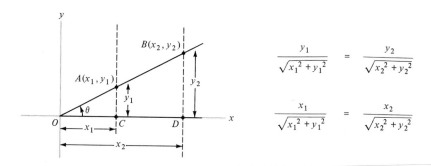

Figure 6-7
The ratios of the x-coordinate and the y-coordinate to the distance of the point (x, y) from the origin do not depend on what point you choose, as long as it is on the terminal side of the angle.

■ Choose an angle in standard position, and any point (x, y) on its terminal side:

> The ratio of the x-coordinate to the distance from the point to the origin is constant, no matter what point you choose.
> The ratio of the y-coordinate to the distance from the point to the origin is constant, no matter what point you choose.

In other words, once the angle has been chosen, these ratios do not depend on the choice of points on its terminal side. In the next section, we shall use these ratios to define the sine and cosine functions.

Example 4
The positive x-axis and the half-line $y = -2x$ for $x \leq 0$ form an angle θ in standard position. Let A be the point $(-1, 2)$, and B the point $(-2, 4)$; both lie on the terminal side of θ (see Figure 6-8). The length of OA is the distance from A to the origin, which is $\sqrt{(-1)^2 + 2^2} = \sqrt{5}$. Similarly, the length of OB is $\sqrt{(-2)^2 + 4^2} = \sqrt{20} = \sqrt{4}\sqrt{5} = 2\sqrt{5}$. The y-coordinate of A divided by the length of OA is $2/\sqrt{5}$; the y-coordinate of B divided by the length of OB is $4/2\sqrt{5} = 2/\sqrt{5}$. The ratios with the x-coordinates are also equal: for A it is $-1/\sqrt{5}$, and for B it is $-2/2\sqrt{5} = -1/\sqrt{5}$.

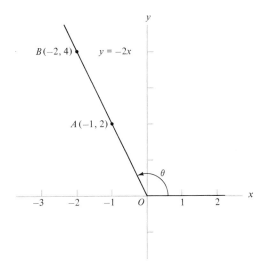

Figure 6-8
The half-line $y = -2x$ for $x \leq 0$ is the terminal side of the angle θ. See Example 4.

Exercises

Convert degrees to radians.
1. $0°$ 2. $30°$ 3. $45°$ 4. $60°$ 5. $90°$
6. $-45°$ 7. $-180°$ 8. $-225°$ 9. $-450°$ 10. $-540°$

Convert radians to degrees.
11. 0 12. $\dfrac{\pi}{6}$ 13. $\dfrac{\pi}{4}$ 14. $\dfrac{\pi}{3}$ 15. $\dfrac{\pi}{2}$

16. $\dfrac{-3\pi}{2}$ 17. $\dfrac{-7\pi}{4}$ 18. $\dfrac{-5\pi}{6}$ 19. $\dfrac{-11\pi}{3}$ 20. $\dfrac{-13\pi}{4}$

Convert degrees to radians (use $\dfrac{\pi}{180} \approx .017$).
21. $22.5°$ 22. $38°$ 23. $-4.3°$ 24. $-17.8°$

Convert radians to degrees (use $\dfrac{180}{\pi} \approx 57.3$).
25. 1 26. 3.2 27. -2.6 28. -6.28

Sketch each angle in standard position.
29. $95°$ 30. $\dfrac{3\pi}{2}$ radians   31. $-460°$ 32. $\dfrac{-8\pi}{3}$ radians

33. $-225°$ 34. $\dfrac{3\pi}{4}$ radians   35. $1080°$ 36. $\dfrac{13\pi}{2}$ radians

Find an angle θ between 0 and 2π radians with the same terminal side as each of the following.
37. $\dfrac{15\pi}{4}$ 38. $\dfrac{15\pi}{6}$ 39. $\dfrac{-62\pi}{3}$ 40. $\dfrac{-7\pi}{2}$

In Exercises 41–44, verify that the ratios of the x and y coordinates to the distance from the origin remain constant, as was done in Example 4.

41. The terminal side of θ is the half-line $y = x$ for $x \geq 0$; $A = (1/\sqrt{2}, 1/\sqrt{2})$ and $B = (3, 3)$.

42. The terminal side is $y = -(1/\sqrt{3})x$ for $x \geq 0$; $A = (1, -1/\sqrt{3})$ and $B = (2, -2/\sqrt{3})$.

43. The terminal side is $y = 3.5x$ for $x \leq 0$; $A = (-2, -7)$ and $B = (-4, -14)$.

44. The terminal side is $y = -4x$ for $x \leq 0$. Choose any two points you wish.

45. If the radius of an automobile wheel is 20 centimeters, what is its angular speed in radians per second when the auto is moving 60 kilometers per hour?

46.   The flywheel of a lathe makes 1500 revolutions per minute. What is the (linear) speed of a point 10 centimeters from the center of the wheel? That is, find out how far the point travels in one minute.

47.   What is the angular speed of the earth in radians per hour? If the radius of the earth is approximately 4000 miles, how fast are you traveling while you are asleep? (Assume you are at the equator.)

48.   A satellite 1000 miles high makes a complete revolution around the earth in 2 hours. How fast is it moving? (Use 4000 miles as the earth's radius.)

49.   If a water wheel with a radius of 6 meters makes 3 revolutions per minute, how fast is the water rushing past it?

50.   Two gear wheels of diameters 15 and 40 centimeters mesh at their rims. If the smaller one rotates at 20 revolutions per minute what is the angular speed of the other in radians per minute?

51.   The wheels of an automobile have a radius of 25 centimeters. If their angular speed is one revolution per second, how fast is the auto traveling, in kilometers per hour?

52.   (Referred to in Section 8-1) Given a circle of radius r that contains a central angle of θ radians, derive a formula, in terms of r and θ, for the area of the pie-shaped region enclosed by θ (see Figure 6-9).

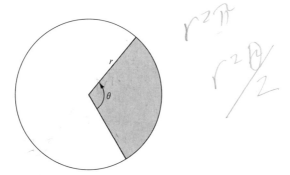

$$r^2 \pi$$

$$r^2 \frac{\theta}{2}$$

Figure 6-9
Find a formula that gives the area of the shaded region in terms of r and θ. See Exercise 52.

6-2
Sine and Cosine. Circular Functions

Let θ be an angle in standard position and let (x, y) be any point on its terminal side. The distance from (x, y) to the origin is $\sqrt{x^2 + y^2}$. We can define two **trigonometric functions**

$$\sin \theta = \frac{y}{\sqrt{x^2 + y^2}} \quad \text{and} \quad \cos \theta = \frac{x}{\sqrt{x^2 + y^2}}$$

read "**sine** theta" and "**cosine** theta." As we saw in Section 6-1, these ratios depend only on θ, not on the point (x, y) that is chosen (see Figure 6-10).

When we write $\sin \theta$ or $\cos \theta$, it is understood that θ is measured in *radians*. Thus, $\sin \theta$ means "the sine of θ radians." If θ is to be measured in degrees, write $\sin \theta°$ or $\cos \theta°$.

■   The sine and cosine are defined for all real numbers. Given any *number* θ, positive, negative, or zero, construct an *angle* of θ radians in standard position. Pick any point (x, y) on its terminal side and then

$$\sin \theta \doteq \frac{y}{\sqrt{x^2 + y^2}} \quad \text{and} \quad \cos \theta = \frac{x}{\sqrt{x^2 + y^2}}$$

Certain values of $\sin \theta$ and $\cos \theta$ occur so frequently that they should be memorized.

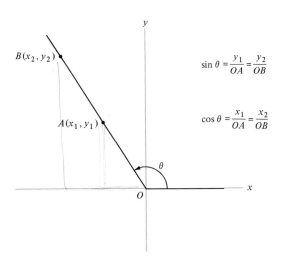

Figure 6-10
To find the sine and the cosine of an angle θ, draw the angle in standard position and choose any point on the terminal side.

The sine of θ is the ratio between the y-coordinate of the point and the distance of the point from the origin. The cosine of θ is the ratio between the x-coordinate of the point and the distance of the point from the origin.

These ratios depend only on θ, not on which point is chosen.

Example 1
Verify and then memorize the entries in the table below;

Radians	0	$\pi/6$	$\pi/4$	$\pi/3$	$\pi/2$	π	$3\pi/2$	2π
Degrees	$0°$	$30°$	$45°$	$60°$	$90°$	$180°$	$270°$	$360°$
$\sin\theta$	0	$1/2$	$\sqrt{2}/2$	$\sqrt{3}/2$	1	0	-1	0
$\cos\theta$	1	$\sqrt{3}/2$	$\sqrt{2}/2$	$1/2$	0	-1	0	1

Solution
To verify a table entry, draw an appropriate angle in standard position, choose *any* point on the terminal side, and calculate the defining ratios. The numbers $\theta = 0, \pi/2, \pi, 3\pi/2$, and 2π are easiest (see Figure 6-11A). For $\theta = 0$, choose the point $(1, 0)$, whose distance from the origin is 1. Then $x = 1$ and $y = 0$, and by definition,

$$\sin 0 = \frac{0}{1} = 0 \quad \text{and} \quad \cos 0 = \frac{1}{1} = 1$$

For $\theta = \pi/2$, choose $(0, 1)$; then $x = 0$ and $y = 1$, and

$$\sin\frac{\pi}{2} = \frac{1}{1} = 1 \quad \text{and} \quad \cos\frac{\pi}{2} = \frac{0}{1} = 0$$

For $\theta = \pi$, choose $(-1, 0)$; for $\theta = 3\pi/2$, choose $(0, -1)$; and for $\theta = 2\pi$, choose $(1, 0)$ again.

The angle $\theta = \pi/4$ is shown in Figure 6-11B; its terminal side is the half-line $y = x$ for $x \geq 0$. For this angle, a convenient point is $(1, 1)$, whose distance from the origin is $\sqrt{1^2 + 1^2} = \sqrt{2}$. Then $x = 1$ and $y = 1$, and

$$\sin\frac{\pi}{4} = \frac{y}{\sqrt{2}} = \frac{1}{\sqrt{2}} \quad \text{and} \quad \cos\frac{\pi}{4} = \frac{x}{\sqrt{2}} = \frac{1}{\sqrt{2}}$$

Rationalize the denominator $(1/\sqrt{2} = \sqrt{2}/2)$ to obtain the entries in the table for $\pi/4$.

Figure 6-11C shows the angle $\theta = \pi/3$, which is the size of each angle in an equilateral triangle. On the terminal side of the angle, it will be convenient to choose the point A that is 2 units away from the origin. To find the coordinates of A, construct the equilateral triangle OAB and draw the perpendicular

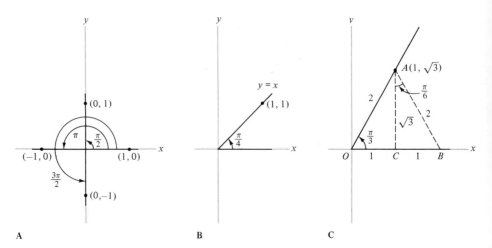

Figure 6-11
(A) The angles $\theta = 0$, $\pi/2$, π, and $3\pi/2$ in standard position. (B) The angle $\theta = \pi/4$ in standard position. (C) The angle $\pi/3$, in standard position, and the angle $\pi/6$. See Example 1.

bisector AC. This forms the right triangle OAC, with side length $OC = 1$ and $AC = \sqrt{3}$. It follows that the coordinates of A are $(1, \sqrt{3})$ and, therefore, that

$$\sin \frac{\pi}{3} = \frac{y}{2} = \frac{\sqrt{3}}{2} \quad \text{and} \quad \cos \frac{\pi}{3} = \frac{x}{2} = \frac{1}{2}$$

To find the sine and cosine of $\theta = \pi/6$, refer again to Figure 6-11C and slide triangle ACB around so that the angle marked $\pi/6$ is in standard position, as shown in Figure 6-12A. Now read off the values:

$$\sin \frac{\pi}{6} = \frac{y}{2} = \frac{1}{2} \quad \text{and} \quad \cos \frac{\pi}{6} = \frac{x}{2} = \frac{\sqrt{3}}{2}$$

The relationship between the trigonometric functions and distance has many applications.

Example 2
The light in a lighthouse makes one revolution per minute. The beam strikes a large rock five seconds after it shines on a ship. The ship is due east of the lighthouse and due south of the rock. If the rock is known to be two miles from the lighthouse, how far is the ship from the rock?

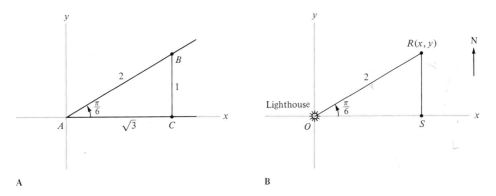

Figure 6-12
(A) The triangle *ABC* in Figure 6-11C has been moved around so that the angle $\pi/6$ is in standard position. See Example 1. (B) The lighthouse, ship, and rock in Example 2.

Solution
Draw a coordinate plane with the lighthouse at the origin, *O*, the ship (*S*) on the positive *x*-axis, and the rock (*R*) due north of the ship (see Figure 6-12B). The distance *OR* is 2, and the *y*-coordinate of the point *R* is the distance between the ship and the rock. One revolution (2π radians) per minute amounts to $\pi/6$ radians in five seconds. Thus, $\angle SOR$ is $\pi/6$. According to the table in Example 1,

$$\sin \frac{\pi}{6} = \frac{1}{2}$$

but you also know that

$$\sin \frac{\pi}{6} = \frac{y}{OR} = \frac{y}{2}$$

Therefore,

$$\frac{1}{2} = \frac{y}{2}$$

and $y = 1$; the ship is one mile from the rock.

Circular functions
Example 2 showed how trigonometry can be used to find straight-line distance, but equally important is the application of trigonometry to arc length, or curved distance. In fact, the trigonometric functions are called **circular functions.** Here is why.

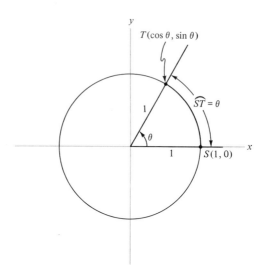

Figure 6-13
The point T is where the terminal side of the angle θ crosses the unit circle. The point S is where the initial side of θ (the x-axis) crosses the unit circle. If θ is measured in radians, the length of the arc ST is θ units.

Construct a circle with center at the origin and radius 1. Such a circle is called the **unit circle.** If an angle θ is in standard position, let T be the point where its terminal side intersects the unit circle (see Figure 6-13). The distance from T to the origin is 1; it follows that the coordinates of T are $(\cos \theta, \sin \theta)$. This is so because

$$\cos \theta = \frac{x}{1} = x \quad \text{and} \quad \sin \theta = \frac{y}{1} = y$$

In the unit circle, an angle of one radian subtends an arc of length 1; thus, an angle of θ radians subtends an arc of length θ (Figure 6-13).

The discussion in the preceding paragraph established a close relationship between circular motion and trigonometry; it may be summarized as follows.

■   Start at the point $(1, 0)$ and move θ units counterclockwise (clockwise if θ is negative) along the unit circle to the point T. Then the coordinates (x, y) of T are given by trigonometric functions:

$$x = \cos \theta \quad \text{and} \quad y = \sin \theta$$

Example 3
The shaft of a horizontal piston is attached to the rim of a wheel at a point P. The radius of the wheel is 1 foot. If the shaft begins from a horizontal position,

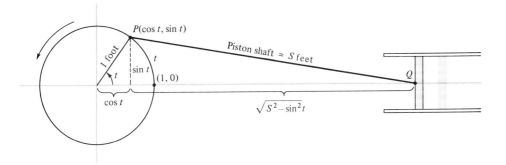

Figure 6-14
A piston is attached by a shaft to a point P on a rotating wheel. See Example 3.

how far from the center of the wheel is the piston head when P moves t feet along the rim of the wheel? $\pi/4$ feet?

Solution
Look at Figure 6-14. Assume that P starts at $(1,0)$. As the wheel rotates counterclockwise, the coordinates of P are given by the circular functions cosine and sine. When P has moved t feet, the distance from the piston head to the center of the wheel is

$$\cos t + \sqrt{S^2 - \sin^2 t}$$

When $t = \pi/4$, then

$$\cos\frac{\pi}{4} + \sqrt{S^2 - \sin^2\frac{\pi}{4}} = \frac{\sqrt{2}}{2} + \sqrt{S^2 - \frac{1}{2}}$$

Question: In case the radius of the wheel is r instead of 1, how far from the center is the piston head when P moves t feet along the rim of the wheel?

Review of basic ideas
Write out the definition of $\sin\theta$ and $\cos\theta$ in terms of an angle in standard position *and* in terms of a point moving along a unit circle.

Without referring to the text, fill in the blanks of the following table. If you cannot remember certain values, draw a picture as an aid. Then check with the table in Example 1. *Memorize* this table.

Radians	Degrees	sin θ	cos θ
0	0	0	1
π/6	30°	1/2	√3/2
π/4	45°	√2/2	√2/2
π/3	60°	√3/2	1/2
π/2	90°	1	0
π	180°	0	-1
3π/2	270°	-1	0
2π	360°	0	1

Exercises

Let θ be an angle in standard position and let (x, y) be a point on its terminal side. Evaluate $\sin \theta$ and $\cos \theta$ when (x, y) is each of the following points.

1. $(3, 4)$ **2.** $(1, 2)$ **3.** $(-3, 4)$ **4.** $(-1, 2)$

5. $(-\sqrt{2}, -1)$ **6.** $(-1, -\sqrt{3})$ **7.** $(2, -\sqrt{3})$ **8.** $(4, -3)$

9. $(-\sqrt{2}/2, \sqrt{2}/2)$ **10.** $(6, 8)$

For what values of θ, $0 \leq \theta \leq \pi/2$, will the trigonometric functions take the following values?

11. $\sin \theta = 0$ **12.** $\cos \theta = 0$ **13.** $\cos \theta = 1/2$

14. $\sin \theta = 1/2$ **15.** $\sin \theta = 1$ **16.** $\cos \theta = 1$

17. $\sin 2\theta = \sqrt{3}/2$ **18.** $\cos 3\theta = \sqrt{3}/2$ **19.** $\cos(\theta/2) = \sqrt{2}/2$

20. $\sin(\theta/3) = 1/2$ **21.** $\sin 5\theta = 1$ **22.** $\cos(\theta/7) = 1$

For what values of θ, $0 \leq \theta \leq \pi$ will the trigonometric functions take the following values?

23. $\sin \theta = \cos \theta$ **24.** $\sin \theta = -\cos \theta$ (See Exercise 9.)

25. $\sin \theta = 0$ **26.** $\cos \theta = -1$

Draw a unit circle with center at the origin of a coordinate plane. Starting at the point $(1, 0)$, move counterclockwise along the circle t units to the point T. What are the coordinates of T if t has the following values?

27. 0   **28.** $\dfrac{\pi}{3}$ **29.** $\dfrac{\pi}{4}$ **30.** π

Answer the same question if the circle has radius 3 and t has the following values.

31. $\dfrac{\pi}{2}$ **32.** $\dfrac{3\pi}{2}$ **33.** $\dfrac{9\pi}{2}$ **34.** 6π

35. Use the definitions of sine and cosine to prove the identity

$$\sin^2\theta + \cos^2\theta = 1 \qquad \text{for all } \theta$$

NOTE: $\sin^2\theta$ means $(\sin\theta)^2$. The notation $\sin^2\theta$, which is easier to write, is commonly used.

36. Use the identity in Exercise 35 to prove the inequalities

$$-1 \leq \sin\theta \leq 1 \quad \text{and} \quad -1 \leq \cos\theta \leq 1 \qquad \text{for all } \theta$$

37. In Example 2, how far is the lighthouse from the ship?

38. A 12-foot ladder is leaned against a house, making an angle of $\pi/3$ with the ground, as shown in Figure 6-15. How high up the wall will the ladder reach?

39. In Example 3, suppose that the shaft of the piston is 5 feet long and is connected to the piston head at point Q (see Figure 6-14). The wheel starts with P at the point $(1, 0)$ and rotates counterclockwise two revolutions (4π radians) per second. How far is Q from the center of the wheel after $\frac{1}{12}$ second? After $\frac{7}{12}$ second? After 1 second?

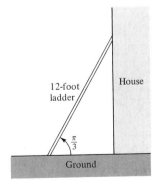

Figure 6-15
A 12-foot ladder leans against a house, making an angle of $\pi/3$ with the ground. See Exercise 38.

6-3
Properties of Sine and Cosine

In the preceding section, the sine and cosine were considered in two different ways.

First, as special ratios called trigonometric functions: Draw an angle θ in standard position, choose any point (x, y) on its terminal side, and define $\sin \theta = y/\sqrt{x^2 + y^2}$ and $\cos \theta = x/\sqrt{x^2 + y^2}$. This interpretation is most useful in problems concerning angles and linear distances (see Example 2 and Exercises 37 and 38 in Section 6-2).

Second, as circular functions: Draw a unit circle, start at the point $(1, 0)$, and move counterclockwise (clockwise if t is negative) along the circumference t units to the point T. Then the coordinates of T are $(\cos t, \sin t)$. This interpretation is most useful in problems concerning angular motion and arc length (see Example 3 and Exercise 39 in Section 6-2).

This section introduces several basic properties of sine and cosine. These properties may be verified by considering either of the interpretations outlined above. In each case we shall use the one that seems most convenient. For example, the important identity

$$\sin^2 t + \cos^2 t = 1 \qquad \text{for all } t$$

and the equally important inequalities

$$-1 \leq \sin t \leq 1 \quad \text{and} \quad -1 \leq \cos t \leq 1 \qquad \text{for all } t$$

are easily verified by a glance at Figure 6-16. This is the circular-function (unit circle) approach. NOTE: The symbol $\sin^2 t$ means $(\sin t)^2$. The notation $\sin^2 t$ is easier to write and is commonly used.

Signs of sine and cosine

If $0 < t < \pi/2$, then the terminal side of the angle of t radians lies in the first quadrant. The coordinates of any point in the first quadrant are both positive; therefore

$$\sin t > 0 \quad \text{and} \quad \cos t > 0 \qquad \text{for } 0 < t < \frac{\pi}{2}$$

If $\pi/2 < t < \pi$, then the terminal side of the angle of t radians lies in the second quadrant. For a point in the second quadrant, the x-coordinate is negative and the y-coordinate is positive; therefore,

$$\sin t > 0 \quad \text{and} \quad \cos t < 0 \qquad \text{for } \frac{\pi}{2} < t < \pi$$

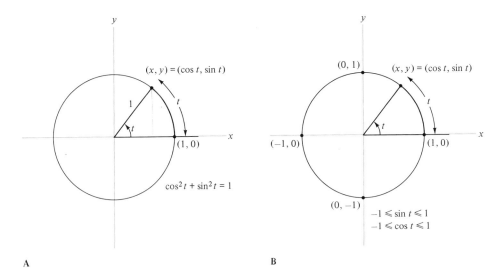

Figure 6-16
The unit circle can be used to prove trigonometric identities and inequalities. (A) Every point (x,y) on the unit circle is 1 unit away from the origin. Therefore,

$$\cos^2 t + \sin^2 t = x^2 + y^2 = 1 \qquad \text{for all } t$$

(B) The coordinates of every point (x,y) on the unit circle lie between -1 and $+1$. Therefore

$$-1 \le x = \cos t \le +1 \quad \text{and} \quad -1 \le y = \sin t \le +1 \qquad \text{for all } t$$

$$\frac{\pi}{2} < t < \pi$$
$$\sin t > 0$$
$$\cos t < 0$$

$$0 < t < \frac{\pi}{2}$$
$$\sin t > 0$$
$$\cos t > 0$$

$$\pi < t < \frac{3\pi}{2}$$
$$\sin t < 0$$
$$\cos t < 0$$

$$\frac{3\pi}{2} < t < 2\pi$$
$$\sin t < 0$$
$$\cos t > 0$$

Figure 6-17
The signs of the sine and cosine functions depend on which quadrant contains the terminal side of the angle t radians (in standard position).

Similar arguments hold when the terminal side lies in the third and in the fourth quadrant. The results are summarized in Figure 6-17.

Values of sine and cosine
The sine and cosine of many angles can be calculated conveniently by using a combination of the two interpretations of these functions.

Example 1

Evaluate $\sin t$ and $\cos t$ for $t = \dfrac{2\pi}{3}$, $t = \dfrac{5\pi}{6}$, and $t = \dfrac{7\pi}{4}$.

Solution

Within a unit circle, draw an angle of $2\pi/3$ radians in standard position. In Figure 6-18A, the point T is the intersection of the angle's terminal side with the unit circle; thus, the coordinates of T are

$$\left(\cos \frac{2\pi}{3}, \sin \frac{2\pi}{3}\right)$$

Now draw an angle of $\pi/3$ radians in standard position. Its terminal side intersects the unit circle at the point S directly across the y-axis from T. Thus, the y-coordinates of S and T are the same, while the x-coordinates have opposite signs with the same absolute value. You already know the coordinates of S:

$$y = \sin \frac{\pi}{3} = \frac{\sqrt{3}}{2} \quad \text{and} \quad x = \cos \frac{\pi}{3} = \frac{1}{2}$$

(Check the table that you completed at the end of Section 6-2.) It follows that

$$\sin \frac{2\pi}{3} = \frac{\sqrt{3}}{2} \quad \text{and} \quad \cos \frac{2\pi}{3} = -\frac{1}{2}.$$

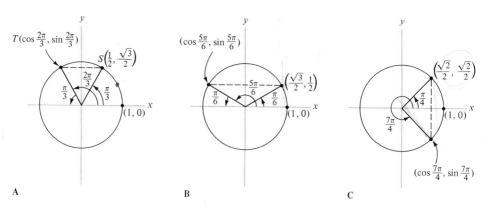

Figure 6-18

(A) Showing that $\sin \dfrac{2\pi}{3} = \dfrac{\sqrt{3}}{2}$ and $\cos \dfrac{2\pi}{3} = -\dfrac{1}{2}$. (B) Showing that $\sin \dfrac{5\pi}{6} = \dfrac{1}{2}$ and $\cos \dfrac{5\pi}{6} = -\dfrac{\sqrt{3}}{2}$. (C) Showing that $\sin \dfrac{7\pi}{4} = -\dfrac{\sqrt{2}}{2}$ and $\cos \dfrac{7\pi}{4} = \dfrac{\sqrt{2}}{2}$. See Example 1.

Similar examination of Figures 6-18B and C shows that

$$\sin\frac{5\pi}{6} = \frac{1}{2} \quad \text{and} \quad \cos\frac{5\pi}{6} = -\frac{\sqrt{3}}{2}$$

$$\sin\frac{7\pi}{4} = -\frac{\sqrt{2}}{2} \quad \text{and} \quad \cos\frac{7\pi}{4} = \frac{\sqrt{2}}{2}$$

Example 2
Find the value of sin t if

(a) $0 < t < \pi/2$ and $\cos^2 t = 1/2$

(b) $3\pi/2 < t < 2\pi$ and $\cos t = 1/\sqrt{3}$.

Solution
(a)   You know that $\sin^2 t + \cos^2 t = 1$; if $\cos^2 t = 1/2$, then $\sin^2 t = 1/2$. Thus sin t is either $1/\sqrt{2}$ or $-1/\sqrt{2}$. Because $0 < t < \pi/2$, the sine of t is positive and, therefore, $\sin t = 1/\sqrt{2} = \sqrt{2}/2$.
(b)   The value of cos $t = 1/\sqrt{3}$, so $\cos^2 t = 1/3$. It follows that $\sin^2 t = 2/3$ and sin t is either $\sqrt{2/3}$ or $-\sqrt{2/3}$. Because $3\pi/2 < t < 2\pi$, the sine of t is negative; thus, $\sin t = -\sqrt{2/3}$.

The sine and cosine of negative angles
In measuring angles, the positive direction is counterclockwise; thus, if an angle is negative, it must be measured in the clockwise direction. Suppose t is a positive number. Starting from $(1, 0)$ on the unit circle, move t units counterclockwise along the circumference; the terminal point has the coordinates (cos t, sin t). Starting again from $(1, 0)$, move t units in the clockwise direction; *this* terminal point has the coordinates $(\cos(-t), \sin(-t))$. The two terminal points are reflections of each other through the x-axis: the x-coordinates are equal, while the y-coordinates are opposite in sign with the same absolute value (see Figure 6-19). The same would be true if you had started with negative t. Thus,

$$\sin(-t) = -\sin t \quad \text{and} \quad \cos(-t) = \cos t \qquad \text{for all } t$$

Example 3
Find sin t and cos t for $t = -\frac{\pi}{3}$, $t = -\frac{5\pi}{6}$, and $t = -\frac{3\pi}{2}$.

Solution

$$\sin\left(-\frac{\pi}{3}\right) = -\sin\frac{\pi}{3} = -\frac{\sqrt{3}}{2}; \quad \cos\left(-\frac{\pi}{3}\right) = \cos\frac{\pi}{3} = \frac{1}{2}$$

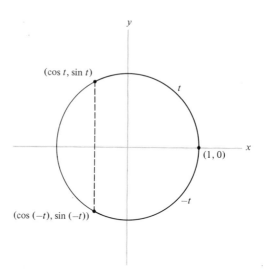

Figure 6-19
Showing that $\cos(-t) = \cos t$ and $\sin(-t) = -\sin t$.

$$\sin\left(-\frac{5\pi}{6}\right) = -\sin\frac{5\pi}{6} = -\frac{1}{2}; \qquad \cos\left(-\frac{5\pi}{6}\right) = \cos\frac{5\pi}{6} = -\frac{\sqrt{3}}{2}$$

(Example 1)

$$\sin\left(-\frac{3\pi}{2}\right) = -\sin\frac{3\pi}{2} = 1; \qquad \cos\left(-\frac{3\pi}{2}\right) = \cos\frac{3\pi}{2} = 0$$

Adding and subtracting π and $\pi/2$
Beginning at $(1, 0)$ on a unit circle, draw arcs of length t and $t + \pi$. Their terminal points lie at opposite ends of a diameter. The same is true of arcs t and $t - \pi$ (see Figure 6-20A). Thus, arcs $t + \pi$ and $t - \pi$ have the same terminal point, and its coordinates are the same as those of the terminal point of arc t, *but with opposite sign.* Therefore,

$$\sin(t \pm \pi) = -\sin t \quad \text{and} \quad \cos(t \pm \pi) = -\cos t \qquad \text{for all } t$$

The terminal points of arcs t and $(\pi/2) - t$ are reflections of each other through the line $y = x$. If the terminal point of t is (x, y), then the terminal point of $(\pi/2) - t$ is (y, x) (see Figure 6-20B). Because the coordinates are reversed, the sine and cosine are interchanged. Therefore,

$$\sin\left(\frac{\pi}{2} - t\right) = \cos t \quad \text{and} \quad \cos\left(\frac{\pi}{2} - t\right) = \sin t \qquad \text{for all } t$$

Thus, if s and t are **complementary numbers,** that is, if their sum is $\pi/2$, then

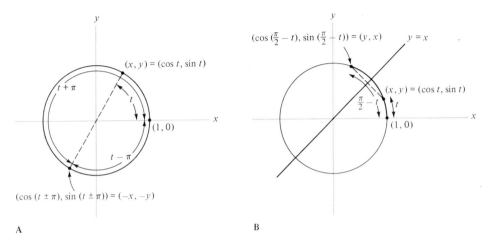

Figure 6-20
(A) On a unit circle, the terminal point of the arcs $t + \pi$ and $t - \pi$ is the opposite end of a diameter from the terminal point of arc t. (B) On a unit circle, the terminal point of arc t and the terminal point of arc $(\pi/2) - t$ are reflections of each other through the line $y = x$.

$\sin s = \cos t$. Incidentally, that is the reason for the *co* in cosine; it is complementary to sine.

The proofs of the following formulas are exercises at the end of this section:

$$\sin(\pi - t) = \sin t \quad \text{and} \quad \cos(\pi - t) = -\cos t \qquad \text{for all } t$$

$$\sin\left(\frac{\pi}{2} + t\right) = \cos t \quad \text{and} \quad \cos\left(\frac{\pi}{2} + t\right) = -\sin t \qquad \text{for all } t$$

$$\sin\left(t - \frac{\pi}{2}\right) = -\cos t \quad \text{and} \quad \cos\left(t - \frac{\pi}{2}\right) = \sin t \qquad \text{for all } t$$

Periodicity
One property of the trigonometric functions which distinguishes them from all the other functions you have studied so far is their periodicity.

■ **Definition**
A function f with domain $\mathbb{R}$ is **periodic** if there is a positive number p such that

$$f(x + p) = f(x) \qquad \text{for all } x \text{ in } \mathbb{R}$$

The smallest positive number p with this property is the **period** of f.

Suppose f is periodic with period p. If the values of f are known for all numbers between some number x_0 and $x_0 + p$, then its values can be determined for all real numbers. This is because the values of f are repeated endlessly, in the same order, on intervals of length p. Periodic functions are used to describe phenomena that exhibit cycles, such as wave motion, harmonic motion, and alternating electric current.

■   The sine and cosine are periodic with period 2π.

This is because, for any number t, the angles t and $t + 2\pi$ in standard position have the same terminal side. Therefore, their sines take the same values, and so do their cosines. The number 2π is the smallest positive value for which this is true. Repeated use of the same reasoning shows that

$$\sin t = \sin(t \pm 2n\pi)$$

$$\cos t = \cos(t \pm 2n\pi)$$

for any $n = 0, 1, 2, \ldots$

Example 4

Evaluate $\cos\dfrac{23\pi}{4}$ and $\sin\left(\dfrac{-19\pi}{2}\right)$.

Solution
First rewrite each angle as some number t between 0 and 2π, plus an *even* multiple of π.

The angle $23\pi/4$ is between 4π and 6π, so write $23\pi/4 = t + 4\pi$ and solve for t. Then $t = 7\pi/4$, so

$$\cos\frac{23\pi}{4} = \cos\frac{7\pi}{4} = \frac{\sqrt{2}}{2} \qquad \text{(Example 1)}$$

The angle $-19\pi/2$ is between -10π and -8π, so write $-19\pi/2 = t - 10\pi$. Then $t = \pi/2$, so

$$\sin\left(\frac{-19\pi}{2}\right) = \sin\frac{\pi}{2} = 1$$

Review of basic ideas
Here is a summary of the basic properties discussed in this section. Remember the diagrams used to justify them.

$$\sin^2 t + \cos^2 t = 1 \qquad \text{for all } t \qquad \text{(Figure 6-16A)}$$

$-1 \leq \sin t \leq 1$ and $-1 \leq \cos t \leq 1$ for all t (Figure 6-16B)

$\sin(-t) = -\sin t$ $\cos(-t) = \cos t$ (Figure 6-19)

$\sin(t \pm \pi) = -\sin t$ $\cos(t \pm \pi) = -\cos t$ (Figure 6-20A)

$\sin(\pi - t) = \sin t$ $\cos(\pi - t) = -\cos t$ (Exercise 42 below)

$\sin\left(\dfrac{\pi}{2} - t\right) = \cos t$ $\cos\left(\dfrac{\pi}{2} - t\right) = \sin t$ (Figure 6-20B)

$\sin\left(\dfrac{\pi}{2} + t\right) = \cos t$ $\cos\left(\dfrac{\pi}{2} + t\right) = -\sin t$ (Exercise 43 below)

$\sin\left(t - \dfrac{\pi}{2}\right) = -\cos t$ $\cos\left(t - \dfrac{\pi}{2}\right) = \sin t$ (Exercise 43 below)

sine and cosine are periodic with period 2π

$\sin t = \sin(t \pm 2n\pi)$ and $\cos t = \cos(t \pm 2n\pi)$ for $n = 0, 1, 2, \ldots$

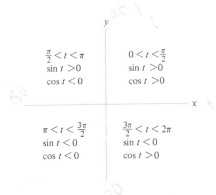

Exercises

Evaluate $\sin t$ and $\cos t$ for the following values of t (use Example 1 as a guide).
1. $7\pi/6$ 2. $4\pi/3$ 3. $5\pi/3$ 4. $11\pi/6$ 5. $3\pi/4$

Evaluate $\sin t$ and $\cos t$ for the following values of t (use Example 3 as a guide).
6. $-\pi/6$ 7. $-\pi/4$ 8. $-7\pi/6$ 9. $-11\pi/6$ 10. $-5\pi/3$

Evaluate $\sin t$ and $\cos t$ for the following values of t (use Example 4 as a guide).
11. $25\pi/4$ 12. $-10\pi/3$ 13. $-79\pi/6$ 14. $11\pi/4$ 15. 52π

Evaluate $\sin t$ and $\cos t$ for the following values of t.

16. $3\pi/4$ 17. $-30\pi/4$ 18. -53π 19. 26π 20. $5\pi/4$

Find all solutions of the following equations.

21. $\sin x = 0$ 22. $\cos x = 0$ 23. $\sin x = 1/2$
24. $\sin x = -\frac{1}{2}$ 25. $\cos x = 1$ 26. $\cos x = -1$

Find all solutions of the following equations.

27. $\sin 2x = \sqrt{2}/2$ 28. $\cos 3x = -\sqrt{3}/2$ 29. $\sin 5x = 1$

Find all solutions of the following equations.

30. $\sin x = \cos x$ 31. $\sin x = -\cos x$ 32. $\cos^2 x + \sin^2 x = 1$
33. $\cos^2 x = \frac{1}{2}$ 34. $\cos x = 2$ 35. $\sin x = -3/2$

Find the value of $\sin u$ (use Example 2 as a guide).

36. $0 < u < \pi/2$ and $\cos^2 u = 3/4$
37. $\pi < u < 3\pi/2$ and $\cos u = -1/\sqrt{3}$
38. $\pi/2 \le u \le \pi$ and $\cos u = -1$

Find the value of $\cos v$.

39. $\pi/2 < v < 3\pi/2$ and $\sin(-v) = \frac{1}{2}$
40. $-\pi/2 < v < \pi/2$ and $\sin(-v) = -\sqrt{3}/2$
41. $-\pi/2 < v < \pi/2$ and $\sin v = 0$

☐   42.   In this section we showed that

$$\sin(t - \pi) = -\sin t \quad \text{and} \quad \cos(t - \pi) = -\cos t$$

Now prove that

$$\sin(\pi - t) = \sin t \quad \text{and} \quad \cos(\pi - t) = -\cos t.$$

[HINT: Write $\pi - t = -(t - \pi)$.]

43.   (Used in next section to graph $y = \cos x$) In this section we showed that sine and cosine are complementary; that is,

$$\sin\left(\frac{\pi}{2} - t\right) = \cos t \quad \text{and} \quad \cos\left(\frac{\pi}{2} - t\right) = \sin t$$

Now prove that

$$\sin\left(\frac{\pi}{2} + t\right) = \cos t \quad \text{and} \quad \cos\left(\frac{\pi}{2} + t\right) = -\sin t$$

$$\left[\text{HINT: Write } \frac{\pi}{2} + t = \frac{\pi}{2} - (-t).\right] \text{Also prove that}$$

$$\sin\left(t - \frac{\pi}{2}\right) = -\cos t \quad \text{and} \quad \cos\left(t - \frac{\pi}{2}\right) = \sin t$$

$$\left[\text{HINT: Write } t - \frac{\pi}{2} \text{ as } -\left(\frac{\pi}{2} - t\right).\right]$$

44.   The living room of a house has a cathedral ceiling. A cross section is shown in Figure 6-21A. How high is the peak from the floor?

45.   (Continuation of Exercise 39 in Section 6-2). How far is Q from the origin after $\frac{1}{6}$, 3, and $\frac{81}{16}$ seconds?

46.   (Anticipation of simple harmonic motion) Imagine a very thin circular disc made of clear plastic with a blue dot painted on its rim. The radius of the disc is one unit. Now let it rotate at a constant angular speed and look at it from the side as in Figure 6-21B. How can you describe the motion of the blue dot? This is called *simple harmonic motion;* it is similar to the motion of a point on a vibrating guitar string. If y represents the distance from the center of the disc to the blue dot (in the side view), and x represents the actual distance that the point moves along the rim (in the front view), write an equation that defines y as a circular function of x. In this way, circular functions are used to describe harmonic motion.

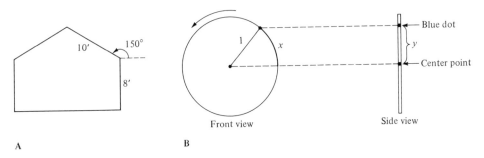

A   B

Figure 6-21
(A) Cross section of the house in Exercise 44. (B) Front and side views of the disc in Exercise 46.

6-4
Graphs of Sine and Cosine

Imagine a clear plastic disc of radius 1 with a point P on its rim (see Figure 6-22). Now let the disc rotate counterclockwise at a constant angular speed. If you view the disc edgewise, P moves up to a point 1 unit above the center, then down to a point 1

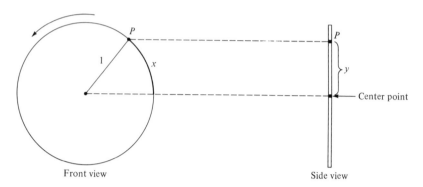

Figure 6-22
When a rotating disc is viewed from the side, a point on its circumference moves up and down in simple harmonic motion.

unit below the center, and up again. The motion is repeated as long as the disc rotates. This up and down movement is similar to the motion of a point on a vibrating string, and it is called **simple harmonic motion.** If x measures the distance that P moves along the circumference of the disc (front view), then $y = \sin x$ measures the distance of the point above or below the horizontal line through the center. In other words, $y = \sin x$ *describes the simple harmonic motion of the point P.*

You can sketch the graph of $y = \sin x$ by using the values and identities obtained in the preceding sections. First, make a table of values for $0 \le x \le \pi$:

x	0	$\pi/6$	$\pi/4$	$\pi/3$	$\pi/2$	$2\pi/3$	$3\pi/4$	$5\pi/6$	π
$y = \sin x$	0	$1/2$	$\sqrt{2}/2$	$\sqrt{3}/2$	1	$\sqrt{3}/2$	$\sqrt{2}/2$	$1/2$	0

The graph from $x = 0$ to $x = \pi$ is shown in Figure 6-23. Because $\sin(\pi + x) = -\sin x$, the part of the graph from $x = \pi$ to $x = 2\pi$ looks just like the part in Figure 6-23, but upside down (see Figure 6-24). Now use that fact that the sine is periodic with period 2π (that is, $\sin(x + 2n\pi) = \sin x$), and also the fact that $\sin(-x) = -\sin x$, to sketch the full graph (Figure 6-25).

The same method can be used to graph the function $y = \cos x$; however, there is an easier way to sketch this graph. In Exercise 43 in the preceding section, you showed that

$$\cos x = \sin\left(x + \frac{\pi}{2}\right)$$

Therefore, the graph of $y = \cos x$ is simply the *translation* of the sine graph $\pi/2$ units to the left (compare Figure 6-26 with Figure 6-25).

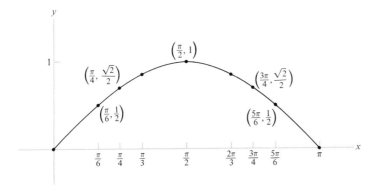

Figure 6-23
The graph of $y = \sin x$ between $x = 0$ and $x = \pi$.

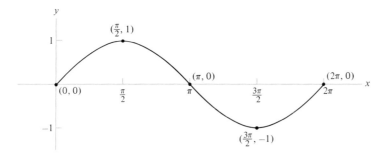

Figure 6-24
The graph of $y = \sin x$ between $x = 0$ and $x = 2\pi$.

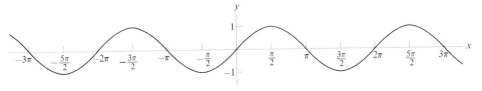

Figure 6-25
The graph of $y = \sin x$.

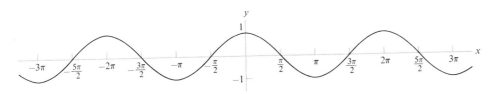

Figure 6-26
The graph of $y = \cos x$. This graph is the graph of $y = \sin x$ translated $\pi/2$ units to the left.

Graphs of $y = a \sin(bx + c)$ and $y = a \cos(bx + c)$

In general, the simple harmonic motion of an oscillating particle, such as a point on a vibrating membrane or a charged particle oscillating in a wire to produce alternating current, can be described by a function

$$y = a \sin(bx + c) \quad \text{or} \quad y = a \cos(bx + c)$$

where a, b, and c are constants; such functions are called **sinusoidal** functions.

The graph of a sinusoidal function $y = a \sin(bx + c)$ is similar to the graph of the sine function. However, the constants a, b, and c alter the graph in the following ways:

■ The values of y will range between $-|a|$ and $|a|$. The number $|a|$ is called the **amplitude** of the function (see Example 1).

■ If $b \neq 0$, the period of the function is $2\pi/b$ (see Example 2).

■ If $b \neq 0$, the graph is shifted $|c/b|$ units to the right or left, depending on whether c/b is negative or positive (see Example 3).

Thus, the graphs of functions $y = a \sin(bx + c)$ and $y = a \cos(bx + c)$ are simply graphs of sine and cosine functions that have been stretched, shrunk, or translated.

Example 1

The amplitude $|a|$ stretches or shrinks the graph of $y = \sin x$ vertically. Graph the functions $y = 2 \sin x$ and $y = \frac{1}{2} \sin x$.

Solution

Both graphs are sine curves, but $y = 2 \sin x$ ranges from $y = -2$ to $y = 2$, and $y = \frac{1}{2} \sin x$ ranges from $y = -\frac{1}{2}$ to $y = \frac{1}{2}$ (see Figure 6-27).

Example 2

The constant b changes the period; this stretches or shrinks the graph of $y = \cos x$ horizontally. Graph the functions $y = \cos 2x$ and $y = \cos \frac{1}{2}x$.

Solution

In the function $y = \cos 2x$, as x goes through a half period (π radians), $2x$ goes through a whole period (2π radians); as x goes through one period, $2x$ goes through two periods; and so on. Thus, *the period of* $\cos 2x$ *is* π, *not* 2π. This has the effect of compressing the graph of the cosine in towards the y-axis (see Figure 6-28).

The function $y = \cos \frac{1}{2}x$ is just the opposite: as x goes through a whole period, $\frac{1}{2}x$ goes through a half period. Thus, the period of $\cos \frac{1}{2}x$ is 4π instead of 2π: the graph is stretched out horizontally (see Figure 6-29).

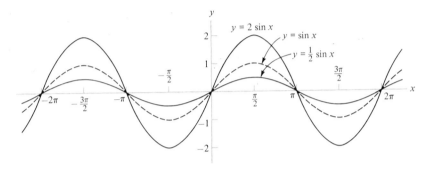

Figure 6-27
The graphs of the functions in Example 1.

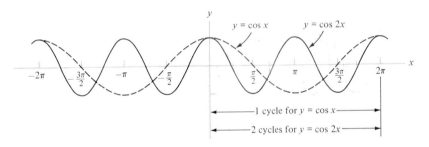

Figure 6-28
The graph of $y = \cos 2x$ is the graph of $y = \cos x$ compressed horizontally by half. See Example 2.

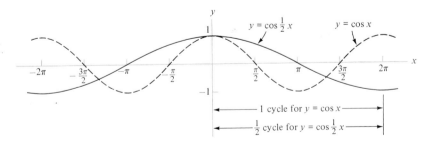

Figure 6-29
The graph of $y = \cos \frac{1}{2}x$ is just the graph of $y = \cos x$ stretched horizontally by a factor of 2. See Example 2.

Example 3

Graph $y = 2 \sin\left(3x + \dfrac{3\pi}{2}\right)$

Solution

First rewrite the equation as $y = 2 \sin 3\left(x + \dfrac{\pi}{2}\right)$. Then, starting with the graph of $y = \sin x$, the constant 2 stretches the graph vertically, the constant 3 shrinks it horizontally (the period is now $2\pi/3$), and the whole curve is translated $\pi/2$ units to the left (see Figure 6-30).

Example 4

Suppose a particle oscillates harmonically along a horizontal line between the points -4 and 4. It starts at the point 2 and moves right to 4, then left to -4, and back to 2. It makes two such oscillations (also called *cycles*) per second. Write a function that describes this motion.

Solution

You can use either a sine or cosine function; try a sine. The independent variable should be t, for time (in seconds); let x be the position at time t. The function that describes this motion has the form

$$x = a \sin(bt + c)$$

Because the particle oscillates between -4 and 4, you want the amplitude to be 4; therefore, set $a = 4$. The particle makes two complete cycles (4π radians) each second. Thus, the period is $\frac{1}{2}$ second, which equals $2\pi/b$, so $b = 4\pi$. So far, then,

$$x = 4 \sin(4\pi t + c)$$

You are told that the particle starts at the point $x = 2$ and moves to the right; that is, when $t = 0$, $2 = 4 \sin(4\pi \cdot 0 + c)$ or $\sin c = \frac{1}{2}$. Thus, c could be $\pi/6$ or $5\pi/6$. Setting $c = 5\pi/6$ would mean that the particle starts moving to the left (when $t = 1/24$, $4\pi t + (5\pi/6) = \pi$ and $x = 4 \sin \pi = 0$, which is to the *left* of 2), so let $c = \pi/6$. Therefore,

$$x = 4 \sin\left(4\pi t + \dfrac{\pi}{6}\right)$$

describes the motion of the particle; the function takes the value $x = 2$ when $t = 0$, it oscillates twice per second, and it varies between 4 and -4.

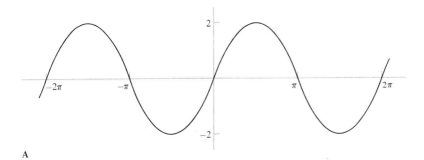

A

B

C

Figure 6-30

Steps toward sketching the graph of $y = 2 \sin \left(3x + \dfrac{3\pi}{2}\right)$. See Example 3. (A) The graph of

$y = 2 \sin x$. (B) The graph of $y = 2 \sin 3x$. (C) The graph of $y = 2 \sin 3 \left(x \pm \dfrac{\pi}{2}\right)$.

Exercises

Graph the following functions for $-2\pi \le x \le 2\pi$.

1. $y = 2 \sin x$ **2.** $y = 3 \cos x$ **3.** $y = -\frac{1}{3} \cos x$

4. $y = -\frac{1}{2} \sin x$ **5.** $y = 2 + \sin x$ **6.** $y = 1 + \cos x$

7. $y = \sin(-x)$ **8.** $y = \cos(-x)$ **9.** $y = \cos 2x$

10. $y = \sin 3x$ **11.** $y = |\sin x|$ **12.** $y = |\cos x|$

13. $y = \cos 2\pi x$ **14.** $y = \sin 4\pi x$ **15.** $y = \sin\left(x - \frac{\pi}{3}\right)$

16. $y = \cos\left(x + \frac{\pi}{6}\right)$ **17.** $y = \cos\left(x - \frac{\pi}{2}\right)$ **18.** $y = \sin\left(x - \frac{\pi}{2}\right)$

19. $y = \sin(2x + \pi)$ **20.** $y = \cos\left(3x - \frac{3\pi}{2}\right)$ **21.** $y = 2\cos\left(3x - \frac{3\pi}{2}\right)$

Tangent function

Let θ be an angle in standard position and let (x, y) be any point on its terminal side. Define the function

$$\tan \theta = \frac{y}{x} \quad \text{if} \quad x \ne 0$$

The symbol $\tan \theta$ is read "tangent theta" (see Figure 6-31A).

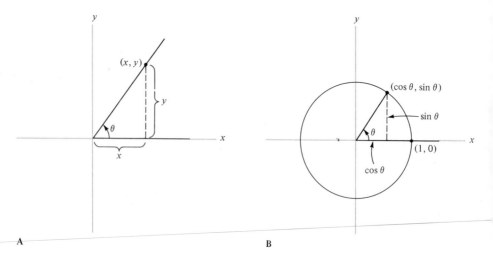

Figure 6-31
(A) $\tan \theta = y/x$, if $x \ne 0$. (B) $\tan \theta = \sin \theta / \cos \theta$, if $\cos \theta \ne 0$. See Exercise 23.

22.   The tangent is undefined for $\theta = \pi/2$. In fact, it is undefined for $\theta = \pi/2 + n\pi$ if $n = 0, \pm 1, \pm 2, \ldots$ Why?

23.   Show that whenever $\tan \theta$ is defined, we have

$$\tan \theta = \frac{\sin \theta}{\cos \theta}$$

(see Figure 6-31B). We shall graph the tangent function in the next section, so you should get used to equations like $y = \tan x$, in which the independent variable is x instead of θ.

24.   Find the value of $\tan x$ if $x = 0, \pi/6, \pi/4$, and $\pi/3$. You may find that the formula $\tan x = \sin x/\cos x$, obtained in Exercise 23, is easier to use than the definition.

25.   In which quadrants is $\tan x$ positive? In which is it negative?

26. $\tan(-x) = $ _____ $\tan\left(x - \dfrac{\pi}{2}\right) = $ _____   (Use $\tan x$ $= \sin x/\cos x$.)

$\tan\left(x + \dfrac{\pi}{2}\right) = $ _____ $\tan(x + \pi) = $ _____

$\tan(\pi - x) = $ _____ $\tan(x + 2\pi) = $ _____

27.   Show that the tangent is periodic with period π.

28.   If the angle of elevation of the sun is $30°$ and the shadow of a flagpole is $20\sqrt{3} \approx 34$ feet long, how tall is the flagpole? [Draw a picture; you may want to use the tangent function defined above.]

29.   A particle moves harmonically on a line between $x = -3$ and $x = 3$. It starts at $x = 0$ and makes 5 oscillations per second. Write a function that describes its motion (see Example 4).

30.   A guitar string is displaced 10 mm (millimeters) by a thumb and is then released. In the absence of a damping effect, the string will make 120 vibrations (complete oscillations) per second. What function describes the motion of the point on the string that was under the thumb?

31.   If the wheel in Figure 6-14 (Section 6-2) starts with P at the point $(0, -1)$ and makes 3 revolutions per second, write a function that describes the harmonic motion of the point Q on the piston head.

32.   Fill in the blanks in the table on the next page.

Degrees	Radians	sin	cos	tan
0	0	0	1	0
30	$\pi/6$	$\frac{1}{2}$	$\frac{\sqrt{3}}{2}$	$\frac{1}{\sqrt{3}}$
45	$\pi/4$	$\frac{\sqrt{2}}{2}$	$\frac{\sqrt{2}}{2}$	1
60	$\pi/3$	$\frac{\sqrt{3}}{2}$	$\frac{1}{2}$	$\sqrt{3}$
90	$\pi/2$	1	0	Undef.
120	$2\pi/3$	$\frac{\sqrt{3}}{2}$	$-\frac{1}{2}$	$-\sqrt{3}$
135	$3\pi/4$	$\frac{\sqrt{2}}{2}$	$-\frac{\sqrt{2}}{2}$	-1
150	$5\pi/6$	$\frac{1}{2}$	$-\frac{\sqrt{3}}{2}$	$-\frac{1}{\sqrt{3}}$
180	π	0	-1	0
210	$7\pi/6$	$-\frac{1}{2}$	$-\frac{\sqrt{3}}{2}$	$\frac{1}{\sqrt{3}}$
270	$3\pi/2$	-1	0	undef.
315	$7\pi/4$	$-\frac{\sqrt{2}}{2}$	$\frac{\sqrt{2}}{2}$	-1

33. Make up and graph a function of the form $y = \sin bx$ and one of the form $y = a\cos(bx + c)$.

34. Make up and solve a problem on simple harmonic motion (similar to Exercises 29, 30, and 31).

35. What sort of function do you think would represent damped harmonic motion; that is, harmonic motion in which the amplitude gradually becomes smaller and smaller (as with an actual vibrating guitar string)?

36. Show that the period of $y = a\sin(bx + c)$ is $2\pi/b$, if $b \neq 0$.

6-5
Other Trigonometric Functions and Their Graphs

In addition to the sine and cosine, there are four other trigonometric functions in common use. All four can be defined in terms of the sine and the cosine.

tangent: $\tan\theta = \dfrac{\sin\theta}{\cos\theta}$

cotangent: $\cot\theta = \dfrac{1}{\tan\theta} = \dfrac{\cos\theta}{\sin\theta}$

secant: $\sec\theta = \dfrac{1}{\cos\theta}$

cosecant: $\csc\theta = \dfrac{1}{\sin\theta}$

■   All properties and all values of these four functions are determined by the corresponding information for sine and cosine.

Example 1
Find $\tan(\pi/6)$, $\cot(\pi/4)$, $\sec(\pi/3)$, and $\csc(\pi/2)$.

Solution

$$\tan(\pi/6) = \sin(\pi/6)/\cos(\pi/6)$$

$$= \frac{1/2}{\sqrt{3}/2} = \frac{1}{\sqrt{3}}$$

$$\cot(\pi/4) = \cos(\pi/4)/\sin(\pi/4)$$

$$= \frac{\sqrt{2}/2}{\sqrt{2}/2} = 1$$

$$\sec(\pi/3) = 1/\cos(\pi/3)$$

$$= \frac{1}{1/2} = 2$$

$$\csc(\pi/2) = 1/\sin(\pi/2) = 1$$

Example 2
Show that $\tan(-\theta) = -\tan\theta$, $\cot\left(\dfrac{\pi}{2} - \theta\right) = \tan\theta$, and $\sec(\pi - \theta) = -\sec\theta$.

Solution

$$\tan(-\theta) = \sin(-\theta)/\cos(-\theta)$$

$$= -\sin\theta/\cos\theta$$

$$= -\tan\theta$$

$$\cot\left(\frac{\pi}{2} - \theta\right) = \cos\left(\frac{\pi}{2} - \theta\right)\Big/\sin\left(\frac{\pi}{2} - \theta\right)$$

$$= \sin\theta/\cos\theta$$

$$= \tan\theta$$

Thus, tangent and cotangent are complementary functions.

$$\sec(\pi - \theta) = 1/\cos(\pi - \theta)$$

$$= 1/-\cos\theta$$

$$= -\sec\theta$$

Let us now examine the graphs of these functions.

Tangent

Make a table of values of $y = \tan x$ for $0 \le x < \pi/2$.

x	0	$\pi/6$	$\pi/4$	$\pi/3$	$\pi/2$
$\sin x$	0	$1/2$	$\sqrt{2}/2$	$\sqrt{3}/2$	1
$\cos x$	1	$\sqrt{3}/2$	$\sqrt{2}/2$	$1/2$	0
$\tan x = \sin x/\cos x$	0	$1/\sqrt{3}$	1	$\sqrt{3}$	Undef.

Notice that $y = \tan x$ increases as x increases, and that it is undefined at $x = \pi/2$. So far, then, the graph looks like Figure 6-32A. Because $\tan(-x) = -\tan x$ (Example 2), you can easily draw the graph for $-\pi/2 < x < \pi/2$, as in Figure 6-32B. The vertical dashed lines at $\pm\pi/2$ are asymptotes of the curve. Notice that the *tangent is periodic with period* π, not 2π because

$$\tan(x + \pi) = \frac{\sin(x + \pi)}{\cos(x + \pi)}$$

$$= \frac{-\sin x}{-\cos x}$$

$$= \tan x$$

The full graph of the tangent function is shown in Figure 6-32C.

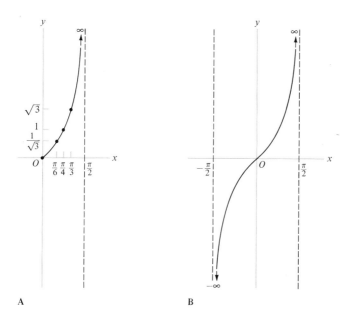

A

B

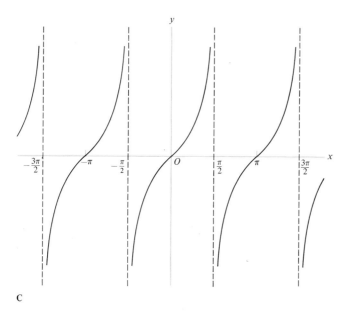

C

Figure 6-32
The graph of $y = \tan x$ (A) for $0 \leq x < \pi/2$; (B) for $-\pi/2 < x < \pi/2$; and (C) for several cycles.

Cotangent

The cotangent is the reciprocal of the tangent. When $|\tan x|$ is very large, $\cot x$ is close to 0; when $\tan x$ is close to 0, $|\cot x|$ is very large. Therefore, the graph of $y = \cot x$ crosses the x-axis at $\pm\pi/2$, $\pm 3\pi/2$, . . . , and the lines $x = 0$, $\pm\pi$, $\pm 2\pi$, . . . are asymptotes (see Figure 6-33).

Secant and cosecant

The secant is the reciprocal of the cosine. Figure 6-34 shows the graph of $y = \cos x$ as a dashed curve, and the graph of $y = \sec x$ as a solid curve. The cosecant and the sine are also reciprocals of each other. Figure 6-35 shows their graphs.

Our observations in Section 6-4 concerning stretching, shrinking, and translation of the graphs of $\sin x$ and $\cos x$ also apply to the graphs of the other trigonometric functions.

Example 3

Graph $y = 3 \tan\left(2x - \dfrac{\pi}{2}\right)$ for $-\pi \le x \le \pi$.

Solution

First, rewrite the function as $y = 3 \tan 2\left(x - \dfrac{\pi}{4}\right)$. The constant 3 stretches the graph of $y = \tan x$ vertically. The constant 2 shrinks the graph of $3 \tan x$ horizontally, because the period of $\tan 2x$ is $\pi/2$ rather than π. Finally, re-

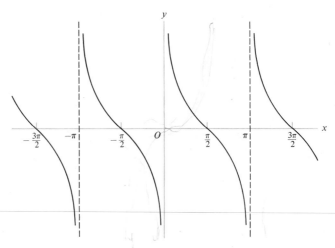

Figure 6-33
The graph of $y = \cot x$.

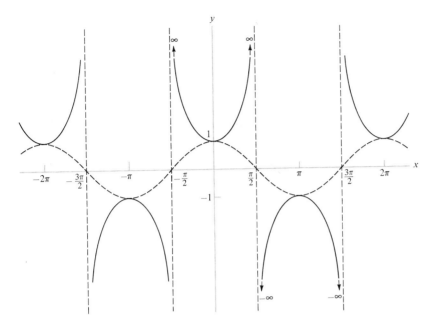

Figure 6-34
The secant is the reciprocal of the cosine. The dashed curve is the graph of $y = \cos x$, and
the solid curves are the graph of $y = \sec x$. Wherever $\cos x = 0$, $y = \sec x$ has an asymptote
(vertical dashed line).

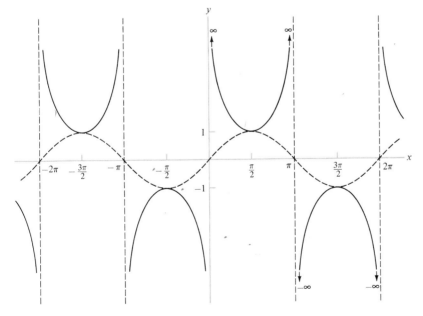

Figure 6-35
The graphs of $y = \sin x$ (dashed curve) and $y = \csc x$ (solid curves).

placing x with $x - \frac{\pi}{4}$ translates the graph of $3 \tan 2x$ to the right $\pi/4$ units. Figure 6-36 shows these three stages in sketching the graph of $y = 3 \tan\left(2x - \frac{\pi}{2}\right)$.

Review of basic ideas
Memorize the definitions

$$\tan x = \frac{\sin x}{\cos x} \qquad \cot x = \frac{\cos x}{\sin x} \qquad \sec x = \frac{1}{\cos x} \qquad \csc x = \frac{1}{\sin x}$$

Fill in the blanks of the table below. If you have forgotten some of the values of sine and cosine, draw a picture as an aid.

Rad.	Deg.	sin	cos	tan	cot	sec	csc
0	0	0	1	0	Undef.	1	Undef.
$\pi/6$	30	$1/2$	$\sqrt{3}/2$	$1/\sqrt{3}$	$\sqrt{3}$	$2/\sqrt{3}$	2
$\pi/4$	45	$\sqrt{2}/2$	$\sqrt{2}/2$	1	1	$2/\sqrt{2}$	$2/\sqrt{2}$
$\pi/3$	60	$\sqrt{3}/2$	$1/2$	$\sqrt{3}$	$1/\sqrt{3}$	2	$2/\sqrt{3}$
$\pi/2$	90	1	0	Undef.	0	undef.	1
$3\pi/4$	135	$\sqrt{2}/2$	$-\sqrt{2}/2$	-1	-1	$-2/\sqrt{2}$	$2/\sqrt{2}$
π	180	0	-1	0	undf.	-1	undf.
$4\pi/3$	240	$-\sqrt{3}/2$	$-1/2$	$\sqrt{3}$	$1/\sqrt{2}$	-2	$-2/\sqrt{3}$
$3\pi/2$	270	-1	0	undf.	0	undf.	-1
$5\pi/3$	300	$-\sqrt{3}/2$	$1/2$	$-\sqrt{3}$	$-1/\sqrt{3}$	2	$-2/\sqrt{3}$

Exercises

Graph the following functions for $-\pi \le x \le \pi$.

1. $y = \frac{1}{2} \tan x$
2. $y = 2 \cot x$
3. $y = 2 \sec x$
4. $y = \frac{1}{2} \csc x$
5. $y = |\cot x|$
6. $y = |\tan x|$

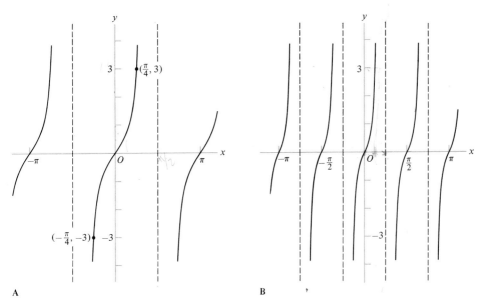

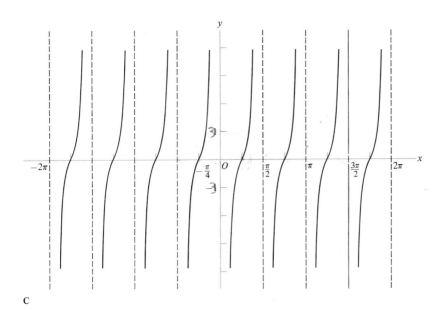

Figure 6-36

Steps in sketching the graph of $y = 3 \tan \left(2x - \dfrac{\pi}{2}\right)$. (A) The graph of $y = 3 \tan x$. (B) The

graph of $y = 3 \tan 2x$. (C) The graph of $y = 3 \tan 2\left(x - \dfrac{\pi}{4}\right) = 3 \tan \left(2x - \dfrac{\pi}{2}\right)$.

7. $y = |\frac{1}{2} \csc x|$ 8. $y = \sec(-x)$ 9. $y = \tan(-x)$
10. $y = 1 + \tan x$ 11. $y = -2 + \cot x$ 12. $y = \frac{1}{2} - \csc x$
13. $y = \tan 2x$ 14. $y = \cot 2x$ 15. $y = \sec 2x$

16. $y = \csc 2x$ 17. $y = \cot\left(x - \dfrac{\pi}{2}\right)$ 18. $y = \tan\left(x - \dfrac{\pi}{4}\right)$

19. $y = \sec(2x + \pi)$ 20. $y = \csc(2x + \pi)$ 21. $y = \tan\left(2x - \dfrac{\pi}{2}\right)$

22. In which quadrants are the tangent, cotangent, secant, and cosecant positive? In which are they negative?

23. What is the period of each of six trigonometric functions?

24. What is the domain and range of each of the six trigonometric functions?

25. $\sec(-x) = $ _____   26. $\csc(-x) = $ _____
27. $\cot(u + \pi) = $ _____   28. $\tan(u + \pi) = $ _____
29. $\csc(u - \pi) = $ _____   30. $\sec(u - \pi) = $ _____
31. $\tan(\pi - t) = $ _____   32. $\cot(\pi - t) = $ _____

33. $\sec\left(\dfrac{\pi}{2} - v\right) = $ _____   34. $\csc\left(\dfrac{\pi}{2} - v\right) = $ _____

35. $\cot\left(\dfrac{\pi}{2} + s\right) = $ _____   36. $\tan\left(\dfrac{\pi}{2} + s\right) = $ _____

Find all solutions of the following equations.

37. $\tan x = \sqrt{3}$ 38. $\cot x = 0$
39. $\sec x = -2/\sqrt{3}$ 40. $\csc x = -2$
41. $\cot 2x = -1$ 42. $\tan 2x = 0$
43. $\csc 3x = 2$ 44. $\sec 4x = 1$

■ 45. (Inverses) The trigonometric functions, being periodic, are not one-to-one on their entire domain. Examine the graph of each of these functions, and pick out a part of its domain on which it is one-to-one. On this part, it will have an inverse. For each function, specify the domain and range of the inverse and sketch the graph. (These inverses will be discussed in Chapter 8, in which you can compare your ideas with those of other mathematicians.)

For example, look at the graph of $y = \sin x$ and choose the domain $-\pi/2 \le x \le \pi/2$. The sine function is one-to-one on this domain and, therefore, it will have an inverse, written $\sin^{-1}x$. The domain of the inverse is $-1 \le x \le 1$, because that is the range of the sine; the range of the inverse is $-\pi/2 \le y \le \pi/2$. (Why?) Now sketch the graph of $y = \sin^{-1}x$ as the reflection of the graph of $y = \sin x$

(on $-\pi/2 \leq x \leq \pi/2$) through the line $y = x$. Compare your sketch with the one in Figure 8-1.

46.   In Figure 6-37 the vertical line L is *tangent* to the unit circle at $(1, 0)$. Find the distance d.

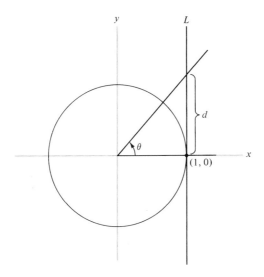

Figure 6-37
The circle and tangent line L in Exercise 46.

Chapter 7

Triangle Trigonometry

The title "Triangle Trigonometry" refers to the classical approach, the original conception of trigonometry as the study of "the ratios of sides of a right triangle." There are some disadvantages to this approach. For one thing, the angles are confined to triangles and, therefore, may range only from 0° to 180°. Another disadvantage is that negative angles make no sense in a triangle. Finally, the ability to describe angular speed and harmonic motion is sacrificed. However, there is one big advantage to the triangle method—it is easy to visualize and to apply to certain types of geometric problems.

Section 7-1 explains how to use trigonometric tables. In Section 7-2, the sine, cosine, and tangent are examined in terms of certain ratios of the sides of a right triangle. Using these ratios and a trigonometric table of values, it is possible to "solve" a right triangle. This means that if you know some parts of a right triangle, say an acute angle and one side, then it is possible to determine the remaining angle and sides.

To solve nonright, or oblique, triangles, we develop the Law of Cosines (Section 7-3) and the Law of Sines (Section 7-4). With the help of these laws, it is possible to solve all triangles. Finally, Section 7-5 introduces the notion of a vector. A vector may be used to represent any quantity, such as force or velocity, that has both magnitude and direction. Triangle trigonometry is combined with vectors to solve force and navigation problems.

7-1
Reference Angles.
Trigonometric Tables

The values of the trigonometric functions are known for all real numbers. Table 2 at the back of this book (p. 488) lists the approximate values for degrees from 0° to 90°, in increments of 10 minutes (60 minutes = 60′ = 1 degree). The corresponding entries for radians from 0 to $\pi/2$ are also given. These values are correct to four places. Although the table ranges only from $0°$ to $90°$, the values for all other angles can be derived from these.

The values of a trigonometric function at $\theta°$ is equal to the value of its cofunction at $(90 - \theta)°$. Thus, sin $15° =$ cos $75°$ and tan $42° =$ cot $48°$. This fact has been used to shorten Table 2. On the left, angles are listed from $0°$ to $45°$ and the columns are headed by Sin, Cos, and so on. On the right, the angles run from $45°$ to $90°$ and each column is footed by the name of the cofunction of the function that heads the column (see Figure 7-1).

Example 1
Find (a) sin $43°20'$ and   (b) sec $88°40'$.

Degrees	Radians	Sin	Cos	Tan	Cot	Sec	Csc		
0° 00′	.0000	.0000	1.0000	.0000	—	1.000	—	1.5708	**90° 00′**
10	.0029	.0029	1.0000	.0029	343.8	1.000	343.8	1.5679	50
20	.0058	.0058	1.0000	.0058	171.9	1.000	171.9	1.5650	40
30	.0087	.0087	1.0000	.0087	114.6	1.000	114.6	1.5621	30
40	.0116	.0116	.9999	.0116	85.94	1.000	85.95	1.5592	20
50	.0145	.0145	.9999	.0145	68.75	1.000	68.76	1.5563	10
1° 00′	.0175	.0175	.9998	.0175	57.29	1.000	57.30	1.5533	**89° 00′**
10	.0204	.0204	.9998	.0204	49.10	1.000	49.11	1.5504	50
20	.0233	.0233	.9997	.0233	42.96	1.000	42.98	1.5475	40
30	.0262	.0262	.9997	.0262	38.19	1.000	38.20	1.5446	30
40	.0291	.0291	.9996	.0291	34.37	1.000	34.38	1.5417	20
50	.0320	.0320	.9995	.0320	31.24	1.001	31.26	1.5388	10
2° 00′	.0349	.0349	.9994	.0349	28.64	1.001	28.65	1.5359	**88° 00′**
43° 00′	.7505	.6820	.7314	.9325	1.072	1.367	1.466	.8203	**47° 00′**
10	.7534	.6841	.7294	.9380	1.066	1.371	1.462	.8174	50
20	.7563	.6862	.7274	.9435	1.060	1.375	1.457	.8145	40
30	.7592	.6884	.7254	.9490	1.054	1.379	1.453	.8116	30
40	.7621	.6905	.7234	.9545	1.048	1.382	1.448	.8087	20
50	.7650	.6926	.7214	.9601	1.042	1.386	1.444	.8058	10
44° 00′	.7679	.6947	.7193	.9657	1.036	1.390	1.440	.8029	**46° 00′**
10	.7709	.6967	.7173	.9713	1.030	1.394	1.435	.8999	50
20	.7738	.6988	.7153	.9770	1.024	1.398	1.431	.8970	40
30	.7767	.7009	.7133	.9827	1.018	1.402	1.427	.7941	30
40	.7796	.7030	.7112	.9884	1.012	1.406	1.423	.7912	20
50	.7825	.7050	.7092	.9942	1.006	1.410	1.418	.7883	10
45° 00′	.7854	.7071	.7071	1.000	1.000	1.414	1.414	.7854	**45° 00′**
		Cos	**Sin**	**Cot**	**Tan**	**Csc**	**Sec**	**Radians**	**Degrees**

Figure 7-1
A small part of Table 2, "Values of Trigonometric Functions," pp. 488–492. See Example 1.

Solution

(a)   In Figure 7-1, find $43°20'$ listed on the left and read across to the column headed by Sin. Thus, sin $43°20' \approx .6862$.

(b)   In Figure 7-1, find $88°40'$ on the *right*. Now read across to the column *footed* by Sec to find sec $88°40' \approx 42.98$.

Example 2

Find (a) cos .1047   and   (b) tan 1.2683.

Solution

Here the unit of measure is radians.

(a)   In Table 2, read down the second column on the left to the entry .1047 and then across to the column headed by Cos. Thus, cos .1047 $\approx .9945$.

(b)   Again look in Table 2, but this time read *up* the second column from the *right* to 1.2683. Now read across to the column *footed* by Tan. It shows that tan 1.2683 ≈ 3.204.

Example 3

Given that $0 < x < \pi/2$ and tan $x \approx 2.112$, find x.

Solution

Because tan $x > 1$, you can conclude that $x > \pi/4$ radians (or $45°$). Therefore, look in the columns *footed* by Tan for the entry 2.112. Now read across to the *right* to find $x \approx 1.1286$ radians (or $64°40'$).

Examples 1–3 show how Table 2 can be used for any angle between $0°$ and $90°$. To find values of the trigonometric functions of other angles, there is a device called the *reference angle*.

■   **Definition**

Suppose θ is in standard position. Then the acute angle θ' between the terminal side of θ and the x-axis is called the **reference angle** for θ.

To find θ', the reference angle of θ, first rewrite θ as a nonnegative angle less than 2π ($360°$) with the same terminal side. For example, rewrite $380°$ as $20°$; and rewrite $-5\pi/4$ as $3\pi/4$. Then use one of the following formulas (see Figure 7-2):

θ in first quadrant; $\theta' = \theta$

θ in second quadrant; $\theta' = \pi - \theta$ (or $180° - \theta°$)

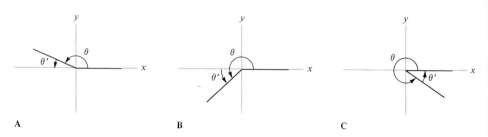

Figure 7-2
Suppose $0 \leq \theta < 2\pi$. (A) If θ is in the second quadrant, then $\theta' = \pi - \theta$. (B) If θ is in the third quadrant, then $\theta' = \theta - \pi$. (C) If θ is in the fourth quadrant, then $\theta' = 2\pi - \theta$.

$$\theta \text{ in third quadrant; } \theta' = \theta - \pi \quad (\text{or } \theta° - 180°)$$

$$\theta \text{ in fourth quadrant; } \theta' = 2\pi - \theta \quad (\text{or } 360° - \theta°)$$

It follows from the various properties of the trigonometric functions that their values at θ and θ' can differ only in sign. For instance, if θ is in the third quadrant, the reference angle is $\theta' = \theta - \pi$. You know that $\sin(\theta - \pi) = -\sin \theta$. Therefore, look up the $\sin \theta'$ in Table 2; then $\sin \theta$ is the negative of that number.

■   To evaluate a trigonometric function at any angle, determine its value at the reference angle and prefix the proper sign.

Example 4
Find (a) $\tan 163°20'$ (b) $\cos 600°$ and (c) $\sec 4.8782$.

Solution
(a) $163°20'$ is in the second quadrant; the reference angle is $180° - 163°20' = 16°40'$. From Table 2, $\tan 16°40' \approx .2994$; however, the tangent is negative in the second quadrant,

$$\tan 163°20' \approx -.2994$$

(b) $600° = 360° + 240°$ lies in the third quadrant. The reference angle is $240° - 180° = 60°$. The cosine is negative in the third quadrant, so

$$\cos 600° = \cos 240° = -\cos 60° = -\tfrac{1}{2}$$

(c)   4.8782 radians is in the fourth quadrant; $2\pi \approx 6.2832$, so the reference angle is $6.2832 - 4.8782 = 1.4050$. The secant is positive in the fourth quadrant, so, from Table 2,

$$\sec 4.878 = \sec 1.405 \approx 6.059$$

In solving problems, the exact angles or numbers needed may not appear in Table 2. When that happens, the easiest thing to do is to *round off* to the nearest entry that does appear in Table 2. The rounding-off method is used in Example 5. However, your professor may want you to use *linear interpolation,* and you should be prepared to do so. The procedure is the same as that used to interpolate logarithms. There are some interpolation exercises at the end of this section.

Example 5

Find all possible values of x if (a) x is in the third quadrant and $\sin x \approx -.6231$; if (b) $\cos x \approx .1849$.

Solution

(a)   In Table 2, look in the *sine* columns for the entry closest to .6231. It is .6225, which is the sine of $38°30'$ or .6720 radians, so $38°30'$ is the reference angle of x. Because x is in the third quadrant, it follows that $x \approx 38°30' + 180° = 218°30'$. But any number of complete revolutions added to this will give an angle in the third quadrant with the same sine. Therefore, the complete answer is

$$x \approx 218°30' + n(360°); \quad n = 0, \pm1, \pm2, \ldots$$

In radians, $x \approx .6720 + \pi + 2n\pi$.

(b)   Look in the *cosine* columns. The closest entry to .1849 is .1851, which is in a column *footed* by Cos. Read across to the *right* to find that .1851 is the cosine of $79°20'$ or 1.3846 radians. You are not told in which quadrant x lies, but because $\cos x$ is positive, you know that x lies in the first or the fourth quadrant. Therefore, $x \approx \pm79°20'$ or ±1.3846 radians. As in part (a), you can add any number of complete revolutions to obtain

$$x \approx \pm79°20' + n(360°); \quad n = 0, \pm1, \pm2, \ldots$$

In radians, $x \approx \pm1.3846 + 2n\pi$.

Example 6

(Snell's law). A fundamental principle of optics is that light travels from one point to another along a path that minimizes the time lapse. That is why a light beam looks "bent" when it travels from one medium to another, for example, from air to water. Figure 7-3 shows a light ray traveling from point A in one medium, where its velocity is V_1, to a point B in a second medium, where its velocity is V_2. The angles θ_1 and θ_2 are the angles between the path of the ray and a vertical line through the boundary between the mediums. Snell's law (which is easily proved in a beginning calculus course) states that, if θ_1 and θ_2 are in radians,

$$\frac{\sin \theta_1}{V_1} = \frac{\sin \theta_2}{V_2}$$

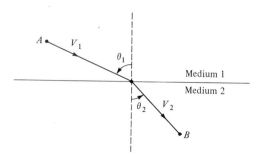

Figure 7-3

Snell's law: $\dfrac{\sin\theta_1}{V_1} = \dfrac{\sin\theta_2}{V_2}$. See Example 6.

If point A is in air, in which $V_1 \approx 186 \times 10^3$ mi/sec, point B is in a medium in which $V_2 \approx 150 \times 10^3$ mi/sec, and $\theta_2 \approx .4300$, find θ_1.

Solution
From Snell's law, it follows that

$$\sin\theta_1 = \frac{V_1 \sin\theta_2}{V_2}$$

$$\approx (186 \times 10^3)(.4173)/(150 \times 10^3)$$

$$\approx .5174$$

There are many angles whose sine is .5174, but Figure 7-3 clearly indicates that this angle must be acute. Look in Table 2 in columns headed or footed by Sin for the entry closest to .5174. You should find $\theta_1 \approx .5440$.

Exercises

Find the value in Table 2. Round off, if necessary, and use the approximation $\pi \approx 3.1416$.

1. $\cos 42°10'$	**2.** $\sin 6°20'$	**3.** $\sin(-64°14')$
4. $\cos(-83°27')$	**5.** $\tan 120°58'$	**6.** $\cot 145°32'$
7. $\cot(-595°20')$	**8.** $\tan 920°$	**9.** $\sec 1003°15'$
10. $\csc 193°38'$	**11.** $\csc 358°$	**12.** $\sec(-234°42')$
13. $\sin 2.6310$	**14.** $\cos 4.6124$	**15.** $\tan(-5.8300)$
16. $\cot(-.8191)$	**17.** $\sec 23$	**18.** $\csc 12.5628$
19. $\cos(-4.1234)$	**20.** $\cot 4.0138$	

As in Example 5, find all possible values of x (round off).
21. x in the third quadrant and $\cos x \approx -.8861$
22. x in the fourth quadrant and $\cos x \approx .1381$
23. $\tan x \approx -1.3411$ **24.** $\csc x \approx 2.8157$
25. $\pi < x < 3\pi/2$ and $\cot x \approx 1.414$
26. $0 < x < \pi/2$ and $\sec x \approx 1.3804$
27. $\sin x = 0$ **28.** $\cos x = .5$
29. $\tan x = 1$ **30.** $\cot x = 0$

Interpolation

Interpolation with trigonometric tables is exactly the same as with log tables. For example, to find the $\tan 37°14'$, assume that it lies $\frac{4}{10}$ of the way between $\tan 37°10' \approx .7581$ and $\tan 37°20' \approx .7627$. Thus,

$$\tan 37°14' \approx .7581 + \tfrac{4}{10}(.7627 - .7581)$$

$$= .7581 + .0018$$

$$= .7599$$

Use interpolation to find
31. $\sin 14°28'$ **32.** $\cot 50°26'$
33. $\cos .6380$ **34.** $\tan .4630$

Here is another example. Find x if $90° < x < 180°$ and $\cos x° \approx -.9500$. The entry .9500 lies $\frac{2}{10}$ of the way between $.9502 \approx \cos 18°10'$ and $.9492 \approx \cos 18°20'$, so $\cos 18°12' \approx .9500$. However, x is in the second quadrant, so $18°12'$ is only the reference angle. It follows that

$$x \approx 180° - 18°12' = 161°48'$$

Use interpolation to find x in degrees and minutes.
35. $0° < x < 180°$ and $\tan x° \approx 1.984$
36. $180° < x < 360°$ and $\cos x° \approx -.9165$

Use interpolation to find x in radians.
37. $\pi < x < 2\pi$ and $\cos x \approx -.4955$
38. $-\pi/2 < x < \pi/2$ and $\sin x \approx .3152$

Exercises 39–40 refer to Snell's law (Example 6).
39. $\theta_1 = .4538, \theta_2 = .5585, V_1 = 186 \times 10^3$. Find V_2.
40. $V_1 = 186 \times 10^3, V_2 = 143 \times 10^3, \theta_2 = 78°10'$. Find θ_1.

41. A particle is traveling in an xy-plane; its coordinates (that is, its location) at any time t is given by the equations $x = \cos t$ and $y = \sin t$. Use Table 2 (round off) to plot its location when $t = 0, 1, 2, 3, 4, 5,$ and 6. What is its path?

42. Use Table 2 to convince yourself that, when h is very close to 0 (positive or negative), then $\sin h \approx 0$, and $\cos h \approx 1$.

43. (There is a wonderful application of this exercise in Exercise 35 of Section 7-2; it is also referred to in Section 8-2.) The ratio

$$\frac{\sin h}{h} \qquad (h \text{ in radians})$$

for values of h close to 0, has many uses. Without using any tables, guess the approximate value of $\dfrac{\sin h}{h}$ for small h. Now use Table 2 to see if your guess was on target. [NOTE: h may be positive or negative.]

44. (Continuation of Exercise 43; this exercise also is referred to in Section 8-2.) Consider the ratio

$$\frac{\cos h - 1}{h} \qquad (h \text{ in radians})$$

Without using any tables, guess its approximate value for very small positive or negative h. Then either check your guess with Table 2 or use this more interesting method: multiply

$$\frac{\cos h - 1}{h} \cdot \frac{\cos h + 1}{\cos h + 1}$$

then apply the identity $\cos^2 h - 1 = -\sin^2 h$ and Exercises 42 and 43. If you have a calculator, use it to compute this ratio for $h = \pm.1, \pm.01,$ and $\pm.001$.

45. (Surprising continuation of 44) Guess the approximate value of

$$\frac{\cos h - 1}{h^2} \qquad (h \text{ in radians})$$

for small h. Then check your guess using either one of the methods suggested in Exercise 44 or your calculator.

7-2
Right Triangles

Let θ be an angle in standard position and A be any point on its terminal side. If A has the coordinates (a, b) and the distance from A to the origin is denoted by c, then $\sin \theta = b/c$, $\cos \theta = a/c$ and $\tan \theta = b/a$. This is how the trigonometric functions

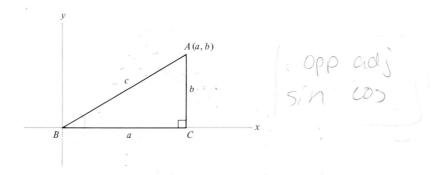

Figure 7-4
A right triangle ABC with the angle B in standard position. The little square in angle C indicates that C is the right angle.

were defined in Chapter 6. In this chapter we shall consider trigonometric functions as ratios of the lengths of sides of a right triangle. In many applications of trigonometry, this approach is the most useful.

Take any right triangle. Place it in an xy-plane so that one of the acute angles, say B, is in standard position and one of the sides is vertical (see Figure 7-4). Suppose that C is the right angle. Suppose the length of side BC is a, the length of side AC is b, and the length of the third side is c. Then the coordinates of point A are (a, b), and it follows that

$$\sin B = \frac{b}{c} \qquad \cos B = \frac{a}{c} \qquad \tan B = \frac{b}{a}$$

■ These ratios depend only on the size of angle B, not on the size of the triangle. Furthermore, the ratios remain the same if the triangle is now moved to any position.

Call AC the **side opposite** B, BC the **side adjacent** to B, and AB the **hypotenuse** (see Figure 7-5A). The ratios above become

$$\sin B = \frac{b}{c} = \frac{\text{side opposite}}{\text{hypotenuse}}$$

$$\cos B = \frac{a}{c} = \frac{\text{side adjacent}}{\text{hypotenuse}}$$

$$\tan B = \frac{b}{a} = \frac{\text{side opposite}}{\text{side adjacent}}$$

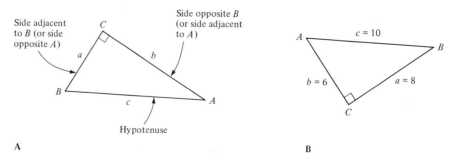

Figure 7-5
(A) Any right triangle. (B) The triangle in Example 1.

Example 1
In the right triangle shown in Figure 7-5B, find sin B and tan A.

Solution

$$\sin B = \frac{\text{side opposite}}{\text{hypotenuse}} = \frac{b}{c} = \frac{6}{10} = \frac{3}{5}$$

$$\tan A = \frac{\text{side opposite}}{\text{side adjacent}} = \frac{a}{b} = \frac{8}{6} = \frac{4}{3}$$

The cotangent, secant, and cosecant can also be defined in this way. Recall that they are the reciprocals of tangent, cosine, and sine, respectively.

$$\text{cotangent} = \frac{\text{side adjacent}}{\text{side opposite}}$$

$$\text{secant} = \frac{\text{hypotenuse}}{\text{side adjacent}}$$

$$\text{cosecant} = \frac{\text{hypotenuse}}{\text{side opposite}}$$

The next example shows how to use the value of one trigonometric function to find the values of others.

Example 2
If $0 < x < \pi/2$ and tan $x = 2$, find sin x and sec x.

Solution
Draw a right triangle with an acute angle x, the side opposite x with length 2, and the side adjacent to x with length 1 (see Figure 7-6A). This triangle satisfies the given conditions, because $\tan x = $ (side opposite)/(side adjacent) $= 2$. By the Theorem of Pythagoras, the hypotenuse then has length $\sqrt{5}$, and you can deduce that

$$\sin x = \frac{\text{side opposite}}{\text{hypotenuse}} = 2/\sqrt{5}$$

$$\sec x = \frac{\text{hypotenuse}}{\text{side adjacent}} = \sqrt{5}$$

Question
If you had drawn a larger triangle, with the side opposite and side adjacent of, say, lengths 10 and 5, would the results have been different? Draw such a triangle and check the results.

Practical applications of trigonometry often require *solving a triangle*. This means using the measurements of some parts of the triangle to find the measurements of all the others.

Example 3
Solve the right triangle in Figure 7-6B.

Solution
$B = 22°$ and $b = 10$ are given; you must find A, a, and c. First, $A = 90° - 22° = 68°$. Next, use $\sin B = $ (side opposite)/(hypotenuse) $= 10/c$

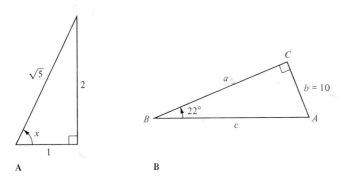

Figure 7-6
(A) Find $\sin x$ and $\sec x$. See Example 2. (B) The right triangle in Example 3.

to solve for c: In Table 2, $\sin 22° \approx .3746$, so $10/c \approx .3746$. It follows that

$$c \approx 10/.3746$$

$$\approx 26.70$$

Similarly, $\tan B = $ (side opposite)/(side adjacent) $= 10/a$. $\tan 22° \approx .4040$, so

$$a \approx 10/.4040$$

$$\approx 24.75$$

Thus, you have solved the triangle. NOTE: You might have chosen to find the unknowns in a different order or in a different way. For example, you could have found c by using the equation $\csc 22° = c/10$.

Example 4

From the top of a building 100 meters high, the angles of depression to two stop signs are $28°30'$ and $57°43'$. If both signs lie in the same direction from the building, how far apart are they?

Solution

Draw a picture. All the information is contained in Figure 7-7. The problem is to find x.

Angle ABC is $90° - 57°43' = 32°17'$, so you can use the equation $\tan 32°17' = b/100$ to solve for b:

$$b = 100 \tan 32°17'$$

$$\approx 100(.6330) \qquad \text{(Round off to } 32°20'.)$$

$$= 63.3 \text{ meters}$$

Angle ABD is $90° - 28°30' = 61°30'$, so you can solve for $b + x$ in triangle ABD. Thus,

$$b + x = 100 \tan 61°30'$$

$$\approx 100(1.842)$$

$$= 184.2 \text{ meters}$$

Thus, the distance between the signs is $(b + x) - b \approx 184.2 - 63.3 = 120.9$ meters.

In navigation, two ways of denoting direction are in common use. One is in degrees measured clockwise from North, as in Figure 7-8A. The other is in degrees east or west of the North–South line, as in Figure 7-8B.

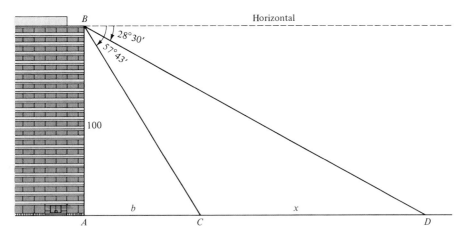

Figure 7-7
The building in Example 4. The stop signs are at C and D.

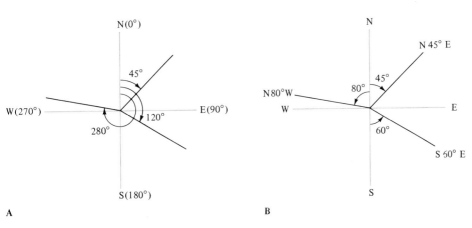

A

B

Figure 7-8
Two ways of showing direction in navigation.

Example 5

A ship leaves New York and sails for 50 miles in the direction S13°E. How far south and east of New York is it?

Solution

Draw a picture. In the triangle of Figure 7-9, solve for x and y.

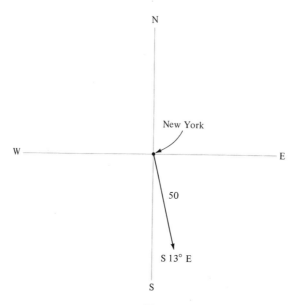

Figure 7-9
The ship in Example 5.

$$x = 50 \sin 13°$$

$$\approx 50(.2250)$$

$$= 11.25 \text{ miles east of New York}$$

$$y = 50 \cos 13°$$

$$\approx 50(.9744)$$

$$= 48.72 \text{ miles south of New York}$$

Exercises

In Exercises 1–18, solve the
triangle below ($\pi/2 \approx 1.5708$).

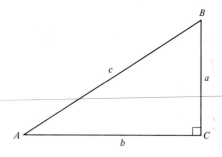

1. $A = 32°, a = 10$
2. $A = 46°40', a = 20$
3. $B = 76°22', b = 4$
4. $B = 49°, b = 5$
5. $A = 59°, b = 2$
6. $A = 13°, b = 4.6$
7. $B = 3°50', a = 2.5$
8. $B = 81°32', a = 7$
9. $A = .4392, c = 10$
10. $A = .5498, c = 20$
11. $B = .3142, c = 1$
12. $B = .1105, c = 3$
13. $a = 3, b = 4$
14. $a = \sqrt{3}, b = 1$
15. $a = 1, c = \sqrt{2}$
16. $a = 4, c = 7$
17. $b = 3, c = 8$
18. $b = 9, c = 13$

In Exercises 19–24, assume that $0 < x < \pi/2$ (see Example 2).

19. If $\tan x = 3$, find $\sin x$ and $\cos x$.
20. If $\sin x = 2/3$, find $\cos x$ and $\tan x$.
21. If $\sec x = \sqrt{5}$, find $\sin x$ and $\cot x$.
22. If $\csc x = 2$, find $\cos x$ and $\tan x$.
23. If $\tan x = 3/4$, find $\sec x$ and $\csc x$.
24. If $\cot x = 1/2$, find $\sin x$ and $\cos x$.

25. If a man 6 feet tall casts a shadow 9 feet long, what is the angle of elevation of the sun?
26. An airplane leaves San Francisco and travels 200 miles in the direction 280° (see Figure 7-8A). How far west and north of San Francisco is it?
27. An airplane leaves Reno bound for Chicago. After traveling 200 miles in a straight line, it is 44 miles north of Reno. In what direction is it flying?
28. An airplane flying at 1000 feet is to drop supplies to a scouting party. When the pilot spots the party, the angle of depression is 27°24'. What is the distance from the plane to the party?
29. A rocket is fired straight up from Cape Canaveral. A tracking unit 1 kilometer from the launch pad observes that the rocket's angle of elevation changes from 45° to 75° in 3 seconds. How far has the rocket traveled in that time period? What is it's average speed in km/sec?
30. From a point on the ground, the angle of elevation to the top of a mountain is 45°. From a point 1 kilometer closer to the base of the mountain, the angle of elevation is 60°. How high is the mountain?
31. When you fly a kite, the angle of elevation of the string should never exceed 50°. If you want to fly a kite to a height of 300 feet, what is the minimum amount of string you must have?
32. Two towns A and B want to draw water from the same pumping station on the river, as pictured in Figure 7-10.

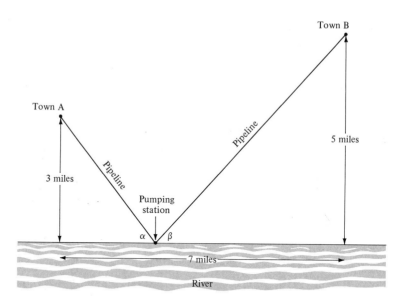

Figure 7-10
Two towns want to draw water from the same pumping station on the river. See Exercise 32.

(a) If $\alpha = 30°$, what is β?
(b) If $\alpha = 30°$, what is the total length of pipe needed?
(c) If you were a city planner who wanted to minimize the length of pipeline needed, approximately where would you locate the pumping station? [HINT: Try $\alpha = 30°$, $45°$, and $60°$; then estimate the answer.]

33. (Used in Exercise 34 and in Section 7-3, Exercise 37) In geometry, it is shown that the area of a triangle is equal to one half the length of its base times its height. Show that the area of triangle ABC in Figure 7-11 is $\frac{1}{2}ab \sin \alpha$, and that the area of triangle DEF is $\frac{1}{2}ed \sin \beta$.

The area of a triangle is equal to one half the product of the lengths of any two sides and the sine of the included angle.

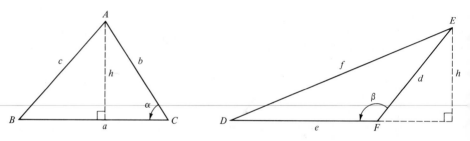

Figure 7-11
Show that the area of triangle ABC is $\frac{1}{2}ab \sin \alpha$, and that the area of triangle DEF is $\frac{1}{2}ed \sin \beta$. See Exercise 33.

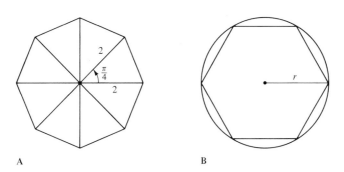

Figure 7-12
(A) The octagon in Exercise 34. (B) A six-sided regular polygon (a regular hexagon) inscribed in a circle C with radius r. See Exercise 35.

34.   (Area of a polygon) Figure 7-12A shows an eight-sided regular polygon (an octagon) that is divided into eight congruent isosceles triangles. In each triangle, the equal sides are 2 units long and the angle at the center of the octagon measures $2\pi/8 = \pi/4$ or $45°$. According to the formula in Exercise 33, the area of each triangle is $\frac{1}{2} \cdot 2 \cdot 2 \sin (\pi/4) = \sqrt{2}$. It follows that the area of the octagon is $8\sqrt{2}$. If P is an n-sided regular polygon in which the distance from the center to any vertex is r, show that

$$\text{area of } P = \frac{n}{2}r^2 \sin \frac{2\pi}{n}$$

35.   (Area of a circle) Let C be a circle of radius r. A regular polygon of any number of sides may be inscribed in C. Figure 7-12B shows a six-sided regular polygon inscribed in C. The area of an inscribed polygon is approximately the area of the circle. It seems logical that, the larger the number of sides of the inscribed polygon, the closer the approximation will be. Use the formula in Exercise 34 and the information from Exercise 43 in Section 7-1 to show that the area of the circle C is indeed πr^2. This is a slick adaptation of what Archimedes did more than 2000 years ago to arrive at the formula for the area of a circle! [NOTE: The solution requires a simple but not obvious algebraic manipulation. It is outlined in the Answers to Selected Exercises.]

36.   It is possible to solve oblique (nonright) triangles. Can you think of a way to solve the triangle below if $C = 30°$, $b = 4$, and $c = 2\sqrt{2}$?
37.   Same as Exercise 36 if $B = \pi/3$, $C = \pi/4$ and $c = 1$.

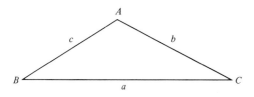

7-3
Law of Cosines. Polar Coordinates

In the preceding section, we solved right triangles in which the lengths of two sides were known, or the length of one side and the size of an acute angle were known. If a triangle does not contain a right angle, it is called an **oblique triangle.** To solve such triangles, we must develop new methods.

Every triangle has six parts, three angles and three sides. In this section and the next, whenever "triangle *ABC*," or simply "a triangle," is referred to, let us agree that its parts are labeled as in Figure 7-13. The letters will also indicate the magnitude of each part. With enough information, trigonometry can be used to solve oblique triangles.

How much information is enough? Knowing only one or two of the six parts is insufficient. Furthermore, knowing all three angles is also insufficient. (Why?) The minimum information needed falls into four categories (S stands for *side* and A stands for *angle*):

SSS: all three sides

SAS: two sides and the included angle

AAS: two angles and any side

SSA: two sides and an angle not included

The first two categories are discussed here and the remaining two will be discussed in the next section.

The Law of Cosines is a relationship between all three sides and one angle of a triangle.

■   **Law of Cosines**
In any triangle, the square of one side equals the sum of the squares of the other two sides minus twice the product of the two sides and the cosine of the angle

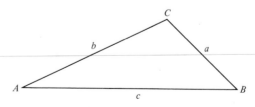

Figure 7-13
The six parts of a triangle.

between them. In symbols,

$$a^2 = b^2 + c^2 - 2bc \cos A$$

The validity of this equation can be proved as follows. Given any triangle ABC, place it in an xy-plane so that angle A is in standard position. Angle A can be any number between 0 and π. Figure 7-14 shows an acute angle, but the argument does not depend on this fact. Now find the coordinates of the points C and B, and express a as the distance between these points. The coordinates of B are $(c, 0)$. The point C is on the terminal side of A at a distance of b units from the origin. If the coordinates of C are (x, y), it follows that $\cos A = x/b$ and $\sin A = y/b$; therefore, $x = b \cos A$ and $y = b \sin A$ (see Figure 7-14). The distance formula yields

$$a = \sqrt{(c - b \cos A)^2 + (0 - b \sin A)^2}$$

Now square both sides and simplify:

$$a^2 = (c - b \cos A)^2 + (0 - b \sin A)^2$$
$$= c^2 - 2bc \cos A + b^2\cos^2 A + b^2\sin^2 A$$
$$= b^2(\cos^2 A + \sin^2 A) + c^2 - 2bc \cos A$$
$$= b^2 + c^2 - 2bc \cos A$$

which is the equation we wanted to prove. Notice that sides a, b, and c, may be interchanged in this equation, if the angle is also changed to the appropriate included angle. Thus,

$$b^2 = a^2 + c^2 - 2ac \cos B \quad \text{and} \quad c^2 = a^2 + b^2 - 2ab \cos C$$

are also valid.

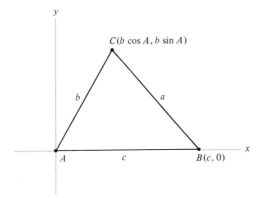

Figure 7-14
Proving the Law of Cosines.

Because the Law of Cosines relates the lengths of all three sides to the cosine of an included angle, it is used to solve triangle problems of the SSS or SAS type.

Example 1
If a triangle has sides $a = 10$, $b = 5$, and $c = 8$, find the angles.

Solution
The information given is SSS. Choose any one of the three forms of the Law of Cosines to find an angle. For instance,

$$a^2 = b^2 + c^2 - 2bc \cos A$$

yields

$$10^2 = 5^2 + 8^2 - 2 \cdot 5 \cdot 8 \cos A$$

and therefore,

$$\cos A = -\frac{11}{80} = -.1375$$

In Table 2, the angle whose cosine is closest to .1375 is $82°10'$. This is the reference angle. Because $\cos A$ is negative, A must be in the second quadrant; therefore, $A \approx 180° - 82°10' = 97°50'$. By the same procedure, it is possible to find angle B. Then $C = 180° - (A + B)°$.

Example 2
Solve the triangle ABC if $a = 10$, $b = 5$, and $C = 38°$.

Solution
This information is the SAS type. Choose the appropriate form of the Law of Cosines to solve for the side opposite the given angle; that is,

$$c^2 = a^2 + b^2 - 2ab \cos C$$

Thus,

$$c^2 = 10^2 + 5^2 - 2 \cdot 10 \cdot 5 \cos 38°$$
$$\approx 46.20$$

Now use logarithms, or a calculator, to find $c \approx \sqrt{46} \approx 6.8$. Having found c, you know all three sides, so you can use the method of Example 1 to find angles A and B.

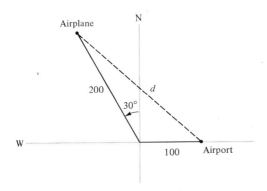

Figure 7-15
The path of the airplane in Example 4.

Example 3
A piece of wire 23 inches long is bent into a triangular shape. One side is 10 inches and another is 8 inches long. What are the angles of the triangle?

Solution
This information is the SSS type: the sides are 10, 8, and 5. In fact, the triangle is the triangle of Example 1, and therefore has the same angles.

Example 4
An airplane leaves O'Hare Airport, in Chicago; it flies due west for 100 miles, and then 200 miles in the direction N30°W. How far is it from the airport?

Solution
Figure 7-15 shows this to be a problem of the SAS type. The sides are 100 and 200, and the included angle is 120°. Solve the triangle for the distance d as in Example 2:

$$d^2 = (100)^2 + (200)^2 - 2(100)(200) \cos 120°$$

$$d \approx 265 \text{ miles}$$

Polar coordinates
One way to locate a point in an xy-plane is to write its rectangular coordinates (x, y). For some uses (reading a radar screen, for example) it is more useful to locate a point by specifying its distance r from the origin and its direction θ from the positive x-axis (see Figure 7-16). The pair $\{r, \theta\}$ used to locate a point in this way are called **polar coordinates**. (In this book, polar coordinates are printed in braces instead of parentheses to distinguish them from rectangular coordinates.) Thus, the point $\{3, \pi/6\}$ is

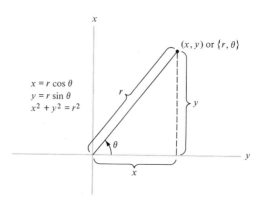

Figure 7-16
Rectangular coordinates (x, y) and polar coordinates $\{r, \theta\}$.

located three units from the origin on the terminal side of the angle $\pi/6$. The point $\{2, 160°\}$ lies two units from the origin on the terminal side of the angle $160°$.

As Figure 7-16 shows, the rectangular and polar systems are related by the equations

$$x^2 + y^2 = r^2 \qquad x = r\cos\theta \qquad y = r\sin\theta$$

Using these equations, it is easy to convert from one system into the other.

Example 5
(a)   Locate the points $\{1, 5\pi/4\}$ and $\{2, -60°\}$.
(b)   Change $\{2, -60°\}$ to rectangular coordinates.
(c)   Change $(-1, \sqrt{3})$ to polar coordinates.

Solution
(a)

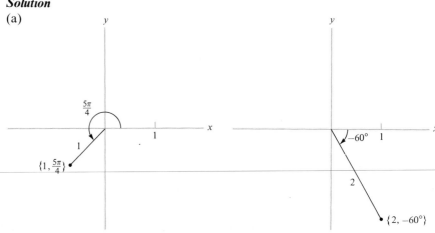

(b) To find the rectangular coordinates of $\{2, -60°\}$, use the conversion equations:

$$x = r \cos \theta \qquad\qquad y = r \sin \theta$$

$$= 2 \cos(-60°) \qquad\qquad = 2 \sin(-60°)$$

$$= 1 \qquad\qquad\qquad = -\sqrt{3}$$

Thus, the rectangular coordinates are $(1, -\sqrt{3})$.
(c) To find the polar coordinates of $(-1, \sqrt{3})$, first find r:

$$r^2 = x^2 + y^2$$

$$= (-1)^2 + (\sqrt{3})^2$$

$$= 4$$

Thus, $r = 2$. By definition, $\cos \theta = x/r = -1/2$ and $\sin \theta = y/r = \sqrt{3}/2$. It follows that θ is in the second quadrant, and $\theta = 2\pi/3$, or $120°$.

Here is a practical application of polar coordinates (more appear in the Exercises).

Example 6
The radar screen at the Denver airport reads out in miles and degrees. It shows a mountaintop at $\{100, 120°\}$ and a plane at $\{150, 65°\}$. How far is the plane from the mountaintop?

Solution
Figure 7-17 shows this is an SAS type problem, with sides 100 and 150 and an included angle of 55°. Solve for the distance as in Example 2 or 4.

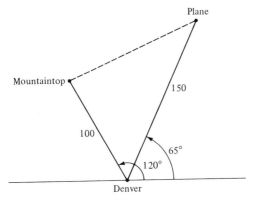

Figure 7-17
The picture on the radar screen in Example 6.

Exercises

Solve the triangle ABC using the Law of Cosines and the following information.

1. $a = 2, b = 4, c = 5$ 2. $a = 14, b = 20, c = 12$
3. $a = 4.6, b = 9.8, c = 10$ 4. $a = 5.3, b = 2.1, c = 4.4$
5. $A = 22°, b = 6, c = 8$ 6. $A = 14°, b = 7, c = 3$
7. $B = 135°, a = 3, c = 2$ 8. $B = 95°, a = 4, c = 5$
9. $C = 2°, a = 100, b = 1$ 10. $C = 178°, a = 1, b = 2$

In Exercises 11–16, state whether or not the Law of Cosines can be used to solve the triangle.

11. $A = 30°, B = 50°, C = 100°$ 12. $A = 20°, b = 4, c = 7$
13. $A = 14°, b = 7, a = 5$ 14. $C = 81°, A = 75°, b = 4$
15. $c = 3, b = 8, B = 10°$ 16. $a = 5, b = 10, c = 20$
17. If your answer to Exercise 16 was *yes,* then go ahead and solve the triangle.

Locate the following points given in polar coordinates.

18. $\{2, 45°\}$ 19. $\{4, 120°\}$ 20. $\{1, 3\pi/2\}$ 21. $\{2, -\pi/4\}$

Change to rectangular coordinates.

22. $\{2, 60°\}$ 23. $\{1, 135°\}$ 24. $\{3, \pi\}$ 25. $\{2, -\pi/6\}$

Change to polar coordinates.

26. $(4, 4)$ 27. $(-2, 2\sqrt{3})$ 28. $(-1, -\sqrt{3})$ 29. $(4\sqrt{3}, 4)$

☐   Some of the following problems cannot be solved by using the Law of Cosines. In those cases, simply write "L of C not applicable" on your homework paper. Drawing a sketch should help you determine which problems they are.

30.   The right field fence at the foul line is marked 315 feet; at dead center field, it is marked 390 feet. What is the straight-line distance between these two points on the fence?

31.   A ship leaves port; it sails 10 kilometers east, and then 12 kilometers in the direction S10°E. How far is it from port?

32.   Pedrick wants to sail his boat from the pier to a point 10 kilometers due north. He reckons it will take two tacks. He sails N30°E and then N50°W to arrive at his destination. How many kilometers did he sail altogether?

33.   Harrington's plane flies at a constant speed of 150 miles per hour. He takes off and flies due north for one hour, and then N75°E for two hours. What direction should he fly now to get back to his airport? How long will it take him?

34.   Two planes leave an airport at the same time. One flies 200 km/hr in the direction 173° (from North) and the other flies 250 km/hr in the direction 320°. How far apart are the planes after 2 hours?

35.   A forest ranger spots a fire in the direction 38° (from due North) from his lookout post. A second ranger in a lookout 10 kilometers due east of the first one spots the same fire; he gives the direction as 13°. How far is the fire from the first ranger?

36.   A hillside slopes at 20° to the horizontal. A 10-meter pole stands upright about halfway up the hill. How long a rope is needed to reach from the top of the pole to a point 20 meters downhill from the base of the pole? How about 20 meters uphill?

37.   A triangular lot is fenced in with sides of 5, 8, and 10 meters. What is the area of the lot? [HINT: See Exercise 33 in Section 7-2.]

38.   (Polar coordinates) A radar tracking station 100 miles due south of O'Hare Airport reports that they have a plane on the radarscope whose (polar) coordinates are $\{32, 47°\}$. Where can the station at O'Hare expect to find the plane on its scope, in polar coordinates? [NOTE: Each station gives coordinates with itself at the origin.]

39.   (Polar coordinates) A ship in distress is located by the San Francisco radar station. The operator radios the Farallon Islands Coast Guard station, which is 3 miles due west of San Francisco, and gives the ship's position as $\{60, 240°\}$. How far is the ship from the Coast Guard station?

40.   Show that in any triangle ABC,

$$a^2 + b^2 + c^2 = 2(bc \cos A + ac \cos B + ab \cos C)$$

41.   Show that, in a triangle ABC, if $C = 60°$, then $(a - b)^2 = c^2 - ab$.

42.   If ABC is an isosceles triangle with $a = b$ and angle A = angle B, show that $c = a\sqrt{2 - 2 \cos C}$.

43.   Given any three positive numbers a, b, and c, will there always be a triangle ABC with sides a, b, and c? (See Exercises 16 and 17.) If not, what conditions on the numbers will insure that there is such a triangle?

44.   Same question as in Exercise 43, with positive numbers a, b, (sides) and C (angle).

45.   Make up and solve a problem of type SSS and one of type SAS.

46.   Make up and solve a word problem that can be solved by using the Law of Cosines. Make up one that cannot.

47.   Derive a formula for the area of a triangle with sides a, b, and c. [HINT: See Exercise 37.]

7-4
Law of Sines

To solve a triangle given all three sides (SSS) or two sides and the included angle (SAS), we have used the Law of Cosines. It is also possible to solve triangles given two angles and any side (AAS) or two sides and an angle not included (SSA). In these cases, we shall use the Law of Sines.

■ **Law of Sines**
In any triangle ABC,

$$\frac{\sin A}{a} = \frac{\sin B}{b} = \frac{\sin C}{c}$$

That is, in any triangle, the ratios obtained by dividing the sine of each angle by the length of the opposite side are all equal.

To prove the Law of Sines, it is necessary only to show that

$$\frac{\sin A}{a} = \frac{\sin B}{b} \tag{1}$$

Draw a triangle ABC and drop a perpendicular from point C to the line through A and B. Figure 7-18 shows two possibilities: $B \leq \pi/2$ and $B > \pi/2$. In each case, the triangle ADC is a right triangle and

$$\sin A = \frac{h}{b} \quad \text{or} \quad h = b \sin A \tag{2}$$

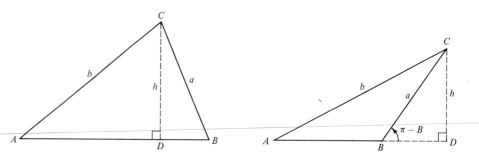

Figure 7-18
Proving the Law of Sines. In triangles ADC, $\sin A = h/b$. In triangles BDC, $\sin B = h/a$.

In each case, triangle BDC also is a right triangle. In the one on the left, $\sin B = h/a$; on the right, $\sin(\pi - B) = h/a$. But $\sin(\pi - B) = \sin B$ (recall Section 6-3) and, therefore, in each case

$$\sin B = \frac{h}{a} \quad \text{or} \quad h = a \sin B \tag{3}$$

Putting Equations (2) and (3) together yields $b \sin A = a \sin B$, from which Equation (1) follows at once. If the perpendicular had been constructed from point B to line AC, then the equality

$$\frac{\sin A}{a} = \frac{\sin C}{c}$$

could have been proved in the same way. This completes the proof of the Law of Sines.

Example 1
Solve the triangle ABC if $a = 3$, $A = 45°$, and $B = 30°$.

Solution
This problem is of the AAS type. First, find angle C:

$$C = 180 - 45 - 30 = 105°$$

Now choose an appropriate pair of ratios from the Law of Sines. Because you know side a, use

$$\frac{\sin A}{a} = \frac{\sin B}{b}$$

and solve for side b:

$$b = a \sin B/\sin A$$
$$= 3 \sin 30°/\sin 45°$$

Because $\sin 30° = 1/2$ and $\sin 45° = \sqrt{2}/2$,

$$b = 3 \cdot \frac{1}{2} \cdot \frac{2}{\sqrt{2}} = \frac{3}{\sqrt{2}}$$

It follows that $b \approx 2.1$. To find c, choose another pair of ratios or use the Law of Cosines.

The only type remaining is SSA: two sides and angle not included. It is slightly more complicated than the others. Data that fit into one of the first three categories determine a unique triangle, but SSA allows several different cases. Suppose sides a and b and angle A are known, and suppose further that $A < \pi/2$. The four possibilities are shown in Figure 7-19.

■ To solve a triangle ABC, you are given a, b, and A, with $A < \pi/2$. If the side opposite the given angle is smaller than the other given side ($a < b$), there are three possibilities:

> I $a = b \sin A$; one right triangle is determined
>
> II $a < b \sin A$; no triangle possible
>
> III $a > b \sin A$; two possible oblique triangles

If the side opposite the given angle is *not* smaller than the other given side ($a \geq b$), then

> IV   One oblique triangle is determined.

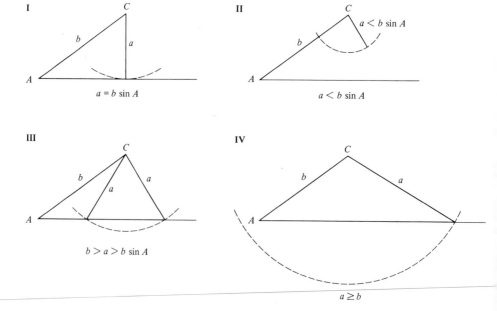

Figure 7-19
To solve a triangle ABC, given a, b, and A, with $A < \pi/2$, there are four possibilities:
I   One right triangle.   II   No triangle possible.   III   Two possible oblique triangles.
IV   One oblique triangle.

Example 2
Solve triangle ABC if $a = 1$, $b = 3$, and $A = 30°$.

Solution
Here $b \sin 30° = 3(\frac{1}{2})$, which is greater than a so there is no triangle. If, perchance, you missed seeing that, and tried to solve for angle B with the Law of Sines, then

$$\frac{\sin A}{a} = \frac{\sin B}{b}$$

would yield $\sin B = (b/a) \sin A = (3/1)(\frac{1}{2}) = 1.5$. But there is *no* angle B whose sine is greater than 1, so you would know that there is no such triangle.

Example 3
Solve triangle ABC if $b = 4$, $c = 8$, and $B = 30°$

Solution
Here, the side opposite the given angle is $b = 4$. Because $c \sin B = 8 \sin 30° = 4$, one right triangle is formed. Again, if you missed noticing that and solved for angle C, then

$$\frac{\sin B}{b} = \frac{\sin C}{c}$$

would yield $\sin C = (c/b) \sin B = (8/4)(\frac{1}{2}) = 1$, and it would follow that $C = 90°$. Now you know that $A = 60°$ and

$$a = \sqrt{8^2 - 4^2} = \sqrt{48} \approx 6.9$$

Example 4
Solve triangle ABC if $c = 5$, $a = 8$, and $C = 30°$.

Solution
The given angle is C and the side opposite it is $c = 5$; this length is between $a = 8$ and $a \sin C = 8 \sin 30° = 4$. Therefore, there are two triangles possible. The equality

$$\frac{\sin A}{a} = \frac{\sin C}{c}$$

yields $\sin A = (a/c) \sin C = (8/5)(\frac{1}{2}) = .8$. There are *two* angles between 0 and 180° whose sine is .8; one is $53°10'$ (rounded off), and the other is $180° - 53°10' = 126°50'$.

CASE 1: If $A = 53°10'$, then $B = 180° - (30° + 53°10') = 96°50'$, and by the Law of Sines

$$b = \frac{c \sin B}{\sin C}$$

$$\approx 5(.9929)/.5$$

$$= 9.929$$

CASE 2: If $A = 126°50'$, then $B = 180° - (30° + 126°50') = 23°10'$, and by the Law of Sines

$$b = \frac{c \sin B}{\sin C}$$

$$\approx 5(.3934)/.5$$

$$= 3.934$$

The two triangles are shown in Figure 7-20.

Example 5

Solve triangle ABC if $b = 5$, $c = 3$, and $B = 23°$.

Solution

The side opposite the given angle is bigger than the other side, so there is one oblique triangle. To find C, use the Law of Sines:

$$\sin C = \frac{c \sin B}{b}$$

$$\approx 3(.3907)/5$$

$$\approx .2344$$

Again, there are two possible angles whose sine is .2344. One is $13°30'$, and the other is $166°30'$. However, the second angle is ruled out, because angle $B = 23°$ and $23° + 166°30' > 180°$. Therefore, the only possibility is $C = 13°30'$. Now you can find A and side a as in the preceding examples.

Review of basic ideas

Memorize the Law of Cosines and the Law of Sines. Write out the type of information to which each law applies. Write out (or, better yet, draw pictures of) the various possibilities if you are given SSA information.

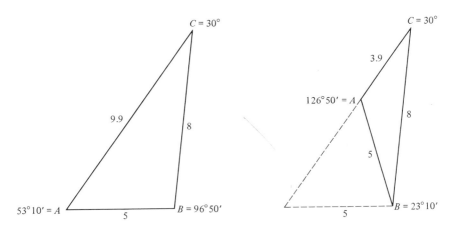

Figure 7-20
There are two triangles ABC that satisfy the conditions $c = 5$, $a = 8$, and $C = 30°$.

Exercises

Solve the triangle ABC.

1. $A = 47°$, $B = 53°$, $b = 4$
2. $B = 10°$, $C = 30°$, $c = 7$
3. $A = 47°$, $B = 53°$, $c = 4$
4. $B = 10°$, $C = 30°$, $a = 7$
5. $B = 130°$, $b = 2$, $c = 10$
6. $A = 35°$, $a = 4$, $c = 8$
7. $A = 40°$, $a = 6$, $b = 6$
8. $C = 18°$, $a = 5$, $c = 20$
9. $C = 60°$, $b = 10$, $c = 9$
10. $A = 150°$, $a = 7$, $b = 14$
11. $B = 30°$, $a = 10$, $b = 5$
12. $B = 20°$, $a = 5$, $b = 10$

In Exercises 13–18, classify the type of information given as SSS, SAS, AAS, or SSA. Write which of the laws, Sine or Cosine, should be used to solve the triangle. If the information is SSA, also write which of the four possibilities hold.

13. $A = 45°$, $b = 3$, $c = 4$
14. $A = 5°$, $a = 4$, $b = 20$
15. $a = 4$, $b = 5$, $c = 8$
16. $A = 5°$, $a = 4$, $b = 200$
17. $A = 13°$, $a = 225$, $b = 1{,}000$
18. $A = 17°$, $B = 95°$, $b = 5$

19. Do Exercise 32 in Section 7-3.
20. Do Exercise 35 in Section 7-3.
21. A 10-foot pole is leaning toward the sun, as shown in Figure 7-21. If the angle of elevation of the sun is 32°, and the shadow of the pole is 12 feet long, what angle does the pole make with the horizontal?
22. (Polar coordinates) The direction from a radar tracking station to Kennedy Airport is N35°E. A plane 200 miles from Kennedy appears on the scope of the

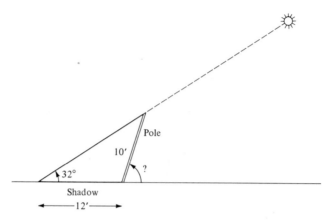

Figure 7-21
The leaning pole and its shadow in Exercise 21.

station at (polar) coordinates {100, 270°}. How far is the radar station from the airport?

23. It is 90 feet from home plate to first base. The center fielder is playing the batter dead center. The angle from home plate to first base to the center fielder is 120°. How far is the center fielder from home plate?

24. Instructions for finding the famous hidden pirate treasure on Nogad Island are as follows:

(a) Locate a tall palm tree and a large rock each marked with a big Y. The imaginary line through them runs east and west and is called the *base line*. The treasure is somewhere on that line.

(b) Starting from the tree, walk exactly 100 yards in the direction N72°E.

(c) Now choose the proper direction so that, when you have walked a distance of exactly 75 yards in that direction, you will be at the base line.

(d) Start digging.

Is it possible to locate the treasure? If so, where is it?

25. Suppose you are standing on one side of the Grand Canyon with a transit to measure angles and a tape to measure distance. How would you go about calculating the width of the canyon?

26. Make up four "solve the triangle" problems illustrating the four possibilities for the SSA category.

27. Make up a word problem with AAS information and solve it.

28. Same as Exercise 27 for SSA information.

29. In the discussion of the SSA category, it was assumed that the given angle was acute. What if the angle is greater than $\pi/2$? Under what conditions will there be a solution? Can there be more than one solution?

7-5
Vectors

Many measurable quantities are determined by magnitude alone: length, area, and temperature, for example. Other quantities, such as force, velocity, and momentum, have both magnitude and direction. These are known as **vector quantities,** or, more simply, as **vectors.** A vector can be represented geometrically by drawing an arrow in the plane. The length and the direction of the arrow indicate the magnitude and the direction of the vector. Two examples are shown in Figure 7-22. When a letter, say *u*, is used to denote a vector, it will be printed **u** to distinguish it from an ordinary number. The magnitude of a vector **u** will be denoted by the symbol $|\mathbf{u}|$.

Vectors are equal if and only if they have the same magnitude *and the same direction*. In Figure 7-23, **u, v,** and **w** all have the same length, but the direction of **w**

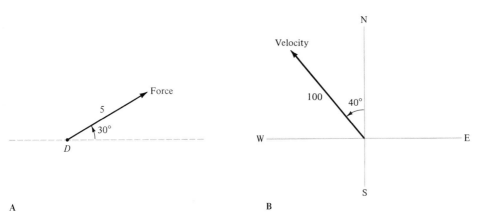

Figure 7-22
Force and velocity are vector quantities. (A) A force of 5 pounds is exerted at point D in the direction 30° above horizontal. (B) An object is moving in the direction N40°W at a speed of 100 miles per hour.

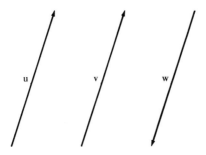

Figure 7-23
Vectors are equal if and only if they have the same magnitude and the same direction. Thus, **u** = **v** but **u** ≠ **w**.

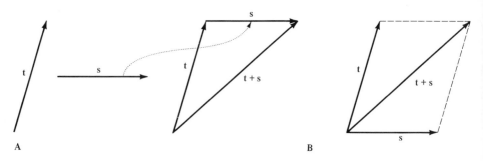

Figure 7-24
(A) The vector **t** + **s** is found by placing the tail of **s** at the head of **t**. (B) The vector **t** + **s** is also the diagonal of the parallelogram formed by putting the tails of **t** and **s** together.

is opposite to the direction of **u** and **v**; thus, **u** = **v**, but **u** ≠ **w**.

Vectors can be added to form a sum, or resultant, which is another vector. To add vectors **s** and **t** geometrically, place the tail of **s** at the head of **t** *without altering the direction of either vector.* Then **t** + **s** is the vector from the tail of **t** to the head of **s** (see Figure 7-24A). The same result can be accomplished by putting the tails of **t** and **s** together. Then draw the parallelogram determined by them; the resultant is the diagonal of the parallelogram (see Figure 7-24B). This method also shows that **t** + **s** = **s** + **t**. In applications to physical problems, the resultant has the same effect as the two vectors combined.

Example 1

An airplane is heading in the direction N45°E with an airspeed of 300 miles per hour. The wind is blowing *from* N20°W at 60 miles per hour. What is the airplane's ground speed and direction?

Solution

Represent the information in terms of vectors (see Figure 7-25). You want to know the length of the resultant OB and the angle θ. Apply the Law of Cosines to triangle OAB, in which angle OAB is 65°:

$$(OB)^2 = (300)^2 + (60)^2 - 2(300)(60)\cos 65°$$

$$\approx 90{,}000 + 3{,}600 - 36{,}000(.4226)$$

$$\approx 78{,}386$$

Therefore, $OB \approx 280$.

To find θ, first find the angle AOB, again by using the Law of Cosines.

$$\cos(AOB) = \frac{(300)^2 - (280)^2 - (60)^2}{-2(280)(60)}$$

$$\approx -.2381$$

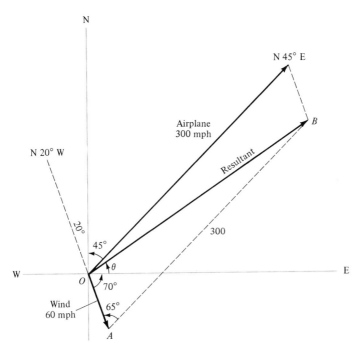

Figure 7-25
A plane flies through the air at 300 miles per hour in the direction N45°E. If the wind is blowing at 60 miles per hour from the direction N20°W, the airplane's ground speed and direction are given by the vector *OB*.

Thus, angle $AOB \approx 103°50'$. Because the wind vector makes an angle of 70° with the horizontal, it follows that $\theta \approx 103°50' - 70° = 33°50'$. Thus, although the airplane is heading through the air in the direction N45°E at 300 miles per hour, its effective ground speed is 280 miles per hour in the direction $N(90° - \theta°)E = N56°10'E$.

Some problems require the **resolution** of a vector into **components.** In other words, given a vector **u,** find vectors **v** and **w,** at right angles to each other, so that **u** = **v** + **w.**

Example 2
A carton is pulled with a force of 100 pounds by a rope that makes an angle of 30° with the horizontal. What part of the force acts to drag the carton across the floor? What part acts to lift it off the floor?

Solution
If **F** is the force along the rope, let $\mathbf{F}_x$ be its horizontal component, the part of

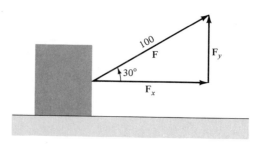

Figure 7-26
A carton is pulled with a force of 100 pounds by a rope that makes an angle of 30° with the horizontal. See Example 2.

F that drags the carton across the floor (see Figure 7-26). The length of $\mathbf{F}_x$ is

$$|\mathbf{F}_x| = 100 \cos 30° \approx 86.60$$

Thus, a force of 100 pounds applied at an angle of 30° has the same horizontal magnitude as a force of about 87 pounds applied horizontally.
The vertical component $\mathbf{F}_y$ has length

$$|\mathbf{F}_y| = 100 \sin 30° = 50$$

Thus, the lifting effect of **F** is 50 pounds.

Example 3
A carton weighing 100 pounds is sitting on an incline of 15°. What force of friction will keep the carton from sliding down the incline?

Solution
The situation is shown in Figure 7-27. Gravity exerts a vertical force of 100

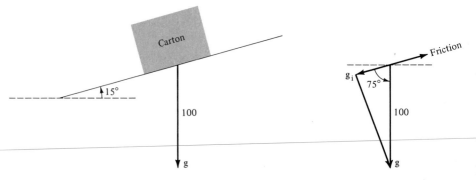

Figure 7-27
Gravity and friction. See Example 3.

pounds (vector **g**); it can be resolved into two components: one perpendicular to the incline and one parallel to the incline. The component $\mathbf{g}_i$ along the incline represents the part of **g** that tends to push the carton down the incline. Friction must be an equal but opposite force if the carton is at rest. The magnitude of $\mathbf{g}_i$ is

$$|\mathbf{g}_i| = 100 \cos 75°$$

$$\approx 25.88$$

Therefore, friction must exert a force of 25.88 pounds in the direction opposite to $\mathbf{g}_i$.

It is often convenient to set up a coordinate system and use rectangular or polar coordinates to specify a vector.

■ $\mathbf{u} = (x, y)$ or $\mathbf{v} = \{r, \theta\}$ means the vector represented by an arrow with its tail at the origin and its tip at the specified point.

For example, the vector $\mathbf{u} = (3, 2)$ has its tail at the origin and its tip at the point $(3, 2)$ (see Figure 7-28A). Then $|\mathbf{u}| = \sqrt{3^2 + 2^2} = \sqrt{13}$ and the direction angle θ has $\cos \theta = 3/\sqrt{13}$, so $\theta \approx 33°40'$. Polar coordinates specify length and direction, and so are very adaptable to vector calculations. For instance, the polar coordinates $\{3, 3\pi/4\}$ specify a vector of length 3 in the direction $3\pi/4 = 135°$ (see Figure 7-28B).
    Recall that the rectangular coordinates (x, y) are related to the polar coordinates $\{r, \theta\}$ by the equations

$$x^2 + y^2 = r^2 \qquad x = r \cos \theta \qquad y = r \sin \theta$$

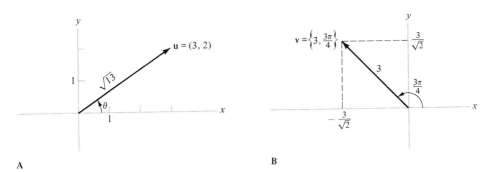

A

B

Figure 7-28
(A) A vector **u** expressed in rectangular coordinates. (B) A vector **v** expressed in polar coordinates.

When vectors are given in terms of rectangular coordinates, it is especially easy to find the resultant algebraically: simply add the x-coordinates and the y-coordinates separately. For example, if $\mathbf{u} = (4, -2)$ and $\mathbf{v} = (-1, 6)$, then $\mathbf{u} + \mathbf{v} = (4 - 1, -2 + 6) = (3, 4)$. In general, if $\mathbf{u} = (x_1, y_1)$ and $\mathbf{v} = (x_2, y_2)$, then

$$\mathbf{u} + \mathbf{v} = (x_1, y_1) + (x_2, y_2) = (x_1 + x_2, y_1 + y_2)$$

You will be asked to verify this in Exercises 9–12.

Example 4
Rework Example 1, about the airplane, using the algebraic method of adding vectors.

Solution
Let $\mathbf{a}$ be the vector of the airplane's velocity through the air; its length is 300 and its direction is N45°E. In rectangular coordinates, $\mathbf{a} = (300 \cos 45°, 300 \sin 45°) \approx (212, 212)$. Let $\mathbf{w}$ be the wind vector; its length is 60 and its direction is S20°E. In rectangular coordinates, $\mathbf{w} = (60 \cos(-70°), 60 \sin(-70°)) \approx (21, -56)$. The resultant, therefore, is

$$\mathbf{u} = \mathbf{a} + \mathbf{w} \approx (212 + 21, 212 - 56) = (233, 156)$$

The length of $\mathbf{u}$ is

$$|\mathbf{u}| = \sqrt{(233)^2 + (156)^2} \approx 280$$

Its direction is θ, where $\cos \theta = 233/280 \approx .8321$; so $\theta \approx 33°40'$. With this method, the Law of Cosines is not needed.

Exercises

Convert the rectangular coordinates to polar coordinates.
1. $(1, \sqrt{3})$ 2. $(0, 5)$ 3. $(-\sqrt{2}, 1)$ 4. $(-3, -4)$

Convert the polar coordinates to rectangular coordinates.
5. $\{3, -15°\}$ 6. $\{4, 30°\}$ 7. $\{2, 3\pi/4\}$ 8. $\{1, 7\pi/6\}$

Find the sum, or resultant, of each of the following pairs of vectors accurately plotting the vectors and completing the parallelogram as in Figure 7-24B. Notice that the coordinates of the resultant are the sums of the corresponding coordinates of the added vectors.
9. $\mathbf{t} = (1, 3)$, $\mathbf{r} = (-4, -2)$ 10. $\mathbf{t} = (-2, -3)$, $\mathbf{s} = (2, 1)$

11. $t = (0, 1)$, $s = (4, -2)$ **12.** $t = (6, 8)$, $s = (-3, -4)$

Find the resultant of each of the following pairs of vectors given in polar coordinates. [HINT: Change to rectangular coordinates.]

13. $\{6, 60°\}$, $\{2, 90°\}$ **14.** $\{3, 105°\}$, $\{1, 180°\}$

15. $\{1, 5\pi/6\}$, $\{4, 3\pi/2\}$ **16.** $\{2, 7\pi/4\}$, $\{1, 3\pi/2\}$

17.   Forces of 20 and 50 pounds act on an object. The angle between them is 40°. Find the magnitude of the resultant force. (Draw a picture.)

18.   An airplane flies on a heading of 280° from North at an airspeed of 200 miles per hour. The wind is blowing at 40 miles per hour from the west. What is the ground speed and direction of the airplane?

19.   A pilot wants to fly a course of 62° from North with a ground speed of 200 miles per hour. The wind is blowing from the direction 120° at 30 miles per hour. What heading and airspeed must be maintained?

20.   A pilot is flying a course of S30°E at an airspeed of 300 miles per hour. His ground speed is 320 miles per hour, and his actual direction is S40°E. What is the direction and speed of the wind?

21.   New York is (approximately) 1000 miles from Chicago in the direction N80°E. If the wind is blowing at 50 miles per hour *in* the direction S60°E, what heading and airspeed must be maintained for a jetliner to make the Chicago-New York run in the scheduled time of 2 hours?

22.   A rope attached to a carton is pulled with a force **F** of 100 pounds. The rope makes an angle of 40° with the horizontal. What are the horizontal and vertical components of **F**? If the force of friction is 75 pounds will the carton move horizontally?

23.   A rope is attached to a carton. The rope makes an angle of 20° with the horizontal. If the force of friction is 50 pounds, what is the minimum force of pull that will move the carton horizontally?

24.   A 150-pound weight rests on an incline of 20°. What is the force of friction?

25.   A 150-pound weight rests on an incline of 25°. How much force in the direction perpendicular to the incline is necessary to lift the weight off the incline? (This principle is used by NASA to simulate weightlessness.)

26.   A 150-pound weight is sitting on a horizontal board. The board is lifted at one end to make an angle θ with the horizontal. At that point it takes a force of 100 pounds perpendicular to the board to lift the weight. Find θ.

Chapter 8

Trigonometric Inverses, Identities, and Equations

The basic concepts of trigonometry have now been presented from three closely related points of view:

■ **Angles in standard position**

Place an angle in standard position, pick any point (x, y) on its terminal side and define the sine and cosine functions as ratios between the coordinates of the point and its distance from the origin.

■ **Unit circle**

Start at the point $(1, 0)$ and move t units counterclockwise along the circle. The coordinates of the terminal point are values of the circular functions $x = \cos t$ and $y = \sin t$.

■ **Right triangles**

Consider the sine and cosine of acute angles as ratios between the sides opposite and adjacent and the hypotenuse of a right triangle.

In this, the final chapter on trigonometry, we return to the functional point of view. There are very few practical applications presented here. Our purpose, rather, is to explore further the nature of the trigonometric functions.

The first topic is trigonometric inverses. The subject is complicated by the fact that the trigonometric functions themselves are not one-to-one. The problem is solved in Section 8-1 by restricting each of them to a part of its domain on which it is one-to-one.

In the next two sections, some useful formulas are introduced, which give the values of the trigonometric functions at sums and differences of angles, and at multiple angles.

Next is a subject included in every text on trigonometry—trigonometric identities. Proving that trigonometric expressions are equivalent to each other will sharpen your manipulative skills and bring into focus the interdependence of the trigonometric functions. Trigonometric equations are considered in Section 8-5.

The contents of this chapter can be considered a summary of your study of trigonometry. At the end you should feel very comfortable with the definitions, the concepts, and the manipulations necessary to make the utmost use of trigonometry in your future work.

8-1
Inverse Trigonometric Functions

The trigonometric functions are periodic and therefore are not one-to-one on their entire domain. In Exercise 45 in Section 6-5, you were asked to pick out a part of the domain of each function on which it is one-to-one; on that part, the restricted function has an inverse. You were asked to sketch the graph of the inverse. In this section we shall develop the topic of trigonometric inverses further.

First, let us briefly review the notion of inverses (refer to Section 5-1 for a more thorough review).

■ **Definition**

Let $f: X \to Y$. If there is a function $g: Y \to X$ such that $g(f(x)) = x$ and $f(g(y)) = y$ for all x in X and all y in Y, then g is called the **inverse** of f and is denoted by the symbol f^{-1} (read "f inverse").

The domain of f is the range of f^{-1}; the range of f is the domain of f^{-1}. Loosely speaking, each function cancels out whatever the other one does: if $f(2) = 3$, then $f^{-1}(3) = 2$. In trigonometry, $\sin(\pi/6) = \frac{1}{2}$, so $\sin^{-1}\frac{1}{2} = \pi/6$.

If a function is one-to-one on a part of its domain, then the function restricted to that part has an inverse. For example, $f(x) = x^2$ is one-to-one for $x \geq 0$, so the restricted function has an inverse $f^{-1}(x) = \sqrt{x}$ for $x \geq 0$. As we shall see, the sine is one-to-one for $-\pi/2 \leq x \leq \pi/2$, so the function restricted to those values of x has an inverse.

Finally, if f and f^{-1} are graphed on the same set of axes, the graphs are reflections of each other through the line $y = x$.

With these facts about inverses in mind, it is easy to define and graph the

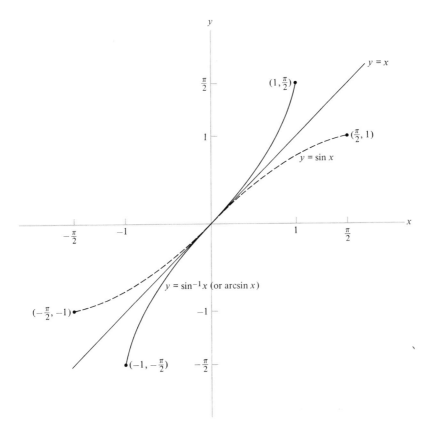

Figure 8-1
If $y = \sin x$ is restricted to the domain $-\pi/2 \le x \le \pi/2$, it has an inverse, $y = \arcsin x$, defined on the domain $-1 \le x \le 1$. The graph of $y = \arcsin x$ (solid curve) is the reflection of the graph of $y = \sin x$ (dashed curve) through the line $y = x$.

inverse trigonometric functions. All that really needs to be done is to decide how to restrict each of the functions so that it is one-to-one.

For the sine function, let us use the domain $-\pi/2 \le x \le \pi/2$. Notice that other intervals, such as $\pi/2 \le x \le 3\pi/2$ or $-3\pi/2 \le x \le -\pi/2$, could also be used, but it is common practice to choose $-\pi/2 \le x \le \pi/2$. On this domain, the sine ranges from -1 to 1. Automatically, then, $\sin^{-1}$ has the domain $-1 \le x \le 1$ and its values range from $-\pi/2$ to $\pi/2$. Its graph is the mirror image of the graph of the sine through the line $y = x$. The function $\sin^{-1}$, is often written **arcsin** and read "arc sine." All of this is shown in Figure 8-1.

It often helps to think of it this way: $y = \arcsin x$ translates to "y is the number between $-\pi/2$ and $\pi/2$ whose sine is x."

Example 1
Find (a) $\arcsin \frac{1}{2}$ and   (b) $\sin^{-1}(-\sqrt{3}/2)$.

Solution

(a) arcsin $\frac{1}{2}$ is the number between $-\pi/2$ and $\pi/2$ whose sine is $\frac{1}{2}$. Therefore, arcsin $\frac{1}{2} = \pi/6$.

(b) $\sin^{-1}(-\sqrt{3}/2)$ is the number between $-\pi/2$ and $\pi/2$ whose sine is $-\sqrt{3}/2$. Thus, $\sin^{-1}(-\sqrt{3}/2) = -\pi/3$.

Defining an inverse of the cosine is done in almost exactly the same way. The domain usually chosen is $0 \le x \le \pi$; the range, of course, is all the numbers from -1 to 1. Thus, the domain of $\cos^{-1}$, or **arccos**, is $-1 \le x \le 1$, and its range is all numbers from 0 to π (see Figure 8-2).

In defining its inverse, the tangent function is usually restricted to the domain $-\pi/2 < x < \pi/2$ (notice that the tangent is not defined at $\pm\pi/2$). The range of the

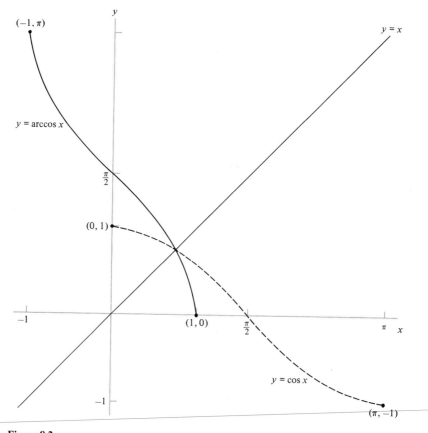

Figure 8-2

If $y = \cos x$ is restricted to the domain $0 \le x \le \pi$, it has an inverse, $y = \arccos x$, defined on the domain $-1 \le x \le 1$. The graph of $y = \arccos x$ (solid curve) is the reflection of the graph of $y = \cos x$ (dashed curve) through the line $y = x$.

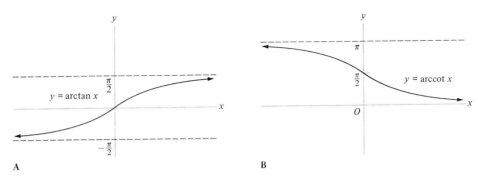

Figure 8-3
(A) If $y = \tan x$ is restricted to the domain $-\pi/2 < x < \pi/2$, then the domain of its inverse, $y = \arctan x$, is the entire real line. The dashed lines $y = \pi/2$ and $y = -\pi/2$ are asymptotes.
(B) If $y = \cot x$ is restricted to the domain $0 < x < \pi$, then the domain of its inverse, $y = \operatorname{arccot} x$, is the entire real line. The dashed line $y = \pi$ and the x-axis are asymptotes.

tangent extends from $-\infty$ to ∞; thus, the domain of $\tan^{-1}$, or **arctan,** is the entire real line, and its range is all the numbers between $-\pi/2$ and $\pi/2$ (see Figure 8-3A). The domain of the cotangent is usually restricted to $0 < x < \pi$; the graph of its inverse, **arccot,** is shown in Figure 8-3B. The inverses of the secant and cosecant are not often used, and we shall not consider them here.

The foregoing definitions are summarized in a table at the end of this section. Look over the entries in that table before you read the rest of this section.

Example 2
Evaluate (a) $\cos^{-1}(-\sqrt{2}/2)$, (b) arctan 1, and (c) $\cot^{-1}(-3.628)$.

Solution
(a) The range of the arccos is all numbers from 0 to π. The $\cos^{-1}(-\sqrt{2}/2)$ is therefore a number between 0 and π whose cosine is $-\sqrt{2}/2$. Thus, $\cos^{-1}(-\sqrt{2}/2) = 3\pi/4$.
(b) arctan 1 is a number between $-\pi/2$ and $\pi/2$ whose tangent is 1. The number is $\pi/4$.
(c) In Table 2, the closest entry to 3.628 in the cotangent column is 3.647, which is the cotangent of .2676. We need the number between 0 and π whose cotangent is -3.628. Because -3.628 is negative, the number must lie between $\pi/2$ and π. It follows that the number must be $\pi - .2676 \approx 2.874$.

Combining trigonometric functions with inverses
Let x be any number from -1 to 1. Then $\sin^{-1}x$ is the number between $-\pi/2$ and $\pi/2$ whose sine is x. In other words $\sin(\sin^{-1}x) = x$. The same reasoning holds for the other functions:

$$\sin(\arcsin x) = x \qquad \cos(\arccos x) = x$$

$$\tan(\arctan x) = x \qquad \cot(\text{arccot } x) = x$$

provided x is in the appropriate domain.

For some values of x, the arcsine of the sine of x might *not* be x. For example, find $\arcsin(\sin 3\pi/4)$. First, find $\sin 3\pi/4 = \sqrt{2}/2$; thus, $\arcsin \sqrt{2}/2$ must be a number from $-\pi/2$ to $\pi/2$ whose sine is $\sqrt{2}/2$; that number is $\pi/4$. Therefore,

$$\arcsin(\sin 3\pi/4) = \pi/4, \quad not \quad 3\pi/4$$

Does this contradict the definition of inverse? No. Recall that, in order to define arcsin, we restricted the domain of sine x to $-\pi/2 \le x \le \pi/2$. The number $3\pi/4$ *is not in this restricted domain,* so we can't expect the inverses to "cancel" each other out. The same precaution applies to the other inverse functions.

Example 3
Find (a) $\sin \arcsin \tfrac{1}{2}$,   (b) $\cot \cot^{-1}32$,   (c) $\tan^{-1}\tan(-\pi/4)$,   and
(d) $\cos^{-1}\cos(-\pi/4)$.

Solution
(a) $\sin \arcsin \tfrac{1}{2} = \tfrac{1}{2}$
(b) $\cot \cot^{-1}32 = 32$
(c)   Start with $\tan(-\pi/4) = -1$;   then $\tan^{-1}\tan(-\pi/4) = \tan^{-1}(-1)$ $= -\pi/4$. [NOTE: $\tan^{-1}\tan(3\pi/4)$ also is $-\pi/4$.]
(d) $\cos(-\pi/4) = \sqrt{2}/2$ and $\cos^{-1}(\sqrt{2}/2) = \pi/4$.
Thus, $\cos^{-1}\cos(-\pi/4) = \pi/4$. [NOTE: $\cos^{-1}\cos(\pi/4)$ also is $\pi/4$.]

It is also possible to combine a trigonometric function with the inverse of another trigonometric function.

Example 4
Evaluate (a) $\cos^{-1}\sin(\pi/2)$,   (b) $\sin \cos^{-1}(4/5)$,   and   (c) $\cos \text{arccot}(-\sqrt{3})$.

Solution
(a) $\sin(\pi/2) = 1$ and $\cos^{-1}1 = 0$; therefore, $\cos^{-1}\sin(\pi/2) = 0$.
(b) $\sin \cos^{-1}(4/5)$. First evaluate $\cos^{-1}(4/5)$, and then find the sine of the result. There are two methods: approximate $\cos^{-1}(4/5)$ by using Table 2; or, to obtain an *exact* answer, draw an angle θ between 0 and π, in standard position, whose cosine is 4/5 (see Figure 8-4A). If the point $(4, y)$ is on the terminal side of θ, then $y = \sqrt{5^2 - 4^2} = 3$. Clearly, then, $\sin \theta = 3/5$. Therefore, $\sin \cos^{-1}(4/5) = 3/5$.

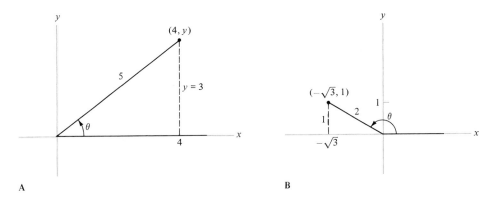

Figure 8-4
(A) Finding sin cos $^{-1}(4/5)$. See Example 4(b). (B) Finding cos arccot$(-\sqrt{3})$. See Example 4(c).

(c)   cos arccot$(-\sqrt{3})$. To find arccot $(-\sqrt{3})$, draw an angle θ whose cotangent is $-\sqrt{3}$. This angle must be in the second quadrant, because the range of arccotangent is 0 to π (see Figure 8-4B). The point $(-\sqrt{3}, 1)$ must be on the terminal side of θ, and the distance of this point from the origin is $\sqrt{(-\sqrt{3})^2 + 1^2} = 2$. Therefore, cos arccot $(-\sqrt{3}) = \cos \theta = -\sqrt{3}/2$.

Example 5
Compute the area of the shaded region in Figure 8-5A.

Solution
Construct the dashed lines shown in Figure 8-5B. The area you seek is the area of the circular sector $OABC$ minus the area of the triangle OAC.

First, compute the area of the circular sector: Let θ be the central angle AOC, and α be the angle DOC, measured in radians. Then $\theta = 2\alpha$ and

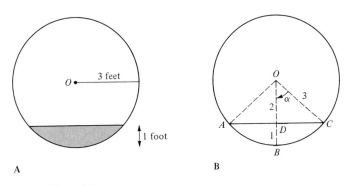

Figure 8-5
Compute the area of the shaded region. See Example 5.

$\alpha = \arccos \frac{2}{3}$. According to Exercise 52 in Section 6-1, the area of $OABC$ is $\frac{1}{2}r^2\theta$; that is

$$\text{area of } OABC = \frac{1}{2} \cdot 3^2 \cdot 2 \arccos \frac{2}{3}$$

$$\approx 9(.8407) \qquad \text{(from Table 2)}$$

$$\approx 7.566 \text{ square feet}$$

Now find the area of triangle OAC: The area is one half the base AC times the height, 2. The length of $AC = 2DC = 2\sqrt{3^2 - 2^2} = 2\sqrt{5}$. Thus,

$$\text{area of } OAC = \frac{1}{2} \cdot 2 \cdot 2\sqrt{5}$$

$$\approx 4.472 \text{ square feet}$$

It follows that the segment in question has an approximate area of $7.566 - 4.472 = 3.094$ square feet.

Review of basic ideas

The following table lists information about domains and ranges of trigonometric functions and their inverses. Square brackets mean that the numbers at the ends of the domain or the range are included; parentheses mean that they are not.

Function	Domain	Range	Inverse	Domain	Range
sin	$[-\pi/2, \pi/2]$	$[-1, 1]$	$\sin^{-1}$	$[-1, 1]$	$[-\pi/2, \pi/2]$
cos	$[0, \pi]$	$[-1, 1]$	$\cos^{-1}$	$[-1, 1]$	$[0, \pi]$
tan	$(-\pi/2, \pi/2)$	$(-\infty, \infty)$	$\tan^{-1}$	$(-\infty, \infty)$	$(-\pi/2, \pi/2)$
cot	$(0, \pi)$	$(-\infty, \infty)$	$\cot^{-1}$	$(-\infty, \infty)$	$(0, \pi)$

Exercises

Evaluate.

1. $\cos^{-1}(\sqrt{3}/2)$
2. $\sin^{-1}(\sqrt{2}/2)$
3. $\arctan \sqrt{3}$
4. $\text{arccot}(1/\sqrt{3})$
5. $\arcsin(1/2)$
6. $\arccos(1/2)$
7. $\tan^{-1}(-1/\sqrt{3})$
8. $\cot^{-1}(-1/\sqrt{3})$
9. $\arccos(-1)$
10. $\arcsin(-\sqrt{3}/2)$
11. $\text{arccot}(-1)$
12. $\tan^{-1}(-1)$

Approximate the following (round off).

13. $\sin^{-1}.3621$
14. $\cos^{-1}.0124$
15. $\tan^{-1}(-2.869)$
16. $\cot^{-1}(-32)$
17. $\arccos(-.8134)$
18. $\sin^{-1}(-.3)$

Find the exact values.

19. $\cos\cos^{-1}.2816$
20. $\sin\sin^{-1}(-1/10)$
21. $\tan\tan^{-1}(10)$
22. $\cot\cot^{-1}(-2.5)$
23. $\sin^{-1}\sin(5\pi/6)$
24. $\cos^{-1}\cos(-\pi)$
25. $\tan^{-1}\tan(-\pi/3)$
26. $\cot^{-1}\cot(5\pi/6)$
27. $\tan\cos^{-1}(1/2)$
28. $\cot\sin^{-1}(\sqrt{3}/2)$
29. $\sin\tan^{-1}2$ (see Example 4)
30. $\cos\cot^{-1}(2/3)$
31. $\tan\arcsin(3/4)$
32. $\cot\arccos(5/7)$
33. $\sin\cos^{-1}(-2/5)$
34. $\cos\sin^{-1}(-9/10)$
35. $\tan\cot^{-1}9$

36. Prove that the area of the circular segment ABC in Figure 8-6 is given by:

$$\text{area} = r^2\arccos\left(\frac{r-h}{r}\right) - (r-h)\sqrt{2rh - h^2}$$

[HINT: Use Example 5 as a guide.]

37. (Continuation of Exercise 36) A drum 6 feet long and 4 feet in diameter is lying on its side. If the depth of the water in it is 1 foot, how many cubic feet of water does it contain? How much if the depth is 3 feet?

38. In a triangle ABC, is it always true that

$$A = \arccos\left(\frac{a^2 - b^2 - c^2}{-2bc}\right)?$$

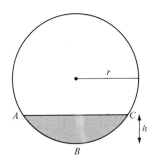

Figure 8-6
What is the area of the shaded region? See Exercise 36.

39. In any triangle *ABC*, is it always true that

$$A = \arcsin\left(\frac{a \sin B}{b}\right)?$$

Careful; this is tricky.

8-2
Addition Formulas

A formula that gives the value of a trigonometric function of a sum of angles or of their difference is called an **addition formula.** Of all such formulas, the one for $\cos(\alpha - \beta)$ is the most important because *every other addition formula can be derived from it.*

The proof of the $\cos(\alpha - \beta)$ formula combines algebraic and geometric arguments. Let α and β be angles in standard position as shown in Figure 8-7A. The terminal sides of α and β meet the unit circle at $A = (\cos \alpha, \sin \alpha)$ and $B = (\cos \beta, \sin \beta)$. According to the distance formula, the distance d between these points satisfies the equation

$$d^2 = (\cos \alpha - \cos \beta)^2 + (\sin \alpha - \sin \beta)^2$$

Now square both terms on the right and use the identity $\sin^2 \theta + \cos^2 \theta = 1$ to simplify as follows:

$$d^2 = \cos^2 \alpha - 2 \cos \alpha \cos \beta + \cos^2 \beta$$
$$+ \sin^2 \alpha - 2 \sin \alpha \sin \beta + \sin^2 \beta$$
$$= (\cos^2 \alpha + \sin^2 \alpha) + (\cos^2 \beta + \sin^2 \beta)$$
$$- 2(\cos \alpha \cos \beta + \sin \alpha \sin \beta)$$
$$= 2 - 2(\cos \alpha \cos \beta + \sin \alpha \sin \beta)$$

So far, so good. But where is $\cos(\alpha - \beta)$? Imagine that the triangle AOB in Figure 8-7A is rotated so that point B now corresponds to the point $(1, 0)$. The result is shown in Figure 8-7B. The distance d has not changed, but the coordinates of A and B have: their new coordinates are $(\cos(\alpha - \beta), \sin(\alpha - \beta))$ and $(1, 0)$. Compute d^2 again, this time with the new coordinates:

$$d^2 = (\cos(\alpha - \beta) - 1)^2 + (\sin(\alpha - \beta) - 0)^2$$
$$= \cos^2(\alpha - \beta) - 2 \cos(\alpha - \beta) + 1 + \sin^2(\alpha - \beta)$$
$$= 2 - 2 \cos(\alpha - \beta)$$

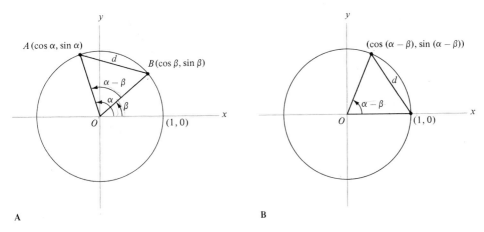

Figure 8-7
Proving that $\cos(\alpha - \beta) = \cos \alpha \cos \beta + \sin \alpha \sin \beta$. (A) $d^2 = (\cos \alpha - \cos \beta)^2 + (\sin \alpha - \sin \beta)^2$ (B) $d^2 = (\cos(\alpha - \beta) - 1)^2 + (\sin(\alpha - \beta) - 0)^2$

Comparing this computation with the preceding one shows that

■ $\cos(\alpha - \beta) = \cos \alpha \cos \beta + \sin \alpha \sin \beta$ (1)

Even though this formula was proved only for the α and β shown in Figure 8-7, it holds for all numbers (or angles) α and β.

Example 1
Find the exact value of $\cos 15°$.

Solution
Table 2 lists $\cos 15°$ as .9659; this is accurate to four places. If you write $15° = 45° - 30°$, then formula (1) yields the *exact* value:

$$\cos 15° = \cos 45° \cos 30° + \sin 45° \sin 30°$$

$$= \frac{\sqrt{2}}{2} \cdot \frac{\sqrt{3}}{2} + \frac{\sqrt{2}}{2} \cdot \frac{1}{2}$$

$$= \frac{\sqrt{6} + \sqrt{2}}{4}$$

Five more addition formulas follow directly from Formula (1).

Replace β by $-\beta$ in Formula (1); recall that $\cos(-\beta) = \cos\beta$ and $\sin(-\beta) = -\sin\beta$. Then

$$\cos(\alpha + \beta) = \cos(\alpha -(-\beta)) = \cos\alpha\cos(-\beta) + \sin\alpha\sin(-\beta)$$
$$= \cos\alpha\cos\beta - \sin\alpha\sin\beta \qquad (2)$$

Recall that "co" functions have equal values at complementary angles. Thus,

$$\sin(\alpha - \beta) = \cos\left(\frac{\pi}{2} - (\alpha - \beta)\right) = \cos\left(\left(\frac{\pi}{2} - \alpha\right) + \beta\right)$$
$$= \cos\left(\frac{\pi}{2} - \alpha\right)\cos\beta - \sin\left(\frac{\pi}{2} - \alpha\right)\sin\beta$$
$$= \sin\alpha\cos\beta - \cos\alpha\sin\beta \qquad (3)$$

Replace β by $-\beta$ in Formula (3) to obtain

$$\sin(\alpha + \beta) = \sin(\alpha - (-\beta)) = \sin\alpha\cos(-\beta) - \cos\alpha\sin(-\beta)$$
$$= \sin\alpha\cos\beta + \cos\alpha\sin\beta \qquad (4)$$

If the sine and cosine of $\alpha + \beta$ are known, then, of course, $\tan(\alpha + \beta)$ $= \sin(\alpha + \beta)/\cos(\alpha + \beta)$. If only $\tan\alpha$ and $\tan\beta$ are known, then

$$\tan(\alpha + \beta) = \frac{\sin(\alpha + \beta)}{\cos(\alpha + \beta)}$$

$$= \frac{\sin\alpha\cos\beta + \cos\alpha\sin\beta}{\cos\alpha\cos\beta - \sin\alpha\sin\beta} \cdot \frac{\dfrac{1}{\cos\alpha\cos\beta}}{\dfrac{1}{\cos\alpha\cos\beta}}$$

$$= \frac{\dfrac{\sin\alpha\cos\beta}{\cos\alpha\cos\beta} + \dfrac{\cos\alpha\sin\beta}{\cos\alpha\cos\beta}}{\dfrac{\cos\alpha\cos\beta}{\cos\alpha\cos\beta} - \dfrac{\sin\alpha\sin\beta}{\cos\alpha\cos\beta}}$$

$$= \frac{\tan\alpha + \tan\beta}{1 - \tan\alpha\tan\beta} \qquad (5)$$

Replacing β by $-\beta$ in Formula (5) gives

$$\tan(\alpha - \beta) = \frac{\tan\alpha - \tan\beta}{1 + \tan\alpha\tan\beta} \qquad (6)$$

Example 2

Find the exact value of (a) $\sin\dfrac{\pi}{12}$ and (b) $\tan\dfrac{5\pi}{12}$.

Solution

(a) Write $\dfrac{\pi}{12} = \dfrac{\pi}{4} - \dfrac{\pi}{6}$. Then use Formula (3):

$$\sin\left(\frac{\pi}{4} - \frac{\pi}{6}\right) = \sin\frac{\pi}{4}\cos\frac{\pi}{6} - \cos\frac{\pi}{4}\sin\frac{\pi}{6}$$

$$= \frac{\sqrt{2}}{2}\cdot\frac{\sqrt{3}}{2} - \frac{\sqrt{2}}{2}\cdot\frac{1}{2}$$

$$= (\sqrt{6} - \sqrt{2})/4$$

(b) Write $\dfrac{5\pi}{12} = \dfrac{\pi}{4} + \dfrac{\pi}{6}$ and use Formula (5):

$$\tan\left(\frac{\pi}{4} + \frac{\pi}{6}\right) = \frac{\tan(\pi/4) + \tan(\pi/6)}{1 - \tan(\pi/4)\tan(\pi/6)}$$

$$= \frac{1 + \dfrac{1}{\sqrt{3}}}{1 - \dfrac{1}{\sqrt{3}}}$$

which may be simplified to $(\sqrt{3} + 1)/(\sqrt{3} - 1)$.

We have derived six addition formulas. They are listed, in pairs, at the end of this section. Take a few moments now to study them and commit the list to memory.

The angle between lines

Recall that a nonvertical line has an equation $y = mx + b$, where m is the slope. Such a line forms a positive angle α with any horizontal line (see Figure 8-8A). It is easy to see that

$$\tan\alpha = m$$

Now let L_1 and L_2 be lines with equations $y = m_1x + b$ and $y = m_2x + b$.

If α_1 is the angle that L_1 makes with the horizontal, then $m_1 = \tan\alpha_1$; if α_2 is the angle that L_2 makes with the horizontal, then $m_2 = \tan\alpha_2$. Let $\theta = \alpha_2 - \alpha_1$. It follows (see Figure 8-8B) that the positive angle from L_1 to L_2 is θ if $\alpha_2 - \alpha_1 \geq 0$ or

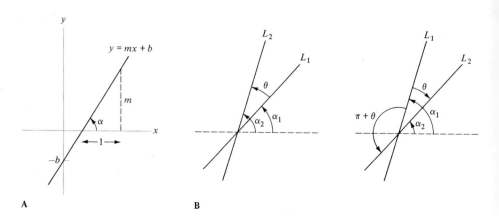

Figure 8-8
(A) The positive angle α between the horizontal (in this case, the x-axis) and the line $y = mx + b$; $\tan \alpha = m$. (B) $\theta = \alpha_2 - \alpha_1$. The positive angle from the line L_1 to the line L_2 is equal to θ or $\pi + \theta$, and

$$\tan \theta = \tan(\alpha_2 - \alpha_1) = \frac{m_2 - m_1}{1 + m_2 m_1}$$

$\pi + \theta$ if $\alpha_2 - \alpha_1 < 0$. The tangent of this angle is the same in both cases, because $\tan(\pi + \theta) = \tan \theta$. Therefore, it is possible to write a formula for the tangent of the angle from line L_1 to line L_2:

$$\tan \theta = \frac{\tan \alpha_2 - \tan \alpha_1}{1 + \tan \alpha_2 \tan \alpha_1} \qquad \text{(Formula (6))}$$

$$= \frac{m_2 - m_1}{1 + m_2 m_1} \qquad (7)$$

Example 3
Find the angle from the line $y = 2x + 4$ to the line $2x + 6y + 7 = 0$. Give the answer accurate to two significant figures.

Solution
Rewrite $2x + 6y + 7 = 0$ as $y = -\frac{1}{3}x - \frac{7}{6}$. The slopes of the lines are 2 and $-\frac{1}{3}$. Thus, θ or $\pi + \theta$ is the angle from the first line to the second, and

$$\tan \theta = \frac{-\dfrac{1}{3} - 2}{1 + \left(-\dfrac{1}{3}\right)(2)} = \frac{-\dfrac{7}{3}}{\dfrac{1}{3}} = -7 \qquad \text{(Formula (7))}$$

From Table 2, 1.4 is the reference angle, so $\theta = -1.4$. Because θ is negative, $\pi + \theta \approx 3.1 - 1.4 = 1.7$ is the angle from the first line to the second.

Rate of change of sine

The rate of change of a function was introduced in Section 2-5. There and in subsequent sections, the rate of change was seen to have many uses. For any function f, the *average rate of change* of f from x to $x + h$ is defined by

$$\text{a.r.c.} f(x, h) = \frac{f(x + h) - f(x)}{h}$$

This is an approximation to the *exact* rate of change of f at x. The smaller h is, the better the approximation. Now let us compute the rate of change of the sine function. Begin with the average rate of change:

$$\text{a.r.c.} \sin(x, h) = \frac{\sin(x + h) - \sin x}{h}$$

$$= \frac{\sin x \cos h + \cos x \sin h - \sin x}{h} \qquad \text{(Formula (4))}$$

which can be rewritten as

$$\text{a.r.c.} \sin(x, h) = \left(\frac{\cos h - 1}{h}\right) \sin x + \left(\frac{\sin h}{h}\right) \cos x \qquad (8)$$

This is the average rate of change from x to $x + h$; it approximates the *exact* rate at x when h is very close to zero. Fortunately, when h is very small, the cumbersome formula above simplifies nicely. When h is very close to zero, then

$$\frac{\cos h - 1}{h} \quad \text{is very close to 0} \quad \text{(Exercise 44 in Section 7-1)}$$

and

$$\frac{\sin h}{h} \quad \text{is very close to 1} \qquad \text{(Exercise 43 in Section 7-1)}$$

Incorporating this information into the right side of Equation (8), it follows that

■ The rate of change of the sine at x is $\cos x$.

Example 4

A particle moves on a straight line in such a way that its position y to the right ($+$) or left ($-$) of a fixed point A at time t is given by the equation $y = \sin t$ (simple harmonic motion). Where is the particle when $t = \pi/3, \pi/2,$ and π? What is its velocity at those times?

Solution

The position is $y = \sin t$; because $\sin(\pi/3) = \sqrt{3}/2$, $\sin(\pi/2) = 1$ and $\sin \pi = 0$, the particle is $\sqrt{3}/2$ units to the right of A when $t = \pi/3$, 1 unit to the right when $t = \pi/2$, and back at A when $t = \pi$.

Now use the fact that the *velocity is the rate of change of position;* thus, the velocity of the point at time t is $\cos t$. Because $\cos(\pi/3) = 1/2$, $\cos(\pi/2) = 0$ and $\cos \pi = -1$, it follows that the speed is $1/2$ and the particle is moving to the right when $t = \pi/3$; it is at rest when $t = \pi/2$; and it is moving to the left at a speed of 1 when $t = \pi$.

Review of basic ideas

Learn the technique used to prove the fundamental formula

$$\cos(\alpha - \beta) = \cos \alpha \cos \beta + \sin \alpha \sin \beta$$

Go over in your mind how to use this cosine formula to prove the other five formulas. The six addition formulas may be paired as follows; memorize them:

$$(1) \text{ and } (2): \quad \cos(\alpha \pm \beta) = \cos \alpha \cos \beta \mp \sin \alpha \sin \beta$$

$$(3) \text{ and } (4): \quad \sin(\alpha \pm \beta) = \sin \alpha \cos \beta \pm \cos \alpha \sin \beta$$

$$(5) \text{ and } (6): \quad \tan(\alpha \pm \beta) = \frac{\tan \alpha \pm \tan \beta}{1 \mp \tan \alpha \tan \beta}$$

Exercises

Find the exact values.

1. $\sin \dfrac{5\pi}{12}$ 2. $\cos \dfrac{5\pi}{12}$ 3. $\cot \dfrac{5\pi}{12}$

4. $\sec \dfrac{7\pi}{12}$ 5. $\csc \dfrac{7\pi}{12}$ 6. $\tan \dfrac{7\pi}{12}$

7. $\cos \dfrac{\pi}{12}$ 8. $\cot \dfrac{\pi}{12}$ 9. $\sin \dfrac{\pi}{12}$

10. $\tan \dfrac{11\pi}{12}$ 11. $\sec \dfrac{11\pi}{12}$ 12. $\sin \dfrac{11\pi}{12}$

13. If $\alpha = \arcsin \frac{1}{2}$ and $\beta = \arccos -\frac{3}{4}$, find $\cos(\alpha + \beta)$.

14. Same α and β as in Exercise 13; find $\sin(\alpha - \beta)$.

15. If $\alpha = \arcsin -\frac{5}{6}$ and $\beta = \arccos \frac{10}{11}$, find $\sin(\alpha + \beta)$.

16. Same α and β as in Exercise 15; find $\cos(\alpha - \beta)$.

17. If $\alpha = \tan^{-1}\frac{1}{2}$ and $\beta = \tan^{-1} -\frac{4}{5}$, find $\tan(\alpha + \beta)$.

18. Same α and β as in Exercise 17; find $\cot(\alpha - \beta)$.

19. Same α and β as in Exercise 17; find $\sin(\alpha + \beta)$.

20. Same α and β as in Exercise 17; find $\cos(\alpha - \beta)$.

Verify the following formulas.

21. $\sin\left(\alpha + \dfrac{\pi}{4}\right) = \dfrac{\sqrt{2}}{2}(\sin \alpha + \cos \alpha)$

22. $\cos\left(\alpha + \dfrac{\pi}{4}\right) = \dfrac{\sqrt{2}}{2}(\cos \alpha - \sin \alpha)$

23. $\cos\left(\dfrac{3\pi}{2} - \alpha\right) = -\sin \alpha$

24. $\tan\left(\dfrac{\pi}{4} + \alpha\right) = \dfrac{\cos \alpha + \sin \alpha}{\cos \alpha - \sin \alpha}$

25. $\sin 2\alpha = 2 \sin \alpha \cos \alpha$ [HINT: $\sin 2\alpha = \sin(\alpha + \alpha)$.]

26. $\cos 2\alpha = \cos^2\alpha - \sin^2\alpha$

27. $\tan 2\alpha = \dfrac{2 \tan \alpha}{1 - \tan^2\alpha}$

28. $\cos(\alpha + \beta) + \cos(\alpha - \beta) = 2 \cos \alpha \cos \beta$

29. Find the angle from line $y = 3x - 2$ to $y = 5x + 1$.

30. Find the angle from line $3x + 2y = 1$ to $x - 5y + 4 = 0$.

31. Same as Exercise 30 for $5x + y - 7 = 0$ and $x - 5y - 13 = 0$. This illustrates the fact that nonvertical lines are perpendicular if and only if the product of their slopes is -1.

32. A particle moves along a straight line so that its position y to the right or to the left of a fixed point A at time t is given by $y = \sin t$. Where does it start? Does it move first to the left or to the right? What is its starting velocity? What is its velocity when $t = \pi/3, \pi/2, 2\pi/3, \pi$, and $3\pi/2$? How would you describe its motion? (See Example 4).

33. Make up three problems about the angle θ between two lines: one in which θ is acute, one in which θ is obtuse, and one in which $\theta = \pi/2$.

34. (Surprise!) What is the exact rate of change of the cosine function?

8-3
Multiple-Angle Formulas

Think of $\cos 2\alpha$ as $\cos(\alpha + \alpha)$ and use the sum formula to obtain

$$\cos 2\alpha = \cos \alpha \cos \alpha - \sin \alpha \sin \alpha$$
$$= \cos^2\alpha - \sin^2\alpha$$

This is the **double-angle formula** for cosine. It also has two other useful formulations, which are shown below. The same method will establish double-angle formulas for sine and tangent:

$$\cos 2\alpha = \cos^2\alpha - \sin^2\alpha \qquad (\cos 2\alpha = \cos(\alpha + \alpha)) \tag{1}$$
$$= 1 - 2\sin^2\alpha \qquad (\cos^2\alpha = 1 - \sin^2\alpha) \tag{1a}$$
$$= 2\cos^2\alpha - 1 \qquad (\sin^2\alpha = 1 - \cos^2\alpha) \tag{1b}$$

$$\sin 2\alpha = 2\sin \alpha \cos \alpha \tag{2}$$

$$\cos^2\alpha + \sin^2\alpha = 1$$

$$\tan 2\alpha = \frac{2\tan \alpha}{1 - \tan^2\alpha} \tag{3}$$

Example 1

If $0 < x < \pi$ and $\tan x = 3/5$, find $\cos 2x$ and $\cos 4x$. In which quadrants are $2x$ and $4x$?

Solution

Because the tangent is positive, x is in the first quadrant. Because $(5, 3)$ is on the terminal side of x, $\sin x = 3/\sqrt{34}$ and $\cos x = 5/\sqrt{34}$ (see Figure 8-9A). Then

$$\cos 2x = \cos^2 x - \sin^2 x$$

$$= \frac{25}{34} - \frac{9}{34} = \frac{16}{34}$$

Evidently, $2x$ is still in the first quadrant.

To find $\cos 4x$, rewrite it as $\cos 2(2x)$ and use Formula (1b) with $\alpha = 2x$:

$$\cos 4x = 2\cos^2(2x) - 1$$

$$= 2(16/34)^2 - 1 \approx -.5571$$

The minus sign means that $4x$ must be in the second quadrant.

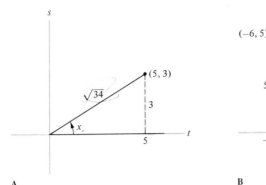

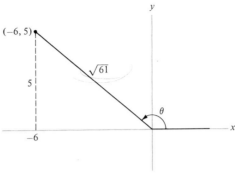

A   B

Figure 8-9
(A) If $0 < x < \pi$ and $\tan x = 3/5$, then $\sin x = 3/\sqrt{34}$ and $\cos x = 5/\sqrt{34}$. See Example 1. (B) If $0 < \theta < \pi$ and $\cot \theta = -6/5$, then $\cos \theta = -6/\sqrt{61}$. See Example 2.

Let us solve Formula (1a) for $\sin \alpha$:

$$\sin \alpha = \pm\sqrt{\frac{1 - \cos 2\alpha}{2}}$$

Because this formula holds for any angle α, we can replace α on both sides by $\beta/2$ to obtain the **half-angle formula**

$$\sin \frac{\beta}{2} = \pm\sqrt{\frac{1 - \cos \beta}{2}} \tag{4}$$

A similar procedure beginning with Formula (1b) yields

$$\cos \frac{\beta}{2} = \pm\sqrt{\frac{1 + \cos \beta}{2}} \tag{5}$$

The choice of sign in Formulas (4) and (5) is determined by the quadrant in which $\beta/2$ lies.

Example 2
If $0 < \theta < \pi$ and $\cot \theta = -6/5$, find $\cos(\theta/2)$ and $\sin(\theta/4)$. In which quadrants are $\theta/2$ and $\theta/4$?

Solution
Because the cotangent is negative, θ must lie in the second quadrant. Because $(-6, 5)$ is on the terminal side of θ, $\cos \theta = -6/\sqrt{61} \approx -.7682$ (see Figure 8-9B). Because θ is in quadrant II, it automatically follows that $\theta/2$ and $\theta/4$

are both in quadrant I. From Formula (5) above,

$$\cos\frac{\theta}{2} = \sqrt{\frac{1 + \cos\theta}{2}}$$

$$\approx \sqrt{\frac{1 - .7682}{2}} \approx .3404$$

To find $\sin\frac{\theta}{4}$, rewrite it as $\sin\frac{\theta/2}{2}$ and use Formula (4) with $\beta = \frac{\theta}{2}$:

$$\sin\frac{\theta}{4} = \sqrt{\frac{1 - \cos(\theta/2)}{2}}$$

$$\approx \sqrt{\frac{1 - .3404}{2}} \approx .5743$$

A half-angle formula for tangent can be derived from the half-angle formulas for sine and cosine:

$$\tan^2\frac{\beta}{2} = \frac{\sin^2\dfrac{\beta}{2}}{\cos^2\dfrac{\beta}{2}}$$

$$= \frac{(1 - \cos\beta)/2}{(1 + \cos\beta)/2}$$

from which it follows that

$$\tan\frac{\beta}{2} = \pm\sqrt{\frac{1 - \cos\beta}{1 + \cos\beta}} \tag{6}$$

Again, the choice of sign is determined by the quadrant in which $\beta/2$ lies. Another formula for the tangent, in which the sign is automatically determined, is

$$\tan\frac{\beta}{2} = \frac{1 - \cos\beta}{\sin\beta} \tag{6a}$$

The derivation of Formula (6a) is an exercise at the end of this section.

Example 3

Find the exact value of $\tan\frac{\pi}{8}$.

Solution

$\pi/8$ is one half of $\pi/4$. Either Formula (6) or Formula (6a) may be used; (6a) seems easier:

$$\tan \frac{\pi}{8} = \frac{1 - \cos(\pi/4)}{\sin(\pi/4)}$$

$$= \frac{1 - (\sqrt{2}/2)}{\sqrt{2}/2}$$

$$= \frac{2 - \sqrt{2}}{\sqrt{2}} = \sqrt{2} - 1$$

Review of basic ideas

Memorize the multiple-angle formulas:

$$\cos 2\alpha = \cos^2 \alpha - \sin^2 \alpha \qquad\qquad \sin \frac{\alpha}{2} = \pm \sqrt{\frac{1 - \cos \alpha}{2}}$$

$$= 1 - 2 \sin^2 \alpha$$

$$= 2 \cos^2 \alpha - 1 \qquad\qquad \cos \frac{\alpha}{2} = \pm \sqrt{\frac{1 + \cos \alpha}{2}}$$

$$\sin 2\alpha = 2 \sin \alpha \cos \alpha \qquad\qquad \tan \frac{\alpha}{2} = \pm \sqrt{\frac{1 - \cos \alpha}{1 + \cos \alpha}}$$

$$\tan 2\alpha = \frac{2 \tan \alpha}{1 - \tan^2 \alpha} \qquad\qquad\qquad = \frac{1 - \cos \alpha}{\sin \alpha}$$

Exercises

In Exercises 1 and 2, assume that $\pi/2 < x < 3\pi/2$.

1. If $\sin x = 2/5$, find $\cos x$, $\cos 2x$, $\sec 4x$, $\cot 2x$, and $\tan(x/2)$.

2. If $\tan x = -4/5$, find $\sin x$, $\sin 2x$, $\tan 2x$, $\cot 4x$, and $\tan(x/2)$.

In Exercises 3 and 4, assume that $-\pi/2 < x < \pi/2$.

3. If $\csc x = -7/2$, find $\tan x$, $\tan 2x$, $\tan 4x$, and $\sec(x/2)$.

4. If $\tan x = 2/3$, find $\sin x$, $\cos x$, $\cos 2x$, and $\cos 4x$.

Find the exact value.

5. $\sin \dfrac{3\pi}{8}$ **6.** $\cos \dfrac{3\pi}{8}$ **7.** $\tan \dfrac{5\pi}{12}$

8. $\sec \dfrac{5\pi}{12}$ 9. $\csc \dfrac{5\pi}{8}$ 10. $\cos \dfrac{5\pi}{8}$

Exercises 11 and 12 show that some care must be taken in choosing the sign in the half-angle formulas.

11. If $3\pi/2 < u < 2\pi$ and $\tan u = -6/7$, find $\cos(u/2)$.
12. If $u = \tan^{-1}(-6/7)$, find $\cos(u/2)$.
13. If $v = \cos^{-1}(-3/5)$, find $\sin(v/2)$.
14. If $-3\pi/2 < v < -\pi$ and $\cos v = -3/5$, find $\sin(v/2)$.

If $0 < x < \pi$ and $\cos x = 1/8$, find the exact value of
15. $\sin 3x$ [HINT: $\sin 3x = \sin(2x + x)$]
16. $\cos 3x$ 17. $\cos 6x$ 18. $\sin 1.5x$

19. Verify Formula (6a):

$$\tan \frac{\beta}{2} = \frac{1 - \cos \beta}{\sin \beta}$$

[HINT: Write $\tan(\beta/2)$ as $\dfrac{\sin(\beta/2)}{\cos(\beta/2)}$; multiply by $\sin(\beta/2)$ divided by itself; the new denominator will look something like Formula (2).]

Hyperbolic functions

The functions sinh and cosh are defined for all real numbers x as follows:

$$\sinh x = \tfrac{1}{2}(e^x - e^{-x})$$

$$\cosh x = \tfrac{1}{2}(e^x + e^{-x})$$

where $e = 2.71828. \ldots$, the irrational number that is the base of the natural logarithm (see Chapter 5). These rather odd-looking functions have many applications to the physical and engineering sciences. In some ways, they are very much like the trigonometric functions. For example,

$$\sinh(-x) = \tfrac{1}{2}(e^{-x} - e^{-(-x)})$$

$$= \tfrac{1}{2}(e^{-x} - e^x)$$

$$= -\tfrac{1}{2}(e^x - e^{-x}) = -\sinh x$$

just like the sine function.

20.   Show that $\cosh(-x) = \cosh x$, just like the cosine.

21.   Show that $\cosh^2 x - \sinh^2 x = 1$, *almost* like the sine and cosine.

22.   Show that

$$\sinh(x + y) = \sinh x \cosh y + \cosh x \sinh y \quad [\text{Like } \sin(x + y)]$$

and

$$\cosh(x + y) = \cosh x \cosh y + \sinh x \sinh y \quad [\text{Almost like } \cos(x + y)]$$

The function sinh is called the **hyperbolic sine.** The function cosh is called the **hyperbolic cosine.** These functions are also related to hyperbolas (discussed in Chapter 10); hence the term *hyperbolic.* There is also a function tanh, the **hyperbolic tangent,** defined by

$$\tanh x = \frac{\sinh x}{\cosh x}$$

23.   Make up and prove a formula for $\tanh(x + y)$.

24.   Make up and prove formulas for $\sinh 2x$, $\cosh 2x$, $\sinh \dfrac{x}{2}$, and $\cosh \dfrac{x}{2}$.

8-4
Trigonometric Identities

Many equations are true only for certain values of the variable. For instance, $2x + 7 = 9$ is true only if $x = 1$, and the equation $\sin 2\alpha = 2 \sin \alpha$ is true only if α is an integral multiple of π. In contrast to these examples, the equation

$$\sin^2 x + \cos^2 x = 1$$

is true for *all* values of x. Such an equation is called an identity.

A **trigonometric identity** is a trigonometric equation true for all values of the variable that are allowed on both sides of the equation. Thus, the double-angle formula

$$\tan 2x = \frac{2 \tan x}{1 - \tan^2 x}$$

is considered to be an identity even though neither side is defined when $x = \pi/4$.

On the inside back cover of this book are printed several identities that we have already proved and that turn up frequently in applications of trigonometry. These will now be used to prove new identities by changing one side of an equation into the other. The new identities are not too important in themselves; more important are the methods employed in proving them.

Example 1

Prove that this equation is an identity:

$$\frac{1}{1 + \cos x} + \frac{1}{1 - \cos x} = 2 \csc^2 x$$

Solution

There is no one method for proving identities, but it usually pays to start with the side that looks more complicatd. In this case, begin by combining the fractions on the left:

$$\frac{1}{1 + \cos x} + \frac{1}{1 - \cos x} = \frac{(1 - \cos x) + (1 + \cos x)}{(1 + \cos x)(1 - \cos x)}$$

$$= \frac{2}{1 - \cos^2 x}$$

$$= \frac{2}{\sin^2 x} \qquad (\sin^2 x + \cos^2 x = 1)$$

$$= 2 \csc^2 x$$

Example 2

Show that

$$\frac{\sin t \sec t}{\tan t + \cot t} = \sin^2 t$$

is an identity.

Solution

If the method of attack is not obvious, then change everything into sines and cosines and simplify. Again, begin with the left side:

$$\frac{\sin t \sec t}{\tan t + \cot t} = \frac{\sin t \cdot \dfrac{1}{\cos t}}{\dfrac{\sin t}{\cos t} + \dfrac{\cos t}{\sin t}}$$

$$= \frac{\dfrac{\sin t}{\cos t}}{\dfrac{\sin^2 t + \cos^2 t}{\cos t \sin t}}$$

$$= \frac{\sin t}{\cos t} \cdot \frac{\cos t \sin t}{1}$$

$$= \sin^2 t$$

Example 3
Verify the identity

$$(\sec u - \tan u)^2 = \frac{1 - \sin u}{1 + \sin u}$$

Solution
There are at least two ways to proceed with this one.

METHOD I. Multiply the left side out:

$$(\sec u - \tan u)^2 = \sec^2 u - 2 \sec u \tan u + \tan^2 u$$

$$= \frac{1}{\cos^2 u} - \frac{2 \sin u}{\cos^2 u} + \frac{\sin^2 u}{\cos^2 u} \quad \text{(Change to sin and cos.)}$$

$$= \frac{1 - 2 \sin u + \sin^2 u}{\cos^2 u}$$

$$= \frac{(1 - \sin u)^2}{1 - \sin^2 u} = \frac{(1 - \sin u)(1 - \sin u)}{(1 - \sin u)(1 + \sin u)}$$

METHOD II. Start with the right side and "rationalize" the denominator:

$$\frac{1 - \sin u}{1 + \sin u} = \frac{1 - \sin u}{1 + \sin u} \cdot \frac{1 - \sin u}{1 - \sin u}$$

$$= \frac{(1 - \sin u)^2}{1 - \sin^2 u}$$

$$= \frac{(1 - \sin u)^2}{\cos^2 u}$$

$$= \left(\frac{1 - \sin u}{\cos u}\right)^2$$

$$= \left(\frac{1}{\cos u} - \frac{\sin u}{\cos u}\right)^2$$

$$= (\sec u - \tan u)^2$$

Example 4
Prove the identity

$$\frac{\sin 2x}{\sin x} - \frac{\cos 2x}{\cos x} = \sec x$$

Solution
Use the double-angle formulas:

$$\frac{\sin 2x}{\sin x} - \frac{\cos 2x}{\cos x} = \frac{2 \cancel{\sin x} \cos x}{\cancel{\sin x}} - \frac{\cos^2 x - \sin^2 x}{\cos x}$$

$$= \frac{2 \cos^2 x - \cos^2 x + \sin^2 x}{\cos x} \quad \text{(Combine fractions.)}$$

$$= \frac{1}{\cos x} = \sec x$$

Trigonometric identities are not very difficult to make up.

Example 5
Start with any algebraic combination of trigonometric functions; for example, let us try

$$\sin x \tan x$$

Now we replace one or both with equivalent expressions. Suppose we write

$$\sin x \tan x = \sin x \cdot \frac{\sin x}{\cos x} = \frac{\sin^2 x}{\cos x}$$

There are a number of paths available now. One is to continue with

$$\sin x \tan x = \frac{\sin^2 x}{\cos x} = \frac{1 - \cos^2 x}{\cos x}$$

$$= \sec x - \cos x$$

The identity we just made up is

$$\sin x \tan x = \sec x - \cos x$$

Example 6
Make up an identity starting with $\dfrac{\cot x}{1 + \sin x}$.

Solution

One possibility is to "rationalize" the denominator:

$$\frac{\cot x}{1 + \sin x} \cdot \frac{1 - \sin x}{1 - \sin x} = \frac{\cot x - \cot x \sin x}{1 - \sin^2 x}$$

The numerator is $\cot x - \cos x$ and the denominator is $1 - \sin^2 x = \cos^2 x$. Dividing gives the identity

$$\frac{\cot x}{1 + \sin x} = \frac{1}{\sin x \cos x} - \frac{1}{\cos x}$$

You can stop here, or go further by substituting $2 \csc 2x$ for $1/\sin x \cos x$, and $\sec x$ for $1/\cos x$. Now the identity is

$$\frac{\cot x}{1 + \sin x} = 2 \csc 2x - \sec x$$

Obviously, you could go on almost indefinitely.

Exercises

Verify the identities.

1. $\csc x - \sin x = \cot x \cos x$

2. $(\sin^2 y)(\csc^2 y - 1) = \cos^2 y$

3. $(\tan^2 u)(1 + \cot^2 u) = \sec^2 u$

4. $(\sec^2 v)(1 - \sin^2 v) = 1$

5. $\dfrac{\sec t}{\cos t} = 1 + \dfrac{\tan t}{\cot t}$

6. $\dfrac{\csc w}{\sin w} - \dfrac{\cot w}{\tan w} = 1$

7. $(\tan x + \cot x)(\cos x + \sin x) = \sec x + \csc x$
8. $(\cos^2 y - 1)(\tan^2 y + 1) = 1 - \sec^2 y$

9. $\dfrac{1}{\tan u + \cot u} = \sin u \cos u$

10. $\dfrac{1}{\sec v - \cos v} = \cot v \csc v$

Show that the following equations are not identities by finding (at least) one value of the variable for which both sides are defined but unequal.

11. $\tan 2x = 2 \tan x$

12. $\cos 2y = 2 \cos y$

13. $\sin u = \sin u \tan^2 u$

14. $\cos v = \cot v \cos v$

15. $\tan t + \sec t = 1$

16. $2 \sin w + \cot w = \csc w$

Some of the following equations are identities; others are not. Decide which is which and prove your decisions.

17. $\sec^2 x - \tan^2 x = 1$

18. $\sin y \tan y + \cos y = \sec y$

19. $\csc 2u \sec 2u = 2 \csc 2u$

20. $\dfrac{\cot v - 1}{1 - \tan v} = \cot v$

21. $\sec^2 t \csc^2 t = \sec^2 t + \csc^2 t$

22. $\cos^4 w + \sin^2 w = \sin^4 w + \cos^2 w$

23. $\tan x + \cot x = \sec x \csc x$

24. $\dfrac{\sec y - \cos y}{\tan y} = \dfrac{\tan y}{\sec y}$

25. $\dfrac{1 + \sec u}{\tan u + \sin u} = \csc u$

26. $\sin 2t \sin t = \cos t$

27. $\sec^2 w + \tan^2 w = (1 - \sin^4 w)(\sec^4 w)$

28. $\dfrac{\cos^2 x - \sin^2 x}{\cos x - \sin x} = 1 + \sin x \cos x$

29. $\dfrac{\cos^3 y - \sin^3 y}{\cos y - \sin y} = 1 + \sin y \cos y$

30. $\dfrac{\sin u + \cos u}{\tan^2 u - 1} = \dfrac{\cos^2 u}{\sin u - \cos u}$

31. $(\cos t)(\tan t - \cot t) = (\csc t)(1 - 2\cos^2 t)$

32. $(\cos w)(\tan w - \sin w) = \dfrac{\sin^2 w}{1 + \cos w}$

33. $(\cos x)(\tan x - \sin x) = \dfrac{\sin^3 x}{1 + \cos x}$

■   Starting with each of the following expressions, make up an identity. Compare your finished products with those of a classmate. There should be quite a variety. Then make up some of your own to exchange and work out.

34. $\dfrac{1 + \cos x}{\sin x}$

35. $\dfrac{1 - \cos y}{1 + \cos y}$

36. $\dfrac{\sec u - \csc u}{\sec u + \csc u}$

37. $\dfrac{\tan^2 v}{\sec v + 1}$

8-5
Trigonometric Equations

Most trigonometric equations that turn up in applications are not identities: they are true only for certain values of the variable. Solving such equations means finding those values. There are three types of solution that may be called for.

Example 1
Solve the equation $2 \sin x - 1 = 0$ for

(a) all values of x (b) $0 \le x < 2\pi$ (c) x in the range of the arcsine

Solution
The first step is to solve for $\sin x$; thus,

$$\sin x = \tfrac{1}{2}$$

(a)   Within one full rotation, only $\sin(\pi/6)$ and $\sin(5\pi/6)$ equal $\tfrac{1}{2}$. To these values you must add all multiples of 2π. Thus, the union

$$\left\{ x \middle| x = \frac{\pi}{6} + 2n\pi \right\} \cup \left\{ x \middle| x = \frac{5\pi}{6} + 2n\pi \right\}$$

is the solution set.
(b)   The solution set is $\{\pi/6, 5\pi/6\}$.
(c)   There is a unique solution, $x = \sin^{-1}\tfrac{1}{2} = \pi/6$.

If an equation contains only one trigonometric function, it is usually possible to transform the trigonometric equation into a familiar algebraic equation. The methods for solving algebraic equations—factoring, applying the quadratic formula, and so on—can then be used to solve the trigonometric equation.

Example 2
Solve $2 \sin^2 x - \sin x = 1$ for $0 \le x < 2\pi$.

Solution
Let $u = \sin x$. Then the equation becomes $2u^2 - u = 1$, which can be solved for u. Rewrite the equation as $2u^2 - u - 1 = 0$ and factor the left side: $(2u + 1)(u - 1) = 0$, so $u = -\tfrac{1}{2}$ or $u = 1$. It follows now that

$$\sin x = -\tfrac{1}{2} \quad \text{or} \quad \sin x = 1$$

and that $\{7\pi/6, 11\pi/6, \pi/2\}$ is the solution set.

Check

$$2 \sin^2 \frac{7\pi}{6} - \sin \frac{7\pi}{6} = 2(-\tfrac{1}{2})^2 - (-\tfrac{1}{2}) = 1$$

The other values also check.

Replacing the function by u can usually be done mentally.

Example 3
Solve $\tan^2 x = 1 - 4 \tan x$ for x in the range of the arctangent function. (Round off to two significant figures.)

Solution
This equation can be rewritten as a quadratic polynomial equal to zero (think of $u^2 + 4u - 1 = 0$). The left side cannot be factored easily, so use the quadratic formula:

$$\tan x = \frac{-4 \pm \sqrt{4^2 - 4(1)(-1)}}{2(1)}$$

$$\approx \frac{-4 \pm 4.5}{2} = .25 \quad \text{or} \quad -4.3$$

The problem calls for x in the range of $\tan^{-1}$, which is $-\pi/2 < x < \pi/2$. According to Table 2,

$$x \approx \tan^{-1}.25 = .24 \quad \text{or} \quad x \approx \tan^{-1}(-4.3) = -1.3$$

Example 4
Solve $10^{(5 \cos u + 1)} = 4$ for $0 \le u < 2\pi$. (Round off to two significant figures.)

Solution
Take the logarithm of each side:

$$5 \cos u + 1 = \log 4 \approx .60 \qquad \text{(Table 1)}$$

so $\cos u \approx -.08$. According to Table 2, the reference angle is 1.5. Because the cosine is negative, it follows that $u \approx \pi - 1.5 \approx 1.6$ or $\pi + 1.5 \approx 4.6$.

If an equation contains more than one trigonometric function, there are two methods of attack. First, try to rewrite the equation with 0 on the right and a product of factors containing only one function each on the left. If this cannot be done, then try using trigonometric identities to reduce the number of functions.

Example 5
Solve $\sin t \tan t = \sin t$ for $0 \le t < 2\pi$.

Solution
Write the equation as $\sin t \tan t - \sin t = 0$ and factor the left side:

$$(\tan t - 1)\sin t = 0$$

Then $\tan t - 1 = 0$ or $\sin t = 0$. From the first equation, $t = \pi/4$ or $5\pi/4$; from the second, $t = 0$ or π. The solution set, therefore is $\{0, \pi/4, \pi, 5\pi/4\}$. Check in the original equation:

$$\sin 0 \tan 0 = 0 \quad \text{and} \quad \sin 0 = 0$$

$$\sin \frac{\pi}{4} \tan \frac{\pi}{4} = \frac{\sqrt{2}}{2} \quad \text{and} \quad \sin \frac{\pi}{4} = \frac{\sqrt{2}}{2}$$

The other values also check. CAUTION: if you had divided both sides of the original equation by $\sin t$ to obtain $\tan t = 1$, then the solutions 0 and π would have been lost. The reason is that for $t = 0$ and π, $\sin t = 0$, and division by 0 is not allowed.

Example 6
Solve $\cos x + 1 = \sin^2 x$ for $0 \le x < 2\pi$.

Solution
Replace $\sin^2 x$ by $1 - \cos^2 x$; then $\cos x + 1 = 1 - \cos^2 x$, or $\cos^2 x + \cos x = 0$. Factoring gives $(\cos x)(\cos x + 1) = 0$, and it follows that $\{\pi/2, \pi, 3\pi/2\}$ is the solution set. Check these values in the original equation.

The double- and half-angle formulas can also be used to advantage.

Example 7
Solve $\cos x = \sin 2x$ for all values of x.

Solution
Use the double-angle formula to write

$$\cos x = 2 \sin x \cos x$$

and proceed as in Example 5. Write

$$\cos x - 2 \sin x \cos x = 0$$

$$\cos x(1 - 2 \sin x) = 0$$

so $\sin x = \frac{1}{2}$ or $\cos x = 0$. The solution set is

$$\left\{ x \mid x = \frac{\pi}{6} + 2n\pi \right\} \cup \left\{ x \mid x = \frac{5\pi}{6} + 2n\pi \right\}$$

$$\cup \left\{ x \mid x = \frac{\pi}{2} + 2n\pi \right\} \cup \left\{ x \mid x = \frac{3\pi}{2} + 2n\pi \right\}$$

Some care must be taken in dealing with multiple angles.

Example 8
Solve $\sin 3x = \frac{1}{2}$ for $0 \leq x < 2\pi$.

Solution
Because $\sin 3x = \frac{1}{2}$, you might be tempted to reason that $3x = \pi/6$ or $5\pi/6$, and conclude that $\{\pi/18, 5\pi/18\}$ is the complete solution set.

The correct reasoning in this case is that, if x can vary from 0 to 2π, then $3x$ can vary from 0 to 6π. Therefore, $3x$ can take any one of the values

$$\frac{\pi}{6}, \frac{5\pi}{6}, \frac{\pi}{6} + 2\pi, \frac{5\pi}{6} + 2\pi, \frac{\pi}{6} + 4\pi, \quad \text{or} \quad \frac{5\pi}{6} + 4\pi$$

and it follows that

$$\left\{ \frac{\pi}{18}, \frac{5\pi}{18}, \frac{\pi}{18} + \frac{2\pi}{3}, \frac{5\pi}{18} + \frac{2\pi}{3}, \frac{\pi}{18} + \frac{4\pi}{3}, \frac{5\pi}{18} + \frac{4\pi}{3} \right\}$$

is the complete solution set of values of x. Check these values.

Exercises

In all these exercises, if approximation is required, round off to only two significant figures. Check your answers.

Solve for all values of x.

1.	$2 \cos x + 1 = 0$	**2.**	$\sin x + 1 = 0$
3.	$\tan x + 1 = .64$	**4.**	$3 \sec x - 4 = 0$
5.	$2 \cos x = \sin 2x$	**6.**	$2 \sin x = \cos 2x$

Solve for x in the range of the inverse function.

7.	$4 \sin^2 x - 3 = 0$	**8.**	$4 \cos^2 - 1 = 0$

9. $2 \cos 3x = 1$

10. $3 \tan^2 3x = 1$

11. $2 \sin^2 x + \sin x - 1 = 0$

12. $6 \cos^2 x + 5 \cos x + 1 = 0$

Solve for $0 \le x < 2\pi$.

13. $\sec^2 x - 2 \sec x = 0$

14. $\csc^2 x + 2 \csc x = 0$

15. $\tan x - \sin x = 0$

16. $\tan x - \sin 2x = 0$

17. $\sec^2 x - 2 \tan x = 0$

18. $\cos^2 x + \sin x = 0$

19. $2 \sin x + \cot x = \csc x$

20. $\sec x + \cos x = \sin x \tan x$

21. $\csc^2 x + 3 \csc x - 18 = 0$

22. $\tan^2 x - 2 \tan x - 8 = 0$

23. $\sin^2 x - 3 \sin x = 4$

24. $\cos^2 x + 2 \cos x = 3$

25. $6 \cos^2 x - \cos x = 2$

26. $12 \sin^2 x + 7 \sin x + 1 = 0$

27. $3 \tan 3x = 1$

28. $\tan 2x = 3$

29. $2 \cos \dfrac{x}{2} = 2$

30. $2 \sin \dfrac{x}{3} = 1$

31. $2 \sin \left(x + \dfrac{\pi}{4} \right) = 1$

32. $\cot \left(x - \dfrac{\pi}{3} \right) = 1$

33. $\sin(\pi - x) + \cos \left(\dfrac{\pi}{2} - x \right) = 1$

34. $\cos(\pi - x) + \sin \left(\dfrac{\pi}{2} - x \right) = 1$

35. $\cos 2x \cos x + \sin 2x \sin x = 1$

36. $\sin 2x \sin x - \cos 2x \cos x + \cos x = 0$

37. $\sin 4x + 2 \sin 2x = 0$

38. $\sin 4x - 2 \sin 2x = 0$

39. $5^{\sin x} = 3$

40. $6^{\cos 2x} = 4$

Chapter 9

Complex Numbers

The two equations $x^2 - 1 = 0$ and $x^2 + 1 = 0$ differ by only a minus sign, but that makes all the difference in the world. The first equation has the solutions $x = \pm 1$; to solve the second, a whole new number system had to be invented.

Imagine a number system that contained the real numbers, preserved the properties of arithmetic, and also contained a number whose square is -1. Let i denote this number. Then $i^2 = -1$, and i would be a solution of $x^2 + 1 = 0$. In such a system it would be possible to take square roots of *all* negative real numbers. For example, $(2i)^2 = 2^2 i^2 = -4$, and therefore $\sqrt{-4} = 2i$. Furthermore, all quadratic equations with real coefficients would have solutions.

Example
Find solutions (in the new system) of $x^2 - 2x + 2 = 0$.

Solution
The quadratic formula yields

$$x = \frac{-(-2) \pm \sqrt{2^2 - 4(1)(2)}}{2(1)}$$

$$= \frac{2 \pm \sqrt{-4}}{2} = \frac{2 \pm 2i}{2}$$

$$= 1 \pm i$$

Check

Let $x = 1 + i$. Then, by the properties of arithmetic,

$$x^2 - 2x + 2 = (1 + i)^2 - 2(1 + i) + 2$$
$$= 1^2 + 2i + i^2 - 2 - 2i + 2$$
$$= 1 + 2i - 1 - 2 - 2i + 2 = 0$$

A similar calculation shows that $x = 1 - i$ also checks.

In Section 9-1, such a system, the complex number system, is defined, with the basic operations of addition, subtraction, multiplication, and division. In Section 9-2 complex numbers are represented geometrically as points in a plane. This representation allows us to give geometric interpretations to the operations defined in Section 9-1.

Section 9-3 contains the important Fundamental Theorem of Algebra, which guarantees that any polynomial with complex coefficients has at least one zero. It then follows that the complex number system is rich enough to contain all solutions of polynomial equations, so that no further enlargements of the number system are needed. Section 9-4 explains how to take large powers and how to find all roots of a complex number. Combining complex numbers with trigonometry, we shall see that each complex number has exactly n distinct nth roots.

9-1
Complex Numbers

There is a system of numbers that contains the real numbers, preserves the usual properties of arithmetic, and also contains a number whose square is -1. This special number is denoted by the letter i, and it is called an **imaginary number.**

■ $i^2 = -1$ or, equivalently, $i = \sqrt{-1}$

The set of numbers in this new system is denoted by **C.** Every real number is in **C.** Therefore, if b is any real number, the product bi must be in **C.** Furthermore, if a is also a real number, the sum $a + bi$ must be in **C.**

■   **Definition**

A **complex number** is any number of the form $a + bi$, where a and b are real numbers.

Examples are $3 + 2i$ and $-\sqrt{2} + \pi i$. If $a = 4$ and $b = -7$, we shall write $4 - 7i$ rather than $4 + (-7)i$. If $b = 0$, then $a + 0i$ will simply be written a; thus each real number a can be thought of as the complex number $a + 0i$. If $a = 0$, then $0 + bi$ is written bi; thus, $i = 1 \cdot i$ is the complex number $0 + i$.

■   **Definition**
Let $a + bi$ and $c + di$ be complex numbers. Then

$$a + bi = c + di \quad \text{if and only if } a = c \text{ and } b = d;$$

$$(a + bi) + (c + di) = (a + c) + (b + d)i; \text{ and}$$

$$(a + bi)(c + di) = (ac - bd) + (ad + bc)i.$$

The set **C** of complex numbers together with equality, addition, and multiplication as defined here is the **complex number system.**

These definitions of addition and multiplication are just what you would expect, given that the properties of arithmetic are preserved in the complex number system.

$$(a + bi) + (c + di) = a + bi + c + di$$

$$= a + c + bi + di \qquad \text{(Commutative)}$$

$$= (a + c) + (b + d)i \qquad \text{(Associative and distributive)}$$

and

$$(a + bi)(c + di) = ac + adi + bci + bdi^2 \qquad \text{(Distributive)}$$

$$= ac - bd + adi + bci \qquad (i^2 = -1)$$

$$= (ac - bd) + (ad + bc)i$$

Notice that multiplication is just the familiar product of factors with two terms each, except that $(bi)(di) = -bd$.

Example 1

(a) $(3 + 2i) + (-4 + 5i) = (3 - 4) + (2 + 5)i = -1 + 7i$

(b) $(-1 + i) + (6 - 3i) = 5 - 2i$

(c) $(2 + 3i)(5 + 4i) = (2 \cdot 5 - 3 \cdot 4) + (2 \cdot 4 + 3 \cdot 5)i$

$$= -2 + 23i$$

(d) $(-1 + i)(2 - i) = [(-1) \cdot 2 - (1)(-1)] + [(-1)(-1) + 1 \cdot 2]i$

$$= -1 + 3i$$

A special product that turns up often is

$$(a + bi)(a - bi) = (a^2 + b^2) + (-ab + ba)i$$
$$= a^2 + b^2$$

Notice that the result of this product is always a nonnegative real number.

Example 2

(a) $(3 + i)(3 - i) = 3^2 + 1^2 = 10$

(b) $(\sqrt{2} + \sqrt{5}i)(\sqrt{2} - \sqrt{5}i) = (\sqrt{2})^2 + (\sqrt{5})^2 = 7$

The letters u, v, w, and z are often used to denote complex numbers. If u and v are any two complex numbers, $u - v$ is another complex number, w, such that $u = w + v$. The formula for subtraction is just what you would expect it to be:

$$(a + bi) - (c + di) = (a - c) + (b - d)i$$

If u and v are complex numbers and $v \neq 0 + 0i$, then u/v is another complex number, w, such that $u = vw$. The formula for division, as usual, is slightly complicated; it must express $(a + bi)/(c + di)$ as a single complex number. We can work it out by "rationalizing" the denominator, using the special product described just before Example 2:

$$\frac{a + bi}{c + di} = \frac{(a + bi)(c - di)}{(c + di)(c - di)}$$

$$= \frac{(ac + bd) + (bc - ad)i}{c^2 + d^2}$$

$$= \frac{ac + bd}{c^2 + d^2} + \frac{bc - ad}{c^2 + d^2}i$$

Example 3

Write $(2 + 4i)/(-6 - 3i)$ as a complex number $a + bi$ and check the answer.

Solution

$$\frac{2 + 4i}{-6 - 3i} = \frac{(2 + 4i)(-6 + 3i)}{(-6 - 3i)(-6 + 3i)}$$

$$= \frac{-24 - 18i}{36 + 9}$$

$$= -\frac{24}{45} - \frac{18}{45}i$$

Check

As usual, division is checked by multiplication:

$$(-6 - 3i)\left(-\frac{24}{45} - \frac{18}{45}i\right) = \left(\frac{144}{45} - \frac{54}{45}\right) + \left(\frac{72}{45} + \frac{108}{45}\right)i$$

$$= 2 + 4i$$

Absolute value

One way of defining the absolute value of a real number a is $|a| = \sqrt{a^2}$. In a similar way, the **absolute value** of a complex number $a + bi$ is defined as

■ $|a + bi| = \sqrt{a^2 + b^2}$

Notice that the absolute value of a complex number is always a nonnegative real number.

Example 4

$$|2 - 4i| = \sqrt{2^2 + (-4)^2} = \sqrt{20} = 2\sqrt{5}$$
$$|-\sqrt{2} + \tfrac{1}{2}i| = \sqrt{(-\sqrt{2})^2 + (\tfrac{1}{2})^2} = \sqrt{\tfrac{9}{4}} = \tfrac{3}{2}$$

The absolute value of a real number has the geometric interpretation "distance from zero." In the next section it will be shown that there is a similar geometric interpretation for complex numbers.

Conjugates

The complex number $a - bi$ is called the **conjugate** of the complex number $a + bi$. The conjugate of a number is denoted by writing a bar over the number:

■ $\overline{a + bi} = a - bi$

Notice that each real number a is its own conjugate:

$$\bar{a} = \overline{a + 0 \cdot i} = a - 0 \cdot i = a$$

There is a close relationship between conjugates and absolute value:

$$(a + bi)\overline{(a + bi)} = (a + bi)(a - bi) = a^2 + b^2 = |a + bi|^2$$

Here is a list of these and other important facts about conjugates:

■   (a)   If a is a real number, then $\bar{a} = a$.

For any complex numbers z and w,
   (b) $\bar{\bar{z}} = z$
   (c) $z\bar{z} = |z|^2$
   (d) $\overline{z + w} = \bar{z} + \bar{w}$ and $\overline{z - w} = \bar{z} - \bar{w}$
   (e) $\overline{zw} = \bar{z}\,\bar{w}$ and $\overline{(z/w)} = \bar{z}/\bar{w}$

Parts (a) and (c) were demonstrated above. The other statements can all be proved in a straightforward manner. For example, let $z = a + bi$. Then

$$\bar{\bar{z}} = \overline{\overline{a + bi}} = \overline{a - bi} = a + bi = z$$

Let $z = a + bi$ and $w = c + di$. Then

$$\overline{z + w} = \overline{(a + c) + (b + d)i} = (a + c) - (b + d)i$$
$$= (a + c) + (-b - d)i$$
$$= (a - bi) + (c - di)$$
$$= \bar{z} + \bar{w}$$

The proofs of the others are left as exercises.

Exercises

Perform the indicated operations and express the answers in the form $a + bi$.
1. $(3 + 4i) + (1 - 2i)$ 2. $(-2 + i) + (3 - i)$
3. $(\frac{1}{2} - \frac{1}{3}i) + (\frac{1}{4} + \frac{1}{9}i)$ 4. $(-2 - i) + (3 + 4i)$
5. $(2 - 4i) - (2 + i)$ 6. $(\frac{3}{4} + \frac{1}{2}i) - (\frac{1}{4} - \frac{1}{2}i)$
7. $(-1 - i) - (4 - \frac{2}{5}i)$ 8. $(-2 - 3i) - (-1 - 5i)$

9. $2i(4 - 3i)$ 10. $i(-1 + i)$

11. $(1 + i)(2 + 3i)$ 12. $(-2 + 3i)(4 - 5i)$

13. $(2.1 + 3i)(.6 - .7i)$ 14. $(7 - i)(-3 - 2i)$

Express as $a + bi$ (as in Example 3).

15. $\dfrac{1}{i}$ 16. $\dfrac{3 + 4i}{i}$ 17. $\dfrac{5}{6 - i}$

18. $\dfrac{2i}{1 + i}$ 19. $\dfrac{3 + 2i}{4 - 5i}$ 20. $\dfrac{1 + i}{1 - i}$

Verify that the indicated complex number is a solution of the given equation.

21. $3x - 6 + 3i = 0$; $x = 2 - i$

22. $4 - 10i - 2x = 0$; $x = 2 - 5i$

23. $x^2 - 2x + 2 = 0$; $x = 1 - i$

24. $x^2 - 3 - 4i = 0$; $x = 2 + i$

25. $x^2 + 2x + 3 = 0$; $x = -1 + \sqrt{2}i$

26. $x^2 - 4x + 13 = 0$; $x = 2 + 3i$

Compute.

27. $|3 - 4i|$ 28. $|(1 + i) - (3 - 2i)|$

29. $|(2 - i)(1 + 3i)|$ 30. $\left|\dfrac{1}{1 + i}\right|$

31. Calculate $i^3, i^4, i^5, \ldots, i^{12}$. Make a general statement about the powers i^n.

32. Compute $i^{17}, i^{220}, i^{5280}$, and i^{-19}

Prove the following statements. They are straightforward; simply let $z = a + bi$ and $w = c + di$ and show that the two sides are equal.

33. $\overline{z + w} = \overline{z} + \overline{w}$ 34. $\overline{z - w} = \overline{z} - \overline{w}$

35. $\overline{zw} = \overline{z}\,\overline{w}$ 36. $\overline{(z/w)} = \overline{z}/\overline{w}$

37. $|\overline{z}| = |z|$ 38. $|zw| = |z|\,|w|$

39. $|z/w| = |z|/|w|$ 40. $\left|\dfrac{z}{|z|}\right| = 1$; $z \neq 0$

The problems encountered in applying fractional exponents to negative real numbers come up when we take complex numbers to fractional powers. For example, $(\sqrt{-4})(\sqrt{-9}) = (2i)(3i) = -6$. On the other hand, if we write $(-4)^{\frac{1}{2}}(-9)^{\frac{1}{2}} = ((-4)(-9))^{\frac{1}{2}}$, the answer is $+6$. This problem is resolved by agreeing to use the first method; that is, *always* express the radicals in terms of i before multiplying.

Compute.

41. $\sqrt{-2}\sqrt{-8}$ **42.** $\sqrt{-3}\sqrt{-12}$

43. $(1 + \sqrt{-2})(3 - \sqrt{-4})$ **44.** $(4 + \sqrt{-2})(1 + \sqrt{-3})$

45. Let $a, b, c,$ and d be any four real numbers. Use what you know about complex numbers to show that

$$(a^2 + b^2)(c^2 + d^2) = (ac - bd)^2 + (ad + bc)^2$$

[HINT: Let $z = a + bi$ and $w = c + di$. Then use Exercise 38 in the form $|z|^2 |w|^2 = |zw|^2$.]

46. (Continuation of Exercise 45) Express 290 as the sum of two perfect squares. [HINT: $10 = 1^2 + 3^2$ and $29 = 2^2 + 5^2$.]

■   **47.** Make up a division problem similar to Exercises 15–20. Divide and check your answer.

48. Make up a quadratic equation with real coefficients that has no real roots. Then find its complex roots and check your work.

49. Make up a problem similar to Exercise 46.

9-2
The Complex Plane. Polar Form

The real numbers can be represented geometrically as a line. The complex numbers can be represented geometrically as a plane.

Each complex number $z = a + bi$ can be thought of as an ordered pair of real numbers (a, b). The number a is called the **real part** of z, and b is called the **imaginary part** of z. Thus, z corresponds to exactly one point in a coordinate plane and, conversely, each point in this plane represents exactly one complex number. The horizontal axis is called the **real axis**; the vertical axis is called the **imaginary axis**. When a plane is considered to represent the set of all complex numbers, it is called a **complex plane** (see Figure 9-1A).

Each of the algebraic operations described in the preceding section has a geometric interpretation in this plane. For example, Figure 9-1B shows that, as with real numbers, $|z|$ is the distance from z to the origin. It also shows that, geometrically, $\bar{z}$ is the reflection of z through the real axis.

Addition and subtraction

Let $z = a + bi$ correspond to the pair (a, b) and $w = c + di$ correspond to (c, d).

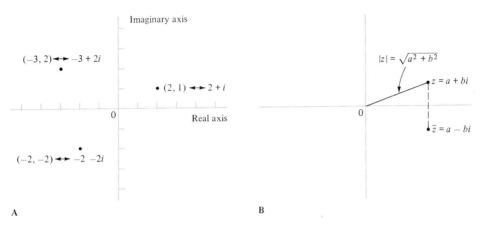

Figure 9-1
(A) Three complex numbers represented in a complex plane. (B) The absolute value of a complex number z is the distance of z from the origin. The conjugate of z is the reflection of z through the real axis.

Then

$$z + w = (a + c) + (b + d)i \quad \text{corresponds to } (a + c, b + d), \quad \text{and}$$

$$z - w = (a - c) + (b - d)i \quad \text{corresponds to } (a - c, b - d).$$

This is precisely the way we added and subtracted vectors in Section 7-5. In other words, each complex number can be thought of as a point in a plane; each point, in turn, determines a vector. Then the sum of the complex numbers is the sum of their corresponding vectors (see Figure 9-2A).

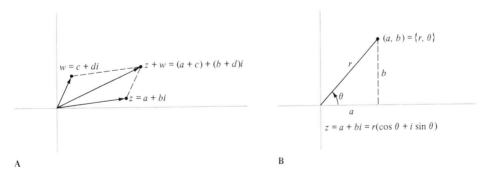

Figure 9-2
(A) The addition of complex numbers in the plane is just like vector addition. (B) If $z = a + bi$ is represented by the point (a, b) in the complex plane, and (a, b) has the polar coordinates $\{r, \theta\}$, then $z = r(\cos \theta + i \sin \theta)$, where $r = \sqrt{a^2 + b^2}$. This is the polar form of z.

Polar form

Each point (a, b) in the plane can also be represented by polar coordinates $\{r, \theta\}$ (see Figure 9-2B). As you learned in Section 7-3,

$$r = \sqrt{a^2 + b^2}, \qquad a = r \cos \theta, \quad \text{and} \quad b = r \sin \theta$$

Now suppose that $z = a + bi$ is any complex number. It corresponds to the point (a, b) in the plane; suppose this point has polar coordinates $\{r, \theta\}$. It follows that $|z| = r$ and

$$z = a + bi = (r \cos \theta) + (r \sin \theta)i$$
$$= r(\cos \theta + i \sin \theta)*$$

This is called the **polar form** of z. When z is represented in polar form, the number r is usually called the **modulus** (rather than absolute value) of z, and θ is called the **argument** of z, written $\theta = \arg z$.

It is often necessary to convert from the rectangular form $a + bi$ to the polar form, or vice versa. This can always be done by making use of the following relationships.

■ Rectangular form: $z = a + bi$ Polar form: $z = r(\cos \theta + i \sin \theta)$

$$a = r \cos \theta \qquad b = r \sin \theta \qquad r = |z| = \sqrt{a^2 + b^2}$$

Both radian and degree measure may be used to express a complex number in polar form.

Example 1

Convert to polar form: (a) $\sqrt{3} - i$ and (b) $-3 + 4i$.

Solution

First find the modulus r; then θ is an angle that satisfies both $\cos \theta = a/r$ and $\sin \theta = b/r$.

(a) $r = |\sqrt{3} - i| = \sqrt{(\sqrt{3})^2 + (-1)^2} = 2$. Therefore, $\cos \theta = \sqrt{3}/2$, and $\sin \theta = -1/2$; it follows that $\theta = (11\pi/6) + 2n\pi$, where n is any integer. If you choose $n = -1$, then $\theta = -\pi/6$, and $z = 2(\cos(-\pi/6) + i \sin(-\pi/6))$ is an answer.

(b) $r = |-3 + 4i| = 5$. Therefore, $\cos \theta = -3/5$ and $\sin \theta = 4/5$. It follows

---

*It is more convenient to write $i \sin \theta$ than $(\sin \theta)i$.

that θ is in the second quadrant and the reference angle (obtained from Table 2) is approximately $53°10'$. Thus, $z \approx 5(\cos 126°50' + i \sin 126°50')$.

Example 2
Convert to rectangular form: (a) $2(\cos(\pi/4) + i \sin(\pi/4))$ and (b) $3(\cos 220° + i \sin 220°)$.

Solution
This is easier than the other conversion. Simply find $a = r \cos \theta$ and $b = r \sin \theta$.
(a) $a = 2 \cos(\pi/4) = \sqrt{2}$ and $b = 2 \sin(\pi/4) = \sqrt{2}$. Thus, $z = \sqrt{2} + \sqrt{2}i$.
(b) $a = 3 \cos 220° \approx 3(-.7660) = -2.298$ and $b = 3 \sin 220° \approx 3(-.6428) = -1.928$. Thus, $z \approx -2.298 - 1.928i$.

Multiplication and division
Sometimes the rather cumbersome expression $\cos \theta + i \sin \theta$ is abbreviated to cis θ. Let $z_1 = r_1$ cis θ_1 and $z_2 = r_2$ cis θ_2 be any two complex numbers in polar form. Then

$$z_1 z_2 = r_1(\cos \theta_1 + i \sin \theta_1) \cdot r_2(\cos \theta_2 + i \sin \theta_2)$$

$$= r_1 r_2[(\cos \theta_1 \cos \theta_2 - \sin \theta_1 \sin \theta_2) + i(\sin \theta_1 \cos \theta_2 + \cos \theta_1 \sin \theta_2)]$$

$$= r_1 r_2(\cos(\theta_1 + \theta_2) + i \sin(\theta_1 + \theta_2)).$$

The last equality follows from the addition formulas for the sine and cosine proved in Section 8-2. It follows that $|z_1 z_2| = r_1 r_2$ and that $\arg(z_1 z_2) = \theta_1 + \theta_2$. These results can be summarized as follows.

■   **Multiplication of complex numbers**
Let $z_1 = r_1$ cis θ_1 and $z_2 = r_2$ cis θ_2. Then

$$z_1 z_2 = r_1 r_2 \operatorname{cis}(\theta_1 + \theta_2)$$

$$|z_1 z_2| = r_1 r_2 = |z_1|\,|z_2|$$

$$\arg(z_1 z_2) = \theta_1 + \theta_2 = \arg z_1 + \arg z_2$$

To multiply two complex numbers, *multiply* their moduli and *add* their arguments (see Figure 9-3).

Example 3
Multiply: (a) $z_1 = 2 \operatorname{cis}(\pi/4)$ and $z_2 = 4 \operatorname{cis}(3\pi/4)$; (b) $u = 1 + i$ and $v = \sqrt{3} - i$.

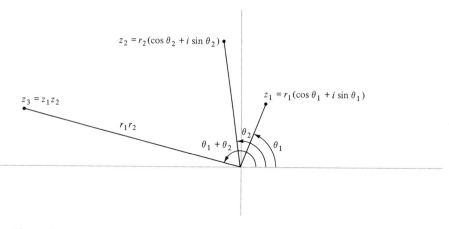

Figure 9-3
To multiply two complex numbers in polar form, multiply their moduli and add their
arguments.

Solution
(a) $z_1 z_2 = 2 \cdot 4 \, \text{cis}[(\pi/4) + (3\pi/4)] = 8 \, \text{cis} \, \pi = 8(\cos \pi + i \sin \pi) = -8$
(b)   Multiplying u and v directly gives $uv = (\sqrt{3} + 1) + (\sqrt{3} - 1)i$. Let us
also convert to polar form and multiply that way:

$$u = 1 + i = \sqrt{2} \, \text{cis} \frac{\pi}{4} \text{ and } v = \sqrt{3} - i = 2 \, \text{cis}\left(-\frac{\pi}{6}\right)$$

Therefore,

$$uv = 2\sqrt{2} \, \text{cis}\left(\frac{\pi}{4} - \frac{\pi}{6}\right) = 2\sqrt{2} \, \text{cis}\frac{\pi}{12}$$

Convert this answer to rectangular form and compare it to the first answer.

From our formula for multiplication, we can work out a division formula. Let
$z_1 = r_1 \text{cis} \, \theta_1$, $z_2 = r_2 \text{cis} \, \theta_2$, and $z_3 = r_3 \text{cis} \, \theta_3$. Then

$$\frac{z_1}{z_2} = z_3 \text{ if and only if } z_1 = z_2 z_3$$

The equation $z_1 = z_2 z_3$ translates to polar form as

$$r_1 \text{cis} \, \theta_1 = r_2 r_3 \text{cis}(\theta_2 + \theta_3)$$

It follows that $r_3 = r_1/r_2$ and $\theta_3 = \theta_1 - \theta_2$. In other words,

$$\frac{z_1}{z_2} = \frac{r_1 \operatorname{cis} \theta_1}{r_2 \operatorname{cis} \theta_2} = \frac{r_1}{r_2} \operatorname{cis}(\theta_1 - \theta_2) = z_3$$

■ **Division of complex numbers**
Let $z_1 = r_1 \operatorname{cis} \theta_1$ and $z_2 = r_2 \operatorname{cis} \theta_2$. Then

$$\frac{z_1}{z_2} = \frac{r_1}{r_2} \operatorname{cis}(\theta_1 - \theta_2)$$

$$|z_1/z_2| = r_1/r_2 = |z_1|/|z_2|$$

$$\arg(z_1/z_2) = \theta_1 - \theta_2 = \arg z_1 - \arg z_2$$

To divide one complex number by another, divide the modulus of the first by the modulus of the second, and subtract the argument of the second from the argument of the first.

Example 4
Divide (a) $6 \operatorname{cis}(-20°)$ by $4 \operatorname{cis} 50°$ and (b) $u = 1 + i$ by $v = \sqrt{3} - i$.

Solution

(a) $\dfrac{6 \operatorname{cis}(-20°)}{4 \operatorname{cis} 50°} = \dfrac{3}{2} \operatorname{cis}(-70°)$

(b)   You could divide $(1 + i)/(\sqrt{3} - i)$ algebraically, in the way described in Section 9-1. However, from Example 3, you know that $u = \sqrt{2} \operatorname{cis}(\pi/4)$ and $v = 2 \operatorname{cis}(-\pi/6)$. Thus, the answer is

$$u/v = \frac{\sqrt{2}}{2} \operatorname{cis}\left(\frac{\pi}{4} + \frac{\pi}{6}\right) = \frac{\sqrt{2}}{2} \operatorname{cis} \frac{5\pi}{12}$$

Exercises

Graph each pair of complex numbers as vectors in the plane. Then find their sum.
1. $2 + i, 3 + 4i$ 2. $-4 + 2i, 5 + i$
3. $-2 - i, -1 + i$ 4. $3 - 2i, 2i$

Graph each pair of complex numbers in the plane and subtract the second from the first.

5. $1 + i, 3 - i$ 6. $-2 + 2i, 1 - 4i$
7. $i, -4$ 8. $5, -3i$

Convert each number to polar form.

9. $1 - i$ 10. $3\sqrt{3} + 3i$
11. $-2 + 2\sqrt{3}i$ 12. $1 - \sqrt{3}i$
13. -2 14. $4i$

Convert to rectangular form.

15. $2 \operatorname{cis} \dfrac{3\pi}{2}$ 16. $2 \operatorname{cis}\left(-\dfrac{\pi}{3}\right)$
17. $\operatorname{cis} 225°$ 18. $4 \operatorname{cis} 180°$

Convert each number to polar form and multiply or divide as indicated. Use Table 2 for approximations, if necessary. Leave the answer in polar form.

19. $(1 + i)(3 + 3\sqrt{3}i)$ 20. $(\sqrt{3} + i)(4 - 4i)$
21. $(1 + \sqrt{3}i)^2$ 22. $(1 - i)^2$
23. $(5i)(5 - 5i)$ 24. $(-6)(2\sqrt{3} - i)$
25. $(3 - 4i)(1 - \sqrt{3}i)$ 26. $(2 + 3i)(6 - i)$
27. $(-3 + i)(-1 - 2i)$ 28. $(-2 - i)(3 + 2i)$
29. $\dfrac{1 + i}{1 - i}$ 30. $\dfrac{1 - i}{1 + \sqrt{3}i}$
31. $\dfrac{2\sqrt{3} - 2i}{-i}$ 32. $\dfrac{3 - 3\sqrt{3}i}{i}$
33. $\dfrac{-3 + 4i}{2 - 5i}$ 34. $\dfrac{6 + 6}{4 + i}$

35. Use the correspondence between addition of complex numbers and addition of vectors to verify the *triangle inequality*

$$|z_1 + z_2| \leq |z_1| + |z_2|$$

[HINT: Draw a picture.]

36. If $z = r \operatorname{cis} \theta$, what are the polar forms of $\bar{z}$ and $-z$? A picture may be helpful.
37. If $z = r \operatorname{cis} \theta$, find z^2, z^3, and z^4. Now write a general formula for z^n in polar form. Find $(1 + i)^4$ and $\left(\dfrac{\sqrt{3}}{2} + \dfrac{1}{2}i\right)^{12}$.

38.   (Continuation of Exercise 37) Show that both $\dfrac{1}{2} + \dfrac{\sqrt{3}}{2}i$ and $\dfrac{1}{2} - \dfrac{\sqrt{3}}{2}i$ are cube roots of -1. Actually, there are three cube roots of -1. Find the other one.

39.   Show that $\dfrac{\sqrt{2}}{2} + \dfrac{\sqrt{2}}{2}i$ is a square root of i. Find another.

40.   Make up a division problem with complex numbers in rectangular form. Convert the numbers to polar form and divide. Check your work.

41.   Find six different complex numbers in rectangular form that are sixth roots of 64 (refer to Exercises 37–39).

9-3
Equations with Complex Solutions

A linear equation with real coefficients has exactly one solution. This is also true if the coefficients happen to be complex numbers.

Example 1
Solve $3x - (2 - i) = ix + 4 + 3i$

Solution
Proceed exactly as if this were an equation with real coefficients.

$$3x - ix = (4 + 3i) + (2 - i) \qquad \text{(Add } (2 - i) \text{ and } -ix)$$

$$(3 - i)x = 6 + 2i \qquad\qquad \text{(Simplify)}$$

$$x = \frac{6 + 2i}{3 - i} \qquad\qquad \text{(Divide)}$$

$$= \frac{6 + 2i}{3 - i} \cdot \frac{3 + i}{3 + i} \qquad\qquad \text{(Simplify)}$$

$$= \frac{16 + 12i}{10} = \frac{8}{5} + \frac{6}{5}i$$

Check

$$3\left(\frac{8}{5} + \frac{6}{5}i\right) - (2 - i) = \frac{24}{5} + \frac{18}{5}i - \frac{10}{5} + \frac{5}{5}i = \frac{14}{5} + \frac{23}{5}i$$

$$i\left(\frac{8}{5} + \frac{6}{5}i\right) + 4 + 3i = \frac{8}{5}i - \frac{6}{5} + \frac{20}{5} + \frac{15}{5}i = \frac{14}{5} + \frac{23}{5}i$$

Unlike a linear equation, a quadratic equation with real coefficients might not have real solutions. The simplest example is $x^2 + 1 = 0$, whose solutions are i and $-i$. For the general equation $ax^2 + bx + c = 0$, the quadratic formula yields the solutions

$$x = \frac{-b \pm \sqrt{b^2 - 4ac}}{2a}$$

They are real if and only if the discriminant $b^2 - 4ac \geq 0$.

Example 2
Solve $2x^2 - 3x + 4 = 0$.

Solution
$a = 2$, $b = -3$, and $c = 4$. Therefore,

$$x = \frac{3 \pm \sqrt{9 - 32}}{4} = \frac{3 \pm \sqrt{-23}}{4}$$

The solutions are

$$\frac{3}{4} + \frac{\sqrt{23}}{4}i \quad \text{and} \quad \frac{3}{4} - \frac{\sqrt{23}}{4}i$$

Notice that the solutions are conjugate complex numbers. As we shall prove later, this is always true if the quadratic has real coefficients.

The procedures that established the quadratic formula used only arithmetic operations. These operations are also valid for complex numbers; therefore, the quadratic formula is valid for equations with complex coefficients.

Example 3
Solve $x^2 + (1 + i)x + 3 - 2i = 0$

Solution
$a = 1$, $b = 1 + i$ and $c = 3 - 2i$. Therefore,

$$x = \frac{-(1 + i) \pm \sqrt{(1 + i)^2 - 4(1)(3 - 2i)}}{2(1)}$$

$$= \frac{-1 - i \pm \sqrt{(1 + 2i - 1) - (12 - 8i)}}{2}$$

$$= \frac{-1 - i \pm \sqrt{-12 + 10i}}{2}$$

Even if a, b, and c are real numbers $\sqrt{b^2 - 4ac}$ might not be a real number. Can it be that, if a, b, and c are complex, then $\sqrt{b^2 - 4ac}$ might not be complex? For instance, in Example 3, is it possible that $\sqrt{-12 + 10i}$ is not a complex number? If the answer is *yes*, then we shall have to enlarge our number system again to handle such equations. Fortunately, the answer is *no:* every complex number has a complex square root. We shall prove that fact in Section 9-4.

Actually, much more is true: *every* polynomial equation with complex coefficients has solutions in the complex number system. Thus, no further enlargements are necessary.

■ **The Fundamental Theorem of Algebra**

Let

$$f(x) = z_n x^n + \cdots + z_1 x + z_0$$

be any polynomial with complex coefficients and degree $n \geq 1$. Then there is a complex number w such that $f(w) = 0$.

The proof of this powerful theorem is far beyond the scope of this book. Notice that it guarantees the existence of a complex zero for each polynomial, but it says nothing about how to find the zero. There are many methods for finding or approximating zeros; we shall consider only the simplest ones.

Because of the Fundamental Theorem, every polynomial can be factored into exactly n linear factors. To prove this fact, notice that, if w_1 is a zero of $f(x)$, then, as in polynomials with real coefficients, $x - w_1$ is a factor of $f(x)$; that is, $f(x) = (x - w_1)g(x)$, where $g(x)$ is a polynomial. The Fundamental Theorem says that $g(x)$ also has a zero, say w_2. It follows now that $f(x) = (x - w_1)(x - w_2)h(x)$ and so on.

■ **Theorem 1**

Let $f(x) = z_n x^n + \cdots + z_1 x + z_0$ with $z_n \neq 0$. Then $f(x)$ has exactly n zeros $w_1, \ldots, w_n$, and $f(x)$ can be written as the product of n linear factors:

$$f(x) = z_n(x - w_1)(x - w_2) \cdots (x - w_n)$$

■ **Definition**

There may be repetitions among the zeros; if a zero appears j times, it is called a **zero of multiplicity j**. A zero with multiplicity 1 appears only once; it is called a **simple zero**.

Example 4

Find the zeros of (a) $x^3 + 1$ and (b) $x^3 + 4ix - 4x$.

Solution
To find zeros try to factor the polynomials.

(a) $x^3 + 1 = (x + 1)(x^2 - x + 1)$

$$= (x + 1)\left(x - \frac{1 + \sqrt{3}i}{2}\right)\left(x - \frac{1 - \sqrt{3}i}{2}\right)$$

The last two factors follow from the quadratic formula. Thus $-1, (1 + \sqrt{3}i)/2$, and $(1 - \sqrt{3}i)/2$ are the three zeros of $x^3 + 1$. They are simple zeros. Notice that the last two are conjugates. As you will see shortly, this always happens when the coefficients are real.

(b) $x^3 + 4ix^2 - 4x = x(x^2 + 4ix - 4)$

$$= x(x + 2i)(x + 2i) \qquad\qquad \text{(Perfect Square)}$$

Thus, 0 and $-2i$ are the zeros; the first is a simple zero and the second has multiplicity 2. Notice that the coefficients are not all real and the zeros are *not* conjugates.

Theorem 1 allows us to reconstruct a polynomial if its zeros are known.

Example 5
Find the polynomial with leading coefficient 3 and simple zeros 1 and $\pm i$.

Solution
A polynomial satisfying these conditions must have linear factors $(x - 1)$, $(x - i)$, and $(x + i)$. Thus,

$$f(x) = 3(x - 1)(x - i)(x + i)$$
$$= 3x^3 - 3x^2 + 3x - 3$$

It was pointed out in Examples 2 and 4 that, when all the coefficients of a polynomial are real, its complex zeros occur in **conjugate pairs.** This is a consequence of the following theorem.

■ **Theorem 2**
If $f(x) = a_n x^n + \cdots + a_1 x + a_0$ has *real* coefficients and w is a complex zero of $f(x)$, then $\bar{w}$ is also a zero of $f(x)$.

This theorem can be proved by using certain facts about conjugates: $\overline{z + w} = \overline{z} + \overline{w}$, $\overline{zw} = \overline{z}\,\overline{w}$, $\overline{z^n} = \overline{z}^n$, $\overline{0} = 0$, and $\overline{a} = a$ if a is real. If $f(w) = 0$, then $a_n w^n + \cdots + a_1 w + a_0 = 0$; take the conjugate of each side of this equation:

$$\overline{a_n w^n + \cdots + a_1 w + a_0} = \overline{0}$$

$$\overline{a_n}\,\overline{w}^n + \cdots + \overline{a_1}\,\overline{w} + \overline{a_0} = \overline{0}$$

$$a_n \overline{w}^n + \cdots + a_1 \overline{w} + a_0 = 0$$

Thus $f(\overline{w}) = 0$ and the proof is complete.

Example 6
Find a real polynomial (that is, with real coefficients) of degree 3 with zeros 1, 2, and $3 + i$.

Solution
This is impossible. According to Theorem 2, if $3 + i$ is a zero, then $3 - i$ is also a zero. Then the polynomial would have degree 3 and have four zeros; but this would contradict Theorem 1.

Example 7
Find a real polynomial of degree 4 with zeros 1, 2, and $3 + i$.

Solution
It follows from Theorem 2 that the zeros are $1, 2, 3 + i$, and $3 - i$. Thus,

$$(x - 1)(x - 2)(x - 3 - i)(x - 3 + i) = x^4 - 9x^3 + 30x^2 - 42x + 20$$

is such a polynomial.

Example 8
Find a real polynomial of degree 4 whose only zeros are 1 and $\pm i$.

Solution
Because there are exactly four zeros, 1 must be a zero of multiplicity 2. (If i appeared twice, so would its conjugate $-i$, resulting in five zeros. Thus, neither i nor $-i$ can be a zero of multiplicity 2.) Therefore,

$$(x - 1)^2(x - i)(x + i) = x^4 - 2x^3 + 2x^2 - 2x + 1$$

is such a polynomial.

The next example deals with solving polynomial equations.

Example 9
(a)   Solve $x^4 + 2x^2 + 1 = 2x^3 + 2x$.
(b)   Solve $x^4 + 7x^2 + 6 = 5x^3 + 5x$, given that one solution is i.

Solution
Rewrite the equations with a polynomial on the left and 0 on the right. The zeros of the polynomial are the solutions of the equation.
(a)   Write $x^4 - 2x^3 + 2x^2 - 2x + 1 = 0$. The polynomial on the left is the one in Example 8; it factors into $(x - 1)^2(x - i)(x + i)$. Thus 1, i, and $-i$ are the solutions of the equation. Check these solutions by substituting them into the original equation.
(b)   Write $x^4 - 5x^3 + 7x^2 - 5x + 6 = 0$. On the left is a real polynomial; call it $f(x)$. Because i is a solution, you know that $f(i) = 0$ and $f(-i) = 0$. Thus,

$$f(x) = (x - i)(x + i)h(x)$$
$$= (x^2 + 1)h(x)$$

for some polynomial $h(x)$. To find $h(x)$, divide $f(x)$ by $x^2 + 1$. This yields $h(x) = x^2 - 5x + 6 = (x - 3)(x - 2)$. Thus,

$$f(x) = (x - i)(x + i)(x - 3)(x - 2)$$

so $\pm i$, 3, and 2 are the solutions.

Exercises

Find all solutions of the following equations.

1. $x + 3 + i = 4x - 5i$ 2. $2x - (1 - 2i) = 5x + 3$
3. $(4 + i)x - (2 + 5i) = 3x - i$ 4. $5ix + 3 = 7x - (2 + 3i)$
5. $x^2 - 6x + 1 = 0$ 6. $9x^2 + x + 1 = 0$
7. $3x^2 + 4 = 2x$ 8. $-x^2 - 7 = 2x$
9. $x^2 = x - 7$ 10. $x^2 = 3x - 4$
11. $x^3 - 1 = 0$ 12. $x^3 + 1 = 0$

Find the real polynomial with leading coefficient 1 that satisfies the given conditions. If there is no such polynomial, say so.
13.   Degree 2; one zero is $3i$.
14.   Degree 2; one zero is $2 - i$
15.   Simple zeros 2 and $1 \pm i$

16. Simple zeros -2 and $-1 \pm 3i$
17. Simple zeros $\pm i$ and a zero 3 with multiplicity 2.
18. Simple zeros $\pm 2i$ and a zero -1 with multiplicity 3.
19. Degree 4; only zeros are $1 \pm i$ and 2.
20. Degree 3; only zeros are $1 + i$ and 4.
21. Degree 3; two zeros are $2i$ and $3i$.
22. Degree 4; two zeros are $2i$ and $3i$.

Solve each of the following equations, given one solution. [HINT: See Example 9(b).]

23. $x^4 - 16 = 0$; $2i$ 24. $x^4 - 81 = 0$; $x = 3i$

25. $x^4 + 16 = 0$; $\sqrt{2} + \sqrt{2}i$ 26. $x^4 + 81 = 0$; $\dfrac{3}{\sqrt{2}} + \dfrac{3}{\sqrt{2}}i$

27. $x^4 + 4x^2 + 3 = 4x^3 + 4x$; i

28. $x^4 + 10x^3 = x + 10$; $-\dfrac{1}{2} + \dfrac{\sqrt{3}}{2}i$

29. $x^3 + 8 = 0$; -2 30. $x^3 + 15 = x^2 + 7x$; -3

31. (a) Compute $(x - 3i)(x + 3i)$ and $(x - 2 + i)(x - 2 - i)$; notice that these products are real quadratic polynomials. (b) Show that, in general, $(x - z)(x - \bar{z})$ is a real quadratic polynomial.

32. Explain why every real polynomial of odd degree must have at least one real zero.

33. (a) Make up a few problems similar to Exercises 13–22. (b) Same for Exercises 23–29. Exchange them with a classmate.

34. Use Exercise 31 to prove that every real polynomial can be written as a product of *real* linear and quadratic factors.

9-4
Powers and Roots of Complex Numbers

If z_0 is a complex number, then each solution of the equation $x^n - z_0 = 0$ is an nth root of z_0. The Fundamental Theorem of Algebra guarantees the existence of at least one such solution. In fact, there are exactly n distinct nth roots of z_0.

First, recall that every complex number z can be written in polar form, $z = r(\cos \theta + i \sin \theta)$, where $|z| = r$ and $\arg z = \theta$. The polar form is often abbreviated to

$z = r \operatorname{cis} \theta$. Next, recall the multiplication rule for complex numbers in polar form: If $z_1 = r_1 \operatorname{cis} \theta_1$ and $z_2 = r_2 \operatorname{cis} \theta_2$, then $z_1 z_2 = r_1 r_2 \operatorname{cis}(\theta_1 + \theta_2)$. It follows that, if $z = r \operatorname{cis} \theta$, then $z^2 = r^2 \operatorname{cis} 2\theta$, $z^3 = r^3 \operatorname{cis} 3\theta$, and, in general,

■ $z^n = r^n \operatorname{cis} n\theta$

This result is called **De Moivre's Theorem.** It can be used to compute large powers of complex numbers.

> ### Example 1
> Find $(1 + i)^{10}$ in rectangular form.
>
> ### Solution
> First express $1 + i$ in polar form: $1 + i = \sqrt{2} \operatorname{cis}(\pi/4)$. Then, according to De Moivre's Theorem,
>
> $$\left(\sqrt{2} \operatorname{cis} \frac{\pi}{4} \right)^{10} = (\sqrt{2})^{10} \operatorname{cis} \left(10 \cdot \frac{\pi}{4} \right)$$
>
> $$= 2^5 \operatorname{cis} \left(\frac{10\,\pi}{4} \right)$$
>
> $$= 32 \operatorname{cis} \frac{\pi}{2} \qquad\qquad \left(\frac{10\pi}{4} = 2\pi + \frac{\pi}{2} \right)$$
>
> Now convert back to rectangular form: $32 \operatorname{cis} \frac{\pi}{2} = 32 \left(\cos \frac{\pi}{2} + i \sin \frac{\pi}{2} \right) = 32i$.
> Thus,
>
> $$(1 + i)^{10} = 32i$$

From De Moivre's Theorem, it is easy to prove the following theorem about the roots of a complex number.

■   **Complex Roots Theorem**
     Let $z = r \operatorname{cis} \theta$. The n distinct nth roots of z are

$$r^{1/n} \operatorname{cis} \left(\frac{\theta}{n} + \frac{2\pi k}{n} \right); \quad k = 0, 1, \ldots, n - 1$$

Or, in terms of degrees,

$$r^{1/n} \operatorname{cis} \left(\frac{\theta^\circ}{n} + \frac{360^\circ \cdot k}{n} \right); \quad k = 0, 1, \ldots, n - 1$$

Before proving this theorem, let us look at some examples of its use.

Example 2
Find the cube roots of $8i$.

Solution
First write $8i = 8 \operatorname{cis}(\pi/2)$. You are looking for cube roots, so $n = 3$; the Complex Roots Theorem states that there will be three distinct cube roots, each of the form

$$8^{\frac{1}{3}} \operatorname{cis}\left(\frac{\pi}{2} \cdot \frac{1}{3} + \frac{2\pi k}{3}\right); \quad k = 0, 1, 2$$

This means to substitute $k = 0$, then $k = 1$, and then $k = 2$:

$$k = 0; \quad 8^{\frac{1}{3}} \operatorname{cis}\left(\frac{\pi}{2} \cdot \frac{1}{3} + \frac{2\pi \cdot 0}{3}\right) = 2 \operatorname{cis}\frac{\pi}{6}$$

$$k = 1; \quad 8^{\frac{1}{3}} \operatorname{cis}\left(\frac{\pi}{2} \cdot \frac{1}{3} + \frac{2\pi \cdot 1}{3}\right) = 2 \operatorname{cis}\frac{5\pi}{6}$$

$$k = 2; \quad 8^{\frac{1}{3}} \operatorname{cis}\left(\frac{\pi}{2} \cdot \frac{1}{3} + \frac{2\pi \cdot 2}{3}\right) = 2 \operatorname{cis}\frac{3\pi}{2}$$

These are the three cube roots of $8i$.

Check
According to De Moivre's Theorem,

$$\left(2 \operatorname{cis}\frac{\pi}{6}\right)^{3} = 2^{3}\operatorname{cis}\frac{\pi}{2} = 8i$$

$$\left(2 \operatorname{cis}\frac{5\pi}{6}\right)^{3} = 2^{3}\operatorname{cis}\frac{5\pi}{2} = 8 \operatorname{cis}\frac{\pi}{2} = 8i$$

$$\left(2 \operatorname{cis}\frac{3\pi}{2}\right)^{3} = 2^{3} \operatorname{cis}\frac{9\pi}{2} = 8 \operatorname{cis}\frac{\pi}{2} = 8i$$

In rectangular coordinates, the roots are $\sqrt{3} + i$, $-\sqrt{3} + i$, and $-2i$. (Check!) These are shown in Figure 9-4. Notice that they are equally spaced $2\pi/3$ radians apart on a circle of radius 2 ($=8^{\frac{1}{3}}$).

In the special case $z = 1$, the nth roots are called the **nth roots of unity.**

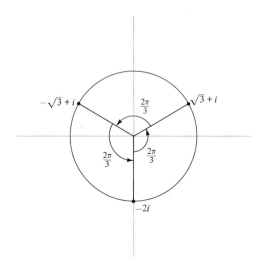

Figure 9-4
The three cube roots of $8i$ are spaced $2\pi/3$ radians apart on a circle of radius 2. See Example 2.

Example 3
Find the sixth roots of unity.

Solution
From the Complex Roots Theorem, we know there are six roots. From the experience of Example 2, we can predict that they are equally spaced 60° apart (360°/6) on the unit circle ($1^{\frac{1}{6}} = 1$). Let us see if this prediction is correct.

Write $1 = \text{cis } 0°$; then the sixth roots of unity are $\text{cis}\left(\dfrac{0°}{6} + \dfrac{360° \cdot k}{6}\right)$; $k = 0, 1, 2, 3, 4, 5$.

$$k = 0; \quad \text{cis}(0° + 0°) = 1$$

$$k = 1; \quad \text{cis}(60°) = \frac{1}{2} + \frac{\sqrt{3}}{2}i$$

$$k = 2; \quad \text{cis}(120°) = -\frac{1}{2} + \frac{\sqrt{3}}{2}i$$

$$k = 3; \quad \text{cis}(180°) = -1$$

$$k = 4; \quad \text{cis}(240°) = -\frac{1}{2} - \frac{\sqrt{3}}{2}i$$

$$k = 5; \quad \text{cis}(300°) = \frac{1}{2} - \frac{\sqrt{3}}{2}i$$

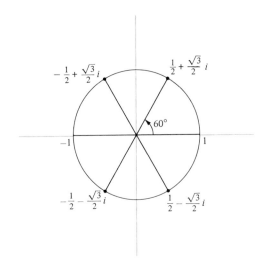

Figure 9-5
The six sixth roots of unity are equally spaced around a circle with radius 1.

Our prediction was correct (see Figure 9-5). Notice that the nonreal roots appear in conjugate pairs; this was to be expected, because they are zeros of the real polynomial $x^6 - 1$. Also notice that the negative of each root is also a root; this was to be expected, because 6 is an even number; if $z^6 = 1$, then $(-z)^6 = 1$.

The next example shows that negative angles may also be used.

Example 4
Find the square roots of $1 - \sqrt{3}i$.

Solution
The absolute value is 2; thus, the square roots will lie on a circle of radius $\sqrt{2}$, and they will be π radians apart. This makes them negatives of each other. Now, $1 - \sqrt{3}i = 2 \operatorname{cis}(-\pi/3)$ and, therefore, its square roots are

$$\sqrt{2} \operatorname{cis}\left(-\frac{\pi}{6} + \frac{2\pi k}{2}\right); \quad k = 0, 1$$

$$k = 0; \quad \sqrt{2} \operatorname{cis}\left(-\frac{\pi}{6}\right) = \sqrt{2}\left(\frac{\sqrt{3}}{2} - \frac{1}{2}i\right) = \sqrt{\frac{3}{2}} - \sqrt{\frac{1}{2}}i$$

$$k = 1; \quad \sqrt{2} \operatorname{cis}\left(\frac{5\pi}{6}\right) = \sqrt{2}\left(-\frac{\sqrt{3}}{2} + \frac{1}{2}i\right) = -\sqrt{\frac{3}{2}} + \sqrt{\frac{1}{2}}i$$

Check to see that using $1 - \sqrt{3}i = 2 \operatorname{cis}(300°)$ yields the same square roots.

The proof of the Complex Roots Theorem is as follows. The theorem asserts that each of the numbers

$$r^{1/n} \operatorname{cis}\left(\frac{\theta}{n} + \frac{2\pi k}{n}\right), \quad \text{for } k = 0, 1, \ldots, n - 1$$

is an nth root of $z = r \operatorname{cis} \theta$. We must show that the nth power of each number is, indeed, equal to z. This follows from De Moivre's Theorem:

$$\left[r^{1/n}\operatorname{cis}\left(\frac{\theta}{n} + \frac{2\pi k}{n}\right)\right]^n = (r^{1/n})^n \operatorname{cis}\left(\frac{\theta}{n} \cdot n + \frac{2\pi k}{n} \cdot n\right)$$

$$= r \operatorname{cis}(\theta + 2\pi k)$$

$$= r \operatorname{cis} \theta = z$$

For $k = 0, 1, \ldots, n - 1$, the angles obtained are different from each other, so n distinct complex roots are obtained. Because there can be at most n solutions to the equation $x^n - z = 0$ (see Theorem 1 in Section 9-3), our proof is complete.

Now that you know how to find complex square roots, you can solve quadratic equations with complex coefficients.

Example 5
Solve $x^2 + 2ix - \sqrt{3}i = 0$.

Solution
Use the quadratic formula

$$x = \frac{-2i \pm \sqrt{-4 + 4\sqrt{3}i}}{2}$$

$$= \frac{-2i \pm 2i\sqrt{1 - \sqrt{3}i}}{2}$$

In Example 4, we found that the square roots of $1 - \sqrt{3}i$ are $\pm(\sqrt{3/2} - \sqrt{1/2}i)$. Choose either one and continue with

$$x = \frac{-2i \pm 2i(\sqrt{3/2} - \sqrt{1/2}i)}{2}$$

$$= -i \pm (\sqrt{3/2}i + \sqrt{1/2})$$

Thus, $x = \sqrt{1/2} + (-1 + \sqrt{3/2})i$ or $x = -\sqrt{1/2} + (-1 - \sqrt{3/2})i$

Exercises

Compute the powers, and give the answer in polar form.

1. $\left(2\,\text{cis}\,\dfrac{\pi}{6}\right)^5$
2. $\left(\text{cis}\,\dfrac{2\pi}{3}\right)^{15}$

3. $(\text{cis}(-45°))^{11}$
4. $(2\,\text{cis}(-30°))^8$

Compute the powers, and give the answer in rectangular form.

5. $\left(\dfrac{1}{2} + \dfrac{\sqrt{3}}{2}i\right)^{14}$
6. $(1 - i)^{10}$

7. $\left(-\dfrac{1}{\sqrt{2}} + \dfrac{1}{\sqrt{2}}i\right)^{100}$
8. $\left(\dfrac{\sqrt{3}}{2} - \dfrac{1}{2}i\right)^{28}$

9. $(-\sqrt{3} + i)^8$
10. $(i/2)^7$

Use Table 2 to approximate these powers. Leave your answer in polar form.

11. $(3 + 4i)^5$
12. $(-4 + 3i)^4$

13. $(-5 - 12i)^4$
14. $(12 - 5i)^3$

15. Find the nth roots of unity for $n = 2, 3, 4, 5,$ and 7 ($n = 6$ was solved in Example 3).

16. Verify that, for each value of n in Exercise 15, *the sum of the nth roots of unity is always* 0.

Find all solutions.

17. $x^3 = 8$
18. $x^5 = 32$
19. $x^6 = -1$

20. $x^4 = -81$
21. $x^5 = i$
22. $x^3 = -i$

23. $x^7 = -\dfrac{\sqrt{3}}{2} - \dfrac{1}{2}i$
24. $x^4 = -\dfrac{1}{2} - \dfrac{\sqrt{3}}{2}i$

Use Table 2 to approximate the solutions to the following equations. Convert each answer to rectangular form rounded off to one decimal place.

25. $x^2 = 15 + 20i$
26. $x^2 = -65 + 156i$

Use your answers to Exercises 25 and 26 to solve the following equations (see Example 5).

27. $x^2 + 4x + (\tfrac{1}{4} - 5i) = 0$

28. $x^2 + 8ix + (\tfrac{1}{4} - 39i) = 0$

Chapter 10

Elements of Analytic Geometry

Analytic geometry unites the study of algebra and geometry. We have been using the principle of analytic geometry throughout this book. Our treatment of many topics (functions, trigonometry, and even complex numbers) has combined algebraic and geometric ideas. In this chapter, we shall use this technique to study several important curves associated with cones.

The curves we shall study are circles, parabolas, ellipses, and hyperbolas. These are called *conic sections* because they were originally studied geometrically as the intersections of planes with cones (see Figure 10-1). Learn the definition, the simple equation, and the general shape of each conic. These basic ideas will carry you through without having to memorize all of the formulas that follow from the definitions.

10-1
The Circle

In geometry, a **circle** with **center** P and **radius** r $(r > 0)$ is defined as the set of all points in the plane that are at distance r from P. Suppose a circle in the coordinate plane has its center at the point $P(h, k)$, and its radius is r (see Figure 10-2). If a point (x, y) is on the circle, then, by definition, its distance from (h, k) is r. In terms of the distance formula,

$$\sqrt{(x - h)^2 + (y - k)^2} = r$$

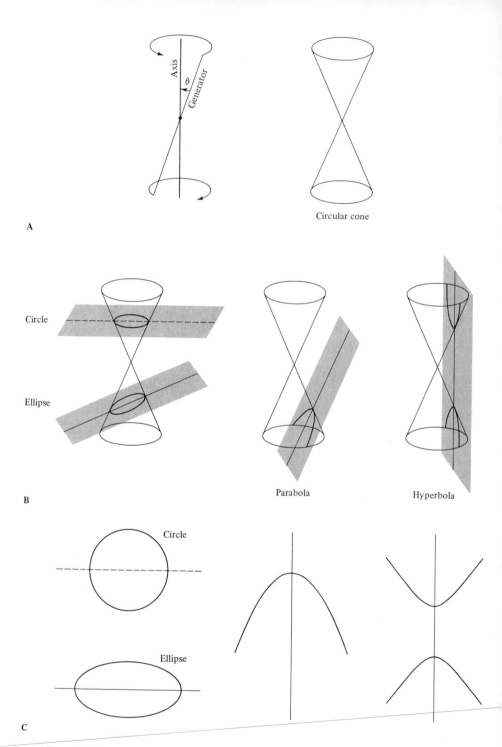

Figure 10-1

(A) Generating a circular cone. A fixed vertical line, called the axis, is attached to another line, the generator, at a fixed point. The generator is free to rotate around the axis, but the angle θ between the lines remains constant. The cone consists of all points through which the generator passes. (B) The intersection of various planes with the cone produces conic sections. (C) The conic sections as seen in their planes of intersection.

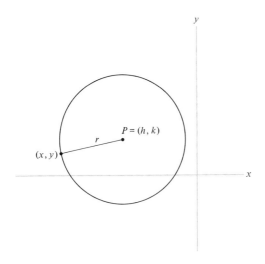

Figure 10-2
A circle with center P and radius r is defined geometrically as the set of all points in the plane that are at distance r from P. If the coordinates of P are (h, k), the same circle can be defined algebraically as the set of all points (x, y) whose coordinates satisfy the equation $(x - h)^2 + (y - k)^2 = r^2$.

Squaring both sides of this equation yields

$$(x - h)^2 + (y - k)^2 = r^2 \tag{1}$$

The coordinates of every point on the circle satisfy this equation.

 Now suppose that the coordinates of a point (x, y) satisfy Equation (1). We may take the (nonnegative) square root of each side, to find that the distance from (x, y) to the point (h, k) is r; thus, the point (x, y) is on the circle. We have shown that Equation (1) is a complete algebraic description of a circle with center (h, k) and radius r. This equation is said to be in **standard form.** Any equation that can be written in this form is an equation of a circle with center (h, k) and radius r.

Example 1
(a)   Find the center and radius of the circle $(x - 3)^2 + (y + 4)^2 = 25$.
(b)   Find an equation of the circle with center at $(-1, 3)$ and radius 2.

Solution
(a) $r^2 = 25$ so the radius is 5. As for the center, it is obvious that $h = 3$; if you think of $y + 4$ as $y - (-4)$, then you can see that $k = -4$; thus, the center is at $(3, -4)$.
(b)   In this circle, $h = -1$, $k = 3$, and $r = 2$. Thus, $(x + 1)^2 + (y - 3)^2 = 4$ is an equation of the given circle.

It often happens that an equation of a circle is written as a quadratic of the form

$$x^2 + y^2 + bx + cy + d = 0 \tag{2}$$

This equation can be put into standard form as follows. Subtract d from both sides and complete the squares:*

$$\left(x^2 + bx + \frac{b^2}{4}\right) + \left(y^2 + cy + \frac{c^2}{4}\right) = -d + \frac{b^2}{4} + \frac{c^2}{4}$$

$$\left(x + \frac{b}{2}\right)^2 + \left(y + \frac{c}{2}\right)^2 = \frac{b^2 + c^2 - 4d}{4}$$

You will recognize this as the standard form of the equation of a circle, *if* $b^2 + c^2 - 4d > 0$; thus, the coordinates of a point (x, y) satisfy Equation (2) if and only if (x, y) lies on the circle with center $(-b/2, -c/2)$ and radius $r = \sqrt{b^2 + c^2 - 4d}/2$. If $b^2 + c^2 - 4d = 0$, *only* the coordinates of $(-b/2, -c/2)$ satisfy Equation (2); if $b^2 + c^2 - 4d < 0$, there is *no* solution of the equation.

Equation (2) is called the **general form** of the equation of a circle. From the general form, it is always possible to find the center and radius, and thus the standard form, by completing squares.

Example 2
Find the center and radius of the circle $x^2 + y^2 - 4x + 6y - 3 = 0$; graph the circle.

Solution
Add 3 to both sides and complete the squares.

$$(x^2 - 4x + 4) + (y^2 + 6y + 9) = 3 + 4 + 9$$
$$(x - 2)^2 + (y + 3)^2 = 16$$

Therefore, the center is $(2, -3)$ and the radius is 4. The graph is shown in Figure 10-3.

A slightly different form for the equation of a circle is $ax^2 + ay^2 + bx + cy + d = 0$, with $a \neq 0$. Dividing this equation by a yields an equation of type (2). For example, $5x^2 + 5y^2 - 20x + 30y - 15 = 0$ represents a circle, because dividing through by 5 yields the equation in Example 2.

---

*Reading Sections 3-3 and 3-4 will refresh your memory of this technique.

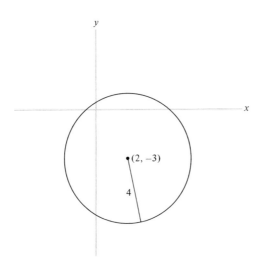

Figure 10-3
The graph of the circle in Example 2.

Most of the exercises at the end of this section will give certain information from which you must find an equation of a circle and draw its graph. For example, if you know the center and radius of a circle, then it is easy to write an equation in standard form. Here are a few of the different ways in which this information can be given:

The center is $(3, 4)$ and the circle passes through $(-1, 2)$. **Solution:** The center is known and the distance from $(3, 4)$ to $(-1, 2)$ is the radius.

The center is $(3, 4)$ and the circle is tangent to the x-axis. **Solution:** A rough sketch will show that the radius must be 4.

The radius is 2 and the circle is tangent to both axes. **Solution:** There are four such circles; their centers are $(2, 2)$, $(-2, 2)$, $(-2, -2)$ and $(2, -2)$.

Information other than the location of the center and the length of the radius may also lead to an equation of a circle. Notice that there are three constants (h, k, and r) in the standard form, and three constants (b, c, and d) in the general form. This suggests that it is sometimes necessary to know three geometric facts to determine the equation of a circle. Again, there are many ways to present these facts.

Example 3
Find an equation of the circle passing through the points $(0, 1)$, $(2, -1)$, and $(4, 1)$. Then graph the equation.

Solution

Use either the standard form or the general form to produce three equations with three unknowns. The general form $(x^2 + y^2 + bx + cy + d = 0)$ is easier because each equation will be linear.

For $(x, y) = (0, 1)$, $0^2 + 1^2 + 0b + 1c + d = 0$

For $(x, y) = (2, -1)$, $2^2 + (-1)^2 + 2b + (-1)c + d = 0$

For $(x, y) = (4, 1)$, $4^2 + 1^2 + 4b + 1c + d = 0$

In other words,

(1) $c + d = -1$

(2) $2b - c + d = -5$

(3) $4b + c + d = -17$

Eliminate c:

$(1) + (2)$ $2b + 2d = -6$

$(2) + (3)$ $6b + 2d = -22$

Subtract the second of these equations from the first to get $-4b = 16$, or $b = -4$; then $d = 1$ and $c = -2$. Therefore, an equation of this circle is

$$x^2 + y^2 - 4x - 2y + 1 = 0$$

Check

For $(x, y) = (0, 1)$, $0^2 + 1^2 - 4 \cdot 0 - 2 \cdot 1 + 1 = 0$

For $(x, y) = (2, -1)$, $2^2 + (-1)^2 - 4 \cdot 2 - 2(-1) + 1 = 0$

For $(x, y) = (4, 1)$, $4^2 + 1^2 - 4 \cdot 4 - 2 \cdot 1 + 1 = 0$

The easiest way to graph the equation is to put it into standard form.

$$(x - 2)^2 + (y - 1)^2 = 4$$

The center is $(2, 1)$ and the radius is 2 (see Figure 10-4).

Example 4

Find an equation of the circle passing through $(-1, 3)$ and $(2, 0)$ whose center lies on the line $x + y = -1$.

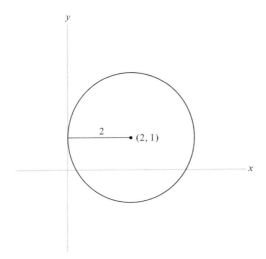

Figure 10-4
The graph of the circle in Example 3.

Solution
This time use the standard form, because you know that the coordinates of the center (h, k) satisfy the equation $x + y = -1$; that is,

$$(1) \quad h + k = -1$$

The coordinates of the two given points yield two more equations:

$$(-1 - h)^2 + (3 - k)^2 = r^2$$

$$(2 - h)^2 + (0 - k)^2 = r^2$$

Multiply out the squared expressions to obtain

$$(2) \quad 1 + 2h + h^2 + 9 - 6k + k^2 = r^2$$

$$(3) \quad 4 - 4h + h^2 \qquad + k^2 = r^2$$

Subtract (3) from (2): the result is

$$(4) \quad 6h - 6k = -6 \quad \text{or} \quad h - k = -1$$

It follows from (1) and (4) that $h = -1$ and $k = 0$. Use any one of the preceding equations to find $r = 3$. Thus, an equation of this circle is

$$(x + 1)^2 + y^2 = 9$$

Translation of axes

When the center of a circle in the xy-plane is the origin, $(h, k) = (0, 0)$, then the standard form reduces to

$$x^2 + y^2 = r^2$$

Thus, the standard form $(x - h)^2 + (y - k)^2 = r^2$ can be thought of as a translation of a circle with radius r and center $(0, 0)$ $|h|$ units to the right (h positive) or to the left (h negative) and $|k|$ units up (k positive) or down (k negative). See Figure 10-5.

To look at it another way, consider the circle given by an equation $(x - h)^2 + (y - k)^2 = r^2$. Draw a new pair of coordinate axes, an x'-axis and a y'-axis parallel to the x- and y-axes, with a new origin at (h, k), the center of the circle (see Figure 10-6). On the circle, each point with coordinates (x, y) in the original coordinate system also has coordinates (x', y') in the *new* coordinate system. Because the center of the circle is at the origin of the new coordinate system, the equation of the circle in the new coordinates is

$$x'^2 + y'^2 = r^2$$

Thus, instead of moving the circle to interpret its equation, we have shifted the *axes,*

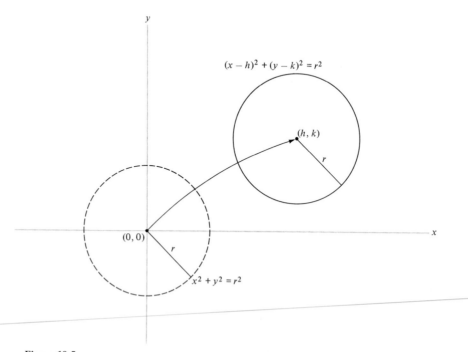

Figure 10-5

The standard form of the equation of a circle translates a circle with its center at the origin to a circle with its center at (h, k).

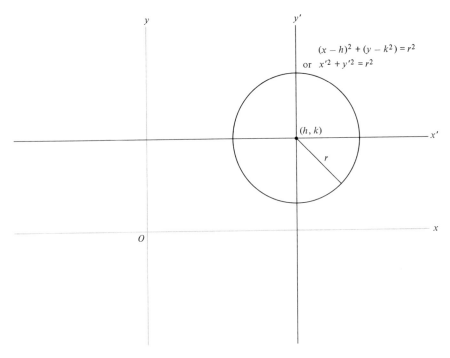

Figure 10-6
Drawing a new set of coordinate axes can simplify the equation of a circle.

which simplified the equation. As you will see later in this chapter, this technique can be used to simplify many other kinds of equations.

A parallel shift of one or both of the coordinate axes is called a **translation of axes;** the result is a new origin and a new set of axes. Figure 10-7 shows a translation of axes: the x-axis has been shifted k units upward to form the new horizontal x'-axis; the y-axis has been translated h units to the right to form the new vertical y'-axis. The new origin O' is located at the point whose xy-coordinates are (h, k). Every point in the plane now has two pairs of coordinates, (x, y) and (x', y'), one for each coordinate system. These coordinates are related by the **equations of translation**

$$x' = x - h \quad \text{and} \quad y' = y - k$$

In general, if the origin of the new coordinate system is at the point (h, k) in the old coordinate system, the old axes are shifted to the right or to the left, upward or downward, according to whether h and k are positive or negative. In any case, the equations of translation are the same.

Example 5
Translate the x-axis 2 units upward and the y-axis 3 units to the left. Find the new coordinates of (1, 2), (−1, 4), and (3, −1).

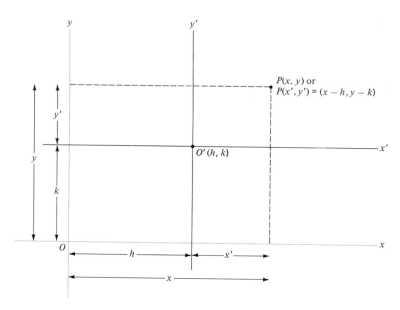

Figure 10-7
A translation of axes. The *x*-axis has been shifted *k* units upward, and the *y*-axis has been
shifted *h* units to the right. The origin O' of the new coordinate system has the coordinates
(h, k) in the old coordinate system. A point *P* whose coordinates were (x, y) in the original
system has coordinates $(x', y') = (x - h, y - k)$ in the new system.

Solution

The origin, which lies on both axes, is shifted 2 units upward and 3 units to the
left. Thus, the new origin is at the point $(h, k) = (-3, 2)$ in the old coordinate
system. According to the equations of translation,

$$(1, 2) \quad \text{becomes} \quad (1 - (-3), 2 - 2) = (4, 0)$$

$$(-1, 4) \quad \text{becomes} \quad (-1 - (-3), 4 - 2) = (2, 2)$$

$$(3, -1) \quad \text{becomes} \quad (3 - (-3), -1 - 2) = (6, -3)$$

A circle with center at the origin and radius *r* has an equation

$$x^2 + y^2 = r^2$$

which we shall call the **simple equation** of a circle. As we have seen, every circle is a
translation of one whose center is at the origin; that is, the equation of any circle can
be transformed, by an appropriate translation of axes, into a simple equation of a
circle.

■ A translation of axes transforms an equation in x and y into an equation in x' and y'. Simply substitute according to the equations of translation.

With an appropriate choice of the equations of translation, this transformation will simplify an equation. For example, if the general form of the equation of a circle is $x^2 + y^2 - 4x + 2y = 0$, then the standard form is $(x - 2)^2 + (y + 1)^2 = 5$. This is equivalent to the simple equation

$$x'^2 + y'^2 = (\sqrt{5})^2$$

if $x' = x - 2$ and $y' = y + 1$. These equations of translation shift the origin to the point $(2, -1)$, which is the center of the given circle. Thus, in discussing circles, we could have studied simple equations first and then treated more complicated equations as transformations of simple ones. In fact, this is what we shall do with parabolas, ellipses, and hyperbolas in the next three sections.

Review of basic ideas

The *standard form* of the equation of a circle with center at (h, k) and radius $r > 0$ is

$$(x - h)^2 + (y - k)^2 = r^2$$

The *general form* of the equation of a circle is

$$x^2 + y^2 + bx + cy + d = 0$$

where $b^2 + c^2 - 4d > 0$. To find the center and the radius, complete the squares and write the general form in the standard form.

The *simple form* of the equation of a circle is

$$x^2 + y^2 = r^2$$

Any equation of a circle can be written in simple form by a translation of the axes.

Exercises

Find an equation of the circle(s) from the given information, and sketch its graph.
1. Center $(-1, 2)$, radius 3
2. Center $(1, 1)$, radius 4.
3. Center $(-2, -1)$, radius $\frac{1}{2}$.
4. Center $(3, 4)$, radius 5.3.
5. Center $(3, 1)$, passing through $(4, 4)$.

6. Center $(-1, 4)$, passing through $(0, 0)$.
7. Center $(-2, -3)$, passing through $(-4, -5)$.
8. Center $(1, -1)$, passing through $(-2, -2)$.
9. Center $(3, 4)$, tangent to y-axis.
10. Center $(-4, 1)$, tangent to y-axis.
11. Center $(-3, -1)$, tangent to x-axis.
12. Center $(4, -3)$, tangent to x-axis.
13. Radius 4, tangent to both axes.
14. Radius 1, tangent to both axes.
15. Endpoints of a diameter are $(1, 3)$ and $(0, 3)$.
16. Endpoints of a diameter are $(1, -4)$ and $(1, 1)$.
17. Endpoints of a diameter are $(1, 2)$ and $(3, 4)$.
18. Endpoints of a diameter are $(-3, 1)$ and $(-1, 5)$.
19. Passing through $(4, 6)$, $(1, 7)$, and $(6, 2)$.
20. Passing through $(-3, 5)$, $(-3, -3)$, and $(1, 1)$.
21. Passing through $(-2, 2)$, $(-1, 3)$, and $(-3, 3)$.
22. Passing through $(0, 0)$, $(3, 1)$, and $(-2, -4)$.
23. Center on y-axis, passing through $(1, 1)$ and $(0, 0)$.
24. Center on x-axis, passing through $(0, 0)$ and $(3, 3)$.
25. Center on $x + y = -1$, passing through $(0, 0)$ and $(3, 1)$.
26. Center on $2x - y = -2$, passing through $(0, 0)$ and $(-5, -1)$.
27. The circle passing through the vertices of the triangle whose sides lie on the lines $y = x$, $y = 0$, and $y = -x + 2$.
28. The circle passing through the vertices of the triangle whose sides lie on the lines $x = 0$, $y = 0$, and $x - y + 2 = 0$.
29. Radius 6 and concentric (same center) with the circle $x^2 + y^2 - 4x - 4y = 0$.
30. Concentric with $x^2 + y^2 + 6x + 8y = 0$ and tangent to the x-axis.

Find the center and the radius, and sketch the graph of the circle defined by each of the following equations (if possible).

31. $x^2 + y^2 = 4$ 32. $x^2 + y^2 = 3$
33. $x^2 + y^2 + 2x - 4y - 3 = 0$ 34. $x^2 + y^2 - 4x + 6y = 0$
35. $x^2 + y^2 - 3x + 5y = 0$ 36. $x^2 + y^2 - 7x + y = 2$
37. $3x^2 + 3y^2 + 6x - 1 = 0$ 38. $4x^2 + 4y^2 - x + y = 8$
39. $x^2 + y^2 - 2x + 4y + 10 = 0$ 40. $x^2 + y^2 = 0$

■ **Parametric equations**

Each point in a plane is located by a pair of rectangular coordinates (x, y). In describing a curve, it is sometimes desirable to express the coordinates as functions of the same single variable, say, $x = f(t)$ and $y = g(t)$. A pair of equations like this locates a point in the plane by specifying a *single* number t. Suppose the coordinates (x, y) of all points on a curve C can be written as functions

$$x = f(t) \quad \text{and} \quad y = g(t) \qquad \text{for } a \le t \le b$$

These are called **parametric equations** of C, and t is called the **parameter.**

41.   Show that

$$x = 3 \cos t \quad \text{and} \quad y = 3 \sin t \qquad \text{for } 0 \le t \le 2\pi$$

are parametric equations of the circle with radius 3 and center at the origin. [HINT: Show that $x^2 + y^2 = 9$.]

42.   (Continuation of Exercise 41) Show that

$$x = (r \cos t) + h \quad \text{and} \quad y = (r \sin t) + k \qquad \text{for } 0 \le t \le 2\pi$$

are parametric equations of the circle with radius r and center at (h, k).

43.   Suppose a particle is moving along a path in a plane and, at any time t, its position is given by the parametric equations $x = (2 \cos t) + 4$ and $y = (2 \sin t) - 3$. Describe the path of the particle. Where will the particle be when $t = 0$? When $t = \pi/2$?

44.   Find an equation of the line tangent to the circle $x^2 + y^2 - 4x + 2y = 0$ at the point $(0, 0)$. [HINT: A tangent line is perpendicular to the radius at the point of tangency. Therefore, the slopes are negative reciprocals. Draw a picture.]

45.   Follow the instructions in Exercise 44 for the circle $x^2 + y^2 - 8x = 0$ and the point $(0, 0)$.

46.   Find an equation of each line (there are two) passing through the origin and tangent to the circle $(x - 5)^2 + y^2 = 16$. [HINT: Draw a picture.]

10-2
The Parabola

In Section 3-3, parabolas were described as graphs of certain quadratic functions. It is also possible to describe them in a more general, completely geometric way.

A **parabola** is the locus, or set, of all points that are equidistant from a fixed point, called the **focus,** and a fixed line, called the **directrix** (see Figure 10-8). The line through the focus that is perpendicular to the directrix is called the **axis;** notice that the parabola is symmetric about its axis. The point where the axis crosses the parabola is called the **vertex;** notice that the vertex lies half way between the focus and the directrix.

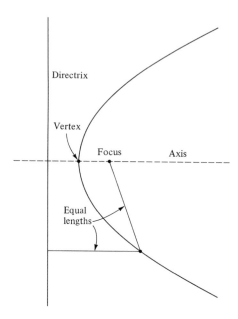

Figure 10-8
A parabola is the curve consisting of all points that are equidistant from a fixed point, called the focus, and a fixed line, called the directrix.

Parabolas occur in nature as the paths followed by some of the comets that appear in our sky. The path of a projectile fired from a gun can be described as a portion of a parabola (if air friction is ignored). If a light source is placed at the focus of a parabolic mirror then the rays will be reflected parallel to the axis to form a powerful beam (see Figure 10-9). That is why the inside surfaces of automobile headlamps and searchlights are parabolic mirrors. Similarly, parallel light rays striking a parabolic mirror will be focused at a single point. That is why parabolic shapes are used in telescopes and solar-energy collecting devices.

A parabola has the simplest possible equation if its vertex is at the origin, its focus lies on one coordinate axis, and its directrix is parallel to the other coordinate axis. Suppose that the focus is on the y-axis at the point $(0, p), p > 0$, and the directrix is the line $y = -p$, which is parallel to the x-axis. The origin, which is equidistant from the focus to the directrix, will be the vertex (see Figure 10-10). A point (x, y) will be on the parabola if and only if its distance from the focus equals its distance to the directrix. It follows that

$$\sqrt{(x - 0)^2 + (y - p)^2} = |y + p|$$

$$(x - 0)^2 + (y - p)^2 = (y + p)^2 \qquad \text{(Square both sides.)}$$

$$x^2 + y^2 - 2py + p^2 = y^2 + 2py + p^2$$

$$x^2 = 4py \qquad\qquad (1)$$

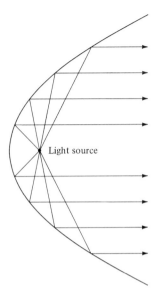

Figure 10-9
Rays from a light source at the focus of a parabolic mirror will be reflected as a beam of parallel rays.

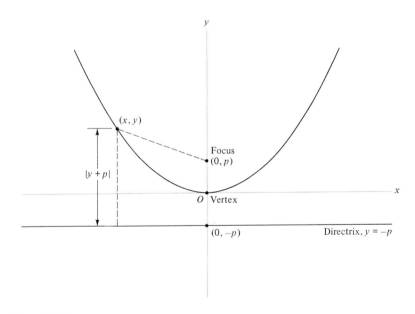

Figure 10-10
If the focus of a parabola is at $(0, p)$, $p > 0$, and the directrix is the horizontal line $y = -p$, then the vertex is at $(0, 0)$, and the coordinates of any point (x, y) on the parabola must satisfy the equation $x^2 = 4py$.

This tells us that if a point is on the parabola, then its coordinates satisfy Equation (1); conversely, because the steps above are completely reversible, if the coordinates of a point satisfy Equation (1) then it is on the parabola. Thus, $x^2 = 4py$ is the equation of the parabola with vertex at the origin, focus at $(0, p)$, and directrix $y = -p$.

There are three other possible ways for a parabola to have a **simple equation.** In each case, the vertex is at the origin.

$$\text{Focus at } (0, -p); \text{ directrix, } y = p: x^2 = -4py \tag{2}$$

$$\text{Focus at } (p, 0); \text{ directrix, } x = -p: y^2 = 4px \tag{3}$$

$$\text{Focus at } (-p, 0); \text{ directrix, } x = p: y^2 = -4px \tag{4}$$

All four possibilities are illustrated in the following example.

Example 1
Find the focus and the directrix and sketch the parabolas

(a) $x^2 = 4y$ (b) $\frac{1}{2}x^2 + y = 0$ (c) $y^2 = 8x$ (d) $y^2 + x = 0$

Solution
(a) $x^2 = 4y$. This is in the form of Equation (1) with $p = 1$. Thus, the focus is $(0, 1)$ and the directrix is the line $y = -1$. To sketch the curve, plot a few points as an aid. The vertex is $(0, 0)$, and it is usually sufficient to plot a few points on only one side of the vertex, because every parabola is symmetrical about its axis (see Figure 10-11A).
(b) $\frac{1}{2}x^2 + y = 0$. Rewrite the equation as $x^2 = -2y$. This is in the form of Equation (2) with $p = \frac{1}{2}$. The focus is $(0, -\frac{1}{2})$ and the directrix is $y = \frac{1}{2}$. Plot the vertex $(0, 0)$ and two other points; a sketch is shown in Figure 10-11B.
(c) $y^2 = 8x$. This is Equation (3) with $p = 2$. The focus is $(2, 0)$ and the directrix is $x = -2$ (see Figure 10-11C).
(d)   Rewrite $y^2 + x = 0$ as $y^2 = -x$. This is Equation (4) with $p = \frac{1}{4}$; the focus is $(-\frac{1}{4}, 0)$ and the directrix is $x = \frac{1}{4}$ (see Figure 10-11D).

Now let us consider the more general parabola whose directrix is parallel to a coordinate axis, but whose vertex is not necessarily at the origin. Suppose the vertex is at (h, k) and the directrix is parallel to the x-axis and is p units $(p > 0)$ below the vertex. Then, as Figure 10-12A shows, the focus is at $(h, k + p)$, the directrix is the line $y = k - p$, and the parabola opens upward.

If the coordinate axes were translated as shown in Figure 10-12B, so as to make (h, k) the new origin, the parabola would have the simple equation

$$x'^2 = 4py'$$

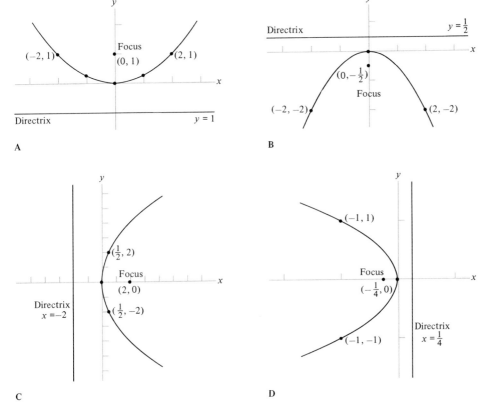

Figure 10-11
(A) The parabola $x^2 = 4y$ opens upward. (B) The parabola $\frac{1}{2}x^2 + y = 0$ opens downward.
(C) The parabola $y^2 = 8x$ opens to the right. (D) The parabola $y^2 + x = 0$ opens to the left.
See Example 1.

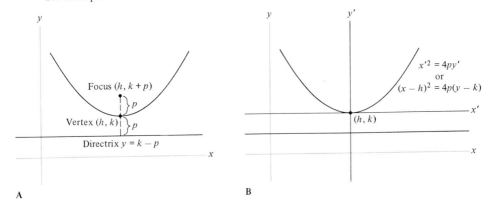

Figure 10-12
(A) Parabola with vertex at (h, k), directrix at distance p below the vertex and parallel to the x-axis. (B) The same parabola after the axes are translated so that (h, k) is the origin.

As we have seen (Section 10-1), such a translation replaces x' by $x - h$ and y' by $y - k$. It follows that the equation of the parabola in the original xy-coordinates is

$$(x - h)^2 = 4p(y - k)$$

This is the **standard form** of the equation of a parabola with vertex (h, k), focus $(h, k + p)$, and directrix $y = k - p$. Similar reasoning applies to a parabola whose directrix is *above* the vertex (h, k), and to a parabola whose directrix is to the *left* or *right* of the vertex and parallel to the y-axis.

■   Any equation that can be put into one of the standard forms below is an equation of a parabola with its vertex at (h, k).

I $(x - h)^2 = 4p(y - k)$ Focus $(h, k + p)$; directrix $y = k - p$; opens upward

II $(x - h)^2 = -4p(y - k)$ Focus $(h, k - p)$; directrix $y = k + p$; opens downward

III $(y - k)^2 = 4p(x - h)$ Focus $(h + p, k)$; directrix $x = h - p$; opens to right

IV $(y - k)^2 = -4p(x - h)$ Focus $(h - p, k)$; directrix $x = h + p$; opens to left

Example 2

Find the vertex, focus, and directrix, and then sketch the graph of

(a) $x^2 + 4x = -2y - 2$ and   (b) $2y^2 - 4y = 6x - 5$

Solution

(a)   The squared term is x, so try to put the equation in standard form I or II by completing the square:

$$x^2 + 4x + 4 = -2y - 2 + 4$$
$$(x + 2)^2 = -2(y - 1)$$

This is form II, so the curve opens downward and $p = \frac{1}{2}$. This is a parabola with vertex $(-2, 1)$, focus $(-2, 1 - \frac{1}{2}) = (-2, \frac{1}{2})$, and directrix $y = 1 + \frac{1}{2} = \frac{3}{2}$. Plot one point on each side of the vertex, say $(-3, \frac{1}{2})$ and $(-1, \frac{1}{2})$, and sketch (see Figure 10-13A).

(b)   Now the squared term is y, so try for type III or IV. Divide through by 2 and complete the square:

$$y^2 - 2y + 1 = 3x - \frac{5}{2} + 1$$
$$(y - 1)^2 = 3(x - \frac{1}{2})$$

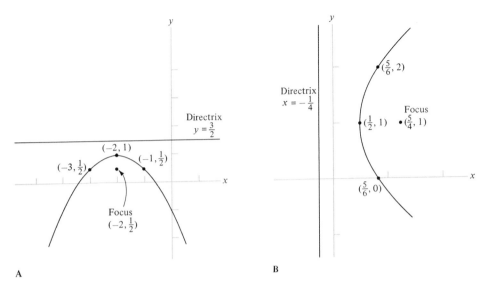

Figure 10-13
(A) The parabola $(x + 2)^2 = -2(y - 1)$. See Example 2(a). (B) The parabola $(y - 1)^2 = 3(x - \frac{1}{2})$. See Example 2(b).

This is form III, so the curve opens to the right and $p = \frac{3}{4}$. The parabola has vertex $(\frac{1}{2}, 1)$, focus $(\frac{1}{2} + \frac{3}{4}, 1) = (\frac{5}{4}, 1)$, and directrix $x = \frac{1}{2} - \frac{3}{4} = -\frac{1}{4}$. Plot a couple of points by letting $y = 0$ and $y = 2$; then sketch (see Figure 10-13B).

The next examples show how to use geometric information to find an equation for a parabola.

Example 3
Find an equation of the parabola with vertex $(3, -4)$ and directrix $y = -3$.

Solution
Make a rough sketch (see Figure 10-14A). The directrix is parallel to the x-axis and is one unit above the vertex. This implies that x will be the squared term, $p = 1$, and the parabola opens downward. The standard form, therefore, is

$$(x - h)^2 = -4p(y - k)$$

Because $h = 3$, $k = -4$, and $p = 1$, you get

$$(x - 3)^2 = -4(y + 4)$$

for an equation of the parabola.

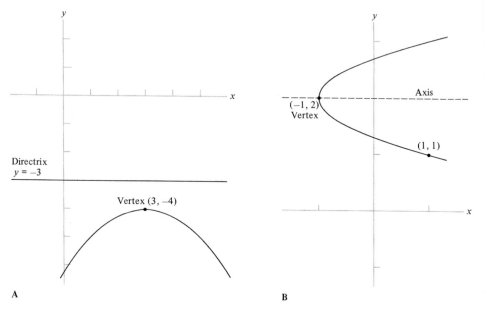

Figure 10-14
(A) The parabola in Example 3. (B) The parabola in Example 4.

Example 4
Find an equation of the parabola that has a horizontal axis, vertex $(-1, 2)$, and passes through $(1, 1)$.

Solution
Make a rough sketch (see Figure 10-14B). It will show that the parabola opens to the right. This means that the standard form is

$$(y - k)^2 = 4p(x - h)$$

You know that $h = -1$ and $k = 2$ so $(y - 2)^2 = 4p(x + 1)$; you can solve for p by using the coordinates of $(1, 1)$, which is on the parabola:

$$(1 - 2)^2 = 4p(1 + 1)$$

$$1 = 8p$$

$$\tfrac{1}{8} = p$$

Therefore, $(y - 2)^2 = \tfrac{1}{2}(x + 1)$ is an equation of the parabola.

Not every parabola has a vertical or horizontal directrix. Parabolas such as the one in

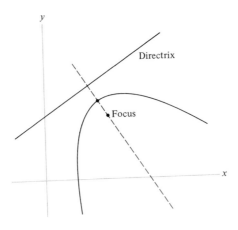

Figure 10-15
A general parabola.

Figure 10-15 can be analyzed by using *rotations* as well as translations of the coordinate axes. This technique is explained in Section 10-5.

Review of basic ideas
Learn the definition of a parabola.
Learn the four simple forms for an equation of a parabola.
Learn these procedures:

■ *Sketching the graph.* A quadratic of the form $Ax^2 + Bx + Cy + D = 0$ or $Ax + By^2 + Cy + D = 0$ is a parabola with a horizontal or vertical directrix. Rewrite it in standard form by completing the square. This form indicates the vertex, focus, and directrix, and how the curve opens. (See Examples 1 and 2.)

Finding an equation. Given geometric information, draw a picture and determine which standard form applies. Then use the information and the standard form to determine h, k, and p. (See Examples 3 and 4.)

Exercises

Find the vertex, focus, and directrix, and sketch the graph.

1. $y^2 - 4x = 0$
2. $y^2 + 6x = 0$
3. $4x^2 = y$
4. $\frac{1}{2}x^2 = -3y$
5. $(x - 1)^2 = 2y$
6. $(y - 3)^2 = 2x + 4$

7. $4(y + 2)^2 + x = 0$ 8. $(y - 3)^2 - 2x + 4 = 0$
9. $x^2 - 2x + 4y = 3$ 10. $y^2 + 4y - x + 2 = 0$
11. $y^2 + 4y + x + 6 = 0$ 12. $2x^2 + 5x - 2y = 3$

Find an equation of the parabola with the given properties.
13. Vertex $(0, 0)$, focus $(0, 3)$.
14. Vertex $(0, 0)$, directrix $x = -2$.
15. Vertex $(-1, 4)$, directrix $y = 0$.
16. Vertex $(3, -2)$, focus $(5, -2)$.
17. Vertex $(-1, -3)$, vertical axis, passes through $(0, 4)$.
18. Vertex $(2, -1)$, horizontal axis, passes through $(5, 0)$.
19. Focus $(6, -1)$, directrix $y = 3$.
20. Focus $(-4, -2)$, directrix $x = 1$.
21. Vertical axis, parabola passes through $(0, 3)$, $(-1, 9)$, and $(2, 3)$. [HINT: Draw a picture, determine which standard form is appropriate, and derive three equations.]
22. Horizontal axis, parabola passes through $(0, -2)$, $(1, 0)$, and $(4, 2)$.

Parametric equations
Parametric equations of a circle were defined just before Exercise 41 in Section 10-1. It is also possible to have parametric equations for a parabola.
23. Show that $x = at$ and $y = bt^2$ $(a, b \neq 0)$ are parametric equations of a parabola with vertex $(0, 0)$ and focus $(0, a^2/4b)$. [HINT: Write $x/a = t$ and show that $x^2 = \dfrac{a^2}{b} y$.]

24. Show that $x = at$ and $y = bt^2 + ct + d$ $(a, b \neq 0)$ are parametric equations of a parabola. Find its vertex.
25. When a shell is fired (from a gun positioned at the origin) with an initial velocity v_0 feet per second (at time $t = 0$) at an angle θ above the ground, its position at any time t is given by the parametric equations

$$x = (v_0 \cos \theta)t \quad \text{and} \quad y = (v_0 \sin \theta)t - 16t^2$$

These equations follow from physical laws; they can be proved by the use of calculus. Show that the trajectory is a parabola.
26. (Continuation of Exercise 25) If a shell is fired with an initial velocity of 1000 ft/sec at an angle of $30°$, how high will it go? When and where will it strike the ground?
27. (Continuation of Exercise 26) At what angle should the gun be aimed to hit a target 5000 ft away?

10-3
The Ellipse

An **ellipse** is the locus, or set, of all points P such that the sum of the distances from P to two distinct fixed points, called **foci** (singular, **focus**), is a constant. The parts of an ellipse are labeled in Figure 10-16. It has two foci, two **axes**—the one through the foci is called the **major axis**—and *four* **vertices**. The **center** is halfway between the foci. An ellipse is symmetric with respect to its center and its axes.

Ellipses occur in nature as paths of orbiting bodies. For example, the orbit of the earth is an ellipse with the sun at one focus. It is also true that waves traveling in a straight line through one focus of an ellipse will be reflected off the boundary through the other focus. Whispering galleries are ellipsoidal, with the whisperer and the listener at the foci.

An ellipse has the simplest equation if the center of the ellipse is at the origin and both foci lie on one coordinate axis. Figure 10-17 shows such an ellipse with foci at $(-c, 0)$ and $(c, 0)$. For all points (x, y) on the ellipse, the sum $d_1 + d_2$ must be a constant greater than $2c$. As you will see, it is convenient to represent the constant by $2a$; notice that $a > c$. Thus, $d_1 + d_2 = 2a$; in terms of the distance formula,

$$\sqrt{(x + c)^2 + (y - 0)^2} + \sqrt{(x - c)^2 + (y - 0)^2} = 2a$$

or

$$\sqrt{(x + c)^2 + y^2} = 2a - \sqrt{(x - c)^2 + y^2}$$

Now square both sides to obtain

$$(x + c)^2 + y^2 = 4a^2 - 4a\sqrt{(x - c)^2 + y^2} + (x - c)^2 + y^2$$

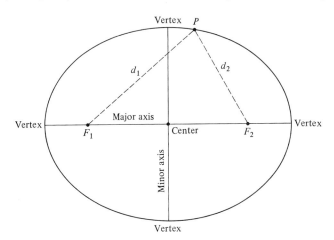

Figure 10-16
An ellipse with foci F_1 and F_2. The sum $d_1 + d_2$ is constant for all points on the ellipse.

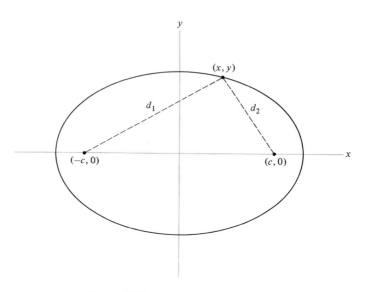

Figure 10-17
An ellipse with foci at $(-c, 0)$ and $(c, 0)$.

Multiply out the terms $(x + c)^2$ and $(x - c)^2$, simplify as much as possible, and isolate the radical on one side. This yields

$$-a^2 + cx = -a\sqrt{(x - c)^2 + y^2}$$

Squaring again, we have

$$a^4 - 2a^2cx + c^2x^2 = a^2(x - c)^2 + a^2y^2$$
$$= a^2x^2 - 2a^2cx + a^2c^2 + a^2y^2$$

which reduces to

$$x^2(a^2 - c^2) + a^2y^2 = a^2(a^2 - c^2)$$

or

$$\frac{x^2}{a^2} + \frac{y^2}{a^2 - c^2} = 1 \qquad\qquad (a > c)$$

If we set $b^2 = a^2 - c^2$, then

$$\frac{x^2}{a^2} + \frac{y^2}{b^2} = 1 \qquad\qquad (1)$$

This is the **simple equation** of an ellipse with center at the origin and foci $(-c, 0)$ and $(c, 0)$, where $c = \sqrt{a^2 - b^2}$ (notice that $a > b$). The vertices are where the curve

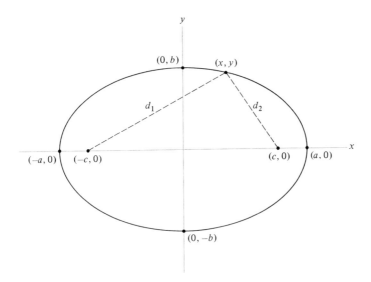

Figure 10-18
The equation of an ellipse whose foci are on the x-axis and whose vertices are at $(\pm a, 0)$
and $(0, \pm b)$ is $\dfrac{x^2}{a^2} + \dfrac{y^2}{b^2} = 1$.

crosses the axes: set $y = 0$ to obtain $(\pm a, 0)$, and $x = 0$ to obtain $(0, \pm b)$. See Figure 10-18.

We have shown that if a point is on the ellipse, its coordinates must satisfy Equation (1). Unlike the derivation of the simple equation for a parabola, these steps are not completely reversible. Nevertheless, it is true that, if the coordinates of a point satisfy Equation (1), then the point is on the ellipse.

An ellipse also has a simple equation if the foci are on the y-axis, say, at $(0, -c)$ and $(0, c)$. The same procedure yields the same equation, but the roles played by a and b are reversed: now $b > a$ and $c = \sqrt{b^2 - a^2}$. In other words,

■ Equation (1) represents an ellipse with its center at the origin and its foci on the x-axis or the y-axis, depending on whether $a > b$ or $b > a$. In either case, the vertices are at $(\pm a, 0)$ and $(0, \pm b)$.

Example 1
Find an equation of the ellipse with foci $(-2, 0)$ and $(2, 0)$, and two of its vertices at $(-3, 0)$ and $(3, 0)$. Sketch the graph.

Solution
The major axis of the ellipse is on the x-axis. The coordinates of the foci and the vertices tell you that $c = 2$ and $a = 3$. It follows from the relationship

$b^2 = a^2 - c^2$ that $b = \sqrt{5}$. The equation, therefore, is

$$\frac{x^2}{9} + \frac{y^2}{5} = 1$$

It is easy to sketch an ellipse if you know where its vertices are. In this case, the vertices are $(\pm 3, 0)$ and $(0, \pm \sqrt{5})$. See Figure 10-19A.

Example 2
Find the vertices and the foci, and sketch the graph of $4x^2 + 2y^2 = 8$.

Solution
First divide by 8 to rewrite the equation in simple form:

$$\frac{x^2}{2} + \frac{y^2}{4} = 1$$

Then $a = \sqrt{2}$ and $b = 2$, so the vertices are $(\pm \sqrt{2}, 0)$ and $(0, \pm 2)$. The foci lie on the y-axis (because $b > a$) and $c^2 = b^2 - a^2 = 2$; thus, the foci are at $(0, \pm \sqrt{2})$. Now locate the vertices and sketch the graph (See Figure 10-19B).

Suppose the major axis of an ellipse lies on the x-axis. The ratio c/a is called the **eccentricity** of the ellipse and is denoted by e. Notice that $e < 1$ because $c < a$. The

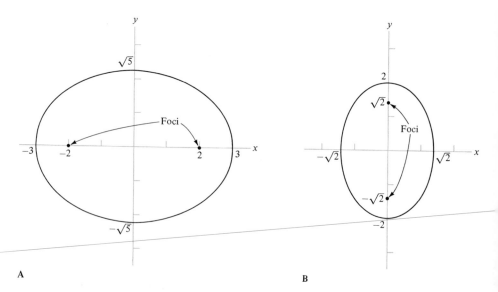

Figure 10-19
(A) The ellipse in Example 1. (B) The ellipse in Example 2.

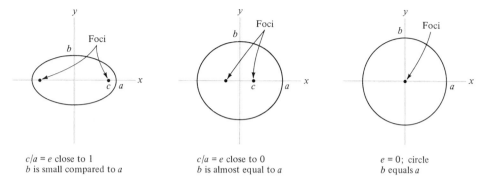

$c/a = e$ close to 1
b is small compared to a

$c/a = e$ close to 0
b is almost equal to a

$e = 0$; circle
b equals a

Figure 10-20
Eccentricity e indicates the shape of an ellipse.

eccentricity determines the shape of an ellipse. When e is close to 1, the ellipse is long and narrow; the closer e is to 0, the rounder the ellipse (see Figure 10-20).

Suppose that the foci come together at the origin. When that happens, $c = 0$, $a = b$, and

$$\frac{x^2}{a^2} + \frac{y^2}{b^2} = 1 \quad \text{becomes} \quad \frac{x^2}{a^2} + \frac{y^2}{a^2} = 1$$

which is equivalent to $x^2 + y^2 = a^2$, a circle. Thus, a circle may be thought of as an ellipse with eccentricity 0. If the foci were on the y-axis, the eccentricity would be c/b.

Suppose the center of an ellipse is at (h, k) and the axes are parallel to the coordinate axes. A translation of axes (see Figure 10-21) to the new origin (h, k) will

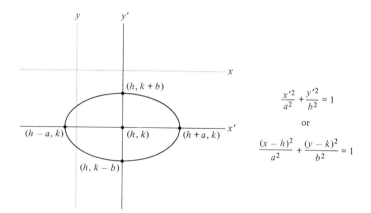

$$\frac{x'^2}{a^2} + \frac{y'^2}{b^2} = 1$$

or

$$\frac{(x - h)^2}{a^2} + \frac{(y - k)^2}{b^2} = 1$$

Figure 10-21
An ellipse with center at (h, k) and with axes parallel to the xy-axes. This ellipse has a simple equation in the $x'y'$ coordinate system obtained by translating the coordinate axes to a new origin at (h, k).

give the ellipse the equation

$$\frac{x'^2}{a^2} + \frac{y'^2}{b^2} = 1$$

Now replace x' by $x - h$ and y' by $y - k$ to obtain

$$\frac{(x - h)^2}{a^2} + \frac{(y - k)^2}{b^2} = 1 \qquad (2)$$

in the original coordinate system. This is the **standard form** of the equation of an ellipse with center (h, k) and axes parallel to the coordinate axes. The foci are on the line $y = k$ or the line $x = h$, depending on whether $a > b$ or $b > a$. In either case, the vertices are at $(h \pm a, k)$ and $(h, k \pm b)$.

Example 3
Find an equation of the ellipse with vertices $(0, 1)$, $(-2, 1)$, $(-1, 3)$, and $(-1, -1)$.

Solution
You must find the center (h, k) and the constants a and b. Plot the four vertices (see Figure 10-22). This shows that the center must be $(-1, 1)$ and that $a = 1$, $b = 2$. Therefore, an equation of this ellipse is

$$(x + 1)^2 + \frac{(y - 1)^2}{4} = 1$$

Example 4
Find an equation of the ellipse with foci $(1, -1)$ and $(3, -1)$, and eccentricity $\frac{3}{4}$.

Solution
First find the center, which lies midway between the foci $(1, -1)$ and $(3, -1)$; it is $(2, -1)$. Now c is the distance from the center to either focus; in this case, $c = 1$. The eccentricity $c/a = \frac{3}{4}$; it follows that $a = \frac{4}{3}$. The relationship $b^2 = a^2 - c^2 = (\frac{4}{3})^2 - 1^2$ shows that $b = \sqrt{7}/3$. Knowing a, b, and the center, you can write

$$\frac{9(x - 2)^2}{16} + \frac{9(y + 1)^2}{7} = 1$$

as the standard equation of this ellipse.

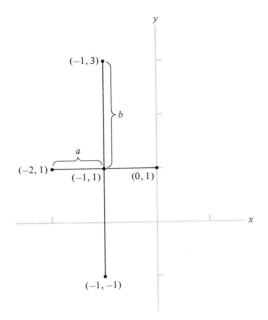

Figure 10-22
Plotting the four vertices of the ellipse in Example 3 shows that the center is at $(-1, 1)$.

Example 5
Find the center, the vertices, and the foci, and sketch the graph of
$4x^2 + y^2 - 16x + 2y + 1 = 0$.

Solution
First complete the squares to obtain the standard form.

$$4(x^2 - 4x \quad) + (y^2 + 2y \quad) = -1$$

$$4(x^2 - 4x + 4) + (y^2 + 2y + 1) = -1 + 16 + 1$$

$$4(x - 2)^2 + (y + 1)^2 = 16$$

$$\frac{(x - 2)^2}{4} + \frac{(y + 1)^2}{16} = 1$$

From this equation, you can gather the following facts:

Center $(2, -1)$

$a = 2, \quad b = 4, \quad c = \sqrt{b^2 - a^2} = 2\sqrt{3}$

Vertices $(0, -1), (4, -1), (2, -5), (2, 3)$

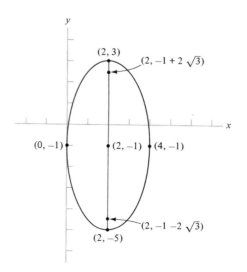

Figure 10-23
The ellipse in Example 5.

$$\text{Foci} \quad (2, -1 - 2\sqrt{3}), (2, -1 + 2\sqrt{3})$$

The graph is shown in Figure 10-23.

The equation $4x^2 + y^2 - 16x + 2y + 1 = 0$ in Example 5 is a special case of the general quadratic equation

$$Ax^2 + By^2 + Cx + Dy + E = 0 \tag{3}$$

Let us assume that A and B are both positive (if they are both negative, multiply each side of the equation by -1 to make A and B positive). Equation (3) can be rewritten as an equation

$$A(x - h)^2 + B(y - k)^2 = F \tag{4}$$

by completing the squares. In Example 5, the equation $4x^2 + y^2 - 16x + 2y + 1 = 0$ is rewritten as $4(x - 2)^2 + (y + 1)^2 = 16$; the constant F in this case is 16. Whenever $F > 0$, we can divide both sides of Equation (4) by F to obtain the standard form of the equation of a circle (if $A = B$) or an ellipse (if $A \neq B$). If it is an ellipse, its axes are parallel to the coordinate axes, and, in any case, its graph is easy to draw. If $F = 0$, the graph of Equation (4) is the single point (h, k). If $F < 0$, there are no solutions at all.

Example 6
Show that
(a) $3x^2 + 2y^2 - 6x + 16y + 29 = 0$ is an equation of an ellipse
(b) $3x^2 + 2y^2 - 6x + 16y + 35 = 0$ has a single solution
(c) $3x^2 + 2y^2 - 6x + 16y + 36 = 0$ has no solutions

Solution
(a)   Complete the squares

$$3(x^2 - 2x \quad\;) + 2(y^2 + 8y \quad\;) = -29$$

$$3(x^2 - 2x + 1) + 2(y^2 + 8y + 16) = -29 + 3 + 32$$

$$3(x - 1)^2 + 2(y + 4)^2 = 6$$

Divide both sides of the equation by 6. The result is

$$\frac{(x - 1)^2}{2} + \frac{(y + 4)^2}{3} = 1$$

This is the standard form of the equation of an ellipse.
(b)   Complete the square as in part (a). The result is

$$3(x - 1)^2 + 2(y + 4)^2 = 0$$

and the only solution is $x = 1, y = -4$.
(c)   The result of completing the squares is

$$3(x - 1)^2 + 2(y + 4)^2 = -1$$

The left side of the equation is nonnegative, so there are no solutions.

Not all ellipses have horizontal and vertical axes. Ellipses such as the one shown in Figure 10-24 are analyzed by rotating the coordinate axes. This is explained in Section 10-5.

Review of basic ideas
Learn the definition of an ellipse.
Learn the simple form for an equation of an ellipse.
Learn the following procedures.

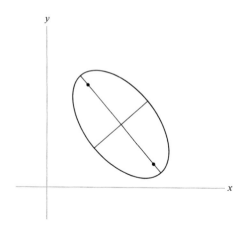

Figure 10-24
A general ellipse.

■ *Sketching the graph.* By completing squares, any equation of the form

$$Ax^2 + By^2 + Cx + Dy + E = 0 \qquad (AB > 0)$$

can be rewritten in standard form. This form tells us whether there is a graph, and, if so, whether it is a point, a circle, or an ellipse, and allows us to sketch the graph easily. Key features: center, axes, vertices, foci. (Refer to Examples 2, 5, and 6.)

Finding an equation. Given geometric information, draw a picture as an aid in finding the center and the constants a and b. Then write an equation in standard form. (Refer to Examples 1, 3, and 4.)

Exercises

Determine which of the equations below represent circles, parabolas, or ellipses. In each case find all the pertinent information and sketch the graph, if possible.

1. $\dfrac{x^2}{4} + \dfrac{y^2}{4} = 1$

2. $4x^2 + 9y^2 = 36$

3. $6x^2 + y = 1$

4. $4x^2 + 4y^2 = 100$

5. $x^2 - 10x + 4y^2 = 0$

6. $3x - 4y^2 + 16y = 1$

7. $\dfrac{(x + 1)^2}{5} + \dfrac{(y - 4)^2}{7} = 1$

8. $\dfrac{x - 2}{5} + \dfrac{(y - 4)^2}{7} = 1$

9. $\dfrac{(x + 1)^2}{5} + \dfrac{(y - 4)^2}{5} = -1$

10. $3x^2 + y^2 - y = 4$

11. $4x^2 + 9y^2 - 16x - 18y = 0$ 12. $2x^2 + y^2 + x + y = 3$

13. $x^2 + 5x + y^2 - 3y = 0$ 14. $x^2 + 5x - 3y = 5$

15. $x^2 + 2y^2 + 4x + 4y + 6 = 0$ 16. $5x^2 + 3y^2 + 6y + 2 = 0$

Find an equation of each ellipse.

17. Vertices $(2, 4)$, $(2, 0)$, $(3, 2)$, and $(1, 2)$.

18. Vertices $(-6, -2)$, $(0, -2)$, $(-3, 2)$, and $(-3, -6)$.

19. Foci $(-3, 2)$, $(1, 2)$ and eccentricity $\frac{1}{3}$.

20. Foci $(1, -2)$, $(1, -4)$ and eccentricity $\frac{4}{5}$.

21. Foci $(0, 3)$, $(4, 3)$ and major axis of length 6.

22. Foci $(2, -1)$, $(2, -6)$ and major axis of length 9.

23. Center $(-3, -2)$ and three vertices $(-7, -2)$, $(-3, 0)$, and $(-3, -4)$.

24. Center $(4, 0)$ and three vertices $(4, 1)$, $(1, 0)$, and $(7, 0)$.

25. One focus $(2, 2)$ and two vertices $(2, 3)$ and $(2, -1)$.

26. One focus $(-1, 4)$ and two vertices $(-3, 4)$ and $(4, 4)$.

Parametric equations

Parametric equations for circles and parabolas were discussed in the Exercises of Sections 10-1 and 10-2. It is also possible to have parametric equations for an ellipse.

27. Show that $x = 2 \cos t$ and $y = 3 \sin t$ are parametric equations of the ellipse $9x^2 + 4y^2 = 36$.

28. Show that $x = (a \cos t) + h$ and $y = (b \sin t) + k$ are parametric equations of an ellipse with center (h, k). Find the vertices and foci.

29. The orbit of the earth is almost an ellipse whose major and minor axes have lengths 18.6×10^7 and 18.58×10^7 miles, respectively. The sun is at one focus. How close does the earth come to the sun? How far away does it get? The amount of solar power reaching the earth is inversely proportional to the square of the distance from the earth to the sun. By what percent is this power increased as the earth moves from the point where it is farthest from the sun to the point where it is closest to the sun? Is it likely that this change has much influence on seasonal temperatures?

10-4
The Hyperbola

A **hyperbola** is the locus, or set, of all points P such that the absolute value of the differences of the distances from P to two distinct fixed points, called **foci**, is a constant. The parts of a hyperbola are labeled in Figure 10-25. It has two **branches** (unconnected parts), two **foci**, two **vertices**, and two **axes**. The line through the foci is called the **transverse axis**. The **center** is midway between the foci. The line through the

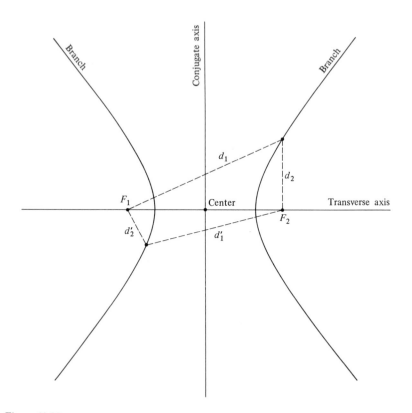

Figure 10-25
The parts of a hyperbola. Points F_1 and F_2 are the foci. The vertices are where the hyperbola crosses the transverse axis. For all points on either branch, $|d_1 - d_2|$ is a constant, which must be smaller than the distance between the foci.

center and perpendicular to the transverse axis is the **conjugate axis.** A hyperbola is symmetric with respect to its center and its axes.

The paths of some comets are hyperbolic, with our sun as a focus. Hyperbolas can also be used to locate a signal source. Suppose two fixed stations report the exact time a signal is received. Then the difference in time multiplied by the speed of the signal is the difference of the distances from the source to the stations. Thus, the source lies on a hyperbola with the two stations as foci. If a third station also reports, the source can be pinpointed at the intersection of two hyperbolas.

The equation of a hyperbola is simplest if the foci are on the x-axis, say, at $(-c, 0)$ and $(c, 0)$; the origin is then the center of the hyperbola. Figure 10-26 shows such a hyperbola. For every point (x, y) on either branch, the number $|d_1 - d_2|$ is a constant, which must be less than $2c$. Again, it is convenient to denote this constant by $2a$; notice that $a < c$. Thus, $|d_1 - d_2| = 2a$; in terms of the distance formula,

$$| \sqrt{(x + c)^2 + (y - 0)^2} - \sqrt{(x - c)^2 + (y - 0)^2} | = 2a$$

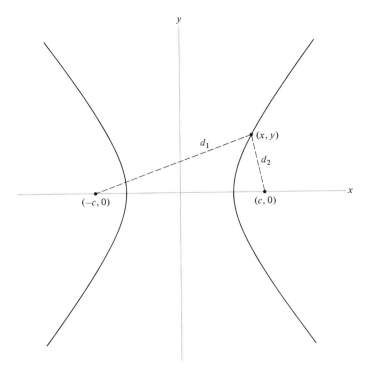

Figure 10-26
A hyperbola whose foci lie on the x-axis.

After some algebraic manipulations similar to those we used to find the equation of an ellipse, the final equation is

$$\frac{x^2}{a^2} - \frac{y^2}{c^2 - a^2} = 1$$

(You are asked to verify this in Exercise 28.) Now set $b^2 = c^2 - a^2$, to get

$$\frac{x^2}{a^2} - \frac{y^2}{b^2} = 1 \tag{1}$$

This is the **simple equation** of a hyperbola with center at the origin and foci $(-c, 0)$ and $(c, 0)$, where $c^2 = a^2 + b^2$. The vertices are where the branches cross the transverse axis (the x-axis in this case). Set $y = 0$ to find the vertices at $(\pm a, 0)$; notice that $|x| \geqslant a$. (Why?) See Figure 10-27.

Figure 10-27 also shows that the two lines $y = \pm\dfrac{b}{a}x$ are **asymptotes** of the

hyperbola: in the first quadrant, when x is very large, y is close to $\dfrac{b}{a}x$; in the second

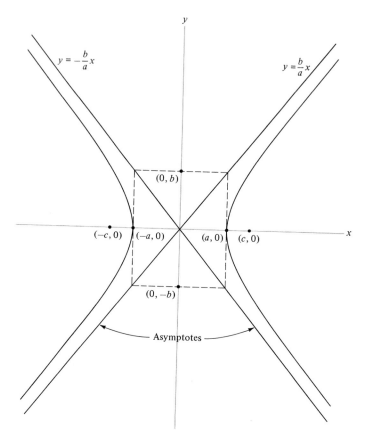

Figure 10-27

The hyperbola $\dfrac{x^2}{a^2} - \dfrac{y^2}{b^2} = 1$. The foci are at $(\pm c, 0)$, where $c^2 = a^2 + b^2$; the vertices are at

$(\pm a, 0)$. The straight lines $y = \pm \dfrac{b}{a}x$ are asymptotes of the hyperbola.

quadrant, when $-x$ is very large, y is very close to $-\dfrac{b}{a}x$; and so on. (See Exercise 29.) The asymptotes are a big help in sketching the graph, as is the box from $x = -a$ to $x = a$ and $y = -b$ to $y = b$ shown in Figure 10-27. The hyperbola stays outside this box, and the asymptotes are extensions of the diagonals of the box.

Example 1

Find the foci, vertices, and asymptotes, and sketch the graph of $\dfrac{x^2}{4} - \dfrac{y^2}{9} = 1$.

Solution

Because $a = 2$ and $b = 3$, you know that $c = \sqrt{a^2 + b^2} = \sqrt{13}$. Thus, the foci

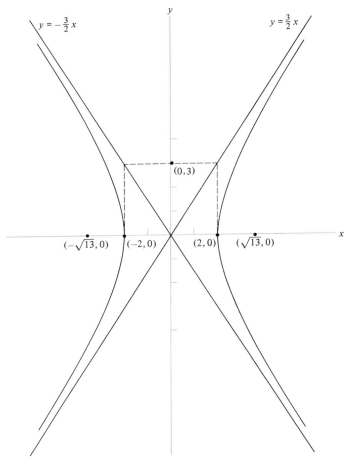

Figure 10-28
The hyperbola in Example 1.

are $(\pm \sqrt{13}, 0)$, the vertices are $(\pm 2, 0)$, and the asymptotes are the lines $y = \pm \frac{3}{2}x$. The graph is shown in Figure 10-28.

A hyperbola also has a simple equation if the foci are on the y-axis, say at $(0, -c)$ and $(0, c)$. This interchanges the roles of x and y; and the resultant equation is

$$\frac{y^2}{b^2} - \frac{x^2}{a^2} = 1 \tag{2}$$

The relationship $b^2 = c^2 - a^2$ still holds; the vertices are now at $(0, \pm b)$; the asymptotes remain the same: $y = \pm \dfrac{b}{a}x$.

Example 2
Find the foci, vertices, and asymptotes, and sketch the graph of $16y^2 - 9x^2 = 144$.

Solution
Rewrite the equation as

$$\frac{y^2}{9} - \frac{x^2}{16} = 1$$

Then $a = 4, b = 3$, and $c = \sqrt{a^2 + b^2} = 5$. Because the positive term contains y, the foci are on the y-axis at $(0, \pm c)$. Thus, the foci are at $(0, \pm 5)$, the vertices are at $(0, \pm 3)$, and the asymptotes are the lines $y = \pm\frac{4}{3}x$. (see Figure 10-29).

Suppose the transverse axis of a hyperbola is parallel to one of the coordinate axes, but

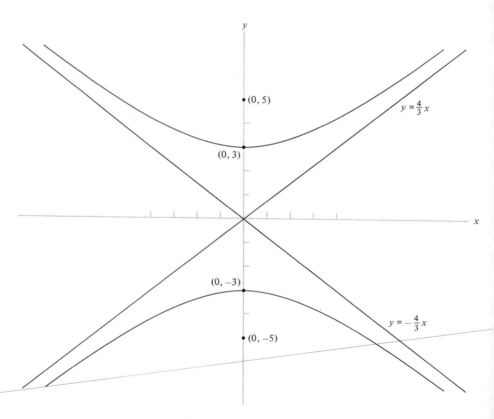

Figure 10-29
The hyperbola in Example 2.

the center is at some point (h, k) not the origin. Then, by the method of translation we used to find the standard equations of ellipses and parabolas, we can show that

$$\frac{(x - h)^2}{a^2} - \frac{(y - k)^2}{b^2} = 1 \quad \text{and} \tag{3}$$

$$\frac{(y - k)^2}{b^2} - \frac{(x - h)^2}{a^2} = 1 \tag{4}$$

are the **standard equations** of hyperbolas with centers at (h, k). In the first case, the transverse axis is horizontal; in the second, it is vertical. If $c^2 = a^2 + b^2$, the foci are at $(h \pm c, k)$ for Equation (3), and at $(h, k \pm c)$ for Equation (4). The vertices are at $(h \pm a, k)$ or at $(h, k \pm b)$, respectively. The asymptotes are translated to $y = \pm \frac{b}{a}(x - h) + k$ in either case.

Example 3
Find the center, foci, vertices, and asymptotes, and sketch the graph of $2x^2 - 4x - 4y^2 - 16y - 6 = 0$.

Solution
Complete the squares.

$$2(x^2 - 2x \quad) - 4(y^2 + 4y \quad) = 6$$

$$2(x^2 - 2x + 1) - 4(y^2 + 4y + 4) = 6 + 2 - 16$$

$$2(x - 1)^2 - 4(y + 2)^2 = -8$$

$$-\frac{(x - 1)^2}{4} + \frac{(y + 2)^2}{2} = 1$$

The center is at $(1, -2)$; because the positive term contains y, the transverse axis is vertical. Now $a = 2, b = \sqrt{2}$, and $c = \sqrt{6}$. The foci are at $(1, -2 \pm \sqrt{6})$, the vertices are at $(1, -2 \pm \sqrt{2})$, and the asymptotes are $y = \pm \frac{\sqrt{2}}{2}(x - 1) - 2$.

The graph is shown in Figure 10-30.
    Notice that, in the original equation, the positive term contained x, which you might have thought would place the transverse axis in a horizontal position. However, in the end this was not so; first appearances can be deceiving.

Suppose the foci of a hyperbola are at $(\pm c, 0)$ and the vertices are at $(\pm a, 0)$. The

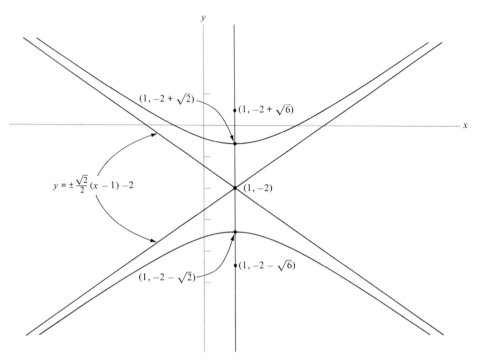

Figure 10-30
The hyperbola in Example 3.

ratio c/a is called the **eccentricity** of the hyperbola and is denoted by e. Unlike the eccentricity of an ellipse, the eccentricity of a hyperbola is greater than 1, because $a < c$. The eccentricity of a hyperbola determines its shape (see Figure 10-31). If the foci are on the y-axis, the eccentricity would be c/b.

Given sufficient geometric information, it is possible to find an equation of a hyperbola. To write the standard equation, it is enough to know the coordinates of the center and the values of the constants a and b.

Example 4
Find an equation of the hyperbola with foci $(-1, 6)$ and $(5, 6)$ and eccentricity 2.

Solution
The foci lie on a horizontal line and are 6 units apart. This tells you three things: the transverse axis is horizontal, so Equation (3) is the standard form; the center is at $(2, 6)$; and $c = 3$. Because the eccentricity $c/a = 2$, you know that $a = \frac{3}{2}$. Finally, $b^2 = c^2 - a^2 = \frac{27}{4}$. It follows that an equation for this hyperbola is

$$\frac{4(x - 2)^2}{9} - \frac{4(y - 6)^2}{27} = 1$$

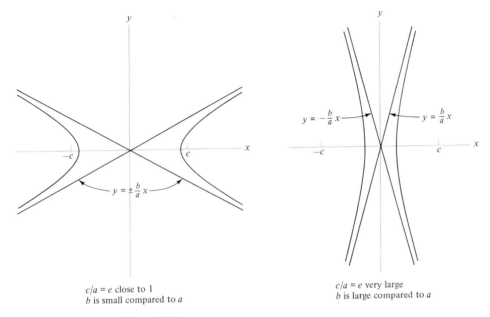

c/a = e close to 1
b is small compared to *a*

c/a = e very large
b is large compared to *a*

Figure 10-31
The eccentricity *e* indicates the shape of the hyperbola.

Example 5
Find an equation of the hyperbola with a vertex at $(2, 0)$ and asymptotes $3y + 2x = 7$ and $3y - 2x = -1$.

Solution
The asymptotes give two pieces of information: they meet at the center and their slopes are $\pm b/a$. Solve the two equations

$$3y + 2x = 7$$

$$3y - 2x = -1$$

simultaneously to find the center at $(2, 1)$. Because the center is at $(2, 1)$ and a vertex is at $(2, 0)$, it follows (draw a picture) that the transverse axis is vertical and that $b = 1$. Finally, notice that the slopes of the asymptotes are $\pm\frac{2}{3}$ which implies that $a = \frac{3}{2}$, because $b = 1$. Thus, the equation is

$$(y - 1)^2 - \frac{4(x - 2)^2}{9} = 1$$

The two equations

$$\frac{x^2}{1^2} - \frac{y^2}{2^2} = 1 \quad \text{and} \quad \frac{x^2}{1^2} - \frac{y^2}{2^2} = -1$$

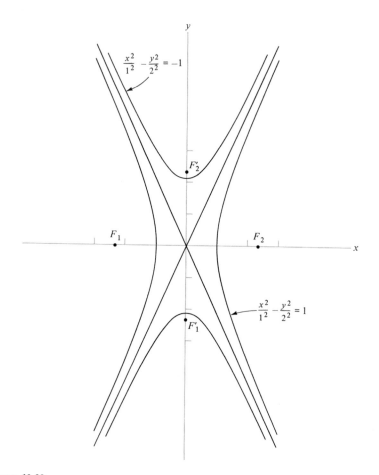

Figure 10-32
Conjugate hyperbolas. The x-axis is the transverse axis of the hyperbola with equation

$$\frac{x^2}{1^2} - \frac{y^2}{2^2} = 1$$

The y-axis is the transverse axis of the hyperbola with equation

$$\frac{x^2}{1^2} - \frac{y^2}{2^2} = -1$$

both determine hyperbolas with asymptotes $y = 2x$ and $y = -2x$ and center $(0, 0)$. Such a pair of hyperbolas are called **conjugates** (see Figure 10-32). The standard form of the second equation would be

$$\frac{y^2}{2^2} - \frac{x^2}{1^2} = 1$$

but the form given above shows how equations for conjugate hyperbolas differ simply in the sign of the constant on the right-hand side.

To sketch the graph of an equation of the form

$$Ax^2 + By^2 + Cx + Dy + E = 0$$

where A and B have opposite signs, simply complete the squares, as in Example 3, and bring the equation into one of the forms

$$\frac{(x - h)^2}{a^2} - \frac{(y - k)^2}{b^2} = 1$$

$$\frac{(x - h)^2}{a^2} - \frac{(y - k)^2}{b^2} = -1$$

$$\frac{(x - h)^2}{a^2} - \frac{(y - k)^2}{b^2} = 0$$

The first two forms give conjugate hyperbolas; they have the same center and the same asymptotes, but they open in different directions (see Figure 10-33). The third form gives a pair of straight lines, because it factors into a product of linear expressions:

$$\left(\frac{x - h}{a} + \frac{y - k}{b}\right)\left(\frac{x - h}{a} - \frac{y - k}{b}\right) = 0$$

Set each factor equal to 0 to obtain the lines

$$y = \pm\frac{b}{a}(x - h) + k$$

which you will recognize as the asymptotes of the two hyperbolas given by the first two forms.

Hyperbolas with tilted axes are analyzed by rotation of axes, which is explained in Section 10-5.

Review of basic ideas
Learn the definition of a hyperbola.
Learn the two simple forms of the equation of a hyperbola.
Learn these procedures:

■   *Sketching the graph.* By completing squares, any expression of the form

$$Ax^2 + By^2 + Cx + Dy + E = 0$$

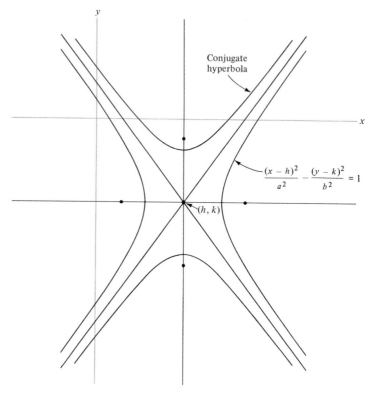

Figure 10-33
A hyperbola with equation

$$\frac{(x - h)^2}{a^2} - \frac{(y - k)^2}{b^2} = 1$$

and its conjugate, with equation

$$\frac{(x - h)^2}{a^2} - \frac{(y - k)^2}{b^2} = -1$$

where A and B have opposite signs, can be put into standard form. This form tells us whether the graph is a hyperbola or a pair of intersecting lines, and allows us to sketch the graph easily. Key features: center, axes, vertices, foci, asymptotes. (Refer to Examples 1, 2, and 3.)

Finding an equation. Given geometric information, draw a picture as an aid. Find the center and the constants a and b. Then write an equation in standard form. (Refer to Examples 4 and 5.)

Exercises

The following equations are conic sections. Determine the necessary information and sketch the graph.

1. $\dfrac{x^2}{4} - \dfrac{y^2}{4} = 1$

2. $\dfrac{x^2}{4} + \dfrac{y^2}{4} = 1$

3. $\dfrac{y^2}{4} - \dfrac{x^2}{9} = 1$

4. $-\dfrac{y^2}{4} - \dfrac{x}{9} + 1 = 0$

5. $-3x^2 - 4y^2 + 12 = 0$

6. $3x^2 - 4y^2 = 1$

7. $\dfrac{(x+1)^2}{16} - \dfrac{(y-2)^2}{9} = 1$

8. $\dfrac{(x+1)^2}{16} + \dfrac{(y-2)^2}{9} = 1$

9. $9(x+1)^2 - 16(y-2)^2 = 144$

10. $8(x+1)^2 + 8(y-2)^2 = 200$

11. $-2x^2 - y^2 - 4x + 2y = -3$

12. $2x^2 - y^2 + x + y = 3$

13. $y^2 - 2x^2 + 8x + 4y = 0$

14. $2x^2 - y + x = 3$

15. $x^2 - 4x - 3y^2 + 6y = -4$

16. $4x^2 + 8x - y^2 = 32$

Find an equation of each hyperbola.
17. Foci $(\pm 4, 0)$ and vertices $(\pm 1, 0)$.
18. Foci $(0, \pm 3)$ and vertices $(0, \pm 2)$.
19. Foci $(1, \pm 3)$ and eccentricity $\frac{3}{2}$.
20. Foci $(2, 0)$ and $(2, 6)$ and eccentricity 4.
21. A vertex $(-3, 2)$ and asymptotes $y = 3x + 5$, $3x + y + 1 = 0$.
22. A vertex $(0, -1)$ and asymptotes $y + 4 = \pm\frac{1}{2}x$.
23. A focus $(0, -1)$ and asymptotes $y - 3 = \pm 2x$.
24. A focus $(0, -1)$ and asymptotes $y = 4x + 7$, $4x + y = -9$.

25. (Parametric equations) Show that $x = 3 \sec t$ and $y = 4 \tan t$ are parametric equations of the hyperbola $16x^2 - 9y^2 = 144$.

26. (Continuation of Exercise 25) Show $x = (a \sec t) + h$ and $y = (b \tan t) + k$ are parametric equations of a hyperbola with center (h, k).

27. (Hyperbolic functions) The hyperbolic cosine and sine were defined in the exercises of Section 8-3. Show that $x = (a \cosh t) + h$ and $y = (b \sinh t) + k$ are parametric equations of a hyperbola with center (h, k).

28. Start with the equation

$$\left| \sqrt{(x+c)^2 + (y-0)^2} - \sqrt{(x-c)^2 + (y-0)^2} \right| = 2a$$

and derive the equation

$$\frac{x^2}{a^2} - \frac{y^2}{c^2 - a^2} = 1$$

[HINT: Remove the absolute value sign and write the right side as $\pm 2a$. Add the second radical to both sides. Then proceed as for an ellipse, taking care with minus signs.]

29. (Asymptotes) Show that the line $y = \frac{b}{a}x$ is an asymptote of the hyperbola

$\frac{x^2}{a^2} - \frac{y^2}{b^2} = 1$ by showing that, in the first quadrant, y is very close to $\frac{b}{a}x$ when x is

very large. [HINT: Solve for y to get $y = \frac{b}{a}\sqrt{x^2 - a^2}$. Then

$$\frac{b}{a}x - y = \frac{b}{a}(x - \sqrt{x^2 - a^2}) = \frac{b}{a}(x - \sqrt{x^2 - a^2})\frac{x + \sqrt{x^2 - a^2}}{x + \sqrt{x^2 - a^2}}$$

$$= \frac{ab}{x + \sqrt{x^2 - a^2}}.$$

When x is very large, the right side of this equation is very close to 0.]

10-5
Rotation of Axes

The most general quadratic equation in two variables has the form

$$Ax^2 + Bxy + Cy^2 + Dx + Ey + F = 0 \tag{1}$$

In the preceding sections, we analyzed and graphed all such equations in which the xy term is not present; that is, in which $B = 0$. In this section, we shall see how a **rotation of axes** can reduce the general form to a form in which the xy term is 0. Thus, the graph of the general quadratic equation is always a conic section, but the conic will have a tipped axis if the xy term is not 0. This illustrates an approach that is often useful in mathematics: learn how to solve a certain kind of problem; then attack a more difficult problem by reducing it to the kind that you already understand.

When axes are rotated, the origin is kept fixed and the coordinate axes are rotated counterclockwise by some angle θ, as shown in Figure 10-34A. This establishes new coordinate axes, which we shall call the x'-axis and the y'-axis. Each point P of the plane has an old pair of coordinates (x, y) and a new pair of coordinates (x', y'). Naturally, these coordinates are related.

If r is the distance from P to the origin (the same in both coordinate systems),

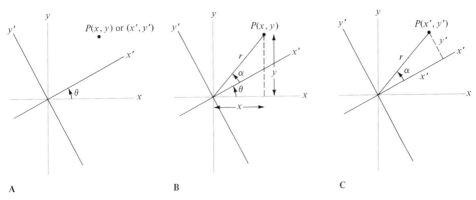

Figure 10-34
Rotation of axes. (A) After rotation, each point P in the plane has two pairs of coordinates. (B) $x = r \cos (\alpha + \theta)$ and $y = r \sin (\alpha + \theta)$. (C) $x' = r \cos \alpha$ and $y' = r \sin \alpha$.

then, as Figure 10-34B shows,

$$x = r \cos(\alpha + \theta) \quad \text{and} \quad y = r \sin(\alpha + \theta)$$

Using the addition formulas for sine and cosine, we have

$$x = r \cos \alpha \cos \theta - r \sin \alpha \sin \theta$$

$$y = r \cos \alpha \sin \theta + r \sin \alpha \cos \theta$$

Figure 10-34C shows that $r \cos \alpha = x'$ and $r \sin \alpha = y'$. Substituting these values in the two equations above yields

$$x = x'\cos \theta - y'\sin \theta \quad \text{and} \quad y = x'\sin \theta + y'\cos \theta \tag{2}$$

These equations produce the old coordinates provided we know the new ones. On the other hand, if the xy-coordinates are known, then the $x'y'$-coordinates can easily be found by solving these equations simultaneously. The result is

$$x' = x \cos \theta + y \sin \theta \quad \text{and} \quad y' = -x \sin \theta + y \cos \theta \tag{3}$$

An easy way to remember these equations is to construct a chart.

	x'	y'
x	$\cos \theta$	$-\sin \theta$
y	$\sin \theta$	$\cos \theta$

The chart is read across to find x and y, and down to find x' and y'. For example, to find x in terms of x' and y', read across the first row: $x = x'\cos\theta - y'\sin\theta$. To find y' in terms of x and y, read down the second column: $y' = -x\sin\theta + y\cos\theta$.

Example 1

(a)   Rotate the axes by $\theta = \pi/3$ and locate the point with $x'y'$-coordinates $(2, 1)$. What are its xy-coordinates?

(b)   Rotate the axes by $\theta = \pi/4$ and find the new coordinates of the point with xy-coordinates $(-3, 2)$.

Solution

(a)   A rotation of axes by an angle $\pi/3$ is shown in Figure 10-35. Use Equations (2) or make a chart and read off the solution.

	x'	y'
x	$\cos(\pi/3)$	$-\sin(\pi/3)$
y	$\sin(\pi/3)$	$\cos(\pi/3)$

$=$

	2	1
x	$1/2$	$-\sqrt{3}/2$
y	$\sqrt{3}/2$	$1/2$

From the chart,

$$x = 2\cdot\frac{1}{2} - 1\cdot\frac{\sqrt{3}}{2} = 1 - \frac{\sqrt{3}}{2} \qquad \text{and} \qquad y = 2\cdot\frac{\sqrt{3}}{2} + 1\cdot\frac{1}{2} = \sqrt{3} + \frac{1}{2}$$

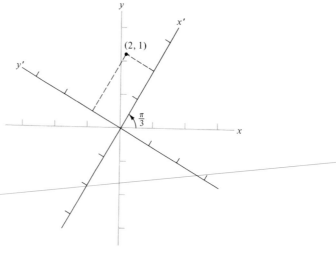

Figure 10-35
The rotation of axes in Example 1(a).

(b) $\theta = \pi/4$. Make a chart or use Equations (3), which yield

$$x' = -3 \cdot \frac{\sqrt{2}}{2} + 2 \cdot \frac{\sqrt{2}}{2} = -\frac{\sqrt{2}}{2}, \qquad y' = -(-3)\frac{\sqrt{2}}{2} + 2\frac{\sqrt{2}}{2} = \frac{5\sqrt{2}}{2}$$

We have seen that a rotation of axes changes the coordinates of a point in a natural way. It follows that a set of points that satisfy an equation in one system will satisfy a corresponding equation in the other system. For instance, take the line $2x + 3y = 7$. Now rotate the axes by $\theta = \pi/3$; then (see the chart in Example 1(a))

$$x = \frac{1}{2}x' - \frac{\sqrt{3}}{2}y' \quad \text{and} \quad y = \frac{\sqrt{3}}{2}x' + \frac{1}{2}y'$$

Thus, the same points whose xy-coordinates satisfy $2x + 3y = 7$ will have $x'y'$-coordinates that satisfy

$$2\left(\frac{1}{2}x' - \frac{\sqrt{3}}{2}y'\right) + 3\left(\frac{\sqrt{3}}{2}x' + \frac{1}{2}y'\right) = 7$$

or

$$\left(1 + \frac{3\sqrt{3}}{2}\right)x' + \left(\frac{3}{2} - \sqrt{3}\right)y' = 7$$

We say the equation $2x + 3y = 7$ is **transformed** into the equation

$$\left(1 + \frac{3\sqrt{3}}{2}\right)x' + \left(\frac{3}{2} - \sqrt{3}\right)y' = 7$$

by a rotation of $\pi/3$.

We shall show that *it is always possible to transform a general quadratic*

$$Ax^2 + Bxy + Cy^2 + Dx + Ey + F = 0$$

into a quadratic in x' and y' in which the coefficient of $x'y'$ is 0. To graph the original equation, we need only graph the simplified equation in the $x'y'$ coordinate system, using the methods developed in the preceding sections.

To transform the general quadratic by a rotation of θ, make the substitutions $x = x'\cos\theta - y'\sin\theta$ and $y = x'\sin\theta + y'\cos\theta$. After multiplying out and collecting like terms, the result will be a new quadratic,

$$A'x'^2 + B'x'y' + C'y'^2 + D'x' + E'y' + F = 0$$

The coefficient B' of the $x'y'$ term will be

$$B' = 2(C - A)\sin\theta\cos\theta + B(\cos^2\theta - \sin^2\theta)$$

$$= (C - A)\sin 2\theta + B\cos 2\theta \tag{4}$$

Checking the first equality is left as an exercise. The second equality is a consequence of the double-angle formulas proved in Section 8-3.

We must find a rotation that eliminates the $x'y'$ term; in other words, find a θ for which $B' = 0$. It follows from Equation (4) that $B' = 0$ when

$$\cot 2\theta = \frac{A - C}{B} \quad \text{or} \quad 2\theta = \cot^{-1}\frac{A - C}{B} \tag{5}$$

If $B \neq 0$, there will always be such an angle, with $0 < 2\theta < \pi$, which is the range of $\cot^{-1}$. Thus, we may choose θ to be in the first quadrant. If $B = 0$, we can analyze and graph the original quadratic without rotation.

The rest of the examples in this section illustrate the use of rotations in graphing quadratics.

Example 2

Locate the principal points and sketch the graph of $8x^2 - 4xy + 5y^2 = 36$.

Solution

(1)   Find the rotation that eliminates the $x'y'$ term. Here, $A = 8$, $B = -4$ and $C = 5$. According to Equation (5), if

$$\cot 2\theta = \frac{A - C}{B} = -\frac{3}{4}$$

then a rotation by θ will eliminate the $x'y'$ term.

(2)   We must find $\sin \theta$ and $\cos \theta$, because these quantities are needed in the substitutions for x' and y'. Because $\cot 2\theta = -3/4$, we know that 2θ is in the second quadrant and $\cos 2\theta = -3/5$, as shown in Figure 10-36A. Referring to

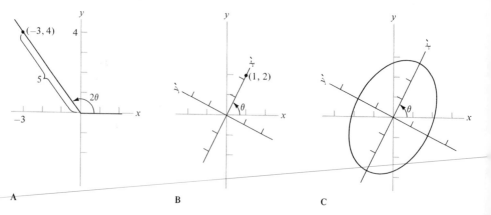

Figure 10-36
(A) Because $\cot 2\theta = -3/4$, the point $(-3, 4)$ is on the terminal side of angle 2θ. Thus, $\cos 2\theta = -3/5$. (B) The rotated $x'y'$-axes in Example 2. (C) The ellipse of Example 2 sketched in the $x'y'$ coordinate system.

the half-angle formulas from Section 8-3, we have

$$\sin \theta = \sqrt{\frac{1 - \cos 2\theta}{2}} = \sqrt{\frac{1 - (-3/5)}{2}} = 2/\sqrt{5}$$

$$\cos \theta = \sqrt{\frac{1 + \cos 2\theta}{2}} = \sqrt{\frac{1 + (-3/5)}{2}} = 1/\sqrt{5}$$

We choose the positive square root, because θ is in the first quadrant.
(3)   Make a chart and read off the substitutions:

	x'	y'
x	$1/\sqrt{5}$	$-2/\sqrt{5}$
y	$2/\sqrt{5}$	$1/\sqrt{5}$

$$x = \frac{x'}{\sqrt{5}} - \frac{2y'}{\sqrt{5}} \quad \text{and} \quad y = \frac{2x'}{\sqrt{5}} + \frac{y'}{\sqrt{5}}$$

The given equation $8x^2 - 4xy + 5y^2 = 36$ becomes

$$8\left(\frac{x' - 2y'}{\sqrt{5}}\right)^2 - 4\left(\frac{x' - 2y'}{\sqrt{5}}\right)\left(\frac{2x' + y'}{\sqrt{5}}\right) + 5\left(\frac{2x' + y'}{\sqrt{5}}\right)^2 = 36$$

Multiply out and collect like terms:

$$\frac{8}{5}(x'^2 - 4x'y' + 4y'^2) - \frac{4}{5}(2x'^2 - 3x'y' - 2y'^2) + (4x'^2 + 4x'y' + y'^2) = 36$$

$$4x'^2 + 9y'^2 = 36$$

(4)   We recognize this last equation as the ellipse $\dfrac{x'^2}{9} + \dfrac{y'^2}{4} = 1$.

(5)   In the $x'y'$ coordinate system, the center of this ellipse is at the origin, its vertices are at $(\pm 3, 0)$ and $(0, \pm 2)$, and its foci are at $(\pm \sqrt{5}, 0)$. Now draw the new $x'y'$-axes in the xy-plane. Because $\cos \theta = 1/\sqrt{5}$ and $\sin \theta = 2/\sqrt{5}$, the x'-axis goes through the point $(1/\sqrt{5}, 2/\sqrt{5})$, so it also passes through the point $(1, 2)$ in the xy coordinate system (see Figure 10-36B).
(6)   Using the information from step (5), sketch the ellipse on the $x'y'$ coordinate system. (See Figure 10-36C.) To express important points in xy coordinates, use the chart in step (3): center $(0, 0)$, vertices $(\pm 3/\sqrt{5}, \pm 6/\sqrt{5})$ and $(\mp 4/\sqrt{5}, \pm 2/\sqrt{5})$, and foci $(\pm 1, \pm 2)$.

Consider the equation $8x^2 - 4xy + 5y^2 = 0$. It is the equation of Example 2, with 36 replaced by 0. It is not clear at once that this equation has only one solution, $(0, 0)$. However, after it is transformed by rotation into $4x'^2 + 9y'^2 = 0$, it is obvious that

(0, 0) is the only solution. Similarly, if 36 were replaced with a negative number, there would be no solutions at all.

Example 3
Locate the principal points and sketch $4x^2 - 12xy + 9y^2 = 13$.

Solution
This equation looks very much like the one in Example 2, but the analysis below will show that it represents quite a different kind of curve.
(1) Find

$$\cot 2\theta = \frac{A - C}{B} = \frac{4 - 9}{-12} = \frac{5}{12}$$

This means that 2θ is in the first quadrant and $\cos 2\theta = 5/13$ (draw a picture).
(2) Find $\sin \theta$ and $\cos \theta$:

$$\sin \theta = \sqrt{\frac{1 - (5/13)}{2}} = 2/\sqrt{13} \qquad \cos \theta = \sqrt{\frac{1 + (5/13)}{2}} = 3/\sqrt{13}$$

(3) Make the substitutions

	x'	y'
x	$3/\sqrt{13}$	$-2/\sqrt{13}$
y	$2/\sqrt{13}$	$3/\sqrt{13}$

$$x = \frac{3x' - 2y'}{\sqrt{13}} \qquad \text{and} \qquad y = \frac{2x' + 3y'}{\sqrt{13}}$$

$$\frac{4}{13}(3x' - 2y')^2 - \frac{12}{13}(3x' - 2y')(2x' + 3y') + \frac{9}{13}(2x' + 3y')^2 = 13$$

$$\frac{4}{13}(9x'^2 - 12x'y' + 4y'^2) - \frac{12}{13}(6x'^2 + 5x'y' - 6y'^2)$$

$$+ \frac{9}{13}(4x'^2 + 12x'y' + 9y'^2) = 13$$

$$13y'^2 = 13$$

(4) The "curve" consists of parallel lines $y' = 1$ and $y' = -1$, or, in the original system, $-2x + 3y = \pm\sqrt{13}$, because

$$y' = \frac{1}{\sqrt{13}}(-2x + 3y)$$

Question
What "curve" does the original equation represent if the constant term is
replaced by 0? By −13?

The next, and final, example shows how to combine translation with rotation to
analyze an equation.

Example 4
Transform $x^2 + 2xy + y^2 + 8\sqrt{2}\,x = 0$ into a simple equation and sketch the
graph.

Solution
(1)   Find the rotation that eliminates the xy term. In this equation, $A = C = 1$
so $(A - C)/B = 0$. It follows that $2\theta = \cot^{-1} 0 = \pi/2$ and $\theta = \pi/4$.
(2)   Because $\sin(\pi/4) = \cos(\pi/4) = \sqrt{2}/2$,

$$x = \frac{\sqrt{2}}{2}(x' - y') \quad \text{and} \quad y = \frac{\sqrt{2}}{2}(x' + y')$$

are the substitutions that eliminate the xy term.
(3)   Substitute in the original equation:

$$\tfrac{1}{2}(x' - y')^2 + (x' - y')(x' + y') + \tfrac{1}{2}(x' + y')^2 + 8(x' - y') = 0$$

which can be simplified to

$$2x'^2 + 8x' - 8y' = 0$$

Now complete the square:

$$2(x'^2 + 4x'\quad\ ) = 8y'$$

$$2(x'^2 + 4x' + 4) = 8y' + 8$$

$$(x' + 2)^2 = 4(y' + 1)$$

This is evidently the equation of a parabola whose vertex is at $(-2, -1)$ in the
$x'y'$ coordinate system.
(4)   Translate the $x'y'$-axes by using the equations

$$x'' = x' + 2 \quad \text{and} \quad y'' = y' + 1$$

The equation $(x' + 2)^2 = 4(y' + 1)$ becomes

$$x''^2 = 4y''$$

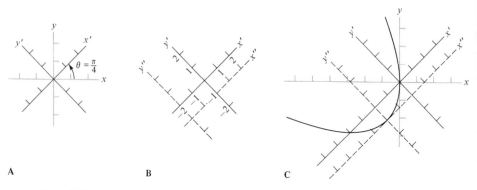

A   B   C

Figure 10-37
(A) Rotate the xy-axes to obtain the $x'y'$-axes. (B) Translate the $x'y'$-axes to obtain the $x''y''$-axes. (C) The rotation and translation transforms $x^2 + 2xy + y^2 + 8\sqrt{2}x = 0$ into $x''^2 = 4y''$, which is the simple equation of the parabola in Example 4.

In the $x''y''$ system, this is the simple equation of a parabola with $p = 1$, focus at $(0, 1)$ and directrix $y'' = -1$.
(5)   Sketch the graph. Rotate the xy-axes by $\theta = \pi/4$ to obtain the $x'y'$-axes (see Figure 10-37A). Translate the $x'y'$-axes 2 units to the left and 1 unit down to obtain the $x''y''$-axes (see Figure 10-37B). Then sketch the parabola $x''^2 = 4y''$ (see Figure 10-37C).

Review of basic ideas
The substitutions for rotation of axes are:

$$x = x'\cos\theta - y'\sin\theta \qquad y = x'\sin\theta + y'\cos\theta$$

$$x' = x\cos\theta + y\sin\theta \qquad y' = -x\sin\theta + y\cos\theta$$

	x'	y'
x	$\cos\theta$	$-\sin\theta$
y	$\sin\theta$	$\cos\theta$

Learn the procedure for analyzing a quadratic equation that contains an xy term:
    (1) Determine the rotation required, using

$$\cot 2\theta = \frac{A - C}{B}$$

Use this to find $\cos 2\theta$.

(2) Apply the half-angle formulas

$$\sin \theta = \sqrt{\frac{1 - \cos 2\theta}{2}} \qquad \cos \theta = \sqrt{\frac{1 + \cos 2\theta}{2}}$$

(3) Make the substitutions in the original equation, multiply out, and simplify.
(4) The simplified version can be put into standard form.
(5) If necessary, use translation to find the simple form.
(6) The $x'y'$-axes are then located relative to the original xy-axes; If necessary, the $x''y''$-axes are then located relative to the $x'y'$-axes. The axis, focus, and so on of the conic are then found relative to the $x'y'$-axes (or the $x''y''$-axes).
(7) The conic can now be sketched from the points and axes located in step (6).

Exercises

Sketch the following curves. Before you sketch, guess what type of curve it will be. (Exercise 25 presents criteria for predicting the type of curve.)

1. $5x^2 - 6xy + 5y^2 = 32$
2. $2x^2 + 3xy + 2y^2 = 9$
3. $3x^2 - 10xy + 3y^2 = -32$
4. $7x^2 + 12xy - 2y^2 = 7$
5. $x^2 - 2xy + y^2 + 1 = 0$
6. $16x^2 - 24xy + 9y^2 = 25$
7. $x^2 - 2xy + y^2 - 3x = 0$
8. $x^2 - 4xy + 4y^2 = 0$
9. $13x^2 - 10xy + 13y^2 = 72$
10. $5x^2 - 8xy + 5y^2 = 9$
11. $xy = 5$
12. $xy = -3$
13. $3x^2 + 10xy + 3y^2 - 2x - 14y - 5 = 0$
14. $4x^2 - 8xy - 2y^2 + 20x - 4y + 15 = 0$
15. $4x^2 + 4xy + y^2 - 24x + 38y - 139 = 0$
16. $16x^2 - 24xy + 9y^2 + 56x - 42y + 49 = 0$
17. $x^2 - 3xy + y^2 + 10x + 10y + 10 = 0$
18. $x^2 - 4xy + 9y^2 - 6y = 0$
19. $x^2 - xy + y^2 - x - y = 20$
20. $x^2 + xy + y^2 + x + y = 20$
21. $5x^2 + 12xy = 4$
22. $x^2 + 2xy + y^2 - x + y = 100$

23. Show that, after a rotation by an angle θ, the coefficient B' of the $x'y'$ term equals $2(C - A)\sin \theta \cos \theta + B(\cos^2\theta - \sin^2\theta)$

24. Show that $A + C$ and $B^2 - 4AC$ are *invariant* under rotation. That is, show that

$$A + C = A' + C' \quad \text{and} \quad B^2 - 4AC = B'^2 - 4A'C'$$

■   **25.**   Use the fact that $B^2 - 4AC$ is invariant under rotation (see Exercise 24) to verify that

   (a)   If $B^2 - 4AC < 0$, the curve is an ellipse, a point, or no curve at all
   (b)   If $B^2 - 4AC > 0$, the curve is a hyperbola or two intersecting lines
   (c)   If $B^2 - 4AC = 0$, the curve is a parabola, two parallel lines, one line, one point, or no curve at all.

Check these statements with the curves in Exercises 1–22.

26.   Show that, if $B \neq 0$, the curve cannot be a circle.

Appendix A

Induction and the Binomial Theorem

A-1
Mathematical Induction

Mathematical induction is a method often used to prove that a statement is true for all positive integers. Consider this statement: *The sum of the first n positive integers is one half the product of n and n + 1.* This sentence represents infinitely many sentences, one for each positive integer. For example, for $n = 1, 2, 3$ and 4, we have

$$S_1: \quad 1 = \tfrac{1}{2}(1)(1 + 1)$$

$$S_2: \quad 1 + 2 = \tfrac{1}{2}(2)(2 + 1)$$

$$S_3: \quad 1 + 2 + 3 = \tfrac{1}{2}(3)(3 + 1)$$

$$S_4: \quad 1 + 2 + 3 + 4 = \tfrac{1}{2}(4)(4 + 1)$$

These are the first four instances of the statement, and they are all true. The original statement can also be written in symbols as

$$1 + 2 + 3 + \cdots + n = \tfrac{1}{2}n(n + 1) \qquad \text{for all positive integers } n$$

Although it is easy to check the validity of this statement for the first four, ten, or even one hundred integers, how can we possibly prove it for *all* positive integers? By using the **principle of mathematical induction.**

■ Every statement in a sequence of statements $S_1, S_2, \ldots, S_n, \ldots$ is true if you can show that
(1) S_1 is true, and
(2)   if S_k is true, then S_{k+1} is true.

You can visualize the principle of induction by imagining an infinite row of dominos placed on end and close to each other. Now suppose the first one is pushed over towards the rest. You need not wait to see that each and every domino topples over; you know they will *all* fall. You know this because

(1)   the first one falls (analogous to "S_1 is true"), and
(2)   whenever one falls, it makes the next one fall (analogous to "if S_k is true, then S_{k+1} is also true").

Applying the principle of induction is a two-step process:
(1)   Prove that S_1 is true. This is usually done by actual computation or verified by observation.
(2)   This is the critical step. We *assume* that the statement is true for any fixed integer k and use this assumption to *prove* that the statement is also true for $k + 1$.

Example 1
Prove by induction that

$$1 + 2 + 3 + \ldots + n = \tfrac{1}{2}n(n + 1)$$

is true for every positive integer n.

Solution
(1) S_1 is true because $1 = \tfrac{1}{2}(1)(1 + 1)$
(2)   Now *assume* that S_k is true; that is, assume that

$$S_k: \quad 1 + 2 + 3 + \ldots + k = \tfrac{1}{2}k(k + 1)$$

for some particular k. You must now show that S_{k+1} is true. It may help to write out the statement S_{k+1}:

$$S_{k+1}: \quad 1 + 2 + \ldots + k + (k + 1) = \tfrac{1}{2}(k + 1)[(k + 1) + 1]$$

Notice that the left side of S_{k+1} is just the left side of S_k with $(k + 1)$ added. Taking this as a hint, add $(k + 1)$ to both sides of S_k. Thus,

$$1 + 2 + 3 + \ldots + k + (k + 1) = \tfrac{1}{2}k(k + 1) + (k + 1)$$

$$= (k + 1)(\tfrac{1}{2}k + 1) \qquad \text{(Factor out } k + 1\text{)}$$

$$= \tfrac{1}{2}(k + 1)(k + 2)$$

$$= \tfrac{1}{2}(k + 1)[(k + 1) + 1]$$

This is precisely the statement "S_{k+1} is true," which completes the induction argument. Therefore, the equation is true for every n.

Example 2

Prove that

$$1 + 3 + 5 + \colon .. + (2n - 1) = n^2$$

for every positive integer n.

Solution

This is the statement "The sum of the first n odd integers is n^2." For example, if $n = 3$, then $1 + 3 + 5 = 3^2$. Use induction:

(1) S_1 is true because $1 = 1^2$.

(2)   Assume that S_k is true; that is, assume

$$S_k: \quad 1 + 3 + \ldots + (2k - 1) = k^2$$

You must show that this implies S_{k+1} is true. Write out the statement S_{k+1}:

$$S_{k+1}: \quad 1 + 3 + \ldots + (2k - 1) + [2(k + 1) - 1] = (k + 1)^2$$

This suggests adding $2(k + 1) - 1$ to both sides of S_k:

$$1 + 3 + \ldots + (2k - 1) + [2(k + 1) - 1] = k^2 + [2(k + 1) - 1]$$

$$= k^2 + 2k + 1$$

$$= (k + 1)^2$$

This is precisely the statement "S_{k+1} is true". Therefore, by induction, the general statement is true for every n.

Example 3

Prove that $n < 2^n$ for all positive n.

Solution

(1) S_1 is true because $1 < 2^1$.

(2)   Now assume that S_k is true; that is, assume

$$S_k: \quad k < 2^k$$

for some unspecified positive integer k. Write out the statement S_{k+1}:

$$S_{k+1}: \quad k + 1 < 2^{k+1}$$

It is not evident that adding 1 to both sides of S_k, to get $k + 1 < 2^k + 1$, will prove statement S_{k+1}. Try another technique, using the fact that $2 \cdot 2^k = 2^{k+1}$. Multiplying both sides of S_k by 2 yields

$$2k < 2^{k+1}$$

Because $1 \le k$, you can conclude that

$$k + 1 \le k + k = 2k < 2^{k+1}$$

Thus, S_{k+1} is true whenever S_k is true and, by induction, the general statement is true for all n.

The next example shows that induction can be used to prove geometric facts. It also shows how the method of induction can be extended to sequences of statements that begin at a number other than 1.

Example 4
Prove that, for every $n \ge 3$, the sum of the interior angles of a polygon with n sides is $(n - 2)180°$.

Solution
A polygon with 3 sides is a triangle, and you know from geometry that the sum of its angles is $180°$. This establishes the truth of

S_3:   The sum of interior angles of a triangle is $(3 - 2)180°$.

Now assume the statement is true for some unspecified $k \ge 3$; that is, assume

S_k: The sum of interior angles of a k-sided polygon is $(k - 2)180°$.

You must show that this forces the truth of

S_{k+1}:   The sum of interior angles of a $(k + 1)$-sided polygon is $[(k + 1) - 2]180°$.

The technique here is quite different from those used in the preceding examples. The picture in Figure A-1 represents any $(k + 1)$-sided polygon with vertices

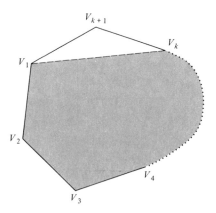

Figure A-1
The polygon in Example 4, proving that the sum of the interior angles of a polygon with n
sides is $(n - 2)180°$.

$V_1, V_2, \ldots, V_k, V_{k+1}$. Divide this polygon into two parts by joining V_1 to V_k to
form the triangle $V_1 V_{k+1} V_k$ and the k-sided polygon that is shaded in the figure.
By your assumption of S_k, you know that the angles of this k-sided polygon add
up to $(k - 2)180°$. You also know that the sum of the angles in the triangle
$V_1 V_{k+1} V_k$ is $180°$. It follows that the sum of the angles of the original $(k + 1)$-
sided polygon is the sum of the angles of the two parts. That is,

$$(k - 2)180° + 180° = (k - 1)180° = [(k + 1) - 2]180°$$

Thus, S_{k+1} is true and the induction proof is complete.

The next example illustrates an abuse of induction. It shows that a sloppy application
can lead to gross errors.

Example 5
Prove that in every group of n dogs, if one is a male, then they are all male.

Solution
The statement is obviously false, so the "proof" below must contain a flaw; see
if you can spot it.
    S_1 is obviously true: in a group of one dog, if one is male, then all are
male. Assume that S_k is true. Let us show that S_{k+1} is true. Suppose

$$\{D_1, D_2, \ldots, D_k, D_{k+1}\}$$

is any group of $k + 1$ dogs, and suppose one of them is a male; say D_1 is male (if it happens that the male was D_2 or D_6, or whatever, just rearrange them so that D_1 is a male). Thus, $\{D_1, D_2, \ldots, D_k\}$ is a group of k dogs and one is a male, so *all* are males, because S_k is assumed true. But this means that $\{D_2, D_3, \ldots, D_k, D_{k+1}\}$ is now a group of k dogs (we left D_1 out) and one is a male (in fact, $D_2, \ldots, D_k$ are males) so they *all* are, including D_{k+1}. Thus, all $k + 1$ dogs are male. This completes our induction argument.

Did you spot the error? It appears as a footnote* on page 446.

Exercises

Use induction to prove the following statements.

1. $1 + 5 + 9 + \ldots + (4n - 3) = n(2n - 1)$

2. $4 + 8 + 12 + \ldots + 4n = 2n(n + 1)$

3. $3 + 6 + 9 + \ldots + 3n = \frac{3}{2}n(n + 1)$

4. $1 + 4 + 7 + \ldots + (3n - 2) = \frac{1}{2}n(3n - 1)$

5. $2 + 4 + 8 + \ldots + 2^n = 2(2^n - 1)$

6. $1^2 + 2^2 + 3^2 + \ldots + n^2 = \frac{1}{6}n(n + 1)(2n + 1)$

7. $1^3 + 2^3 + 3^3 + \ldots + n^3 = \frac{1}{4}n^2(n + 1)^2$

8. $\dfrac{1}{1 \cdot 2} + \dfrac{1}{2 \cdot 3} + \dfrac{1}{3 \cdot 4} + \cdots + \dfrac{1}{n(n + 1)} = \dfrac{n}{n + 1}$

9. $5 + 5^2 + 5^3 + \ldots + 5^n = \frac{5}{4}(5^n - 1)$

10. $\left(1 + \dfrac{1}{1}\right)\left(1 + \dfrac{1}{2}\right)\left(1 + \dfrac{1}{3}\right) \cdots \left(1 + \dfrac{1}{n}\right) = n + 1$

11. $3^{2n} - 1$ is divisible by 8

12. $7^{2n} + 16n - 1$ is divisible by 64

13. (De Moivre's Theorem) $[r(\cos \theta + i \sin \theta)]^n = r^n(\cos n\theta + i \sin n\theta)$

14. $2^n + 10n < 3^n$ for $n \geq 4$

15. $1 \cdot 2 \cdot 3 \cdot \ldots \cdot n \geq n^3$ for $n \geq 6$

A-2
Sequences and Sums

The word *sequence* usually implies that one object or event follows another in some sort of order, like a sequence of cards or a sequence of plays in football. Here, we shall confine our attention to sequences of numbers. For example,

$$2, 8, 5, 10, \ldots$$

is a sequence. Each member of the sequence is called a **term.** In this example, the first term is 2, the second term is 8, and so on.

We may also think of a sequence as a real valued function a whose domain is the positive integers. It is customary not to use the usual notation $a(1), a(2), \ldots$, but rather $a_1, a_2, \ldots$. Thus, in the example above, $a_1 = 2$, $a_2 = 8$, $a_3 = 5$, and so on.

It often happens that the terms in a sequence can be calculated by a general rule or formula. For example, in the sequence

$$1, 3, 5, \ldots, 2n - 1, \ldots$$

any term can be found from the formula $a_n = 2n - 1$. Thus, $a_1 = 2 \cdot 1 - 1 = 1$, $a_2 = 2 \cdot 2 - 1 = 3$, and $a_{17} = 2 \cdot 17 - 1 = 33$. The nth term $a_n = 2n - 1$ is called the **general term.** If the general term of a sequence is not given, it can often be discovered from the pattern set by the first few terms.

Example 1
Find the general term of each sequence below and use it to find a_6.
(a) $2, 4, 6, 8, \ldots$. The pattern set here is the sequence of even numbers. The general term is $a_n = 2n$ and $a_6 = 12$.
(b) $4, 8, 16, 32, \ldots$. The pattern here is that each term is a power of 2, but the sequence begins with $4 = 2^2$. Thus, $a_n = 2^{n+1}$ and $a_6 = 2^{6+1} = 2^7 = 128$.
(c) $1, -\frac{1}{2}, \frac{1}{4}, -\frac{1}{8}, \ldots$. Each term of this sequence is a power of $-\frac{1}{2}$, and the first term is $1 = (\frac{1}{2})^0$. The general term is $a_n = (-\frac{1}{2})^{n-1}$ and $a_6 = -\frac{1}{32}$.

A sequence may be defined by specifying its first few terms and a rule for computing each succeeding term from those already known. This is called a **recursive definition,** and it is often the best way to define a sequence that has no simple formula for the nth term.

Example 2
Find the first five terms of these sequences defined recursively.
(a) $a_1 = 3$; $a_{k+1} = (-1)^k a_k / 3$ for $k \geq 1$.

$$a_1 = 3$$
$$a_2 = (-1)^1 a_1 / 3 = -3/3 = -1$$
$$a_3 = (-1)^2 a_2 / 3 = -1/3 = -\tfrac{1}{3}$$
$$a_4 = (-1)^3 a_3 / 3 = (-1)(-\tfrac{1}{3})/3 = \tfrac{1}{9}$$
$$a_5 = (-1)^4 a_4 / 3 = (\tfrac{1}{9})/3 = \tfrac{1}{27}$$

The sequence is $3, -1, -\frac{1}{3}, \frac{1}{9}, \frac{1}{27}, \ldots$ (no general term).

(b)   *Fibonacci sequence.*† The first two terms are $a_1 = a_2 = 1$, and $a_{k+1} = a_k + a_{k-1}$ for $k \geq 3$. Thus,

$$a_1 = 1$$
$$a_2 = 1$$
$$a_3 = a_2 + a_1 = 2$$
$$a_4 = a_3 + a_2 = 3$$
$$a_5 = a_4 + a_3 = 5$$

The sequence is $1, 1, 2, 3, 5, \ldots$ (no simple formula for a_n).‡

Let us now take a quick look at two simple but important types of sequences.
An **arithmetic sequence** is a sequence in which the difference $a_{k+1} - a_k$ of any two successive terms is a constant. The constant is denoted by d, and it is called the **common difference.**

■   The general term of an arithmetic sequence is $a_n = a_1 + d(n - 1)$.

You will be asked to verify this in an exercise. Here are some examples:

$2, 6, 10, 14, \ldots$ $a_1 = 2;\ d = 4;\ a_n = 2 + 4(n - 1)$

$1, -1, -3, -5, \ldots$ $a_1 = 1;\ d = -2;\ a_n = 1 - 2(n - 1)$

$-\frac{1}{4}, \frac{1}{4}, \frac{3}{4}, \frac{5}{4}, \ldots$ $a_1 = -\frac{1}{4};\ d = \frac{1}{2};\ a_n = -\frac{1}{4} + \frac{1}{2}(n - 1)$

A **geometric sequence** is a sequence in which the quotient a_{k+1}/a_k of any two successive terms is a constant. This constant is denoted by r, and it is called the **common ratio.**

■   The general term of a geometric sequence is $a_n = a_1 r^{n-1}$.

---

*Answer to the question posed in Example 5: The deduction that S_k implies S_{k+1} is correct whenever $k \geq 2$. However, *it does not hold for* $k = 1$; that is, the argument fails to prove that if S_1 is true, then S_2 is also true.

† This is a well-known sequence, named after the mathematician Leonardo Fibonacci (twelfth and thirteenth centuries).

‡ In fact

$$a_n = \frac{1}{\sqrt{5}}\left[\left(\frac{1 + \sqrt{5}}{2}\right)^n - \left(\frac{1 - \sqrt{5}}{2}\right)^n\right]$$

The proof is left as an exercise. Here are some examples:

$$1, 2, 4, 8, \ldots \qquad a_1 = 1; r = 2; a_n = (1)2^{n-1}$$

$$1, \tfrac{1}{2}, \tfrac{1}{4}, \tfrac{1}{8}, \ldots \qquad a_1 = 1; r = \tfrac{1}{2}; a_n = (1)(\tfrac{1}{2})^{n-1}$$

$$4, -1, \tfrac{1}{4}, -\tfrac{1}{16}, \ldots \qquad a_1 = 4; r = -\tfrac{1}{4}; a_n = 4(-\tfrac{1}{4})^{n-1}$$

Sums

Sigma notation. The Greek letter Σ, capital *sigma,* is used extensively in mathematics to denote a sum. For example, the symbol

$$\sum_{n=1}^{4} 2n$$

is read "the sum from $n = 1$ to $n = 4$ of $2n$." This means to let $n = 1, 2, 3$ and 4; then evaluate $2n$ at each value of n and add up the terms. Thus,

$$\sum_{n=1}^{4} 2n = 2 \cdot 1 + 2 \cdot 2 + 2 \cdot 3 + 2 \cdot 4$$

$$= 2 + 4 + 6 + 8$$

Here are some other examples.

Example 3
Write out the following sums.

(a) $\displaystyle\sum_{n=1}^{3} (2n + 1) = (2 \cdot 1 + 1) + (2 \cdot 2 + 1) + (2 \cdot 3 + 1)$

$$= 3 + 5 + 7$$

(b) $\displaystyle\sum_{k=0}^{4} (\tfrac{1}{2})^k = (\tfrac{1}{2})^0 + (\tfrac{1}{2})^1 + (\tfrac{1}{2})^2 + (\tfrac{1}{2})^3 + (\tfrac{1}{2})^4$

$$= 1 + \tfrac{1}{2} + \tfrac{1}{4} + \tfrac{1}{8} + \tfrac{1}{16}$$

(c) $\displaystyle\sum_{j=3}^{7} j = 3 + 4 + 5 + 6 + 7$

If the general term is known, a sum can be converted to sigma notation.

> **Example 4**
> Express the following sums in sigma notation. (The particular letters used—
> n, k, j—are unimportant; any letters will do.)
> (a) $1 + 3 + 5 + 7 + 9$. The general term is $2n - 1$, and n takes the values
> $1, 2, \ldots, 5$. The sum in sigma notation is
>
> $$\sum_{n=1}^{5} (2n - 1)$$
>
> (b) $1 + 2 + 4 + 8$. The general term is 2^k with k starting at 0. (Why?) The
> sum is
>
> $$\sum_{k=0}^{3} 2^k$$
>
> (c) $\sqrt{6} + \sqrt{7} + \sqrt{8}$. The sum is
>
> $$\sum_{j=6}^{8} \sqrt{j}$$

Sums of a sequence. For a sequence $a_1, a_2, a_3, \ldots$, we shall let s_n stand for the sum of
the first n terms. Thus,

$$s_n = \sum_{k=1}^{n} a_k = a_1 + a_2 + \cdots + a_n$$

We shall now use this notation to derive formulas for the sums of arithmetic and
geometric sequences.

Sums of an arithmetic sequence. Suppose you want to find the sum of the first four
terms of the arithmetic sequence 4, 8, 12, $\ldots, a_n, \ldots$ In sigma notation,

$$s_4 = \sum_{n=1}^{4} a_n = 4 + 8 + 12 + 16$$

Because the order of addition is immaterial, the terms can be written in reverse order:

$$s_4 = 16 + 12 + 8 + 4$$

If s_4 is added to itself,

$$
\begin{aligned}
s_4 &= 4 + 8 + 12 + 16 \\
s_4 &= 16 + 12 + 8 + 4 \\
\hline
2s_4 &= 20 + 20 + 20 + 20
\end{aligned}
$$

Notice that all the terms in the final sum are the same; in fact, each one is equal to $a_1 + a_4$. In general, the sum of the first n terms of an arithmetic sequence $a_1, a_2, \ldots,$ $a_n, \ldots$ is

$$
s_n = \frac{n}{2}(a_1 + a_n)
$$

Proof
Write s_n as usual and then in reverse order.

$$
s_n = a_1 + a_2 + a_3 + \cdots + a_n
$$

$$
s_n = a_n + a_{n-1} + a_{n-2} + \cdots + a_1
$$

Now add the two equations to obtain

$$
2s_n = (a_1 + a_n) + (a_2 + a_{n-1}) + (a_3 + a_{n-2}) + \cdots + (a_1 + a_n)
$$

There are n terms in this sum, and each of them equals $a_1 + a_n$. For example, if d is the common difference, then $a_2 + a_{n-1} = a_1 + d + a_{n-1} = a_1 + a_n$ and $a_3 + a_{n-2} = a_1 + 2d + a_{n-2} = a_1 + a_n$. Thus, $2s_n = n(a_1 + a_n)$, which is equivalent to the formula we wanted to prove.

A corollary to the above result is obtained by replacing a_n by $a_1 + d(n-1)$, which is the formula for the general term of an arithmetic sequence.

■   The sum of the first n terms of an arithmetic sequence with first term a_1 and common difference d is

$$
s_n = \frac{n}{2}(a_1 + a_n) \quad \text{or} \quad s_n = \frac{n}{2}(2a_1 + d(n-1))
$$

Sums of a geometric sequence. Suppose you want to add the first four terms of the geometric sequence 2, 6, 18, $\ldots,$ $a_n,$ $\ldots,$ with common ratio $r = 3$. In sigma notation,

$$
s_4 = \sum_{n=1}^{4} a_n = 2 + 6 + 18 + 54
$$

If you multiply s_4 by $-r = -3$, then

$$-3s_4 = -6 - 18 - 54 - 162$$

If you add the two equations, then

$$
\begin{aligned}
s_4 &= 2 + 6 + 18 + 54 \\
-3s_4 &= \quad\; -6 - 18 - 54 - 162 \\
\hline
-2s_4 &= 2 + 0 + \; 0 + \; 0 - 162
\end{aligned}
$$

Notice that, in the final sum, all terms are zero except a_1 and $-3a_4$.

Now consider any geometric sequence $a_1, a_2, a_3, \ldots$, with common ratio r. Then the sum of the first n terms is

$$s_n = a_1 + a_1 r + a_1 r^2 + \ldots + a_1 r^{n-1}$$

Multiply both sides by $-r$ to obtain

$$-rs_n = -a_1 r - a_1 r^2 - a_1 r^3 \ldots - a_1 r^n$$

and now add the two equations. As in the example, all terms are zero except a_1 and $-a_1 r^n$:

$$(1 - r)s_n = a_1 - a_1 r^n = a_1(1 - r^n)$$

If $r \neq 1$, divide through by $1 - r$ to get

■   The sum of the first n terms of a geometric sequence with first term a_1 and common ratio $r \neq 1$ is

$$s_n = \frac{a_1(1 - r^n)}{1 - r}$$

Example 5

(a)   Find s_{20} for the sequence 3, 6, 9, ... This is an arithmetic sequence, but we do not know the 20th term, so let us use $s_n = \dfrac{n}{2}(2a_1 + d(n - 1))$:

$$s_{20} = \frac{20}{2}(2 \cdot 3 + 3 \cdot 19)$$

$$= (10)(63) = 630$$

(b) Find the sum $\sum\limits_{k=0}^{5} (\frac{1}{2})^k$. This is s_6 of the geometric sequence $1, \frac{1}{2}, \frac{1}{4}, \ldots,$

with $r = \frac{1}{2}$. The formula derived above yields

$$s_6 = \frac{1(1 - (\frac{1}{2})^6)}{1 - \frac{1}{2}} = \frac{63}{32}$$

Exercises

In each of the following arithmetic sequences, find a_{20} and the sum $s_{10} = \sum\limits_{k=1}^{10} a_k$.

1. $-3, 3, 9, \ldots$ 2. $5, 7, 9, \ldots$ 3. $2, -2, -6, \ldots$

4. $1, -4, -9, \ldots$ 5. $\frac{1}{2}, \frac{7}{10}, \frac{9}{10}, \ldots$ 6. $-\frac{1}{3}, -\frac{1}{12}, \frac{1}{6}, \ldots$

In each of the following geometric sequences, find a_5 and the sum $s_6 = \sum\limits_{k=1}^{6} a_k$.

7. $\frac{1}{4}, \frac{1}{8}, \frac{1}{16}, \ldots$ 8. $4, 2, 1, \ldots$ 9. $8, -2, \frac{1}{2}, \ldots$

10. $6, -2, \frac{2}{3}, \ldots$ 11. $1, \frac{1}{3}, \frac{1}{9}, \ldots$ 12. $-3, 1, -\frac{1}{3}, \ldots$

Find the following sums.

13. $-2 + 1 + 4 + \ldots + 100$ 14. $8 + 7 + 6 + \ldots + (-13)$

15. $1 + 2 + 4 + \ldots + 128$ 16. $3 + 1 + \frac{1}{3} + \ldots \frac{1}{81}$

17. $\sum\limits_{k=1}^{100} 2k$ 18. $\sum\limits_{j=4}^{100} (5 + 3j)$ 19. $\sum\limits_{n=0}^{50} (3 - 5n)$

20. $\sum\limits_{m=1}^{9} 6m$ 21. $\sum\limits_{p=0}^{5} (-\frac{1}{2})^p$ 22. $\sum\limits_{q=1}^{4} (\frac{1}{3})^q$

23. A certain ball always bounces up to one half the height from which it falls. If it is dropped from a height of six feet, how far will it rise on the fifth bounce? How far has it traveled when it is at the top of its fifth bounce? Will it ever come to rest?

24. Prove by induction that the general term of an arithmetic sequence with first term a_1 and common difference d is

$$a_n = a_1 + d(n - 1)$$

25.   Prove, by induction, that the general term of a geometric sequence with first term a_1 and common ratio r is

$$a_n = a_1 r^{n-1}$$

A-3
Counting Methods.
Binomial Coefficients

How many three-digit numbers can be formed with the numbers 1, 2, and 3? One way to answer this question is to make a list of all the numbers: 123, 111, 332, and so on. This is tedious, because there are a large number of possibilities. Let us see if there is a better way.

There are three choices for the first, or *hundreds,* digit: it could be 1, 2, or 3. For each of these choices, there are three choices for the second, or *tens,* digit. So far, then, there are three times three, or nine, choices for the first two digits. For each of those nine choices, there are three choices for the final digit. Therefore, we can conclude that there are $3 \cdot 3 \cdot 3 = 27$ different numbers possible.

Now suppose there are three pieces of paper, each marked with the number 1, 2, or 3. How many three-digit numbers may be formed by placing the pieces of paper side by side? This problem is different from the one above in that no number may be repeated. Again, we could make a list: 123, 213, 231, and so on. A better way is to analyze the choices that can be made. There are three choices for the first digit. But for each of these choices, now there are only two choices for the second digit, because repetitions are not allowed. Once we have selected the first two digits there is only one choice left for the final digit. Therefore, the answer is that there are $3 \cdot 2 \cdot 1 = 6$ distinct possible numbers. These examples illustrate the

■   **First Counting Principle**
If n actions are performed in order, with the first having m_1 possible outcomes, the second having m_2 possible outcomes, and so on, then the total number of possible outcomes of performing all n actions is the product $m_1 m_2 \dots m_n$.

Example 1
With the numbers 1, 2, 3, and 4,
(a)   How many four-digit numbers can be formed? *Answer:* $4 \cdot 4 \cdot 4 \cdot 4 = 256$.
(b)   How many two-digit numbers can be formed? *Answer:* $4 \cdot 4 = 16$.
(c)   How many four-digit numbers can be formed if repetitions are not allowed? *Answer:* $4 \cdot 3 \cdot 2 \cdot 1 = 24$.

You may have noticed that disallowing repetitions gives rise to a number like $n(n-1)(n-2) \dots$ This product turns up so frequently that there is a symbol to denote that number. The symbol $n!$ (read "n **factorial**") is defined recursively by $0! = 1$, $1! = 1$, and $n! = n[(n-1)!]$ for $n \geq 2$. Thus,

$$2! = 2 \cdot 1! = 2 \cdot 1 = 2$$
$$3! = 3 \cdot 2! = 3 \cdot 2 \cdot 1 = 6$$
$$4! = 4 \cdot 3! = 4 \cdot 3 \cdot 2 \cdot 1 = 24$$

In general, for $n > 0$,

$$n! = n(n-1)(n-2) \cdots 2 \cdot 1$$

Example 2
(a) How many different ways can five children line up? *Answer:* $5 \cdot 4 \cdot 3 \cdot 2 \cdot 1 = 5! = 120$
(b) How many ways can ten different colored beads be strung on a wire? *Answer:* $10! = 3,628,800$. (Factorials get very large very fast—even faster than exponentials!)

Suppose the five children of Example 2(a) are at camp and must be assigned to beds. There are two rooms, A and B. Room A has three beds and B has two. If we number the beds 1 through 5 and assign each child to a bed, there will again be $5! = 120$ different possible arrangements. On the other hand, what if we merely assign each child to a room, three to A and two to B? Now how many possible roommate arrangements are there? The difference between this problem and the preceding one, in which the beds were numbered, is that once three children are chosen to share room A, the other two are automatically assigned to B, and the answer does not depend on which beds they decide to sleep in. The question could be rephrased as follows: "How many ways can three children be chosen from five children."

To figure this out, let us number the children 1 through 5, ask them to line up, and then assign the first three on the left to room A. As we have seen, there are $5! = 120$ ways for them to line up, but suppose that children 1, 2, and 3 have decided to room together in room A. Thus, they must take the first three places in line, but otherwise it doesn't matter how they line up; there are $3! = 6$ ways for them to do this, namely,

$$
\begin{array}{ccc}
1 & 2 & 3 \\
1 & 3 & 2 \\
2 & 1 & 3 \\
2 & 3 & 1 \\
3 & 1 & 2 \\
3 & 2 & 1 \\
\end{array}
$$

For each of these possible line-ups, the remaining two children can line up as they choose in the remaining two places in line. There are $2! = 2$ ways that they can do this, namely,

$$4 \ 5 \quad \text{and} \quad 5 \ 4$$

Thus, there are $3!2!$ different line-ups of the five children that will assign children 1, 2, and 3 to room A, namely,

1	2	3	4	5		1	2	3	5	4
1	3	2	4	5		1	3	2	5	4
2	1	3	4	5		2	1	3	5	4
2	3	1	4	5		2	3	1	5	4
3	1	2	4	5		3	1	2	5	4
3	2	1	4	5		3	2	1	5	4

If any other group of three children had decided to room together in room A, there would also be $3!2!$ different line-ups that would give them their wish. Thus, although there are $5!$ different line-ups, there are only $5!/3!2!$ different ways to assign the children to the two rooms. To answer the rephrased question above, there are $5!/3!2! = 120/12 = 10$ ways to choose three children from a group of five children.

Although we shall not do so here, we could use a similar argument to prove the following important fact.

■   **Second Counting Principle**

Let n be a positive integer and r be a nonnegative integer, with $r \leq n$.

Let $\binom{n}{r}$ be the number of ways to choose r objects from n distinct objects. Then

$$\binom{n}{r} = \frac{n!}{r!(n-r)!}$$

It may seem odd to let $r = 0$, so that

$$\binom{n}{0} = \frac{n!}{0!(n-0)!} = \frac{n!}{n!} = 1 \qquad\qquad (0! = 1)$$

However, if you decide to choose *no* objects from a set of n objects, there is indeed only one way to do it.

Example 3
(a) How many three-member committees can be chosen from a seven-member organization? *Answer:*

$$\binom{7}{3} = \frac{7!}{3!4!} = \frac{7 \cdot \cancel{6} \cdot 5 \cdot \cancel{4} \cdot \cancel{3} \cdot \cancel{2} \cdot \cancel{1}}{\cancel{3} \cdot \cancel{2} \cdot 1 \cdot \cancel{4} \cdot \cancel{3} \cdot \cancel{2} \cdot \cancel{1}} = 35$$

(b) How many ways can a football team with a ten-game schedule wind up with a 7–3 win–loss record? *Answer:*

$$\binom{10}{7} = \frac{10!}{7!3!} = 120 \qquad \text{(Check.)}$$

The next example and several of the exercises should be interesting to card players.

Example 4
A deck of 52 cards is shuffled and a five-card hand is dealt.
(a) How many possible hands are there? *Answer:*

$$\binom{52}{5} = \frac{52!}{5!47!} = \frac{52 \cdot 51 \cdot 50 \cdot 49 \cdot 48}{5 \cdot 4 \cdot 3 \cdot 2 \cdot 1} = 2,598,960$$

(b) How many of those hands will be a poker hand of a pair of aces?
(c) What percentage of all possible hands contain exactly one pair?

Solution
(b) The hand must contain exactly two aces and no other pair or three of a kind. There are four aces in all, so there are $\binom{4}{2}$ ways to get two of them. There are three other cards in the hand. For the first card, there are 48 choices (anything but an ace); for the next, there are 44 choices (we cannot pair up with the other card); and for the final card, there are 40 choices. Thus there are $48 \cdot 44 \cdot 40$ choices for the other three cards received *in order.* But order is not important here. Because each group of three cards can be received in $3! = 6$ different ways, we have to divide by 3!. Therefore, there are exactly

$$\binom{4}{2} \cdot \frac{48 \cdot 44 \cdot 40}{3!} = 84,480$$

poker hands of a pair of aces.

(c) There are 84,480 hands of a pair of aces. Each of the other pairs is just as likely as aces. Therefore, there are $(13)(84,480) = 1,098,240$ hands of one pair.

Because there are 2,598,960 hands in all, the percentage of hands with one pair is

$$\frac{1,098,240}{2,598,960} \approx .42 \quad \text{or} \quad 42\%$$

Exercises

Evaluate.

1. $\binom{3}{2}$ 2. $\binom{3}{1}$ 3. $\binom{7}{2}$ 4. $\binom{8}{4}$

5. $\binom{6}{0}$ 6. $\binom{4}{0}$ 7. $\binom{6}{6}$ 8. $\binom{4}{4}$

9. How many four-digit numbers can be formed with the numbers 1, 2, 3, 4?
10. How many three-digit numbers can be formed with the numbers 5, 6, 7?
11. How many four-digit numbers can be formed with the numbers 1, 2, 3, 4, 5, 6?
12. How many three-digit numbers can be formed with the numbers 5, 6, 7, 8, 9?
13. California license plates have three numbers followed by three letters or three letters followed by three numbers. How many possible license plates are there?
14. A coin with a head and a tail is tossed six times. How many possible outcomes are there? (An outcome is a list noting the results, heads or tails, of each toss. For example, TTHTHH is one possible outcome.)
15. (Continuation of Exercise 14) How many of the outcomes result in one tail and five heads? How many result in three heads and three tails?
16. How many different ways are there to answer a ten-question multiple choice exam if each question has three possible answers? What are the chances of a student getting a perfect score if he guesses at each answer?
17. In how many ways can seven children be assigned to two rooms with four in one and three in the other?
18. Same question as in Exercise 17, except that now Bob and Roy, who are brothers, must room together.
19. In how many ways can 4 children be assigned to two rooms?
20. Let $A = \{1, 2, 3\}$ and $B = \{1, 2\}$. How many functions $f{:}A \rightarrow B$ are there?
21. Same as Exercise 20 for $f{:}A \rightarrow A$.

Poker
Have you ever wondered why a straight beats three of a kind and why a flush beats a straight? The reasons are mathematical, as the next few exercises show. (Refer to Example 4.)

22.   How many (five card) poker hands of three aces are there?

23.   How many poker hands of three of a kind are there?

24.   How many poker hands are straights? [HINT: A straight is five cards with consecutive numbers or names. First count the straights with Ace, 2, 3, 4, 5.]

25.   How many hands are flushes? [HINT: A flush is five cards of the same suit. First count the spade flushes.]

In Section A-4 we shall need to know that $\binom{n}{r} + \binom{n}{r+1} = \binom{n+1}{r+1}$.

26.   Verify the following

(a) $\binom{4}{2} + \binom{4}{3} = \binom{5}{3}$ here, $n = 4$ and $r = 2$

(b) $\binom{5}{1} + \binom{5}{2} = \binom{6}{2}$ here, $n = 5$ and $r = 1$

(c) $\binom{1}{0} + \binom{1}{1} = \binom{2}{1}$ here, $n = 1$ and $r = 0$

27.   Show that

$$\binom{n}{r} + \binom{n}{r+1} = \binom{n+1}{r+1}$$

[HINT: Write out each form on the left as a quotient of factorials (see the Second Counting Principle), find the LCD, and add the fractions.]

A-4
The Binomial Theorem

In this section, we shall develop a general formula for expanding the powers of a binomial; that is, a formula for writing $(x + y)^n$ as a sum of terms. For $n = 2$ or 3, you already know the expansions:

$$(x + y)^2 = x^2 + 2xy + y^2$$
$$(x + y)^3 = x^3 + 3x^2y + 3xy^2 + y^3$$

The general formula will give the expansion for any n.

Let us use the methods of the previous section to see what the formula should be. Suppose we want to expand

$$(x + y)^5 = (x + y)(x + y)(x + y)(x + y)(x + y)$$

By definition, any such product is the sum of all products obtained by choosing one term from each factor and multiplying them together. All the factors of $(x + y)^5$ are alike: they are all $x + y$. From each factor, we must choose an x or a y. Suppose we pick zero y's; then all choices are x and the product of five x's is x^5, or x^5y^0. In how many ways can we pick zero y's from the five factors? The answer is $\binom{5}{0}$. Thus, the expansion must contain $\binom{5}{0}$ terms of the form x^5y^0. Now suppose we pick one y; the other four choices are x's, so the term equals x^4y, or x^4y^1. In how many ways can we pick one y from five factors? The answer is $\binom{5}{1}$. Thus, the expansion must contain $\binom{5}{1}$ terms of the form x^4y^1. In similar fashion, we can show that there will be $\binom{5}{2}$ terms of the form x^3y^2, $\binom{5}{3}$ terms x^2y^3, and so on. Notice that the sum of the exponents is always 5, so that each term has the form $x^{5-r}y^r$ and the expansion can be written

$$(x + y)^5 = \sum_{r=0}^{5} \binom{5}{r} x^{5-r} y^r$$

$$= \binom{5}{0}x^5 + \binom{5}{1}x^4y + \binom{5}{2}x^3y^2 + \binom{5}{3}x^2y^3 + \binom{5}{4}xy^4 + \binom{5}{5}y^5$$

$$= x^5 + 5x^4y + 10x^3y^2 + 10x^2y^3 + 5xy^4 + y^5$$

A similar argument can prove the following general formula for the expansion of any power of a binomial expression.

■   **Binomial Theorem**
For any nonzero real numbers x and y and any positive integer n,

$$(x + y)^n = \sum_{r=0}^{n} \binom{n}{r} x^{n-r} y^r = x^n + \binom{n}{1}x^{n-1}y + \ldots + \binom{n}{n-1}xy^{n-1} + y^n$$

The numbers $\binom{n}{r}$ are called the **binomial coefficients.**

Notice that the exponents of x and y in each term always add up to n. The exponent r in $x^{n-r}y^r$ identifies the coefficient $\binom{n}{r}$ of that term.

If we write the coefficients of the powers $(x + y)^n$ in a triangle, beginning with $n = 0$, they form **Pascal's triangle,** named after the seventeenth-century French mathematician and theologian Blaise Pascal:

$n = 0$						1						
$n = 1$					1		1					
$n = 2$				1		2		1				
$n = 3$			1		3		3		1			
$n = 4$		1		4		6		4		1		
$n = 5$	1		5		10		10		5		1	

Notice that, except for the 1's at the ends of each row, each number is the sum of the two numbers above it. Thus, to find the row corresponding to $n = 6$, first write a 1; for the next entry, add 1 and 5 from the row above (corresponding to $n = 5$); then add 5 and 10; and so on:

$$1 \quad 6 \quad 15 \quad 20 \quad 15 \quad 6 \quad 1$$

For $n = 7$, this method yields

$$1 \quad 7 \quad 21 \quad 35 \quad 35 \quad 21 \quad 7 \quad 1$$

Check these out by using the Binomial Theorem to find the coefficients of $(x + y)^6$ and $(x + y)^7$.

Now let us prove the Binomial Theorem by induction. First, we must show that it is true for $n = 1$:

$$(x + y)^1 = \binom{1}{0} x^{1-0} y^0 + \binom{1}{1} x^{1-1} y^1$$

$$= x + y$$

Now we shall suppose that it is true for some unspecified $k \geq 1$; that is,

$$(x + y)^k = \sum_{r=0}^{k} \binom{k}{r} x^{k-r} y^r$$

Then

$$(x + y)^{k+1} = (x + y)(x + y)^k$$

$$= (x + y) \sum_{r=0}^{k} \binom{k}{r} x^{k-r} y^r$$

$$= x \sum_{r=0}^{k} \binom{k}{r} x^{k-r} y^r + y \sum_{r=0}^{k} \binom{k}{r} x^{k-r} y^r$$

$$= \left[x^{k+1} + \cdots + \binom{k}{r} x^{k+1-r} y^r + \binom{k}{r+1} x^{k-r} y^{r+1} + \cdots + xy^k \right]$$

$$+ \left[x^k y + \cdots + \binom{k}{r-1} x^{k+1-r} y^r + \binom{k}{r} x^{k-r} y^{r+1} + \cdots + y^{k+1} \right]$$

$$= x^{k+1} + \cdots + \left[\binom{k}{r-1} + \binom{k}{r} \right] x^{k+1-r} y^r + \left[\binom{k}{r} + \binom{k}{r+1} \right] x^{k-r} y^{r+1}$$
$$+ \cdots + y^{k+1}$$

$$= x^{k+1} + \cdots + \binom{k+1}{r} x^{k+1-r} y^r + \binom{k+1}{r+1} x^{k-r} y^{r+1} + \cdots + y^{k+1}$$

[See Exercise 27 in Section A-3.]

$$= \sum_{r=0}^{k+1} \binom{k+1}{r} x^{k+1-r} y^r$$

This completes the induction argument.

Example 1
Use Pascal's triangle to expand $(x + y)^4$.

Solution
The fifth row of the triangle, which corresponds to $n = 4$, reads 1   4   6   4   1.
Thus,

$$(x + y)^4 = x^4 + 4x^3 y + 6x^2 y^2 + 4xy^3 + y^4$$

Example 2
Use the Binomial Theorem to expand $(2a - 3b)^4$.

Solution
Here $x = 2a$ and $y = -3b$. Either find the coefficients in Pascal's triangle or use
the formula for $\binom{4}{r}$. Thus,

$$(2a - 3b)^4 = \sum_{r=0}^{4} \binom{4}{r} (2a)^{4-r} (-3b)^r$$

$$= (2a)^4 + 4(2a)^3 (-3b) + 6(2a)^2 (-3b)^2 + 4(2a)(-3b)^3 + (-3b)^4$$

$$= 16a^4 - 96a^3 b + 216a^2 b^2 - 216ab^3 + 81b^4$$

Example 3
Find the fourth term in the expansion of $(u - 2v)^7$.

Solution
Here, $x = u$ and $y = -2v$, and the fourth term in $(x + y)^7$ is $\binom{7}{3}x^4y^3$. (Check!)

Thus,

$$\binom{7}{3}u^4(-2v)^3 = 35(u^4)(-8v^3)$$

$$= -280u^4v^3$$

is the fourth term in the expansion of $(u - 2v)^7$.

Example 4
Compute $(1.1)^5$.

Solution
Write 1.1 as $1 + .1$; thus, $x = 1$ and $y = .1$. Then,

$$(1.1)^5 = (1 + .1)^5 = \sum_{r=0}^{5} \binom{5}{r}(1)^{5-r}(.1)^r$$

$$= 1 + 5(.1) + 10(.01) + 10(.001) + 5(.0001) + .00001$$

$$= 1 + .5 + .1 + .01 + .0005 + .00001$$

$$= 1.61051$$

Exercises

Use the Binomial Theorem or Pascal's triangle to expand the following.

1. $(a + b)^3$	**2.** $(a - b)^3$	**3.** $(2x - y)^4$
4. $(x - 2y)^4$	**5.** $(s^2 + t^3)^4$	**6.** $(s^3 + t^2)^4$
7. $\left(\dfrac{1}{u} - v\right)^5$	**8.** $\left(u - \dfrac{1}{v}\right)^5$	**9.** $\left(1 + \dfrac{1}{x}\right)^6$
10. $(1.1)^4$	**11.** $(1.01)^4$	**12.** $(2.1)^4$
13. $(.99)^3$	**14.** $(2.1)^4$	**15.** $(1.9)^5$

Find the specified term.

16. The fifth term in $(2x - y)^8$.

17. The sixth term in $\left(1 + \dfrac{1}{x}\right)^{10}$.

18. The fourth term in $(x^2 - y^3)^8$.

19. The third term in $\left(\dfrac{1}{x} - \dfrac{1}{y^2}\right)^7$.

20. Expand $(1 + x)^n$ for $n = 2, 3, 4,$ and 5.

21. Evaluate $\left(1 + \dfrac{1}{n}\right)^n$ for $n = 2, 3, 4,$ and 5. That is, compute $(1 + \tfrac{1}{2})^2$, $(1 + \tfrac{1}{3})^3$, $(1 + \tfrac{1}{4})^4$, and $(1 + \tfrac{1}{5})^5$. As n gets larger and larger, these numbers approach the number $e \approx 2.71828. \ldots$

Systems of Linear Equations

B-1
Equivalent Systems

In applications of mathematics, it often happens that several conditions must be met simultaneously. This gives rise to a **system of equations.** Examples are given in Exercises 21–32 in Section 3-2. There are many methods for solving systems of equations. The method of **elimination,** described in Section 3-2, is the one used most often. In this method, one of the equations in a system is replaced by its sum with a constant multiple of one of the other equations. Because this transformation is reversible, the new system has the same solutions as the original one; the two systems are **equivalent** (see Exercise 33 in Section 3-2). The object is to eliminate some of the unknowns in some equations, making the new system easier to solve than the original one was.

Example 1
Solve the system

$$(1) \quad 2x - 3y = 4$$

$$(2) \quad 3x + y = 1$$

Solution
To eliminate y from the first equation, simply replace the first equation by its sum with three times the second equation:

$$(1') \quad 11x \quad\ \ = 7 \qquad\qquad [(1) + 3 \cdot (2)]$$

$$(2') \quad 3x + y = 1 \qquad\qquad [\text{Same as (2)}]$$

This system is equivalent to the original one, and it is easy to solve. From Equation (1'), it follows that $x = \frac{7}{11}$; substituting this value for x into Equation (2') yields $y = 1 - 3(\frac{7}{11}) = -\frac{10}{11}$. Thus, the ordered pair $(x, y) = (\frac{7}{11}, -\frac{10}{11})$ is the solution. Check (in the *original* equations):

$$2(\tfrac{7}{11}) - 3(-\tfrac{10}{11}) = 4 \quad \text{and} \quad 3(\tfrac{7}{11}) + (-\tfrac{10}{11}) = 1$$

Example 2
Solve

$$(1) \qquad 3x + 2y - z = 6$$

$$(2) \qquad x - 4y + z = 1$$

$$(3) \qquad -2x + 6y + z = 0$$

Solution
It looks like z is the easiest unknown to eliminate. First, replace Equation (2) by (1) + (2), and then replace Equation (3) by (1) + (3), to obtain the equivalent system

$$(1') \quad 3x + 2y - z = 6 \qquad \text{[Same as (1)]}$$

$$(2') \quad 4x - 2y \quad\quad = 7 \qquad \text{[(1) + (2)]}$$

$$(3') \quad x + 8y \quad\quad = 6 \qquad \text{[(1) + (3)]}$$

Now work with Equations (2') and (3') to eliminate x or y, whichever seems easier. For example, replace Equation (2') with $-4 \cdot (3') + (2')$, to eliminate x. This yields the equivalent system

$$(1'') \quad 3x + 2y - z = 6 \qquad \text{[Same as (1')]}$$

$$(2'') \quad\quad -34y \quad\quad = -17 \qquad [-4 \cdot (3') + (2')]$$

$$(3'') \quad x + 8y \quad\quad = 6 \qquad \text{[Same as (3')]}$$

This system is easily solved. From Equation (2''), it is clear that $y = \frac{1}{2}$; then Equation (3'') yields $x + 8(\frac{1}{2}) = 6$, so $x = 2$; finally, Equation (1'') now reads $3(2) + 2(\frac{1}{2}) - z = 6$, so $z = 1$. The solution is the ordered triple $(x, y, z) = (2, \frac{1}{2}, 1)$. Check this out in the *original* system.

Each system in Examples 1 and 2 had only one solution. It is possible to have a system with no solution. For example, $3x + 2y$ cannot equal both 1 and 2 simultaneously; therefore,

$$3x + 2y = 1$$

$$3x + 2y = 2$$

has no solution. Such a system is called **inconsistent.**

The next example shows that a system may have infinitely many solutions. Such a system is called **dependent.**

Example 3
Solve

$$(1) \quad 2x - y + 4z = 0$$

$$(2) \quad x + y - 6z = 0$$

$$(3) \quad -x + 2y - 10z = 0$$

Solution
It seems that y is a likely candidate for elimination from Equations (2) and (3).

$$(1') \quad 2x - y + 4z = 0 \qquad\qquad \text{[Same as (1)]}$$

$$(2') \quad 3x \qquad - 2z = 0 \qquad\qquad \text{[(1) + (2)]}$$

$$(3') \quad 3x \qquad - 2z = 0 \qquad\qquad \text{[2 · (1) + (3)]}$$

Subtracting Equation (2') from Equation (3') yields the equivalent system

$$(1'') \quad 2x - y + 4z = 0$$

$$(2'') \quad 3x \qquad - 2z = 0$$

$$(3'') \qquad\qquad\quad 0 = 0 \qquad\qquad \text{[−1 · (2') + (3')]}$$

This system can be solved. Equation (2'') shows that $x = \frac{2}{3}z$; substituting this value for x into Equation (1'') yields

$$2(\tfrac{2}{3}z) - y + 4z = 0$$

so $y = \frac{16}{3}z$. Here, z *can have any value whatsoever,* and any ordered triple $(\frac{2}{3}z, \frac{16}{3}z, z)$ will be a solution. For example, if $z = 3$, then $x = \frac{2}{3} \cdot 3 = 2$,

$y = \frac{16}{3} \cdot 3 = 16$, and $z = 3$. Thus, $(2, 16, 3)$ is a solution. Check this out in the original system. Now let $z = -6$. Calculate the values of x and y and check this solution in the original system.

■   **The method of elimination**

Eliminate unknowns by replacing any equation in the system by its sum with a constant multiple of any other equation in the system. This forms an *equivalent* system. Continue this procedure until you find an equivalent system that can be solved easily.

B-2
Echelon Form

In solving systems of equations by the method of elimination, it is often difficult to decide which unknown to eliminate. In this section, we shall develop a procedure that reduces the guesswork to a minimum. This procedure also has the advantage that it can be programmed for a computer.

■   **Definition**

The first nonzero coefficient in any equation is called the **leading coefficient** of that equation. A system of equations is said to be in **echelon form** if the leading coefficient in each equation is 1 and the corresponding unknown does not appear in any succeeding equation.

For example,

$$x_1 + 2x_2 - 3x_3 + 2x_4 = 7$$

$$x_2 \qquad\qquad -x_4 = -2$$

$$x_3 + 2x_4 = 6$$

$$x_4 = 9$$

is in echelon form: the leading coefficient is 1 in each equation and the corresponding unknowns are absent in the succeeding equations. *Notice that a system in this form is easy to solve:* the last equation gives $x_4 = 9$; from the third equation, we see that $x_3 + 2(9) = 6$, so $x_3 = -12$; and so on. The system

$$x_1 - 3x_2 + x_3 \quad\quad = 1$$

$$2x_2 \quad\quad + 4x_4 = -2$$

$$x_1 \quad\quad + x_3 \quad -x_4 = 0$$

$$x_4 = 2$$

is *not* in echelon form. It fails on two counts: the leading coefficient of the second equation is not 1, but 2; and the unknown x_1, which corresponds to the leading coefficient in the first equation, also appears in the third equation.

A system in echelon form is easy to solve, but it is even easier to solve if it is in *reduced* echelon form.

■ **Definition**
A system is said to be in **reduced echelon form** if it is in echelon form and the unknowns corresponding to the leading coefficients are absent in *all* other equations of the system.

For example,

$$x_1 \quad\quad = 0 \quad\quad\quad\quad x_1 \quad + 3x_4 = 8$$

$$x_2 \quad = 1 \quad\text{and}\quad x_2 \quad - x_4 = 0$$

$$x_3 \quad = -3 \quad\quad\quad\quad x_3 + 2x_4 = 2$$

$$x_4 = 2 \quad\quad\quad\quad\quad x_5 = 3$$

are two systems in reduced echelon form. In the first system, each unknown appears in only one equation, and the solution $(0, 1, -3, 2)$ is obvious. In the second system, each unknown x_1, x_2, x_3, and x_5, corresponding to a leading coefficient appears in only one equation. Notice that x_4 does not correspond to any leading coefficient and, therefore, may appear in several equations. Again, the solution is easy to read off: $x_5 = 3$, $x_3 = 2 - 2x_4$, $x_2 = x_4$, $x_1 = 8 - 3x_4$, and x_4 can be *any number we choose*. Thus, the system is dependent.

■   If a given system is equivalent to a system in reduced echelon form, then the solution to the original system is easily obtained from the reduced system.

Is every system equivalent to a system in reduced echelon form? The answer is *yes*. The reduced system may be found by employing the following operations:

Interchange any two equations.

Multiply any equation by a nonzero constant.

Replace any one of the equations by its sum with a constant multiple of any other equation.

These three operations are called **elementary operations.** They obviously yield new equations with the same solutions as the original ones, so that

■ If one system is obtained by applying any combination of elementary operations to a given system, the two systems are equivalent.

Any system can be transformed to reduced echelon form by using only the elementary operations, as shown in the following examples.

Example 1
Reduce and solve

$$(1) \qquad 3x + 2y - z = 6$$

$$(2) \qquad x - 4y + z = 1$$

$$(3) \qquad -2x + 6y + z = 0$$

Solution
Work with the first unknown, x. To make the first equation have a leading coefficient 1, you could multiply through by $\frac{1}{3}$ to get the equation $x + \frac{2}{3}y - \frac{1}{3}z = 2$. However, it is convenient to avoid fractions by, instead, interchanging Equations (1) and (2):

$$(1') \qquad x - 4y + z = 1$$

$$(2') \qquad 3x + 2y - z = 6$$

$$(3') \qquad -2x + 6y + z = 0$$

Next, eliminate x's from all other equations:

$$(1'') \quad x - \quad 4y + \quad z = 1 \qquad\qquad \text{[Same as } (1')]$$

$$(2'') \qquad\qquad 14y - 4z = 3 \qquad\qquad [-3 \cdot (1') + (2')]$$

$$(3'') \qquad\qquad -2y + 3z = 2 \qquad\qquad [2 \cdot (1') + (3')]$$

Now start to work on the second unknown, y. Multiply (2″) by $\frac{1}{14}$ to obtain Equation (2‴) $= y - \frac{2}{7}z = \frac{3}{14}$, which has a leading coefficient of 1 (we cannot avoid these fractions). Next eliminate y from the other two equations, to obtain

$$(1‴)\ x\ -\tfrac{1}{7}z = \tfrac{13}{7} \qquad\qquad [4\cdot(2‴)+(1″)]$$

$$(2‴)\ \ y -\tfrac{2}{7}z = \tfrac{3}{14} \qquad\qquad [\tfrac{1}{14}\cdot(2″)]$$

$$(3‴)\ \ \ \ \tfrac{17}{7}z = \tfrac{17}{7} \qquad\qquad [2\cdot(2‴)+(3″)]$$

The final step is to multiply (3‴) by $\frac{7}{17}$, to obtain $z = 1$. Then eliminate z in the other equations. The final result is

$$x\ \ = 2$$

$$y\ = \tfrac{1}{2}$$

$$z = 1$$

and the solution is $(x, y, z) = (2, \tfrac{1}{2}, 1)$. Check this solution in the original system.

Example 2
Reduce and solve

$$x_3 + \ \ x_4 = 2$$

$$x_1 \qquad\qquad -x_3 \qquad = 7$$

$$2x_1 + \ \ x_2 \qquad\qquad -x_4 = 3$$

$$-2x_2 + \ \ x_3 + \ \ x_4 = -4$$

Solution
Begin by interchanging the first and second equations and then proceed as indicated below. Cover the solution at each stage, and try to guess the next step; then check. There are many possible paths to the answer.

$$x_1 \qquad - x_3 \qquad = 7 \qquad\qquad\qquad x_1 \qquad\qquad -x_3 \qquad = 7$$

$$x_3 + x_4 = 2 \qquad\qquad\qquad\qquad x_3 + x_4 = 2$$

$$\qquad\qquad\qquad\qquad\qquad \longrightarrow \qquad\qquad\qquad\qquad\qquad\qquad\qquad \longrightarrow$$

$$2x_1 + x_2 \qquad - x_4 = 3 \qquad\qquad\qquad x_2 + 2x_3 - x_4 = -11$$

$$- 2x_2 + x_3 + x_4 = -4 \qquad\qquad\qquad -2x_2 + x_3 + x_4 = -4$$

$$x_1 \qquad -x_3 \qquad = 7$$
$$x_2 + 2x_3 - x_4 = -11$$
$$x_3 + x_4 = 2$$
$$-2x_2 + x_3 + x_4 = -4$$

$\longrightarrow$

$$x_1 \qquad -x_3 \qquad = 7$$
$$x_2 + 2x_3 - x_4 = -11$$
$$x_3 + x_4 = 2$$
$$5x_3 - x_4 = -26$$

$\longrightarrow$

$$x_1 \qquad +x_4 = 9$$
$$x_2 \qquad -3x_4 = -15$$
$$x_3 + x_4 = 2$$
$$-6x_4 = -36$$

$\longrightarrow$

$$x_1 \qquad = 3$$
$$x_2 \qquad = 3$$
$$x_3 \qquad = -4$$
$$x_4 = 6$$

The solution is the quadruple $(3, 3, -4, 6)$. Check.

If, at any stage in reducing a system, one equation takes the form $0 = c$, where c is a nonzero constant, then the original system is inconsistent (no solution).

Example 3
Reduce and solve

$$x - 2y + 4z = 2$$
$$y \quad - z = -1$$
$$3x - 5y + 11z = 4$$

Solution
Eliminate x from the third equation; then proceed as usual to eliminate y from the first and third equations:

$$x - 2y + 4z = 2$$
$$y - z = -1$$
$$y - z = -2$$

$\longrightarrow$

$$x \quad + 2z = 0$$
$$y - z = -1$$
$$0 = -1$$

You need reduce no further. The last equation indicates that the original system is inconsistent. (In the system on the left, $y - z$ equals both -1 and -2; impossible.)

Suppose a system is in reduced echelon form and that some of the unknowns do not correspond to leading coefficients. When this happens the system can have infinitely many solutions; it is dependent.

Example 4
Reduce and solve

$$2x - 6y + 8z = 0$$

$$4x - 10y + 6z = 0$$

$$y - 5z = 0$$

Solution
Multiply the first equation by $\frac{1}{2}$, then eliminate x from the second equation; then work on y:

$$x - 3y + 4z = 0 \qquad\qquad x - 11z = 0$$

$$2y - 10z = 0 \qquad\longrightarrow\qquad y - 5z = 0$$

$$y - 5z = 0 \qquad\qquad 0 = 0$$

This is in reduced form, and z is not a leading unknown. Both the leading unknowns, x and y, can be written in terms of z; that is, $x = 11z$ and $y = 5z$. Therefore, every solution must be of the form $(11z, 5z, z)$, and z can have any value. For instance, if $z = 2$, then $(22, 10, 2)$ is a solution (check); if $z = -1$, then $(-11, -5, -1)$ is a solution (check).

Exercises

Bring each of the following systems into reduced echelon form. Solve each system, or indicate that it has no solutions (if it is inconsistent). Check your answer in the original system of equations.

1. $x - 2y = 1$
   $3x + 7y = 2$

2. $4x + y = 0$
   $-2x + 3y = 2$

3. $x - 3y + z = 0$
   $-x + y + z = 2$
   $2x + 2y - 3z = -5$

4. $2x - 3y + z = -4$
   $x + y - 2z = 3$
   $3x - 2y = -2$

5. $2x + 2y - z = 1$
   $x - y + z = 2$
   $5x + 3y - z = 5$

6. $x - y + z = 0$
   $3x + y - 2z = -2$
   $2x + 2y - 3z = 2$

7. $\begin{aligned} x - y + z &= 1 \\ y - 2z &= 3 \\ 2x - y &= 5 \end{aligned}$

8. $\begin{aligned} 2x + y - 3z &= -3 \\ x + y + z &= 4 \\ x + 2y + 6z &= 15 \end{aligned}$

9. $\begin{aligned} x_1 + 2x_2 - 3x_3 + x_4 &= 1 \\ -x_2 + x_3 &= 0 \\ 2x_1 - 5x_3 + x_4 &= 3 \\ 2x_3 - 5x_4 &= 8 \end{aligned}$

10. $\begin{aligned} 3x_1 - 2x_2 + x_4 - x_5 &= 3 \\ x_1 - x_2 + x_3 + x_5 &= 1 \\ x_3 + x_4 - 2x_5 &= 0 \\ 2x_4 + 4x_5 &= 6 \end{aligned}$

11. $\dfrac{1}{x} - \dfrac{1}{y} = 7$

 $\dfrac{2}{x} + \dfrac{3}{y} = 8$

[HINT: Let $u = 1/x$ and $v = 1/y$]

12. $\begin{aligned} x^2 - 2y^3 + z^2 &= 0 \\ y^3 - 3z^2 &= 4 \\ 2x^2 + z^2 &= 8 \end{aligned}$

[HINT: Let $u = x^2, v = y^3, w = z^2$]

13. $\begin{aligned} \sin x - \cos y + \tan z &= 1 \\ 2 \sin x + \cos y - 2 \tan z &= 1 \\ -\sin x + 2 \cos y - \tan z &= 0 \end{aligned}$

B-3
Matrices

The procedure that transforms a system of equations to reduced echelon form can also be applied to rectangular arrays of numbers. For example, consider the array

$$\begin{bmatrix} 2 & 3 & -1 & -1 \\ 1 & -2 & -2 & -1 \\ 1 & -1 & -1 & 0 \end{bmatrix}$$

Any such arrangement of numbers is called a **matrix.** This matrix can be put into reduced form by applying the three elementary operations to its rows:

Interchange rows one and two.   Add -2 times row one to row two; add -1 times row one to row three.

$$\begin{bmatrix} 1 & -2 & -2 & -1 \\ 2 & 3 & -1 & -1 \\ 1 & -1 & -1 & 0 \end{bmatrix} \longrightarrow \begin{bmatrix} 1 & -2 & -2 & -1 \\ 0 & 7 & 3 & 1 \\ 0 & 1 & 1 & 1 \end{bmatrix} \longrightarrow$$

Interchange rows two and three.

$$\begin{bmatrix} 1 & -2 & -2 & -1 \\ 0 & 1 & 1 & 1 \\ 0 & 7 & 3 & 1 \end{bmatrix} \longrightarrow$$

Add 2 times row two to row one;
add -7 times row two to row three.

$$\begin{bmatrix} 1 & 0 & 0 & 1 \\ 0 & 1 & 1 & 1 \\ 0 & 0 & -4 & -6 \end{bmatrix} \longrightarrow$$

Multiply third row by $-\frac{1}{4}$.

$$\begin{bmatrix} 1 & 0 & 0 & 1 \\ 0 & 1 & 1 & 1 \\ 0 & 0 & 1 & \frac{3}{2} \end{bmatrix} \longrightarrow$$

Add -1 times row three to row two.

$$\begin{bmatrix} 1 & 0 & 0 & 1 \\ 0 & 1 & 0 & -\frac{1}{2} \\ 0 & 0 & 1 & \frac{3}{2} \end{bmatrix}$$

In the final matrix, the first nonzero entry in each row is a 1 and all other entries in the corresponding columns are zero. We shall say that such a matrix is in **reduced echelon form.**

You may have already realized the significance of what we have done: matrices can be used to solve systems of equations. In solving a system, it is the relationship between the coefficients that is important. The particular letters used to indicate the unknowns are of no consequence; why keep writing them down? For example, the row of numbers

$$2 \quad 3 \quad -1 \quad -1$$

can represent the equation

$$2x + 3y - z = -1$$

The row of numbers 1 -2 -2 -1 can be thought of as the equation $x - 2y - 2z = -1$, and 1 -1 -1 0 could represent $x - y - z = 0$. Thus, a matrix can be used to represent a system of linear equations. When that matrix is put in reduced form, it is the same thing as putting the system in reduced form. Then the solution is easily found.

Example 1
Solve

$$2x + 3y \quad -z = -1$$

$$x - 2y - 2z = -1$$

$$x \quad - y \quad - z = 0$$

Solution

Write all the coefficients and constants as a matrix, with each row representing the corresponding equation.

$$\begin{array}{cccc} x & y & z & \text{const.} \end{array}$$
$$\left[\begin{array}{ccc|c} 2 & 3 & -1 & -1 \\ 1 & -2 & -2 & -1 \\ 1 & -1 & -1 & 0 \end{array}\right]$$

Here, each column is labeled and a vertical line separates the "unknown" columns from the "constant" column. Both the line and the labels serve merely as reminders; neither is at all necessary.

■   **Definition**

The matrix consisting of the "unknown" columns is called the **coefficient matrix** of the system. The entire matrix is called the **augmented matrix** of the system.

The augmented matrix above is the matrix that was put into reduced echelon form at the beginning of this section. Thus, after six applications of the elementary operations, we have

$$\begin{array}{cccc} x & y & z & \text{const.} \end{array} \qquad \begin{array}{cccc} x & y & z & \text{const.} \end{array}$$
$$\left[\begin{array}{ccc|c} 2 & 3 & -1 & -1 \\ 1 & -2 & -2 & -1 \\ 1 & -1 & -1 & 0 \end{array}\right] \longrightarrow \left[\begin{array}{ccc|c} 1 & 0 & 0 & 1 \\ 0 & 1 & 0 & -\frac{1}{2} \\ 0 & 0 & 1 & \frac{3}{2} \end{array}\right]$$

The first row of the reduced form represents the equation $x + 0 \cdot y + 0 \cdot z = 1$, or $x = 1$. The second and third rows represent $y = -\frac{1}{2}$ and $z = \frac{3}{2}$. Thus, $(1, -\frac{1}{2}, \frac{3}{2})$ is the solution to the system. A quick check in the original system shows that this is correct.

When an unknown is missing from one of the equations, the corresponding entry in the coefficient matrix is 0.

Example 2
Solve

$$x - y + 3z = 1$$

$$x \qquad -2z = 0$$

$$-y + z = 4$$

Solution

Write the augmented matrix and reduce as follows:

$$-1 \text{ times row one plus row two.}$$

$$\begin{bmatrix} 1 & -1 & 3 & | & 1 \\ 1 & 0 & -2 & | & 0 \\ 0 & -1 & 1 & | & 4 \end{bmatrix} \longrightarrow \begin{bmatrix} 1 & -1 & 3 & | & 1 \\ 0 & 1 & -5 & | & -1 \\ 0 & -1 & 1 & | & 4 \end{bmatrix} \longrightarrow$$

Add row two to row one;
add row two to row three. Multiply row three by $-\frac{1}{4}$.

$$\begin{bmatrix} 1 & 0 & -2 & | & 0 \\ 0 & 1 & -5 & | & -1 \\ 0 & 0 & -4 & | & 3 \end{bmatrix} \longrightarrow \begin{bmatrix} 1 & 0 & -2 & | & 0 \\ 0 & 1 & -5 & | & -1 \\ 0 & 0 & 1 & | & -\frac{3}{4} \end{bmatrix} \longrightarrow$$

Add 5 times row three to row two; add 2 times row three to row one. The final matrix in reduced form is

$$\begin{array}{ccc} x & y & z & \text{const.} \end{array}$$

$$\begin{bmatrix} 1 & 0 & 0 & | & -\frac{3}{2} \\ 0 & 1 & 0 & | & -\frac{19}{4} \\ 0 & 0 & 1 & | & -\frac{3}{4} \end{bmatrix}$$

Now read off the solution, $(x, y, z) = (-\frac{3}{2}, -\frac{19}{4}, -\frac{3}{4})$. Check this solution in the original system.

If, at any stage in the reduction, a row takes the form

$$0 \quad 0 \ldots 0 | c$$

with $c \neq 0$, then the original system is inconsistent (no solutions).

Example 3

Solve

$$3x_1 + 4x_2 \qquad - x_4 = 2$$

$$x_1 + x_2 - 2x_3 \qquad = 0$$

$$x_2 + 6x_3 - x_4 = 7$$

Solution

Write the augmented matrix and reduce. You should supply the reasons at each step.

$$\begin{array}{ccccc} x_1 & x_2 & x_3 & x_4 & \text{const.} \end{array}$$

$$\left[\begin{array}{cccc|c} 3 & 4 & 0 & -1 & 2 \\ 1 & 1 & -2 & 0 & 0 \\ 0 & 1 & 6 & -1 & 7 \end{array}\right] \longrightarrow \left[\begin{array}{cccc|c} 1 & 1 & -2 & 0 & 0 \\ 3 & 4 & 0 & -1 & 2 \\ 0 & 1 & 6 & -1 & 7 \end{array}\right] \longrightarrow$$

$$\left[\begin{array}{cccc|c} 1 & 1 & -2 & 0 & 0 \\ 0 & 1 & 6 & -1 & 2 \\ 0 & 1 & 6 & -1 & 7 \end{array}\right] \longrightarrow \left[\begin{array}{cccc|c} 1 & 0 & -8 & 1 & -2 \\ 0 & 1 & 6 & -1 & 2 \\ 0 & 0 & 0 & 0 & 5 \end{array}\right]$$

Stop! The last row indicates that there is no solution. Why? Because it represents the equation $0 \cdot x_1 + 0 \cdot x_2 + 0 \cdot x_3 + 0 \cdot x_4 = 5$.

The next example shows how to use matrices to solve a dependent system of equations.

Example 4
Solve

$$3x_1 + 4x_2 \qquad - x_4 = 2$$

$$x_1 + x_2 - 2x_3 \qquad = 0$$

$$x_2 + 6x_3 - x_4 = 2$$

Solution

Write the augmented matrix and reduce as in Example 3. This time, the last row will be all 0's:

$$\begin{array}{ccccc} x_1 & x_2 & x_3 & x_4 & \text{const.} \end{array} \qquad \begin{array}{ccccc} x_1 & x_2 & x_3 & x_4 & \text{const.} \end{array}$$

$$\left[\begin{array}{cccc|c} 3 & 4 & 0 & -1 & 2 \\ 1 & 1 & -2 & 0 & 0 \\ 0 & 1 & 6 & -1 & 2 \end{array}\right] \xrightarrow[\text{(Example 3)}]{} \left[\begin{array}{cccc|c} 1 & 0 & -8 & 1 & -2 \\ 0 & 1 & 6 & -1 & 2 \\ 0 & 0 & 0 & 0 & 0 \end{array}\right]$$

The two nonzero rows represent the equations

$$x_1 \qquad - 8x_3 + x_4 = -2$$

$$x_2 + 6x_3 - x_4 = 2$$

Solving these for x_1 and x_2 gives

$$x_1 = -2 + 8x_3 - x_4 \quad \text{and} \quad x_2 = 2 - 6x_3 + x_4$$

Thus, for any values of x_3 and x_4, the quadruple

$$(-2 + 8x_3 - x_4, 2 - 6x_3 + x_4, x_3, x_4)$$

is a solution of the original system of equations. For instance, if $x_3 = 0$ and $x_4 = 1$, then $(-3, 3, 0, 1)$ is a solution (check). For $x_3 = -1$ and $x_4 = 2$, the quadruple $(-12, 10, -1, 2)$ is a solution (check).

Exercises

Use matrix notation to solve each of the following systems of equations (if there is a solution). Check your answer in the original system of equations.

1. $\quad x + 2y = 4$
   $\quad -2x + 7y = -8$

2. $\quad 5x - 10y = 1$
   $\quad x + 2y = 3$

3. $\quad x - 3y + z = 5$
   $\quad -x + 4y - 3z = 1$
   $\quad 2x - 6y + 3z = 0$

4. $\quad 3x - y = 4$
   $\quad x - \frac{2}{3}y + z = 0$
   $\quad 2y - 3z = -2$

5. $\quad x + \frac{1}{2}y - 2z = 1$
   $\quad -2x + z = 4$
   $\quad x - \frac{1}{2}y + z = 5$

6. $\quad 4x + 3y - 2z = 0$
   $\quad y + 4z = 0$
   $\quad x + \frac{7}{4}y + \frac{1}{2}z = 0$

7. $\quad x - 3y + z = 1$
   $\quad y - 2z = -3$
   $\quad 2x - 7y + 4z = 5$

8. $\quad x + y + z = 9$
   $\quad -x + 2y - 4z = -2$
   $\quad -x + 8y - 10z = 11$

9. $\quad x_1 + 3x_2 - x_4 = 1$
   $\quad x_2 + 2x_3 + 3x_4 = 0$
   $\quad 2x_1 - x_2 - x_3 + 2x_4 = 8$
   $\quad 3x_1 + 4x_4 = -2$

10. $\quad 3x_1 - 2x_2 + x_3 - x_5 = 0$
    $\quad x_1 - x_2 + x_4 = 5$
    $\quad x_3 - 2x_4 + 2x_5 = -2$
    $\quad 2x_2 + x_4 - 3x_5 = 1$

11. $\quad \dfrac{1}{x} - \dfrac{3}{y} = 2$

    $\quad \dfrac{5}{x} + \dfrac{2}{y} = 4$ [HINT: Let $u = 1/x$ and $v = 1/y$]

12. $\quad 3x^3 - 2y^2 + 4 \sin z = 1$
    $\quad x^3 + y^2 + \sin z = 0$
    $\quad 2x^3 + \sin z = -1$

B-4
Determinants. Cramer's Rule

When the number of unknowns equals the number of equations, and the system has a unique solution, it can be found by using Cramer's Rule. The statement of this rule requires the definition of several new terms.

A **square matrix** is any matrix with the same number of rows and columns. Thus,

$$A = \begin{bmatrix} 3 & -4 \\ 1 & 0 \end{bmatrix} \quad \text{and} \quad B = \begin{bmatrix} 1 & 2 & 3 \\ 0 & -1 & 2 \\ 4 & 6 & 1 \end{bmatrix}$$

are square matrices; A is a 2×2 (two by two) matrix, and B is a 3×3 (three by three) matrix. There are also 4×4, 5×5, and, in general, $n \times n$ matrices.

Given any square matrix M, a **minor** M_{ij} is defined as the matrix obtained from M by deleting the ith row and jth column. Given the 3×3 matrix B above, for example,

$$B_{11} = \begin{bmatrix} 1 & 2 & 3 \\ 0 & -1 & 2 \\ 4 & 6 & 1 \end{bmatrix} = \begin{bmatrix} -1 & 2 \\ 6 & 1 \end{bmatrix}$$

is obtained by deleting row one and column one from B. Similarly,

$$B_{21} = \begin{bmatrix} 1 & 2 & 3 \\ 0 & -1 & 2 \\ 4 & 6 & 1 \end{bmatrix} = \begin{bmatrix} 2 & 3 \\ 6 & 1 \end{bmatrix} \qquad \text{(Delete row two and column one.)}$$

$$B_{32} = \begin{bmatrix} 1 & 2 & 3 \\ 0 & -1 & 2 \\ 4 & 6 & 1 \end{bmatrix} = \begin{bmatrix} 1 & 3 \\ 0 & 2 \end{bmatrix} \qquad \text{(Delete row three and column two.)}$$

Notice that, if M is an $n \times n$ matrix, then M_{ij} is an $(n-1) \times (n-1)$ matrix.

To each square matrix M, we can assign a real number called its **determinant,** denoted either by det M or by $|M|$. For example, if M is the 2×2 matrix $\begin{bmatrix} a & b \\ c & d \end{bmatrix}$, its determinant may be written as

$$\det \begin{bmatrix} a & b \\ c & d \end{bmatrix} \quad \text{or} \quad \begin{vmatrix} a & b \\ c & d \end{vmatrix}$$

The determinant of a 2 × 2 matrix is defined as

$$\begin{vmatrix} a & b \\ c & d \end{vmatrix} = ad - bc$$

Example 1

(a) $\begin{vmatrix} 1 & 2 \\ 3 & 4 \end{vmatrix} = 1 \cdot 4 - 2 \cdot 3 = -2$

(b) $\det \begin{bmatrix} -2 & 0 \\ 4 & -1 \end{bmatrix} = (-2)(-1) - 0 \cdot 4 = 2$

(c) $\begin{vmatrix} 0 & 3 \\ 1 & 6 \end{vmatrix} = 0 \cdot 6 - 3 \cdot 1 = -3$

The determinant of a 3 × 3 matrix is defined in terms of its minors, as follows: Let

$$M = \begin{bmatrix} a_1 & b_1 & c_1 \\ a_2 & b_2 & c_2 \\ a_3 & b_3 & c_3 \end{bmatrix}$$

Then

$$|M| = a_1 |M_{11}| - a_2 |M_{21}| + a_3 |M_{31}|$$

$$= a_1 \begin{vmatrix} b_2 & c_2 \\ b_3 & c_3 \end{vmatrix} - a_2 \begin{vmatrix} b_1 & c_1 \\ b_3 & c_3 \end{vmatrix} + a_3 \begin{vmatrix} b_1 & c_1 \\ b_2 & c_2 \end{vmatrix}$$

Example 2

(a) $\begin{vmatrix} 6 & 0 & 3 \\ -2 & 4 & 1 \\ -1 & 2 & 3 \end{vmatrix} = 6 \begin{vmatrix} 4 & 1 \\ 2 & 3 \end{vmatrix} - (-2) \begin{vmatrix} 0 & 3 \\ 2 & 3 \end{vmatrix} + (-1) \begin{vmatrix} 0 & 3 \\ 4 & 1 \end{vmatrix}$

$\qquad\qquad = 6(4 \cdot 3 - 1 \cdot 2) + 2(0 \cdot 3 - 3 \cdot 2) - (0 \cdot 1 - 3 \cdot 4)$

$\qquad\qquad = 60 - 12 + 12 = 60$

(b) $\begin{vmatrix} 0 & 1 & 4 \\ -2 & 4 & 1 \\ -1 & 2 & 3 \end{vmatrix} = 0 \begin{vmatrix} 4 & 1 \\ 2 & 3 \end{vmatrix} - (-2) \begin{vmatrix} 1 & 4 \\ 2 & 3 \end{vmatrix} + (-1) \begin{vmatrix} 1 & 4 \\ 4 & 1 \end{vmatrix}$

$\qquad\qquad = 0 \cdot 10 + 2 \cdot (-5) - 1 \cdot (-15) = 5$

Determinants of larger matrices are defined in a similar way. The determinant of an $n \times n$ matrix is defined as the sum of the products of the entries in the first column with the determinants of the corresponding $(n - 1) \times (n - 1)$ minors, the terms of this sum alternating in sign. For example, if

$$M = \begin{bmatrix} a_1 & b_1 & c_1 & d \\ a_2 & b_2 & c_2 & d_2 \\ a_3 & b_3 & c_3 & d_3 \\ a_4 & b_4 & c_4 & d_4 \end{bmatrix}$$

then

$$|M| = a_1 |M_{11}| - a_2 |M_{21}| + a_3 |M_{31}| - a_4 |M_{41}|$$

Example 3
Find the determinant of

$$M = \begin{bmatrix} -1 & 0 & 1 & 4 \\ 9 & 6 & 0 & 3 \\ 0 & -2 & 4 & 1 \\ 0 & -1 & 2 & 3 \end{bmatrix}$$

Solution

$$\det M = (-1) \begin{vmatrix} 6 & 0 & 3 \\ -2 & 4 & 1 \\ -1 & 2 & 3 \end{vmatrix} - 9 \begin{vmatrix} 0 & 1 & 4 \\ -2 & 4 & 1 \\ -1 & 2 & 3 \end{vmatrix} + 0 \begin{vmatrix} 0 & 1 & 4 \\ 6 & 0 & 3 \\ -1 & 2 & 3 \end{vmatrix} - 0 \begin{vmatrix} 0 & 1 & 4 \\ 6 & 0 & 3 \\ -2 & 4 & 1 \end{vmatrix}$$

The first two 3×3 determinants are those in Example 2; the last two are multiplied by 0 and need not be calculated. Thus, $\det M = (-1)(60) - 9(5) + 0 + 0 = -105$.

■   **Cramer's Rule**
Suppose there is a system of n equations with n unknowns $x_1, x_2, \ldots, x_n$. Let M be the $n \times n$ coefficient matrix and let M_j be the matrix M with the jth column replaced by the constants of the n equations (the numbers to the right of the equal signs). If $|M| \neq 0$, then there is a unique simultaneous solution, and

$$x_j = \frac{|M_j|}{|M|} \text{ for each } j = 1, 2, \ldots, n$$

Example 4
Use Cramer's Rule to solve the system

$$6x \qquad + 3z = 1$$

$$-2x + 4y + z = 0$$

$$-x + 2y + 3z = -1$$

Solution
The coefficient matrix is

$$M = \begin{bmatrix} 6 & 0 & 3 \\ -2 & 4 & 1 \\ -1 & 2 & 3 \end{bmatrix}$$

Let x be the first unknown, y the second, and z the third. According to Cramer's Rule, if $|M| \neq 0$, then there is a unique solution

$$x = \frac{|M_1|}{|M|} \qquad y = \frac{|M_2|}{|M|} \qquad z = \frac{|M_3|}{|M|}$$

where M_j is the matrix M with column j replaced by the column of constants

$$\begin{matrix} 1 \\ 0 \\ -1 \end{matrix}$$

Thus,

$$M_1 = \begin{bmatrix} 1 & 0 & 3 \\ 0 & 4 & 1 \\ -1 & 2 & 3 \end{bmatrix} \qquad M_2 = \begin{bmatrix} 6 & 1 & 3 \\ -2 & 0 & 1 \\ -1 & -1 & 3 \end{bmatrix} \qquad M_3 = \begin{bmatrix} 6 & 0 & 1 \\ -2 & 4 & 0 \\ -1 & 2 & -1 \end{bmatrix}$$

In Example 2(a), you found that $|M| = 60$. The determinant of M_1 is

$$|M_1| = 1 \begin{vmatrix} 4 & 1 \\ 2 & 3 \end{vmatrix} - 0 \begin{vmatrix} 0 & 3 \\ 2 & 3 \end{vmatrix} + (-1) \begin{vmatrix} 0 & 3 \\ 4 & 1 \end{vmatrix} = 22$$

Similarly, $|M_2| = 17$, and $|M_3| = -24$. The solution, therefore, is

$$x = \tfrac{22}{60} \qquad y = \tfrac{17}{60} \qquad z = \tfrac{-24}{60}$$

Check

$$6(\tfrac{22}{60}) \qquad\quad + 3(\tfrac{-24}{60}) = \tfrac{132}{60} - \tfrac{72}{60} = 1$$

$$-2(\tfrac{22}{60}) + 4(\tfrac{17}{60}) + \ (\tfrac{-24}{60}) = -\tfrac{44}{60} + \tfrac{68}{60} - \tfrac{24}{60} = 0$$

$$-(\tfrac{22}{60}) + 2(\tfrac{17}{60}) + 3(\tfrac{-24}{60}) = -\tfrac{22}{60} + \tfrac{34}{60} - \tfrac{72}{60} = -1$$

Example 5

Use determinants to solve

$$-x_1 \qquad\quad + x_3 + 4x_4 = 2$$

$$9x_1 + 6x_2 \qquad\quad + 3x_4 = 1$$

$$-2x_2 + 4x_3 \ + x_4 = 0$$

$$-x_2 + 2x_3 + 3x_4 = 0$$

Solution

The coefficient matrix is

$$M = \begin{bmatrix} -1 & 0 & 1 & 4 \\ 9 & 6 & 0 & 3 \\ 0 & -2 & 4 & 1 \\ 0 & -1 & 2 & 3 \end{bmatrix}$$

whose determinant was found to be -105 in Example 3. The matrices M_j are

$$M_1 = \begin{bmatrix} 2 & 0 & 1 & 4 \\ 1 & 6 & 0 & 3 \\ 0 & -2 & 4 & 1 \\ 0 & -1 & 2 & 3 \end{bmatrix} \qquad M_2 = \begin{bmatrix} -1 & 2 & 1 & 4 \\ 9 & 1 & 0 & 3 \\ 0 & 0 & 4 & 1 \\ 0 & 0 & 2 & 3 \end{bmatrix}$$

$$M_3 = \begin{bmatrix} -1 & 0 & 2 & 4 \\ 9 & 6 & 1 & 3 \\ 0 & -2 & 0 & 1 \\ 0 & -1 & 0 & 3 \end{bmatrix} \qquad M_4 = \begin{bmatrix} -1 & 0 & 1 & 2 \\ 9 & 6 & 0 & 1 \\ 0 & -2 & 4 & 0 \\ 0 & -1 & 2 & 0 \end{bmatrix}$$

Now find the determinants:

$$|M_1| = 2 \begin{vmatrix} 6 & 0 & 3 \\ -2 & 4 & 1 \\ -1 & 2 & 3 \end{vmatrix} - 1 \begin{vmatrix} 0 & 1 & 4 \\ -2 & 4 & 1 \\ -1 & 2 & 3 \end{vmatrix} + 0 \begin{vmatrix} 0 & 1 & 4 \\ 6 & 0 & 3 \\ -1 & 2 & 3 \end{vmatrix} - 0 \begin{vmatrix} 0 & 1 & 4 \\ 6 & 0 & 3 \\ -2 & 4 & 1 \end{vmatrix}$$

$$= 2(60) - 1(5) + 0 + 0 = 115$$

Similarly, $|M_2| = -190$, $|M_3| = -95$, and $|M_4| = 0$. Therefore, the solution is

$$x_1 = \frac{|M_1|}{|M|} = -\tfrac{115}{105} \qquad x_2 = \frac{|M_2|}{|M|} = \tfrac{190}{105}$$

$$x_3 = \frac{|M_3|}{|M|} = \tfrac{95}{105} \qquad x_4 = \frac{|M_4|}{|M|} = 0$$

Check these values in the original equations.

To solve a system of n equations with n unknowns, first find the determinant of the coefficient matrix M. If $|M| \neq 0$, then Cramer's Rule applies and there will be a unique solution. If $|M| = 0$, then the methods described in earlier sections must be used to solve the system. There may be no solution (inconsistent system) or infinitely many solutions (dependent system).

Example 6
Solve the system

$$3x + 2y = 4$$

$$6x + 4y = 9$$

Solution
The coefficient matrix is

$$M = \begin{bmatrix} 3 & 2 \\ 6 & 4 \end{bmatrix}$$

so $|M| = 0$. Cramer's Rule does not apply, so you must use another method. Reduce the augmented matrix:

$$\begin{bmatrix} 3 & 2 & | & 4 \\ 6 & 4 & | & 9 \end{bmatrix} \longrightarrow \begin{bmatrix} 3 & 2 & | & 4 \\ 0 & 0 & | & 1 \end{bmatrix}$$

The last line shows that the system has no solution.

Example 7
Solve the system

$$x - 2y + z = -1$$

$$y - 3z = 4$$

$$x - y - 2z = 3$$

Solution
Let M be the coefficient matrix. Then

$$|M| = \begin{vmatrix} 1 & -2 & 1 \\ 0 & 1 & -3 \\ 1 & -1 & -2 \end{vmatrix} = 1 \begin{vmatrix} 1 & -3 \\ -1 & -2 \end{vmatrix} - 0 \begin{vmatrix} -2 & 1 \\ -1 & -2 \end{vmatrix} + 1 \begin{vmatrix} -2 & 1 \\ 1 & -3 \end{vmatrix}$$

$$= -5 - 0 + 5 = 0$$

Cramer's Rule does not apply, so reduce the augmented matrix:

$$\begin{bmatrix} 1 & -2 & 1 & | & -1 \\ 0 & 1 & -3 & | & 4 \\ 1 & -1 & -2 & | & 3 \end{bmatrix} \longrightarrow \begin{bmatrix} 1 & -2 & 1 & | & -1 \\ 0 & 1 & -3 & | & 4 \\ 0 & 1 & -3 & | & 4 \end{bmatrix}$$

$$\longrightarrow \begin{bmatrix} 1 & 0 & -5 & | & 7 \\ 0 & 1 & -3 & | & 4 \\ 0 & 0 & 0 & | & 0 \end{bmatrix}$$

Thus $x = 7 + 5z$, $y = 4 + 3z$, and z any number is the solution. This system is dependent; it has infinitely many solutions.

Exercises

Find the determinants.

1. $\begin{vmatrix} 2 & -1 \\ 3 & -2 \end{vmatrix}$

2. $\begin{vmatrix} 0 & 2 \\ -1 & 3 \end{vmatrix}$

3. $\begin{vmatrix} 1 & 2 & 3 \\ -2 & 1 & 0 \\ -2 & 4 & 1 \end{vmatrix}$

4. $\begin{vmatrix} 0 & -2 & 4 \\ 2 & 1 & 0 \\ 3 & 2 & 1 \end{vmatrix}$

5. $\begin{vmatrix} 1 & 0 & 2 & 0 \\ 0 & 1 & 0 & 2 \\ -2 & 0 & 0 & 1 \\ 0 & 1 & 3 & 1 \end{vmatrix}$

6. $\begin{vmatrix} -1 & 2 & 0 & 1 \\ 4 & 0 & 0 & 3 \\ 0 & 1 & 0 & 2 \\ 1 & 1 & 1 & 1 \end{vmatrix}$

Solve the following systems. Use Cramer's Rule if possible. If not, use other methods.
Then check your answers.

7. $2x - 3y = 1$
    $x + 4y = 7$

8. $\frac{1}{2}x - \frac{2}{3}y = \frac{1}{4}$
    $\frac{5}{6}x - \frac{1}{4}y = \frac{1}{5}$

9. $x - 2y + z = 0$
    $2x + 3y - z = 4$
    $4x - 7y + z = 5$

10. $x - 2y + z = 2$
    $2x - 3y + 2z = 0$
    $-x + 2y + z = 4$

11. $x_1 - 2x_2 \qquad + x_4 = 1$
    $\qquad x_2 - x_3 \qquad = 2$
    $-2x_1 + 4x_2 + x_3 \qquad = 1$
    $-x_1 + 3x_2 + x_3 + x_4 = 4$

12. $2x_1 + x_2 - x_3 \qquad = -2$
    $x_1 \qquad - 2x_3 + x_4 = 0$
    $\qquad x_2 \qquad - x_4 = 0$
    $3x_1 + 2x_2 - 3x_3 \qquad = 3$

Table 1. Common Logarithms of Numbers between 1 and 10

	0	1	2	3	4	5	6	7	8	9
1.0	.0000	.0043	.0086	.0128	.0170	.0212	.0253	.0294	.0334	.0374
1.1	.0414	.0453	.0492	.0531	.0569	.0607	.0645	.0682	.0719	.0755
1.2	.0792	.0828	.0864	.0899	.0934	.0969	.1004	.1038	.1072	.1106
1.3	.1139	.1173	.1206	.1239	.1271	.1303	.1335	.1367	.1399	.1430
1.4	.1461	.1492	.1523	.1553	.1584	.1614	.1644	.1673	.1703	.1732
1.5	.1761	.1790	.1818	.1847	.1875	.1903	.1931	.1959	.1987	.2014
1.6	.2041	.2068	.2095	.2122	.2148	.2175	.2201	.2227	.2253	.2279
1.7	.2304	.2330	.2355	.2380	.2405	.2430	.2455	.2480	.2504	.2529
1.8	.2553	.2577	.2601	.2625	.2648	.2672	.2695	.2718	.2742	.2765
1.9	.2788	.2810	.2833	.2856	.2878	.2900	.2923	.2945	.2967	.2989
2.0	.3010	.3032	.3054	.3075	.3096	.3118	.3139	.3160	.3181	.3201
2.1	.3222	.3243	.3263	.3284	.3304	.3324	.3345	.3365	.3385	.3404
2.2	.3424	.3444	.3464	.3483	.3502	.3522	.3541	.3560	.3579	.3598
2.3	.3617	.3636	.3655	.3674	.3692	.3711	.3729	.3747	.3766	.3784
2.4	.3802	.3820	.3838	.3856	.3874	.3892	.3909	.3927	.3945	.3962
2.5	.3979	.3997	.4014	.4031	.4048	.4065	.4082	.4099	.4116	.4133
2.6	.4150	.4166	.4183	.4200	.4216	.4232	.4249	.4265	.4281	.4298
2.7	.4314	.4330	.4346	.4362	.4378	.4393	.4409	.4425	.4440	.4456
2.8	.4472	.4487	.4502	.4518	.4533	.4548	.4564	.4579	.4594	.4609
2.9	.4624	.4639	.4654	.4669	.4683	.4698	.4713	.4728	.4742	.4757
3.0	.4771	.4786	.4800	.4814	.4829	.4843	.4857	.4871	.4886	.4900
3.1	.4914	.4928	.4942	.4955	.4969	.4983	.4997	.5011	.5024	.5038
3.2	.5051	.5065	.5079	.5092	.5105	.5119	.5132	.5145	.5159	.5172
3.3	.5185	.5198	.5211	.5224	.5237	.5250	.5263	.5276	.5289	.5307
3.4	.5315	.5328	.5340	.5353	.5366	.5378	.5391	.5403	.5416	.5428
3.5	.5441	.5453	.5465	.5478	.5490	.5502	.5514	.5527	.5539	.5551
3.6	.5563	.5575	.5587	.5599	.5611	.5623	.5635	.5647	.5658	.5670
3.7	.5682	.5694	.5705	.5717	.5729	.5740	.5752	.5763	.5775	.5786
3.8	.5798	.5809	.5821	.5832	.5843	.5855	.5866	.5877	.5888	.5899
3.9	.5911	.5922	.5933	.5944	.5955	.5966	.5977	.5988	.5999	.6010
4.0	.6021	.6031	.6042	.6053	.6064	.6075	.6085	.6096	.6107	.6117
4.1	.6128	.6138	.6149	.6160	.6170	.6180	.6191	.6201	.6212	.6222
4.2	.6232	.6243	.6253	.6263	.6274	.6284	.6294	.6304	.6314	.6325
4.3	.6335	.6345	.6355	.6365	.6375	.6385	.6395	.6405	.6415	.6425
4.4	.6435	.6444	.6454	.6464	.6474	.6484	.6493	.6503	.6513	.6522
4.5	.6532	.6542	.6551	.6561	.6571	.6580	.6590	.6599	.6609	.6618
4.6	.6628	.6637	.6646	.6656	.6665	.6675	.6684	.6693	.6702	.6712
4.7	.6721	.6730	.6739	.6749	.6758	.6767	.6776	.6785	.6794	.6803
4.8	.6812	.6821	.6830	.6839	.6848	.6857	.6866	.6875	.6884	.6893
4.9	.6902	.6911	.6920	.6928	.6937	.6946	.6955	.6964	.6972	.6981
5.0	.6990	.6998	.7007	.7016	.7024	.7033	.7042	.7050	.7059	.7067
5.1	.7076	.7084	.7093	.7101	.7110	.7118	.7126	.7135	.7143	.7152
5.2	.7160	.7168	.7177	.7185	.7193	.7202	.7210	.7218	.7226	.7235
5.3	.7243	.7251	.7259	.7267	.7275	.7284	.7292	.7300	.7308	.7316
5.4	.7324	.7332	.7340	.7348	.7356	.7364	.7372	.7380	.7388	.7396
	0	**1**	**2**	**3**	**4**	**5**	**6**	**7**	**8**	**9**

Table 1 487

Table 1 (concluded)

	0	1	2	3	4	5	6	7	8	9
5.5	.7404	.7412	.7419	.7427	.7435	.7443	.7451	.7459	.7466	.7474
5.6	.7482	.7490	.7497	.7505	.7513	.7520	.7528	.7536	.7543	.7551
5.7	.7559	.7566	.7574	.7582	.7589	.7597	.7604	.7612	.7619	.7627
5.8	.7634	.7642	.7649	.7657	.7664	.7672	.7679	.7686	.7694	.7701
5.9	.7709	.7716	.7723	.7731	.7738	.7745	.7752	.7760	.7767	.7774
6.0	.7782	.7789	.7796	.7803	.7810	.7818	.7825	.7832	.7839	.7846
6.1	.7853	.7860	.7868	.7875	.7882	.7889	.7896	.7903	.7910	.7917
6.2	.7924	.7931	.7938	.7945	.7952	.7959	.7966	.7973	.7980	.7987
6.3	.7993	.8000	.8007	.8014	.8021	.8028	.8035	.8041	.8048	.8055
6.4	.8062	.8069	.8075	.8082	.8089	.8096	.8102	.8109	.8116	.8122
6.5	.8129	.8136	.8142	.8149	.8156	.8162	.8169	.8176	.8182	.8189
6.6	.8195	.8202	.8209	.8215	.8222	.8228	.8235	.8241	.8248	.8254
6.7	.8261	.8267	.8274	.8280	.8287	.8293	.8299	.8306	.8312	.8319
6.8	.8325	.8331	.8338	.8344	.8351	.8357	.8363	.8370	.8376	.8382
6.9	.8388	.8395	.8401	.8407	.8414	.8420	.8426	.8432	.8439	.8445
7.0	.8451	.8457	.8463	.8470	.8476	.8482	.8488	.8494	.8500	.8506
7.1	.8513	.8519	.8525	.8531	.8537	.8543	.8549	.8555	.8561	.8567
7.2	.8573	.8579	.8585	.8591	.8597	.8603	.8609	.8615	.8621	.8627
7.3	.8633	.8639	.8645	.8651	.8657	.8663	.8669	.8675	.8681	.8686
7.4	.8692	.8698	.8704	.8710	.8716	.8722	.8727	.8733	.8739	.8745
7.5	.8751	.8756	.8762	.8768	.8774	.8779	.8785	.8791	.8797	.8802
7.6	.8808	.8814	.8820	.8825	.8831	.8837	.8842	.8848	.8854	.8859
7.7	.8865	.8871	.8876	.8882	.8887	.8893	.8899	.8904	.8910	.8915
7.8	.8921	.8927	.8932	.8938	.8943	.8949	.8954	.8960	.8965	.8971
7.9	.8976	.8982	.8987	.8993	.8998	.9004	.9009	.9015	.9020	.9025
8.0	.9031	.9036	.9042	.9047	.9053	.9058	.9063	.9069	.9074	.9079
8.1	.9085	.9090	.9096	.9101	.9106	.9112	.9117	.9122	.9128	.9133
8.2	.9138	.9143	.9149	.9154	.9159	.9165	.9170	.9175	.9180	.9186
8.3	.9191	.9196	.9201	.9206	.9212	.9217	.9222	.9227	.9232	.9238
8.4	.9243	.9248	.9253	.9258	.9263	.9269	.9274	.9279	.9284	.9289
8.5	.9294	.9299	.9304	.9309	.9315	.9320	.9325	.9330	.9335	.9340
8.6	.9345	.9350	.9555	.9360	.9365	.9370	.9375	.9380	.9385	.9390
8.7	.9395	.9400	.9405	.9410	.9415	.9420	.9425	.9430	.9435	.9440
8.8	.9445	.9450	.9455	.9460	.9465	.9469	.9474	.9479	.9484	.9489
8.9	.9494	.9499	.9504	.9509	.9513	.9518	.9523	.9528	.9533	.9538
9.0	.9542	.9547	.9552	.9557	.9562	.9566	.9571	.9576	.9581	.9586
9.1	.9590	.9595	.9600	.9605	.9609	.9614	.9619	.9624	.9628	.9633
9.2	.9638	.9643	.9647	.9652	.9657	.9661	.9666	.9671	.9675	.9680
9.3	.9685	.9689	.9694	.9699	.9703	.9708	.9713	.9717	.9722	.9727
9.4	.9731	.9736	.9741	.9745	.9750	.9754	.9759	.9763	.9768	.9773
9.5	.9777	.9782	.9786	.9791	.9795	.9800	.9805	.9809	.9814	.9818
9.6	.9823	.9827	.9832	.9836	.9841	.9845	.9850	.9854	.9859	.9863
9.7	.9868	.9872	.9877	.9881	.9886	.9890	.9894	.9899	.9903	.9908
9.8	.9912	.9917	.9921	.9926	.9930	.9934	.9939	.9943	.9948	.9952
9.9	.9956	.9961	.9965	.9969	.9974	.9978	.9983	.9987	.9991	.9996
	0	1	2	3	4	5	6	7	8	9

Table 2. Values of Trigonometric Functions

Degrees	Radians	Sin	Cos	Tan	Cot	Sec	Csc		
0° 00′	.0000	.0000	1.0000	.0000	—	1.000	—	1.5708	**90° 00′**
10	.0029	.0029	1.0000	.0029	343.8	1.000	343.8	1.5679	50
20	.0058	.0058	1.0000	.0058	171.9	1.000	171.9	1.5650	40
30	.0087	.0087	1.0000	.0087	114.6	1.000	114.6	1.5621	30
40	.0116	.0116	.9999	.0116	85.94	1.000	85.95	1.5592	20
50	.0145	.0145	.9999	.0145	68.75	1.000	68.76	1.5563	10
1° 00′	.0175	.0175	.9998	.0175	57.29	1.000	57.30	1.5533	**89° 00′**
10	.0204	.0204	.9998	.0204	49.10	1.000	49.11	1.5504	50
20	.0233	.0233	.9997	.0233	42.96	1.000	42.98	1.5475	40
30	.0262	.0262	.9997	.0262	38.19	1.000	38.20	1.5446	30
40	.0291	.0291	.9996	.0291	34.37	1.000	34.38	1.5417	20
50	.0320	.0320	.9995	.0320	31.24	1.001	31.26	1.5388	10
2° 00′	.0349	.0349	.9994	.0349	28.64	1.001	28.65	1.5359	**88° 00′**
10	.0378	.0378	.9993	.0378	26.43	1.001	26.45	1.5330	50
20	.0407	.0407	.9992	.0407	24.54	1.001	24.56	1.5301	40
30	.0436	.0436	.9990	.0437	22.90	1.001	22.93	1.5272	30
40	.0465	.0465	.9989	.0466	21.47	1.001	21.49	1.5243	20
50	.0495	.0494	.9988	.0495	20.21	1.001	20.23	1.5213	10
3° 00′	.0524	.0523	.9986	.0524	19.08	1.001	19.11	1.5184	**87° 00′**
10	.0553	.0552	.9985	.0553	18.07	1.002	18.10	1.5155	50
20	.0582	.0581	.9983	.0582	17.17	1.002	17.20	1.5126	40
30	.0611	.0610	.9981	.0612	16.35	1.002	16.38	1.5097	30
40	.0640	.0640	.9980	.0641	15.60	1.002	15.64	1.5068	20
50	.0669	.0669	.9978	.0670	14.92	1.002	14.96	1.5039	10
4° 00′	.0698	.0698	.9976	.0699	14.30	1.002	14.34	1.5010	**86° 00′**
10	.0727	.0727	.9974	.0729	13.73	1.003	13.76	1.4981	50
20	.0756	.0756	.9971	.0758	13.20	1.003	13.23	1.4952	40
30	.0785	.0785	.9969	.0787	12.71	1.003	12.75	1.4923	30
40	.0814	.0814	.9967	.0816	12.25	1.003	12.29	1.4893	20
50	.0844	.0843	.9964	.0846	11.83	1.004	11.87	1.4864	10
5° 00′	.0873	.0872	.9962	.0875	11.43	1.004	11.47	1.4835	**85° 00′**
10	.0902	.0901	.9959	.0904	11.06	1.004	11.10	1.4806	50
20	.0931	.0929	.9957	.0934	10.71	1.004	10.76	1.4777	40
30	.0960	.0958	.9954	.0963	10.39	1.005	10.43	1.4748	30
40	.0989	.0987	.9951	.0992	10.08	1.005	10.13	1.4719	20
50	.1018	.1016	.9948	.1022	9.788	1.005	9.839	1.4690	10
6° 00′	.1047	.1045	.9945	.1051	9.514	1.006	9.567	1.4661	**84° 00′**
10	.1076	.1074	.9942	.1080	9.255	1.006	9.309	1.4632	50
20	.1105	.1103	.9939	.1110	9.010	1.006	9.065	1.4603	40
30	.1134	.1132	.9936	.1139	8.777	1.006	8.834	1.4573	30
40	.1164	.1161	.9932	.1169	8.556	1.007	8.614	1.4544	20
50	.1193	.1190	.9929	.1198	8.345	1.007	8.405	1.4515	10
7° 00′	.1222	.1219	.9925	.1228	8.144	1.008	8.206	1.4486	**83° 00′**
10	.1251	.1248	.9922	.1257	7.953	1.008	8.016	1.4457	50
20	.1280	.1276	.9918	.1287	7.770	1.008	7.834	1.4428	40
30	.1309	.1305	.9914	.1317	7.596	1.009	7.661	1.4399	30
40	.1338	.1334	.9911	.1346	7.429	1.009	7.496	1.4370	20
50	.1367	.1363	.9907	.1376	7.269	1.009	7.337	1.4341	10
8° 00′	.1396	.1392	.9903	.1405	7.115	1.010	7.185	1.4312	**82° 00′**
10	.1425	.1421	.9899	.1435	6.968	1.010	7.040	1.4283	50
20	.1454	.1449	.9894	.1465	6.827	1.011	6.900	1.4254	40
30	.1484	.1478	.9890	.1495	6.691	1.011	6.765	1.4224	30
40	.1513	.1507	.9886	.1524	6.561	1.012	6.636	1.4195	20
50	.1542	.1536	.9881	.1554	6.435	1.012	6.512	1.4166	10
9° 00′	.1571	.1564	.9877	.1584	6.314	1.012	6.392	1.4137	**81° 00′**
		Cos	Sin	Cot	Tan	Csc	Sec	**Radians**	**Degrees**

(continued)

Table 2 (continued)

Degrees	Radians	Sin	Cos	Tan	Cot	Sec	Csc		
9° 00′	.1571	.1564	.9877	.1584	6.314	1.012	6.392	1.4137	81° 00′
10	.1600	.1593	.9872	.1614	6.197	1.013	6.277	1.4108	50
20	.1629	.1622	.9868	.1644	6.084	1.013	6.166	1.4079	40
30	.1658	.1650	.9863	.1673	5.976	1.014	6.059	1.4050	30
40	.1687	.1679	.9859	.1703	5.871	1.014	5.955	1.4021	20
50	.1716	.1708	.9853	.1733	5.769	1.015	5.855	1.3992	10
10° 00′	.1745	.1736	.9848	.1763	5.671	1.015	5.759	1.3963	80° 00′
10	.1774	.1765	.9843	.1793	5.576	1.016	5.665	1.3934	50
20	.1804	.1794	.9838	.1823	5.485	1.016	5.575	1.3904	40
30	.1833	.1822	.9833	.1853	5.396	1.017	5.487	1.3875	30
40	.1862	.1851	.9827	.1883	5.309	1.018	5.403	1.3846	20
50	.1891	.1880	.9822	.1914	5.226	1.018	5.320	1.3817	10
11° 00′	.1920	.1908	.9816	.1944	5.145	1.019	5.241	1.3788	79° 00′
10	.1949	.1937	.9811	.1974	5.066	1.019	5.164	1.3759	50
20	.1978	.1965	.9805	.2004	4.989	1.020	5.089	1.3730	40
30	.2007	.1994	.9799	.2035	4.915	1.020	5.016	1.3701	30
40	.2036	.2022	.9793	.2065	4.843	1.021	4.945	1.3672	20
50	.2065	.2051	.9787	.2095	4.773	1.022	4.876	1.3643	10
12° 00′	.2094	.2079	.9781	.2126	4.705	1.022	4.810	1.3614	78° 00′
10	.2123	.2108	.9775	.2156	4.638	1.023	4.745	1.3584	50
20	.2153	.2136	.9769	.2186	4.574	1.024	4.682	1.3555	40
30	.2182	.2164	.9763	.2217	4.511	1.024	4.620	1.3526	30
40	.2211	.2193	.9757	.2247	4.449	1.025	4.560	1.3497	20
50	.2240	.2221	.9750	.2278	4.390	1.026	4.502	1.3468	10
13° 00′	.2269	.2250	.9744	.2309	4.331	1.026	4.445	1.3439	77° 00′
10	.2298	.2278	.9737	.2339	4.275	1.027	4.390	1.3410	50
20	.2327	.2306	.9730	.2370	4.219	1.028	4.336	1.3381	40
30	.2356	.2334	.9724	.2401	4.165	1.028	4.284	1.3352	30
40	.2385	.2363	.9717	.2432	4.113	1.029	4.232	1.3323	20
50	.2414	.2391	.9710	.2462	4.061	1.030	4.182	1.3294	10
14° 00′	.2443	.2419	.9703	.2493	4.011	1.031	4.134	1.3265	76° 00′
10	.2473	.2447	.9696	.2524	3.962	1.031	4.086	1.3235	50
20	.2502	.2476	.9689	.2555	3.914	1.032	4.039	1.3206	40
30	.2531	.2504	.9681	.2586	3.867	1.033	3.994	1.3177	30
40	.2560	.2532	.9674	.2617	3.821	1.034	3.950	1.3148	20
50	.2589	.2560	.9667	.2648	3.776	1.034	3.906	1.3119	10
15° 00′	.2618	.2588	.9659	.2679	3.732	1.035	3.864	1.3090	75° 00′
10	.2647	.2616	.9652	.2711	3.689	1.036	3.822	1.3061	50
20	.2676	.2644	.9644	.2742	3.647	1.037	3.782	1.3032	40
30	.2705	.2672	.9636	.2773	3.606	1.038	3.742	1.3003	30
40	.2734	.2700	.9628	.2805	3.566	1.039	3.703	1.2974	20
50	.2763	.2728	.9621	.2836	3.526	1.039	3.665	1.2945	10
16° 00′	.2793	.2756	.9613	.2867	3.487	1.040	3.628	1.2915	74° 00′
10	.2822	.2784	.9605	.2899	3.450	1.041	3.592	1.2886	50
20	.2851	.2812	.9596	.2931	3.412	1.042	3.556	1.2857	40
30	.2880	.2840	.9588	.2962	3.376	1.043	3.521	1.2828	30
40	.2909	.2868	.9580	.2994	3.340	1.044	3.487	1.2799	20
50	.2938	.2896	.9572	.3026	3.305	1.045	3.453	1.2770	10
17° 00′	.2967	.2924	.9563	.3057	3.271	1.046	3.420	1.2741	73° 00′
10	.2996	.2952	.9555	.3089	3.237	1.047	3.388	1.2712	50
20	.3025	.2979	.9546	.3121	3.204	1.048	3.356	1.2683	40
30	.3054	.3007	.9537	.3153	3.172	1.049	3.326	1.2654	30
40	.3083	.3035	.9528	.3185	3.140	1.049	3.295	1.2625	20
50	.3113	.3062	.9520	.3217	3.108	1.050	3.265	1.2595	10
18° 00′	.3142	.3090	.9511	.3249	3.078	1.051	3.236	1.2566	72° 00′
		Cos	Sin	Cot	Tan	Csc	Sec	Radians	Degrees

(*continued*)

489

Table 2 (continued)

Degrees	Radians	Sin	Cos	Tan	Cot	Sec	Csc		
18° 00′	.3142	.3090	.9511	.3249	3.078	1.051	3.236	1.2566	**72° 00′**
10	.3171	.3118	.9502	.3281	3.047	1.052	3.207	1.2537	50
20	.3200	.3145	.9492	.3314	3.018	1.053	3.179	1.2508	40
30	.3229	.3173	.9483	.3346	2.989	1.054	3.152	1.2479	30
40	.3258	.3201	.9474	.3378	2.960	1.056	3.124	1.2450	20
50	.3287	.3228	.9465	.3411	2.932	1.057	3.098	1.2421	10
19° 00′	.3316	.3256	.9455	.3443	2.904	1.058	3.072	1.2392	**71° 00′**
10	.3345	.3283	.9446	.3476	2.877	1.059	3.046	1.2363	50
20	.3374	.3311	.9436	.3508	2.850	1.060	3.021	1.2334	40
30	.3403	.3338	.9426	.3541	2.824	1.061	2.996	1.2305	30
40	.3432	.3365	.9417	3.574	2.798	1.062	2.971	1.2275	20
50	.3462	.3393	.9407	.3607	2.773	1.063	2.947	1.2246	10
20° 00′	.3491	.3420	.9397	.3640	2.747	1.064	2.924	1.2217	**70° 00′**
10	.3520	.3448	.9387	.3673	2.723	1.065	2.901	1.2188	50
20	.3549	.3475	.9377	.3706	2.699	1.066	2.878	1.2159	40
30	.3578	.3502	.9367	.3739	2.675	1.068	2.855	1.2130	30
40	.3607	.3529	.9356	.3772	2.651	1.069	2.833	1.2101	20
50	.3636	.3557	.9346	.3805	2.628	1.070	2.812	1.2072	10
21° 00′	.3665	.3584	.9336	.3839	2.605	1.071	2.790	1.2043	**69° 00′**
10	.3694	.3611	.9325	.3872	2.583	1.072	2.769	1.2014	50
20	.3723	.3638	.9315	.3906	2.560	1.074	2.749	1.1985	40
30	.3752	.3665	.9304	.3939	2.539	1.075	2.729	1.1956	30
40	.3782	.3692	.9293	.3973	2.517	1.076	2.709	1.1926	20
50	.3811	.3719	.9283	.4006	2.496	1.077	2.689	1.1897	10
22° 00′	.3840	.3746	.9272	.4040	2.475	1.079	2.669	1.1868	**68° 00′**
10	.3869	.3773	.9261	.4074	2.455	1.080	2.650	1.1839	50
20	.3898	.3800	.9250	.4108	2.434	1.081	2.632	1.1810	40
30	.3927	.3827	.9239	.4142	2.414	1.082	2.613	1.1781	30
40	.3956	.3854	.9228	.4176	2.394	1.084	2.595	1.1752	20
50	.3985	.3881	.9216	.4210	2.375	1.085	2.577	1.1723	10
23° 00′	.4014	.3907	.9205	.4245	2.356	1.086	2.559	1.1694	**67° 00′**
10	.4043	.3934	.9194	.4279	2.337	1.088	2.542	1.1665	50
20	.4072	.3961	.9182	.4314	2.318	1.089	2.525	1.1636	40
30	.4102	.3987	.9171	.4348	2.300	1.090	2.508	1.1606	30
40	.4131	.4014	.9159	.4383	2.282	1.092	2.491	1.1577	20
50	.4160	.4041	.9147	.4417	2.264	1.093	2.475	1.1548	10
24° 00′	.4189	.4067	.9135	.4452	2.246	1.095	2.459	1.1519	**66° 00′**
10	.4218	.4094	.9124	.4487	2.229	1.096	2.443	1.1490	50
20	.4247	.4120	.9112	.4522	2.211	1.097	2.427	1.1461	40
30	.4276	.4147	.9100	.4557	2.194	1.099	2.411	1.1432	30
40	.4305	.4173	.9088	.4592	2.177	1.100	2.396	1.1403	20
50	.4334	.4200	.9075	.4628	2.161	1.102	2.381	1.1374	10
25° 00′	.4363	.4226	.9063	.4663	2.145	1.103	2.366	1.1345	**65° 00′**
10	.4392	.4253	.9051	.4699	2.128	1.105	2.352	1.1316	50
20	.4422	.4279	.9038	.4734	2.112	1.106	2.337	1.1286	40
30	.4451	.4305	.9026	.4770	2.097	1.108	2.323	1.1257	30
40	.4480	.4331	.9013	.4806	2.081	1.109	2.309	1.1228	20
50	.4509	.4358	.9001	.4841	2.066	1.111	2.295	1.1199	10
26° 00′	.4538	.4384	.8988	.4877	2.050	1.113	2.281	1.1170	**64° 00′**
10	.4567	.4410	.8975	.4913	2.035	1.114	2.268	1.1141	50
20	.4596	.4436	.8962	.4950	2.020	1.116	2.254	1.1112	40
30	.4625	.4462	.8949	.4986	2.006	1.117	2.241	1.1083	30
40	.4654	.4488	.8936	.5022	1.991	1.119	2.228	1.1054	20
50	.4683	.4514	.8923	.5059	1.977	1.121	2.215	1.1025	10
27° 00′	.4712	.4540	.8910	.5095	1.963	1.122	2.203	1.0996	**63° 00′**
		Cos	**Sin**	**Cot**	**Tan**	**Csc**	**Sec**	**Radians**	**Degrees**

(*continued*)

Table 2 (continued)

Degrees	Radians	Sin	Cos	Tan	Cot	Sec	Csc		
27° 00′	.4712	.4540	.8910	.5095	1.963	1.122	2.203	1.0996	63° 00′
10	.4741	.4566	.8897	.5132	1.949	1.124	1.190	1.0966	50
20	.4771	.4592	.8884	.5169	1.935	1.126	1.178	1.0937	40
30	.4800	.4617	.8870	.5206	1.921	1.127	2.166	1.0908	30
40	.4829	.4643	.8857	.5243	1.907	1.129	2.154	1.0879	20
50	.4858	.4669	.8843	.5280	1.894	1.131	2.142	1.0850	10
28° 00′	.4887	.4695	.8829	.5317	1.881	1.133	2.130	1.0821	62° 00′
10	.4916	.4720	.8816	.5354	1.868	1.134	2.118	1.0792	50
20	.4945	.4746	.8802	.5392	1.855	1.136	2.107	1.0763	40
30	.4974	.4772	.8788	.5430	1.842	1.138	2.096	1.0734	30
40	.5003	.4797	.8774	.5467	1.829	1.140	2.085	1.0705	20
50	.5032	.4823	.8760	.5505	1.816	1.142	2.074	1.0676	10
29° 00′	.5061	.4848	.8746	.5543	1.804	1.143	2.063	1.0647	61° 00′
10	.5091	.4874	.8732	.5581	1.792	1.145	2.052	1.0617	50
20	.5120	.4899	.8718	.5619	1.780	1.147	2.041	1.0588	40
30	.5149	.4924	.8704	.5658	1.767	1.149	2.031	1.0559	30
40	.5178	.4950	.8689	.5696	1.756	1.151	2.020	1.0530	20
50	.5207	.4975	.8675	.5735	1.744	1.153	2.010	1.0501	10
30° 00′	.5236	.5000	.8660	.5774	1.732	1.155	2.000	1.0472	60° 00′
10	.5265	.5025	.8646	.5812	1.720	1.157	1.990	1.0443	50
20	.5294	.5050	.8631	.5851	1.709	1.159	1.980	1.0414	40
30	.5323	.5075	.8616	.5890	1.698	1.161	1.970	1.0385	30
40	.5352	.5100	.8601	.5930	1.686	1.163	1.961	1.0356	20
50	.5381	.5125	.8587	.5969	1.675	1.165	1.951	1.0327	10
31° 00′	.5411	.5150	.8572	.6009	1.664	1.167	1.942	1.0297	59° 00′
10	.5440	.5175	.8557	.6048	1.653	1.169	1.932	1.0268	50
20	.5469	.5200	.8542	.6088	1.643	1.171	1.923	1.0239	40
30	.5498	.5225	.8526	.6128	1.632	1.173	1.914	1.0210	30
40	.5527	.5250	.8511	.6168	1.621	1.175	1.905	1.0181	20
50	.5556	.5275	.8496	.6208	1.611	1.177	1.896	1.0152	10
32° 00′	.5585	.5299	.8480	.6249	1.600	1.179	1.887	1.0123	58° 00′
10	.5614	.5324	.8465	.6289	1.590	1.181	1.878	1.0094	50
20	.5643	.5348	.8450	.6330	1.580	1.184	1.870	1.0065	40
30	.5672	.5373	.8434	.6371	1.570	1.186	1.861	1.0036	30
40	.5701	.5398	.8418	.6412	1.560	1.188	1.853	1.0007	20
50	.5730	.5422	.8403	.6453	1.550	1.190	1.844	.9977	10
33° 00′	.5760	.5446	.8387	.6494	1.540	1.192	1.836	.9948	57° 00′
10	.5789	.5471	.8371	.6536	1.530	1.195	1.828	.9919	50
20	.5818	.5495	.8355	.6577	1.520	1.197	1.820	.9890	40
30	.5847	.5519	.8339	.6619	1.511	1.199	1.812	.9861	30
40	.5876	.5544	.8323	.6661	1.501	1.202	1.804	.9832	20
50	.5905	.5568	.8307	.6703	1.492	1.204	1.796	.9803	10
34° 00′	.5934	.5592	.8290	.6745	1.483	1.206	1.788	.9774	56° 00′
10	.5963	.5616	.8274	.6787	1.473	1.209	1.781	.9745	50
20	.5992	.5640	.8258	.6830	1.464	1.211	1.773	.9716	40
30	.6021	.5664	.8241	.6873	1.455	1.213	1.766	.9687	30
40	.6050	.5688	.8225	.6916	1.446	1.216	1.758	.9657	20
50	.6080	.5712	.8208	.6959	1.437	1.218	1.751	.9628	10
35° 00′	.6109	.5736	.8192	.7002	1.428	1.221	1.743	.9599	55° 00′
10	.6138	.5760	.8175	.7046	1.419	1.223	1.736	.9570	50
20	.6167	.5783	.8158	.7089	1.411	1.226	1.729	.9541	40
30	.6196	.5807	.8141	.7133	1.402	1.228	1.722	.9512	30
40	.6225	.5831	.8124	.7177	1.393	1.231	1.715	.9483	20
50	.6254	.5854	.8107	.7221	1.385	1.233	1.708	.9454	10
36° 00′	.6283	.5878	.8090	.7265	1.376	1.236	1.701	.9425	54° 00′
		Cos	Sin	Cot	Tan	Csc	Sec	Radians	Degrees

(*continued*)

Table 2 (concluded)

Degrees	Radians	Sin	Cos	Tan	Cot	Sec	Csc		
36° 00′	.6283	.5878	.8090	.7265	1.376	1.236	1.701	.9425	**54° 00′**
10	.6312	.5901	.8073	.7310	1.368	1.239	1.695	.9396	50
20	.6341	.5925	.8056	.7355	1.360	1.241	1.688	.9367	40
30	.6370	.5948	.8039	.7400	1.351	1.244	1.681	.9338	30
40	.6400	.5972	.8021	.7445	1.343	1.247	1.675	.9308	20
50	.6429	.5995	.8004	.7490	1.335	1.249	1.668	.9279	10
37° 00′	.6458	.6018	.7986	.7536	1.327	1.252	1.662	.9250	**53° 00′**
10	.6487	.6041	.7969	.7581	1.319	1.255	1.655	.9221	50
20	.6516	.6065	.7951	.7627	1.311	1.258	1.649	.9192	40
30	.6545	.6088	.7934	.7673	1.303	1.260	1.643	.9163	30
40	.6574	.6111	.7916	.7720	1.295	1.263	1.636	.9134	20
50	.6603	.6134	.7898	.7766	1.288	1.266	1.630	.9105	10
38° 00′	.6632	.6157	.7880	.7813	1.280	1.269	1.624	.9076	**52° 00′**
10	.6661	.6180	.7862	.7860	1.272	1.272	1.618	.9047	50
20	.6690	.6202	.7844	.7907	1.265	1.275	1.612	.9018	40
30	.6720	.6225	.7826	.7954	1.257	1.278	1.606	.8988	30
40	.6749	.6248	.7808	.8002	1.250	1.281	1.601	.8959	20
50	.6778	.6271	.7790	.8050	1.242	1.284	1.595	.8930	10
39° 00′	.6807	.6293	.7771	.8098	1.235	1.287	1.589	.8901	**51° 00′**
10	.6836	.6316	.7753	.8146	1.228	1.290	1.583	.8872	50
20	.6865	.6338	.7735	.8195	1.220	1.293	1.578	.8843	40
30	.6894	.6361	.7716	.8243	1.213	1.296	1.572	.8814	30
40	.6923	.6383	.7698	.8292	1.206	1.299	1.567	.8785	20
50	.6952	.6406	.7679	.8342	1.199	1.302	1.561	.8756	10
40° 00′	.6981	.6428	.7660	.8391	1.192	1.305	1.556	.8727	**50° 00′**
10	.7010	.6450	.7642	.8441	1.185	1.309	1.550	.8698	50
20	.7039	.6472	.7623	.8491	1.178	1.312	1.545	.8668	40
30	.7069	.6494	.7604	.8541	1.171	1.315	1.540	.8639	30
40	.7098	.6517	.7585	.8591	1.164	1.318	1.535	.8610	20
50	.7127	.6539	.7566	.8642	1.157	1.322	1.529	.8581	10
41° 00′	.7156	.6561	.7547	.8693	1.150	1.325	1.524	.8552	**49° 00′**
10	.7185	.6583	.7528	.8744	1.144	1.328	1.519	.8523	50
20	.7214	.6604	.7509	.8796	1.137	1.332	1.514	.8494	40
30	.7243	.6626	.7490	.8847	1.130	1.335	1.509	.8465	30
40	.7272	.6648	.7470	.8899	1.124	1.339	1.504	.8436	20
50	.7301	.6670	.7451	.8952	1.117	1.342	1.499	.8407	10
42° 00′	.7330	.6691	.7431	.9004	1.111	1.346	1.494	.8378	**48° 00′**
10	.7359	.6713	.7412	.9057	1.104	1.349	1.490	.8348	50
20	.7389	.6734	.7392	.9110	1.098	1.353	1.485	.8319	40
30	.7418	.6756	.7373	.9163	1.091	1.356	1.480	.8290	30
40	.7447	.6777	.7353	.9217	1.085	1.360	1.476	.8261	20
50	.7476	.6799	.7333	.9271	1.079	1.364	1.471	.8232	10
43° 00′	.7505	.6820	.7314	.9325	1.072	1.367	1.466	.8203	**47° 00′**
10	.7534	.6841	.7294	.9380	1.066	1.371	1.462	.8174	50
20	.7563	.6862	.7274	.9435	1.060	1.375	1.457	.8145	40
30	.7592	.6884	.7254	.9490	1.054	1.379	1.453	.8116	30
40	.7621	.6905	.7234	.9545	1.048	1.382	1.448	.8087	20
50	.7650	.6926	.7214	.9601	1.042	1.386	1.444	.8058	10
44° 00′	.7679	.6947	.7193	.9657	1.036	1.390	1.440	.8029	**46° 00′**
10	.7709	.6967	.7173	.9713	1.030	1.394	1.435	.7999	50
20	.7738	.6988	.7153	.9770	1.024	1.398	1.431	.7970	40
30	.7767	.7009	.7133	.9827	1.018	1.402	1.427	.7941	30
40	.7796	.7030	.7112	.9884	1.012	1.406	1.423	.7912	20
50	.7825	.7050	.7092	.9942	1.006	1.410	1.418	.7883	10
45° 00′	.7854	.7071	.7071	1.000	1.000	1.414	1.414	.7854	**45° 00′**
		Cos	**Sin**	**Cot**	**Tan**	**Csc**	**Sec**	**Radians**	**Degrees**

Answers to Selected Exercises

Chapter 1
Section 1-1 (page 15)

1. -11 3. $-7/3$ 5. $-25/8$ 7. $35/12$ 9. 11.43 11. $13/18$ 13. $1/15$
15. -2 17. ≈ 2.78 19. 24 21. $1/45$ 23. $-7/30$ 25. 144 27. -1
29. $8/125$ 31. $-1/125$ 33. 16 35. $25/4$ 37. $1/256$ 39. $1/64$ 41. 6
43. -4 45. -10 47. 2 49. -17 51. 36 53. $-27/8$ 55. -8 57. $-43/36$
59. $1/36$ 61. 1 63. $416/27$ 65. -4 67. $3/16$ 69. $-16\sqrt[3]{-4}$ 71. $1/4$
73. $\sqrt{2}$ 75. 0 77. 0 79. -4 81. The direction of the inequality remains
unchanged in parts (a) (b) and (c) but is reversed in part (d). For instance,
$-3 < 2$ and $-3 + (-5) < 2 + (-5)$, BUT because $-5 < 0$, we have
$(-3)(-5) > 2(-5)$. 82. The direction of the inequality remains unchanged
when it is divided by 2, but is reversed when it is divided by -2. 83. In parts
(a) and (c), the direction of the inequality is reversed: $2 < 6$, but $1/2 > 1/6$; and
$-2 > -6$, but $-1/2 < -1/6$. In part (b), we have $-6 < 2$ and $-1/6 < 1/2$.
GENERAL RULE: if $0 < a < b$ or $a < b < 0$, then $1/a > 1/b$, BUT if $a < 0 < b$,
then $1/a < 1/b$.

Section 1-2 (page 22)

1. $x^2 + x - 1$ 3. $a + 2b - 2c$ 5. $5x^2 - 4y + 3z$ 7. $9p - q + 4r$
9. $\frac{1}{6}a - \frac{7}{12}b$ 11. $9x^2 + 6x + 1$ 13. $7u^2 + 6\sqrt{7}uv + 9v^2$ 15. $9x^2 - 6x + 1$
17. $7u^2 - 6\sqrt{7}uv + 9v^2$ 19. $9x^2 - 1$ 21. $7u^2 - 9v^2$ 23. $x^3 + 3x^2 + 3x + 1$
25. $8x^3 - 36x^2y + 54xy^2 - 27y^3$ 27. $2x^2 - 11x - 21$ 29. $\frac{1}{4}x^2 - 25$
31. $2x^3 + 5x^2y - 5xy^2 + y^3$ 33. $x^3 + 1$ 35. $27x^3 - 64$
37. $2x^2 - xy - xz - 3y^2 + 4yz - z^2$ 39. $2x^4 - x^3y - 4x^2y^2 + 4xy^3 - y^4$
41. $2x^2/y$ 43. $3a^5c^3/4b^5$ 45. $4r^7/27s^{11}$ 47. $xy^3/72$ 49. $0, 0$ 50. $0, 0$ 51. $0, 0$

Section 1-3 (page 29)

1. $3x(3x + 1)$ **3.** $3t^2(t^2 - 3t + 9)$ **5.** $5x^2(x - 2) + (x - 2) = (x - 2)(5x^2 + 1)$
7. $(x + 6)^2$ **9.** $(2x + 3y)^2$ **11.** $(t - \sqrt{3})^2$ **13.** $(x + 5)(x - 5)$
15. $(s - 3 + 9)(s - 3 - 9) = (s + 6)(s - 12)$
17. $\left(x + \dfrac{b + \sqrt{b^2 - 4ac}}{2a}\right)\left(x + \dfrac{b - \sqrt{b^2 - 4ac}}{2a}\right)$ **19.** $(x + 4)(x^2 - 4x + 16)$
21. $(u^3 - 5v)(u^6 + 5u^3v + 25v^2)$
23. $(t + 1 - 2)((t + 1)^2 + 2(t + 1) + 4) = (t - 1)(t^2 + 4t + 7)$
25. $(x + 7)(x + 2)$ **27.** $(t - 6)(t + 5)$ **29.** $(y - 3z)(y - 19z)$
31. $(3x - 2)(x + 1)$ **33.** $(4x + 5)(2x + 7)$ **35.** $(-3x - 2)(x - 1)$
37. $(x + 1 + 3)(x + 1 - 3) = (x + 4)(x - 2)$ **39.** $(x - 15y)(x - y)$
41. $(t^2)^3 - (\frac{1}{3})^3 = (t^2 - \frac{1}{3})(t^4 + \frac{1}{3}t^2 + \frac{1}{9})$ **43.** $(5x - 1)(x + 8)$
45. $(s - (t - 4))(s + (t - 4)) = (s - t + 4)(s + t - 4)$ **47.** $(x - 5)(x - 3)$
49. $(4x^2)^2 - (\frac{1}{4})^2 = (4x^2 + \frac{1}{4})(4x^2 - \frac{1}{4}) = (4x^2 + \frac{1}{4})(2x + \frac{1}{2})(2x - \frac{1}{2})$
51. $(3y - 2)(3y - 1)$ **52.** $(96 + 4)(96 + 3) = 9900$
53. $(9y + 8)(y - 4)$ at $y = 14$ is $(126 + 8)(10) = 1340$
54. $(2t + 3)(t + 7)$ at $t = -1.5$ is $(0)(1.5 + 7) = 0$ **55.** 0 **56.** $x = -7, 2$
57. $y = 6, 7$ **58.** $x = -3/2, 1$ **59.** $u = \pm 3/5$

Section 1-4 (page 36)

1. $3x$ (replacements: before, neither x nor y can be 0; after, x can be any
number) **3.** $(x + 3)/(x + 8)$ **5.** $(y - 5)/y$ **7.** $2(t^2 + 2t + 4)/(t + 3)$ **9.** $3xy$
11. $3xy(x^2 + y^2)/(x + y)^2$ **13.** $3(x - 4)(x + 7)/x$ **15.** $2(s - 4t)/(s^2 - t^2)$
17. $-x(2x + 11)/(x + 4)^2(x + 1)$ **19.** $(-y + 5)/(y - 3)(y + 2)(y - 1)$
21. $(y - x)(3y - 5x)/x^2y^2$ **23.** $(x^2 - 1)/(x^2 + 1)$
25. $-3x(3x + 1)/(3x^2 + 8x - 27)$ **27.** $5\sqrt{8}/8 = 5\sqrt{2}/4$
29. $3x(x - \sqrt{3})/(x^2 - 3)$ **31.** $5(\sqrt{3} - \sqrt{5})/-2$ **33.** $105/2(5\sqrt{6} + 3\sqrt{5})$
35. $1/(\sqrt{x + h} + \sqrt{x})$ **36.** -1.35 (without a calculator)

Section 1-5 (page 41)

1. $1/4$ **3.** 8 **5.** Write $\sqrt[4]{(81)^3} = (\sqrt[4]{81})^3 = 3^3 = 27$ **7.** 3 **9.** $\approx .763$
11. $(8)^{1/6} = (2^3)^{1/6} = 2^{1/2} \approx 1.414$ **13.** $7^{7/12}$ **15.** $((x^{10})^{1/4})^{1/5} = x^{1/2}$ **17.** x^2
19. $5x^2(2x)^{1/2}$ **21.** $x^{23/60}$ **23.** $\sqrt[20]{x^{17}}$ **25.** $t^2\sqrt[3]{t}$ **27.** $xy^2\sqrt{x}$ **29.** T **31.** F
33. T **35.** F **37.** F **39.** -2 **41.** $-1/4$ **43.** -1 **45.** $1/2$ **47.** $5\sqrt[6]{x}/x$
49. $2x\sqrt[5]{(x + 1)^3}/(x + 1)$ **51.** $-2(x^{2/3} + (4x)^{1/3} + 4^{2/3})/(x - 4)$

Section 1-6 (page 49)

1. -5 **3.** $-1/2$ **5.** 0 **7.** $-8/7$ **9.** $-8/9.1 \approx -.88$ **11.** 2 **13.** $11/9$ **15.** 1
17. $\{1/2, -4\}$ **19.** $\{\sqrt{2}, -\sqrt{3}\}$ **21.** $\{-2, -3\}$ **23.** $\{-2, 9\}$

25. $y = (4x - 7)/3$ **27.** $y = (2x - 5)/4$
29. $x + (x + 1) + (x + 2) + (x + 3) = 90$; $x = 21$
30. $2x + (2x + 2) + (2x + 4) + (2x + 6) = 76$; $x = 8$; the numbers are
16, 18, 20, 22. **32.** $.07x = 500$; $x \approx \$7,143$ **34.** $.15(x + 5) = .25(5)$;
$x = 50/15 \approx 3.33$ **35.** $x =$ gal. of 25% solution; $10 - x =$ gal. of 40% solution;
$.25x + .40(10 - x) = .35(10)$; $x = 50/15 \approx 3.33$ gal. **37.** wind speed 50 mph;
plane speed 550 mph **38.** $x =$ ave. speed; $300/x =$ time for trip; $300/(x + 10)$
$= (300/x) - 1$. Multiply through by $x(x + 10)$ to clear fractions. Then $x^2 + 10x$
$- 3000 = 0$; $x = 50$ mph. **39.** Dimensions: 4 by 14 inches. **40.** When it hits
the ground, $h = 0$; thus, $-16t^2 + 160t = 0$; $t = 10$ sec

Chapter 2
Section 2-1 (page 57)

1. $-6, -6, -6$ **3.** $4, 4, u^2$ **5.** $-7, -1, (y - 3)/2, 25u - 12$
7. $-6, 0, 4t + 4h + 2, 16t + 10$ **8.** $16, -2, -4, (t + k)^2 - 3(t + k) - 2$
9. $-2, 3, 4\sqrt{3}, -z^2 + 2z + 6$ **11.** $-1/4, -3, 1/(t + h), b$ **13.** $3, 3/2, 0, t^2$
15. $7, -13, (1 - u + u^2 + u^3)/u^3$ **17.** All x **19.** All x **20.** All x **21.** $x \geq -1$
22. $|x| \leq 1$ **23.** $|x| \geq 1$ **25.** $x \neq \pm\sqrt{2}$ **26.** (a) 900; (b) $25x^2$; (c) 99,980,000
27. $f(5) = 25, F(5) = 32$; $g(-4) = -64, G(-4) = 1/81$; $h(8) = 4, H(8) = 256/6561$
28. $2^{100} = (2^{10})^{10} = (1024)^{10} > (10^3)^{10} = 10^{30}$
29. (a) When $x = 24, y = 6$; if $y = 6$, then $x = 6y - 12 = 24$
30. (a) 13; (b) 7; (c) $4x^2 - 12x + 13$; (d) $t^4 + 8t^2 + 20$; (e) $2u^2 + 4u + 7$
31. (a) -3; (b) 14; (c) 0; (d) -2; (e) $g(f(x)) = g(2x - 3) = \frac{1}{2}(2x - 3) + \frac{3}{2} = x$
32. If $x \geq 0$, then $\sqrt{x^2} = x = |x|$; if $x < 0$, then $\sqrt{x^2} = -x = |x|$
33. If $x \geq 0$, then $|x| = x$, so $|x|^2 = x^2$; if $x < 0$, then $|x| = -x$,
so $|x|^2 = (-x)^2 = x^2$

Section 2-2 (page 66)

1.

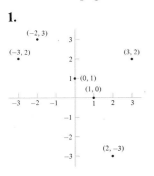

2.

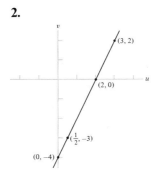

5.

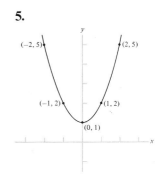

7.

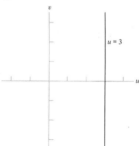

9.

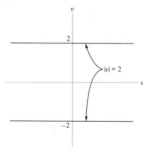

11.

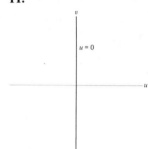

13.

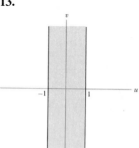

17.

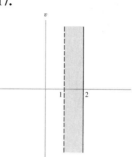

21.

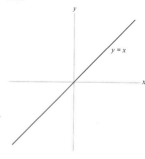

22.

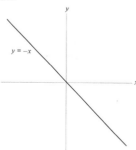

23.

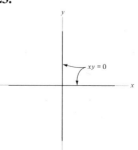

24.

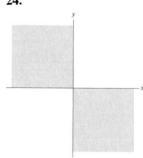

25. $\sqrt{50}$ **27.** $\sqrt{45}$ **29.** 5.46 **31.** 4 sq mi **33.** (3, 1) **35.** 14.71 km
36. $|xy| = \sqrt{(xy)^2} = \sqrt{x^2y^2} = \sqrt{x^2}\,\sqrt{y^2} = |x|\,|y|$ **37.** −1 or 7
39. $-\sqrt{2} \pm 1/2$ **41.** −17/20 or −13/20

Section 2-3 (page 76)

1. (a) Translates $y = x$ two units down (b) Translates $s = -t$ seven units up.
2. (a) Translates $y = |x|$ one unit left and three units down (b) Translates
$y = |x|$ two units right and one unit up **3.** (a) Translates $s = t^2$ three units
right and one unit down (b) Translates $v = u^2 + u$ one unit left **4.** (0, 7) and

$(1 + h, 5 - 2h)$ **6.** $(a + 2, a^2 + 4a)$ and $(b, b^2 - 4)$ **8.** $(4, 3)$ and $(-2, 2)$
9. $a = -4, b = 11$ **11.** $a = 1/7, b = -4/7$ **12.** $c = \pm 3, d = 0$

13.

15.

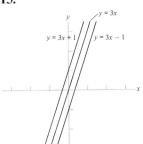

17.

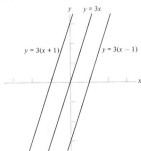

19.

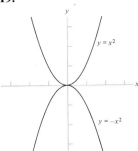

21.

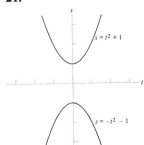

22.

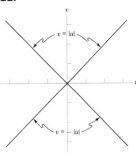

23.

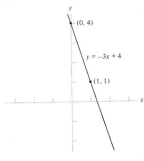

25.

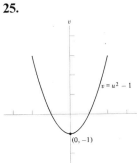

27.

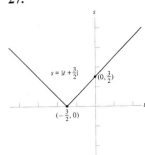

29.

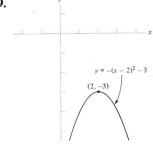

31.

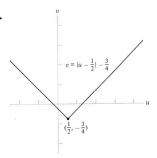

33. (a) Constant; (b) $y = ax$; (c) $y = x + 1$; (d) $y = |x - 1| + 2$

34. (a) No, because it assigns many values of y to the same value of x; (b) A can, but B cannot for the same reason as given for the first part; (c) a curve may be part of a graph of some function if it meets each vertical line in at most one point. **35.** (a) $-1, 5, t, z + 7$; (b) $3, 3$; (c) x, t; (e) (x, y) is on the graph of f if and only if $y = f(x)$, which happens if and only if $x = g(y)$; the latter happens if and only if (y, x) is on the graph of g. Therefore, (x, y) is on the graph of f if and only if (y, x) is on the graph of g.

35. (f)

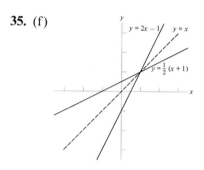

Section 2-4 (page 84)

1. -2 **3.** -4 **5.** $-1, 5, 5$ **7.** $1, 6, 5$

9.

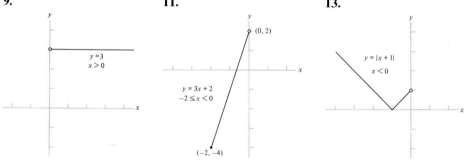

11.

13.

15.

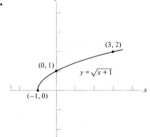

17.

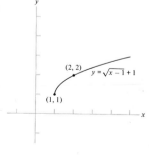

18.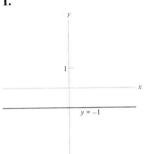

19.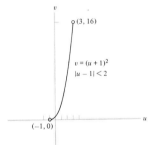

22. $3, 4, 20$ **23.** $1, -3, 11/24$ **24.** $-5, 13, -1$

25. $F = \begin{cases} .80 + .35[8M] & \text{if } M \neq \frac{1}{8}, \frac{2}{8}, \ldots \\ .80 + .35([8M] - 1) & \text{if } M = \frac{1}{8}, \frac{2}{8}, \ldots \end{cases}$

26. $C = \begin{cases} 2.00 + .30([2M] + 1) & \text{if } M \neq \frac{1}{2}, \frac{2}{2}, \frac{3}{2}, \ldots \\ 2.00 + .30[2M] & \text{if } M = \frac{1}{2}, \frac{2}{2}, \frac{3}{2}, \ldots \end{cases}$

27. 5.8¢   **28.** $V = x(10 - 2x)(8 - 2x), 0 < x < 4$
29. $W = 110x - 4x^2, 0 < x < 25/2$ **30.** $c = .05$; 125/3 ohms   **31.** $\pi(r_2{}^2 - r_1{}^2)$
32. (a) $2\pi h$; (b) 2π ft; (c) $2\pi \approx 6.28$ ft

Section 2-5 (page 93)

3. 0   **5.** 3   **7.** 11   **9.** 17   **11.** $(4 - \sqrt{11})/5$ **13.** 0   **15.** -2 **17.** $6x + 3h$
19. $-6x^2 - 6xh - 2h^2 + 1$ **21.** $1/(\sqrt{x + h - 4} + \sqrt{x - 4})$
23. $0, -2, 30, -149, 1/2$ **25.** $-1/x^2$ **28.** -16 ft/sec, -80 ft/sec, -128 ft/sec
29. No, yes   **32.** $.718, .696, .693; (2^2)(.693) = 2.77$

Chapter 3
Section 3-1 (page 106)

1.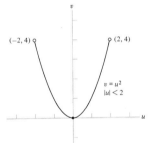

3.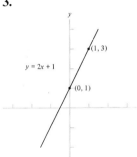

5.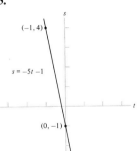

7.

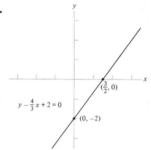

$y - \frac{4}{3}x + 2 = 0$

$\left(\frac{3}{2}, 0\right)$

$(0, -2)$

9.

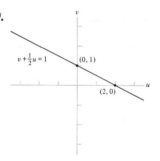

$v + \frac{1}{2}u = 1$

$(0, 1)$

$(2, 0)$

11.

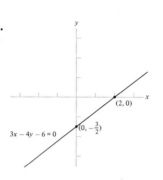

$3x - 4y - 6 = 0$

$(2, 0)$

$\left(0, -\frac{3}{2}\right)$

13.

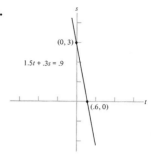

$(0, 3)$

$1.5t + .3s = .9$

$(.6, 0)$

15. Parallel: 5 and 13; Perpendicular: 3 and 9
17. $y - 1 = -(x - 4)/5$; decreasing   **19.** $y - 2 = 5(x + 3)$; increasing
21. $y + 3 = 4x/3$; increasing   **23.** $y - 7 = 2(x + 4)/5$; increasing
24. $y - 3 = 3(x - 2)$; increasing   **25.** $y = (x - 2)/2$; increasing
27. (a) $y - \sqrt{2/3} = -(x - \sqrt{1/3})/\sqrt{2}$; (b) 0; no slope at $(1, 0)$

29.

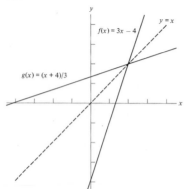

$y = x$

$f(x) = 3x - 4$

$g(x) = (x + 4)/3$

30. (a)

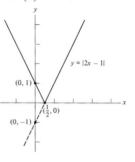

$y = |2x - 1|$

$(0, 1)$

$\left(\frac{1}{2}, 0\right)$

$(0, -1)$

(b)

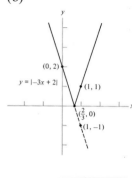

$(0, 2)$

$y = |-3x + 2|$

$(1, 1)$

$\left(\frac{2}{3}, 0\right)$

$(1, -1)$

32. $55,000; $5000/year; slope is the rate of increase
33. $8000; $18,000; $15,000

Section 3-2 (page 117)

1.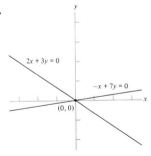

3.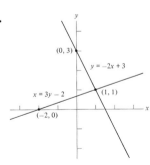

4. $s = -1, t = -1$ **6.** $v = -1/2, u = 21/8$ **7.** $x = 5, y = 9$
10. $s = -1, t = 2$ **12.** $u = 4, v = 3$ **13.** $x = 1, y = 2, z = -1$
15. $u = 2, v = 0, w = 3$ **17.** No solution **19.** $a = b = c = 1$
21. $m = -1/3, b = 10/3$ **22.** $a = 0, b = 1, c = -1$ **25.** 56/5 and 16/5
26. $x = 1/10, y = 7/30, z = 1/3$ **27.** 35 **28.** 100/3 g of 20% copper and
200/3 g of 35% copper **29.** row 16/5 km/hr; current 4/5 km/hr
31. meat \$1.75/kilo; butter \$1.00/kilo **32.** 10 nickels, 15 dimes, 5 quarters

Section 3-3 (page 132)

1.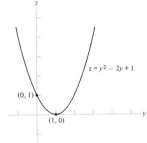

3.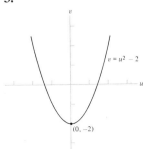

5.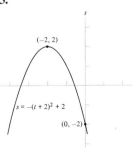

7.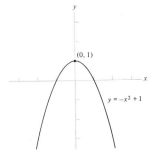

9.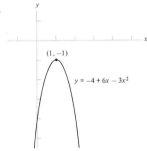

11.

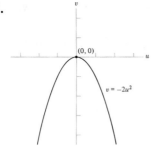

$(0, 0)$

$v = -2u^2$

13.

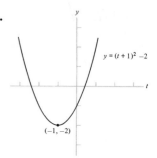

$y = (t + 1)^2 - 2$

$(-1, -2)$

15.

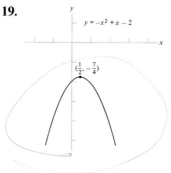

$v = u^2 + 6u + 8$

$(-3, -1)$

17.

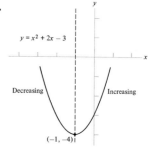

$y = -3 + 2t - t^2$

$(1, -2)$

19.

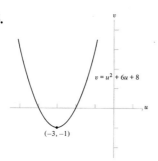

$y = -x^2 + x - 2$

$\left(\frac{1}{2}, -\frac{7}{4}\right)$

21.

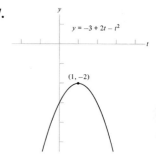

$y = x^2 + 2x - 3$

Decreasing   Increasing

$(-1, -4)$

22. $8x; 2x; x/2$

23. (a)

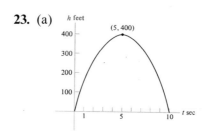

h feet

$(5, 400)$

400
300
200
100

1   5   10 t sec

(b) 400 ft after 5 sec; (c) *increasing* means the projectile is rising; (d) after 10 sec

25. 25 ft by 50 ft   **26.** $10,000   **27.** $x = 3, y = 4$ **28.** Both shapes yield the same maximum area.   **29.** If $x =$ increase in price, then $S = (10 + x)$ $\times (400 - 10x)$; maximum sales occur when $x = 15$; he should charge 25¢

30.

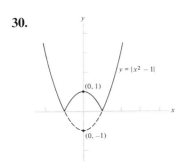

32.

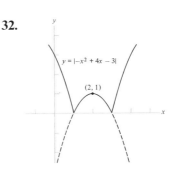

33. If the discriminant $b^2 - 4ac \leq 0$ **34.** $h = -b/2a, k = (4ac - b^2)/4a$

Section 3-4 (page 140)

1. -1 **3.** No real solution   **5.** $2, 1$ **7.** $-1, 1/4$ **9.** No real solutions
11. $-1, 1/2$ **13.** $-7, 5$ **15.** Clear fractions; then $u = (6 \pm \sqrt{132})/16$ **17.** $0, 2$
19. No real solutions   **21.** (a) 15 meters; (b) 7 meters; (c) 5 sec
22. (a) 128 ft; (b) 128 ft; (c) no; the ball is rising at 1 sec and falling at 3 sec;
(d) set $h = 0$; then $t = 5$ sec   **23.** 144 ft   **24.** (a) 16 ft; (b) 80 ft; (c) 144 ft;
(e) 10 sec   **25.** a.r.c.$f(t, h) = -32t - 16h$; exact rate of change is $-32t$;
-64 ft/sec; -160 ft/sec; -320 ft/sec   **26.** 50   **27.** 52¢/plate
28. (b) $-b = -2 + 3 = 1$ so $b = -1, c = (-2)(3) = -6$; $b = -2, c = -2$;
$b = 1/3, c = -1/36$

29. $f(x) = 2\left(x - \dfrac{-3 + \sqrt{17}}{4}\right)\left(x - \dfrac{-3 - \sqrt{17}}{4}\right)$

$g(t) = -\left(t - \dfrac{1 + \sqrt{5}}{2}\right)\left(t - \dfrac{1 - \sqrt{5}}{2}\right)$

31. $x^4 = 16$; $x = \pm 2$ **32.** $(x^2 - 4)(x^2 - 1) = 0$; $x = \pm 2$ or ± 1

Section 3-5 (page 146)

1.

3.

5.

7.

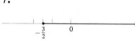

9.

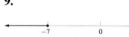

11.

13.

15.

17.

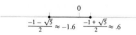

19. No solution

21.

23.

25.

27.

29.

31.

33.

35.

37.

39.

41.

43.

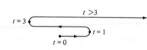

45. From $300/7 \approx 42.9$ to 60 mph

Chapter 4
Section 4-1 (page 156)

1. $x^5 + 3x^4 + 2x^3 - x^2 - 3$ 3. $\frac{1}{4}y^7 + \frac{2}{3}y^5 - y^4 - y^2$ 5. $3x^4 - 3x^2 - x + 1$
7. $y^3 - 2y^2 - 2y - 3$ 9. $x^5 - 2x^3 + 10x^2 - 9x + 7$
14. $f(0) = 0,\ F(0) = 0,\ G(1) = 0$ 15. $f'(x) = 6x^2 + 6x - 2;\ g'(x) = 4x^3 - 2;$
$h'(x) = 4x^3 - 2;\ F'(x) = 5x^4 + 3x^2;\ G'(x) = -6x^2;\ H'(x) = 0$
16. $(f + g)(x) = x^4 + 2x^3 + 3x^2 - 4x + 1;\ (f + g)'(x) = 4x^3 + 6x^2 + 6x - 4;$
$(f' + g')(x) = (6x^2 + 6x - 2) + (4x^3 - 2) = 4x^3 + 6x^2 + 6x - 4$
17. $(F - G)(x) = x^5 + 3x^3 + 2;\ (F - G)'(x) = 5x^4 + 9x^2 = (F' - G')(x)$
18. $(FG)(x) = -2x^8 - 2x^6 + 2x^5 + 2x^3;\ (FG)'(x) =$
$-16x^7 - 12x^5 + 10x^4 + 6x^2;\ (FG')(x) = -6x^7 - 6x^5;\ (GF')(x) =$
$-10x^7 - 6x^5 + 10x^4 + 6x^2;\ (FG)'(x) = (FG' + GF')(x)$
21. $a = 0,\ b = -2,\ c = 1,\ d = -3$ 23. $a = 0,\ b = -1,\ c = 1,\ d = 1,\ e = -1$
25. $f(-1, 1) = 8;\ f(0, 2) = 4;\ f(\sqrt{2}, \sqrt{2}) = 4;\ g(3, 4) = 25;\ g(0, 0) = 0;$
$g(1/\sqrt{2}, 1/\sqrt{2}) = 1$ 27. $V = \pi r^2 h$ 28. $S = 2\pi r h$ 29. $V = whl$
30. $S = 2lw + 2hl + 2hw$

Section 4-2 (page 162)

1. $x^2 + 3 - \dfrac{1}{x^2}$ 3. $6y^2 - 9 + \dfrac{y + 7}{y^2 + 1}$ 5. $q = t^2 - t + 1;\ r = -(t^2 + 1)$

7. $2m^4 - m + 1$ 9. $q = 9x + 15;\ r = 34$ 11. $q = 3t^4 - 3t^3 + 2t^2 - 2t + 3;$
$r = -3$ 13. $q = 8m^2 - 5m + \frac{11}{2};\ r = -3/4$ 15. $r^4 + r^3 + r^2 + r + 1$
20. $F/G = t^4 + t^3 + t^2 + t + 1;\ (F/G)' = 4t^3 + 3t^2 + 2t + 1;\ GF' =$
$5t^5 - 5t^4;\ FG' = t^5 - 1;\ G^2 = t^2 - 2t + 1;\ (GF' - FG')/G^2 =$
$(4t^5 - 5t^4 + 1)/(t^2 - 2t + 1) = 4t^3 + 3t^2 + 2t + 1$
25. $q = t^2;\ r = -t^4 + t^3 + t^2 - 1;\ [(t^2)(t^5 - 1) + (-t^4 + t^3 + t^2 - 1)]' =$
$(t^2)(5t^4) + (t^5 - 1)(2t) + (-4t^3 + 3t^2 + 2t) = 7t^6 - 4t^3 + 3t^2 = H'$
28. (a) $t = 3;$ (b) $y = -1$

Section 4-3 (page 169)

1. $(x + 5)(x - 1)(x + 2);\ -5, 1, -2$ 3. $(u^2 + 2u + 2)(u - 3);\ 3$ 5. $-3, 2, 5/2$
7. $-7, 4, \pm\sqrt{2}$ 9. $0, -1$ 11. $\pm 1/\sqrt{3}, \pm 1/2$ 13. $\pm 2, 3$ 15. $\pm\sqrt{2}, 1, \pm\sqrt{3}$
17. $f(x)$ has one change of sign and there is one positive zero; $f(-x)$ has two changes of sign and there are two negative zeros   21. $h(u)$ has no change of sign and there are no positive zeros; $h(-u)$ has three changes of sign and there is one negative zero   23. (a) $p(x) = x^3 - x - 1$ has one change of sign so there is a positive zero; (b) yes   24. (a) No; $x - x^2 - 1 = -(x^2 - x + 1)$ has

no real zeros by the quadratic formula; (c) if n is odd, then $p(-x) = -x + x^n - 1 = x^n - x - 1$ has one change of sign, so there is one negative zero.   **26.** $x = -5, 1, -2$ **27.** $t = -3, 2, 5/2$ **28.** $x = -7, 4, \pm\sqrt{2}$
35. There are two positive zeros of $x^2 - 2x + 1 = (x - 1)(x - 1)$; both zeros are equal to 1.

Section 4-4 (page 179)

1. $13/30$ **3.** $-(\sqrt{6} - \sqrt{3})/\sqrt{2}$ **5.** $-9, 3$ **7.** $1/2, -4/3$ **9.** $2 \pm \sqrt{10}$
11. $-5, -2, 1$ **13.** 3 **15.** $-3, 5/2, 2$
17. $-7, 4$, and two irrational solutions: $-2 < a_1 < -1$ and $1 < a_2 < 2$
19. $1/2$ and $3/2$ are the only solutions **21.** No solutions
23. Three irrational solutions: $-3 < a_1 < -2$, $-1 < a_2 < 0$, and $2 < a_3 < 3$
25. -1 and two irrational solutions: $-3 < a_1 < -2$ and $2 < a_2 < 3$
27. 0 and one irrational root: $1 < a_1 < 2$ **29.** ± 2 are the only solutions
31. ± 1 and ± 2 are the only possible rational zeros

Section 4-5 (page 188)

5.

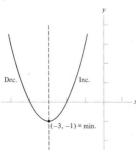

7.

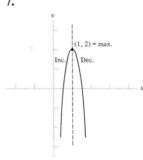

9.

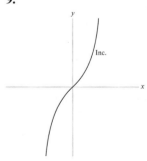

11.

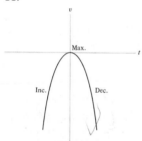

13.

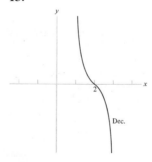

15.

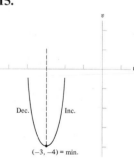

17.

19.

21.

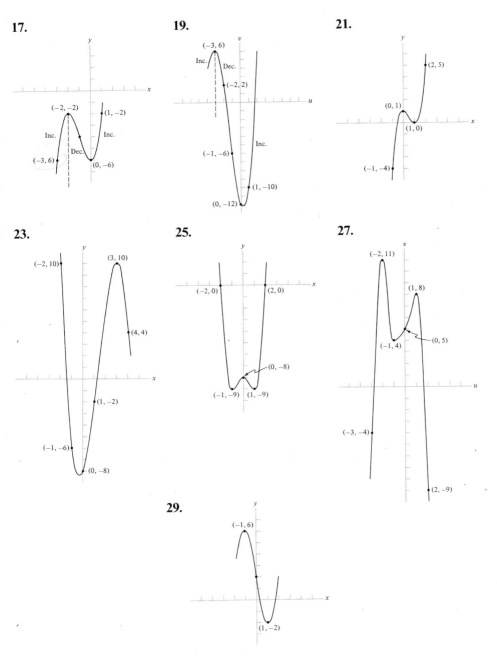

23.

25.

27.

29.

31. $f'(x) = 3x^2 + 6x$; the zeros of f' are -2 and 0; f' is negative between its zeros. **33.** Use S' or sketch the graph. At $t = 1$ the sales are decreasing. The sales are at a minimum when $t = 2$; buy then. **35.** When $t = 3$

36. The function behaves like x^4 for large $|x|$. Yes, it will be positive; in fact, it has a minimum but *no* maximum.

Section 4-6 (page 195)

1. $(7x - 1)/2x$ **3.** $(t^2 - 1)/t$ **5.** $-15/y(y + 3)$ **7.** $(-x^2 + 5x + 5)/(x + 1)$
9. $(x^2 + 2x + 4)/(x + 2)(x + 3)$ **11.** $(u^2 - 11u - 2)/(u - 4)^2(u + 2)$
13. $(x + 5)/(x - 2)$ **15.** $(t^2 + t + 1)/(t + 1)(t + 2)$ **17.** $x + 2y$
19. $(3x - 5)/x^3(x - 1)$ **21.** 3

23.

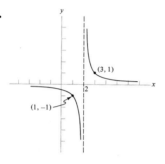

25.

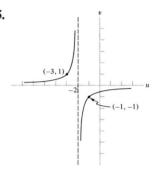

27.

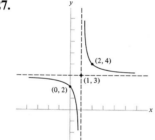

31.

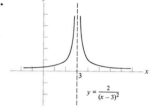

33.

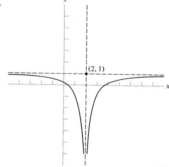

35. $c = 98$; (a) $98/25$ and $98/4$; (b) 6.86, increasing   **36.** $-1/x^2$
37. (a) $-1/80$ ft/sec; (b) $-1/64$ ft/sec; (c) toward the point; (d) no
38. $C = 2.13 + 60,000/x$

Chapter 5
Section 5-1 (page 206)

1.

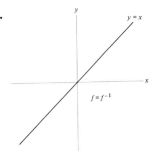

3.

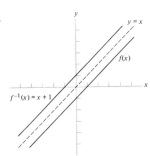

5.

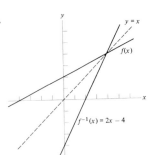

7.

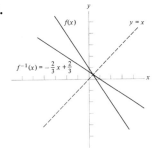

9.

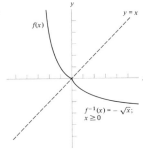

11.

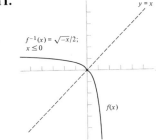

13.

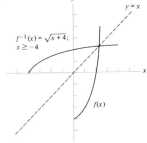

15.

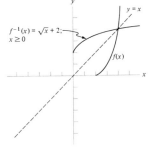

21.
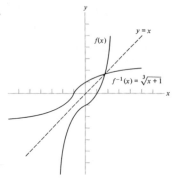

25.
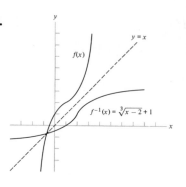

27.
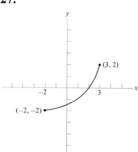

28.
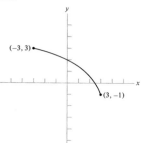

29.
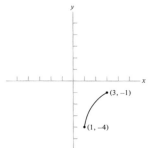

30.
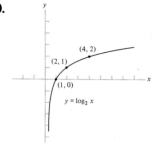

31.
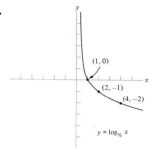

32. $L(1/16) = -4$, $L(1) = 0$, $L(4) = 2$, $L(2^3) = 3$, $2^{L(4)} = 4$

33. $L(1/2) = 1$, $L(1) = 0$, $L(2) = -1$, $(1/2)^{L(4)} = 4$

Section 5-2 (page 213)

1. 8 **3.** 1 **5.** 1000 **7.** $y = 2^3 = 8$ **9.** $1/\sqrt{2}$ **11.** 2 **13.** $1/9 = 3^x$; $x = -2$
15. 1/4 **17.** 1 **19.** $b^3 = 8$; $b = 2$ **21.** π **23.** 7

25. **27.** **29.**

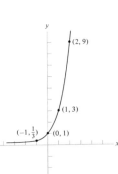

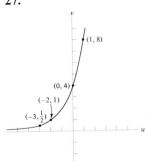

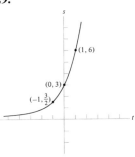

31. Maximum at $x = 3$ is 27; minimum at $x = -2$ is $1/9$
32. Maximum at $t = -1$ is 4; minimum at $t = 2$ is $1/16$

33.

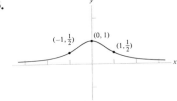

Max. = 1, no minimum, no inverse

34. Over \$10 billion   **35.** (a) $Q(t) = Q(1/2)^{t/2}$; (b) $Q/16$; (c) no
37. (a) 4 (b) $-1/16$ (c) $3/64$ (d) -32 **38.** (a) Q; (b) $Q2^9$; (c) $Q2^{99}$

Section 5-3 (page 219)

1. $x = 4^2 = 16$ **3.** $1/32$ **5.** $1/4$ **7.** $b^2 = 4$; $b = 2$ **9.** $1/9$ **11.** $1/3$
13. $(1/3)^y = 81$; $y = -4$ **15.** -5 **17.** 0   **19.** 1.176   **21.** $-.2219$ **23.** 2.352

27. **28.**

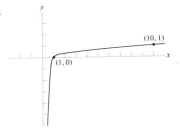

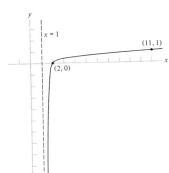

29.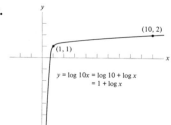

30.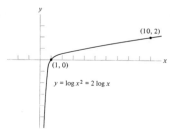

31.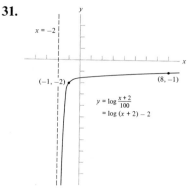

32. (a) -2; (b) -2 **34.** (a) Set $b = 10$, $a = 3$, and $x = 5$.
Then $\log_3 5 = (\log 5)/(\log 3) = .6990/.4771 = 1.4651$
35. (a) $.3010 - 2 = -1.6990$; (b) $-.6990$; (c) 1.3010; (d) 2.3010; (e) $n + .3010$

Section 5-4 (page 226)

1. 1.4713 **3.** -2.5287 **5.** 3.1614 **6.** 4.1614 **11.** 3.7474 **13.** 851 **15.** $.001$
17. 1 **19.** $.1$ **21.** $.0002$ **23.** 4400 **25.** $3 \log 3.27 + 4 \log .0628 - \log 591 =$
$-6.0361 = .9639 - 7$; the antilogarithm is 9.2×10^{-7} **27.** 2.99×10^{-4}
29. 812 **31.** 3.25 **33.** 3.858 **35.** 2.637 **37.** (a) $-.9080$; (b) $.0004$; (c) 0
38. (a) 1035; (b) $.01184$; (c) $.04181$

Section 5-5 (page 232)

1. $323,830$ cu. in. **3.** $123,551$ cu. in. **5.** 5.74 sec **7.** $.0448$ lb/cu. in.
9. 2.45 cu. ft. **11.** 2.1 **13.** $.692$ **15.** $x = -\dfrac{1}{R}\ln(1 - RI)$ **17.** 8×10^9
19. $x = 10^{(Q-S)/R} - 1$ **21.** $\$2208$ **22.** $\$12,191$ **23.** 139 months or 11.6 years
25. $\left(1 + \dfrac{1}{n}\right)^n \approx 2$, 2.59, 2.70, and 2.717 when $n = 1$, 10, 100, and 1000

26. $k = 3.85 \times 10^{-5}$; $P = (.68)P_0$
27. $P_0 = 202$, $k = 2.92 \times 10^{-3}$; $P = 227$ million in the year 2000 **28.** 88.6 g

Chapter 6
Section 6-1 (page 242)

1. 0 **2.** $\pi/6$ **3.** $\pi/4$ **4.** $\pi/3$ **5.** $\pi/2$ **7.** $-\pi$ **9.** $-5\pi/2$ **11.** $0°$ **12.** $30°$
13. $45°$ **14.** $60°$ **15.** $90°$ **17.** $-315°$ **19.** $-660°$ **21.** .383 **23.** $-.0731$
25. $57.3°$ **27.** $-149°$ **37.** $7\pi/4$ **39.** $4\pi/3$ **41.** For point A, the distance is 1; for point B, the distance is $\sqrt{18} = 3\sqrt{2}$. The ratios $1/\sqrt{2}$ to 1 and 3 to $3\sqrt{2}$ are equal. **43.** For point A, the distance is $\sqrt{53}$; for point B, the distance is $\sqrt{212} = 2\sqrt{53}$. The ratios are $-2/\sqrt{53} = -4/2\sqrt{53}$ and $-7/\sqrt{53} = -14/2\sqrt{53}$ **45.** 83.33 rad/sec $\approx$ 13 rev/sec **47.** $\pi/12$ rad/hr; 1047 mph
49. $36\pi \approx 113$ m/min **52.** Area $= r^2\theta/2$

Section 6-2 (page 250)

1. 4/5 and 3/5 **3.** 4/5 and $-3/5$ **5.** $-1/\sqrt{3}$ and $-\sqrt{2}/\sqrt{3}$
9. $\sqrt{2}/2$ and $-\sqrt{2}/2$ **11.** 0 **13.** $\pi/3$ **15.** $\pi/2$ **17.** $\pi/6$ and $\pi/3$ **19.** $\pi/2$
21. $\pi/10$ and $\pi/2$ **23.** $\pi/4$ **25.** 0 and π **27.** $(1, 0)$ **29.** $(1/\sqrt{2}, 1/\sqrt{2})$
31. $\left(\dfrac{3\sqrt{3}}{2}, \dfrac{3}{2}\right)$ **33.** $(0, -3)$ **37.** $\sqrt{3} \approx 1.73$ miles **38.** $6\sqrt{3} \approx 10.4$ ft

Section 6-3 (page 259)

1. $-1/2$ and $-\sqrt{3}/2$ **3.** $-\sqrt{3}/2$ and $1/2$ **5.** $\sqrt{2}/2$ and $-\sqrt{2}/2$
6. $-1/2$ and $\sqrt{3}/2$ **8.** $1/2$ and $-\sqrt{3}/2$ **10.** $\sqrt{3}/2$ and $1/2$
11. $\sqrt{2}/2$ and $\sqrt{2}/2$ **13.** $1/2$ and $-\sqrt{3}/2$ **15.** 0 and 1
21. $\{n\pi \,|\, n \text{ any integer}\}$
23. $\left\{\dfrac{\pi}{6} + 2n\pi \,\middle|\, n \text{ any integer}\right\} \cup \left\{\dfrac{5\pi}{6} + 2n\pi \,\middle|\, n \text{ any integer}\right\}$
25. $\{2n\pi \,|\, n \text{ any integer}\}$ **27.** $\left\{\dfrac{\pi}{8} + n\pi \,\middle|\, n \text{ any integer}\right\} \cup \left\{\dfrac{3\pi}{8} + n\pi \,\middle|\, n \text{ any integer}\right\}$
29. $\left\{\dfrac{\pi + 4n\pi}{10} \,\middle|\, n \text{ any integer}\right\}$ **30.** $\left\{\dfrac{\pi}{4} + n\pi \,\middle|\, n \text{ any integer}\right\}$
32. All x **34.** No solution (because $|\cos x| \le 1$) **36.** 1/2 **38.** 0
39. $-\sqrt{3}/2$ **41.** 1 **44.** 13 ft
46. It will move upward to a point one unit above the center, then downward to a point one unit below the center, then upward again. It will continue this up-and-down motion as long as the disc rotates; $y = \sin x$.

Section 6-4 (page 268)

1.

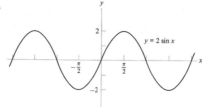

$y = 2 \sin x$

3.

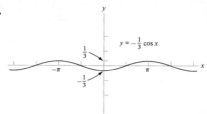

$y = -\frac{1}{3} \cos x$

5.

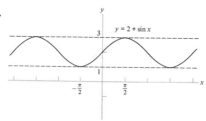

$y = 2 + \sin x$

7.

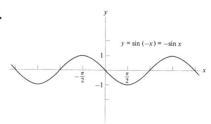

$y = \sin(-x) = -\sin x$

9.

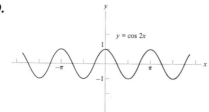

$y = \cos 2x$

11.

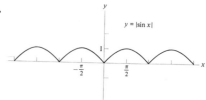

$y = |\sin x|$

13.

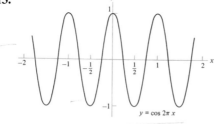

$y = \cos 2\pi x$

15.

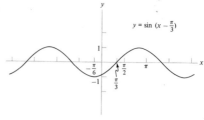

$y = \sin \left(x - \frac{\pi}{3}\right)$

17.

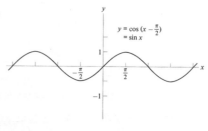

$y = \cos \left(x - \frac{\pi}{2}\right)$
$= \sin x$

19.

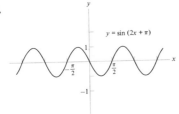

21.

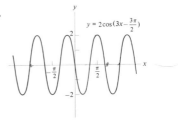

22. When $\theta = \pi/2$, the x-coordinate of the terminal point is 0.

24. $0, 1/\sqrt{3}, 1, \sqrt{3}$ **25.** First and third; second and fourth

26. $\tan(-x) = -\tan x$; $\tan\left(x - \dfrac{\pi}{2}\right) = -1/\tan x$; $\tan\left(x + \dfrac{\pi}{2}\right) = -1/\tan x$;

$\tan(x + \pi) = \tan x$; $\tan(\pi - x) = -\tan x$; $\tan(x + 2\pi) = \tan x$ **28.** 20 ft

29. $x = 3 \cos\left(10\pi t - \dfrac{\pi}{2}\right)$ or $x = 3 \sin 10\pi t$ **30.** $y = 10 \sin\left(240\pi t - \dfrac{\pi}{2}\right)$

assuming that the motion starts from a point 10 mm below the original position.

Section 6-5 (page 276)

1.

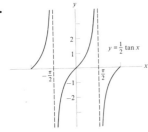

3.

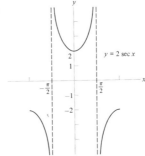

5.

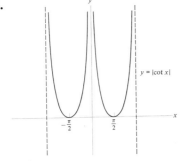

7.

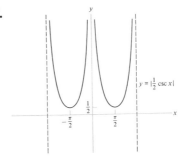

9.

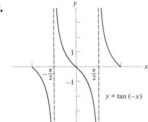

$y = \tan(-x)$

11.

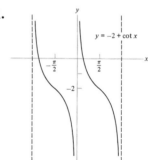

$y = -2 + \cot x$

13.

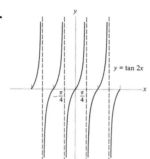

$y = \tan 2x$

15.

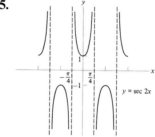

$y = \sec 2x$

17.

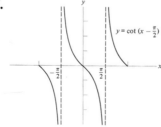

$y = \cot\left(x - \frac{\pi}{2}\right)$

19.

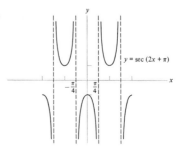

$y = \sec(2x + \pi)$

21.

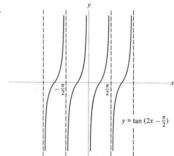

$y = \tan\left(2x - \frac{\pi}{2}\right)$

22. 23. 24.

	Quad 1	Quad 2	Quad 3	Quad 4	Period	Domain	Range
sin	+	+	−	−	2π	All x	$-1 \le y \le 1$
cos	+	−	−	+	2π	All x	$-1 \le y \le 1$
tan	+	−	+	−	π	$x \neq \dfrac{\pi}{2} \pm n\pi$	All y
cot	+	−	+	−	π	$x \neq \pm n\pi$	All y
sec	+	−	−	+	2π	$x \neq \dfrac{\pi}{2} \pm n\pi$	$-\infty < y \le -1$ or $1 \le y < \infty$
csc	+	+	−	−	2π	$x \neq \pm n\pi$	$-\infty < y \le -1$ or $1 \le y < \infty$

25. $\sec x$ **27.** $\cot u$ **29.** $-\csc u$ **31.** $-\tan t$ **33.** $\csc v$ **35.** $-\tan s$

37. $\left\{ \dfrac{\pi}{3} + n\pi \,\middle|\, n \text{ any integer} \right\}$

39. $\left\{ \dfrac{5\pi}{6} + 2n\pi \,\middle|\, n \text{ any integer} \right\} \cup \left\{ \dfrac{7\pi}{6} + 2n\pi \,\middle|\, n \text{ any integer} \right\}$

41. $\left\{ \dfrac{3\pi}{8} + \dfrac{n\pi}{2} \,\middle|\, n \text{ any integer} \right\}$

43. $\left\{ \dfrac{\pi}{18} + \dfrac{2n\pi}{3} \,\middle|\, n \text{ any integer} \right\} \cup \left\{ \dfrac{5\pi}{18} + \dfrac{2n\pi}{3} \,\middle|\, n \text{ any integer} \right\}$

Chapter 7
Section 7-1 (page 286)

(Many of the answers for Chapter 7 were derived using a calculator and may differ slightly from calculations using Table 2.)

1. .7412 **3.** −.9001 **5.** −1.6666 **7.** −.6916 **9.** 4.3363 **11.** −28.6537
13. .4887 **15.** .4870 **17.** −1.8768 **19.** −.5555 **21.** $207°40' \pm n360°$
23. $126°40' \pm n180°$ **25.** 3.7571 **27.** $\pm n\pi$ **29.** $\pi/4 \pm n\pi$ **31.** .2498 **33.** .8033
35. $63°15'$ **37.** 4.0213 **39.** 225×10^3 **41.** The unit circle
43. $(\sin h)/h \approx 1$ for small h **44.** $(\cos h - 1)/h \approx 0$ for small h
45. $(\cos h - 1)/h^2 \approx -\frac{1}{2}$ for small h

Section 7-2 (page 294)

1. $B = 58°, b = 16, c = 18.9$ **5.** $B = 31°, a = 3.3, c = 3.9$
9. $B = 1.1316, a = 4.2522, b = 9.0509$ **13.** $c = 5, A = .6435, B = .9273$
17. $a = \sqrt{55} \approx 7.4, A = 1.1864, B = .3844$ **19.** $\sin x = 3/\sqrt{10}, \cos x = 1/\sqrt{10}$
21. $\sin x = 2/\sqrt{5}, \cot x = 1/2$ **23.** $\sec x = 5/4, \csc x = 5/3$ **25.** $33°40'$
27. N77°20′E   **29.** 2.73 km, .91 km/sec   **30.** 2.4 km
32. (a) $70°10'$; (b) 11.3 mi; (c) between $\alpha = 45°$ and $\alpha = 60°$

35. $\dfrac{n}{2}r^2 \sin\dfrac{2\pi}{n} = \pi r^2 \left(\dfrac{n}{2\pi}\right)\sin\dfrac{2\pi}{n} = \pi r^2 \left[\dfrac{\sin\dfrac{2\pi}{n}}{\dfrac{2\pi}{n}}\right]$. If n is very large, the

expression in brackets is very close to 1 (see Exercise 43 in Section 7-1).
36. HINT: Draw a line from A perpendicular to side a; then solve each of the right triangles formed.

Section 7-3 (page 304)

1. $A = 22°20', B = 49°30', C = 108°10'$ **5.** $a = 3.3, B = 42°30', C = 115°30'$
9. Because the sum of the lengths of any two sides of a triangle must be larger than the third side, c must be greater than 99. Using a calculator with eight significant figures, $c = 99.000615$.   **11.** No   **12.** Yes   **13.** Yes   **14.** No   **15.** Yes
16. See Exercise 17   **17.** No triangle can have sides of length 5, 10, and 20 because $5 + 10 < 20$ (see answer to Exercise 9 above).
22. $(1, \sqrt{3})$ **24.** $(-3, 0)$ **26.** $\{\sqrt{32}, \pi/4\}$ **28.** $\{2, 4\pi/3\}$ **30.** 278.5 ft
32. L of C not applicable   **33.** S 51°50′W, about 2 hrs 27 min
35. L of C not applicable   **36.** 25.2 ft, 19.1 ft   **37.** 19.8 m²   **38.** $\{79.6, -74°10'\}$
39. 58.6 miles   **43.** The sum of any two must be larger than the third
44. $0° < C < 180°$ **47.** Area $= \frac{1}{2}ab \sin C$, where C is the angle between $0°$ and $180°$ whose cosine is $(a^2 + b^2 - c^2)/2ab$

Section 7-4 (page 311)

1. $a = 3.7, C = 80°, c = 4.9$ **5.** No triangle   **7.** $B = 40°, C = 100°, c = 9.2$
9. $B = 74°10', A = 45°50', a = 7.5$; or $B = 105°50', A = 14°10', a = 2.5$
11. $A = 90°, C = 60° \ c = \sqrt{75} \approx 8.7$ **13.** SAS   **14.** SSA; two triangles
15. SSS   **16.** SSA; no triangle   **17.** SSA; two triangles   **18.** AAS   **19.** 13 km
20. 23 km   **22.** 110 miles   **23.** 301 ft

Section 7-5 (page 318)

1. $\{2, 60°\}$ **3.** $\{\sqrt{3}, 144°45'\}$ **5.** $(2.9, -.8)$ **7.** $(-\sqrt{2}, \sqrt{2})$

9. 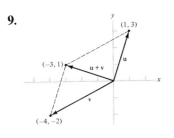   **11.**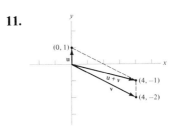

13. $(3, 2 + 3\sqrt{3}) \approx (3, 7.2)$ **15.** $(-\sqrt{3}/2, -7/2) \approx (-.86, 3.5)$ **17.** 67 lb
19. 217 mph, 68°40′ (from North)   **21.** 463 mph, N76°E
22. $\mathbf{F}_x = 76.6$ lb, $\mathbf{F}_y = 64.3$ lb   **23.** about 54 lb   **25.** 136 lb   **26.** 48°10′

Chapter 8
Section 8-1 (page 328)

1. $\pi/6$ **3.** $\pi/3$ **5.** $\pi/6$ **7.** $-\pi/6$ **9.** π **11.** $3\pi/4$ **13.** .3705   **15.** -1.235
17. 2.521   **19.** .2816   **21.** 10   **23.** $\pi/6$ **25.** $-\pi/3$ **27.** $\sqrt{3}$ **29.** $2/\sqrt{5}$
31. $3/\sqrt{7}$ **33.** $\sqrt{21}/5$ **35.** $1/9$ **37.** About 15 ft³, 60 ft³
38. Yes, by the Law of Cosines.   **39.** Only if $0 < A < \pi/2$

Section 8-2 (page 336)

1. $(\sqrt{6} + \sqrt{2})/4$ **3.** $\left(1 - \dfrac{1}{\sqrt{3}}\right)\Big/\left(1 + \dfrac{1}{\sqrt{3}}\right) = (\sqrt{3} - 1)/(\sqrt{3} + 1)$

7. $(\sqrt{6} + \sqrt{3})/4$ **11.** Write $11\pi/12$ as $2\pi/3$ plus $\pi/4$ to obtain $-4/(\sqrt{2} + \sqrt{6})$
13. $-(3\sqrt{3} + \sqrt{7})/8$ **15.** $(-50 + \sqrt{231})/66$ **17.** $-3/14$ **29.** .1244 rad   **31.** $\pi/2$
32. Starts at point A; to the right; 1; 1/2 to the right at $\pi/3$; at rest at $\pi/2$; 1/2
to the left at $2\pi/3$; at rest at $3\pi/2$; simple harmonic motion   **34.** $-\sin x$

Section 8-3 (page 341)

1. $-\sqrt{21}/5$; $17/25$; -13.3; $-17/4\sqrt{21}$; $(5 + \sqrt{21})/2$
3. $-2/\sqrt{45}$; $-4\sqrt{45}/41$; $-328\sqrt{45}/961$; 1.01   **5.** $\sqrt{(2 + \sqrt{2})}/2$

7. $2 + \sqrt{3}$ **9.** $2/\sqrt{2 + \sqrt{2}}$ **11.** $-\sqrt{\dfrac{1 + \dfrac{7}{\sqrt{85}}}{2}}$ **12.** $\sqrt{\dfrac{1 + \dfrac{7}{\sqrt{85}}}{2}}$

15. $-15\sqrt{63}/128$ **17.** $1 - 2(15\sqrt{63}/128)^2 \approx -.7303$
21. $\cosh^2 x - \sinh^2 x = \frac{1}{4}[(e^{2x} + 2 + e^{-2x}) - (e^{2x} - 2 + e^{-2x})] = 1$
23. $\tanh(x + y) = (\tanh x + \tanh y)/(1 + \tanh x \tanh y)$
24. $\sinh 2x = \sinh(x + x) = 2 \sinh x \cosh x$; etc.

Section 8-4 (page 347)

1. $\dfrac{1}{\sin x} - \sin x = \dfrac{1 - \sin^2 x}{\sin x} = \dfrac{\cos x}{\sin x} \cdot \cos x$ **3.** $\dfrac{\sin^2 u}{\cos^2 u} \cdot \dfrac{1}{\sin^2 u} = \dfrac{1}{\cos^2 u}$

5. $\dfrac{\sec t}{\cos t} = \sec^2 t = 1 + \tan^2 t$

7. $\left(\dfrac{\sin x}{\cos x} + \dfrac{\cos x}{\sin x}\right)(\cos x + \sin x) = \sin x + \dfrac{\sin^2 x}{\cos x} + \dfrac{\cos^2 x}{\sin x} + \cos x$

$$= \dfrac{\sin^2 x + \cos^2 x}{\sin x} + \dfrac{\sin^2 x + \cos^2 x}{\cos x}$$

9. $\tan u + \cot u = (\sin^2 u + \cos^2 u)/\cos u \sin u$ **11.** $x = \pi/3$ **13.** $u = \pi/3$
15. $t = \pi/4$ **17.** Identity   **19.** Not an identity   **21.** Identity   **23.** Identity
25. Identity   **27.** Identity   **29.** Identity (Factor $\cos^3 y - \sin^3 y$ as the difference of cubes.)   **31.** Identity   **33.** Identity

Section 8-5 (page 352)

1. $\left\{\dfrac{2\pi}{3} + 2n\pi\right\} \cup \left\{\dfrac{4\pi}{3} + 2n\pi\right\}$ **3.** $\{-.35 + n\pi\}$ **5.** $\left\{\dfrac{\pi}{2} + n\pi\right\}$ **7.** $\pm\pi/3$
9. $0 \le x \le \pi$ so $0 \le 3x \le 3\pi$; $\{\pi/9, 5\pi/9, 7\pi/9\}$ **11.** $\{\pi/6, -\pi/2\}$
13. $\{\pi/3, 5\pi/3\}$ **15.** $\{0, \pi\}$ **17.** $\{\pi/4, 5\pi/4\}$ **19.** $\{2\pi/3, 4\pi/3\}$
(0 is not a solution)   **21.** $\{2\pi - .17, \pi + .17, .34, \pi - .34\}$ **23.** $3\pi/2$
25. $\{2\pi/3, 4\pi/3, .84, 5.44\}$ **27.** $\{.11 + n\pi/3; n = 0, 1, \ldots, 5\}$ **29.** 0
31. $\{7\pi/12, 23\pi/12\}$ (remember, $0 \le x < 2\pi$)   **33.** $\{\pi/6, 5\pi/6\}$
35. $\{0\}$ **37.** $\{0, \pi/2, \pi, 3\pi/2\}$ **39.** $\{.75, \pi - .75\}$

Chapter 9
Section 9-1 (page 360)

1. $4 + 2i$ **3.** $\frac{3}{4} - \frac{2}{9}i$ **5.** $-5i$ **7.** $-5 - \frac{3}{5}i$ **9.** $6 + 8i$ **11.** $-1 + 5i$
13. $3.36 + .33i$ **15.** $-i$ **17.** $\frac{30}{37} + \frac{5}{37}i$ **19.** $\frac{2}{41} + \frac{23}{41}i$ **27.** 5   **29.** $5\sqrt{2}$
31. $i^3 = -i, i^4 = 1, i^5 = i, i^6 = -1, \ldots, i^{12} = 1$;

$$i^n = \begin{cases} 1 & \text{if } n = 4m \\ i & \text{if } n = 4m + 1 \\ -1 & \text{if } n = 4m + 2 \\ -i & \text{if } n = 4m + 3 \end{cases} \quad \text{for some integer } m.$$

32. $17 = 4 \cdot 4 + 1$ so $i^{17} = i$; $220 = 4 \cdot 55$ so $i^{220} = 1$; $5280 = 4 \cdot 1320$
so $i^{5280} = 1$; $-19 = 4(-5) + 1$ so $i^{-19} = i$
41. -4 **43.** $(3 + 2\sqrt{2}) + (3\sqrt{2} - 2)i$ **46.** $290 = (13)^2 + (11)^2$

Section 9-2 (page 367)

1. $5 + 5i$ **3.** -3 **5.** $-2 + 2i$ **7.** $4 + i$ **9.** $\sqrt{2}(\cos(-\pi/4) + i\sin(-\pi/4))$
11. $4(\cos 2\pi/3 + i\sin 2\pi/3)$ **13.** $2(\cos \pi + i\sin \pi)$ **15.** $-2i$
17. $-(\sqrt{2} + \sqrt{2}i)/2$ **19.** $6\sqrt{2}(\cos 7\pi/12 + i\sin 7\pi/12)$
21. $4(\cos 2\pi/3 + i\sin 2\pi/3)$ **23.** $25\sqrt{2}(\cos \pi/4 + i\sin \pi/4)$
29. $\cos \pi/2 + i\sin \pi/2$ **31.** $4(\cos \pi/3 + i\sin \pi/3)$
36. $\bar{z} = r(\cos(-\theta) + i\sin(-\theta))$; $-z = r(\cos(\theta + \pi) + i\sin(\theta + \pi))$
37. $z^n = r^n(\cos n\theta + i\sin n\theta)$; $1 + i = \sqrt{2}(\cos \pi/4 + i\sin \pi/4)$ so
$(1 + i)^4 = 4(\cos \pi + i\sin \pi) = -4$; $(\sqrt{3}/2) + (1/2)i = \cos \pi/6 + i\sin \pi/6$ so
$((\sqrt{3}/2) + (1/2)i)^{12} = \cos 2\pi + i\sin 2\pi = 1$ **38.** -1 **39.** $-(\sqrt{2}/2) - (\sqrt{2}/2)i$
41. In polar form, the roots are $2(\cos n\pi/3 + i\sin n\pi/3)$, $n = 0, 1, \ldots, 5$ (Check).
In rectangular form, the roots are 2 ($n = 0$), $(1 + \sqrt{3}i)$ ($n = 1$), $(-1 + \sqrt{3}i)$
($n = 2$), and so on.

Section 9-3 (page 374)

1. $1 + 2i$ **3.** $3 + i$ **5.** $3 \pm 2\sqrt{2}$ **7.** $(1 \pm \sqrt{11}i)/3$ **9.** $(1 \pm 3\sqrt{3}i)/2$
11. $1, -\sqrt{3}/2 \pm i/2$ **13.** $x^2 + 9$ **15.** $x^3 - 4x^2 + 6x - 4$
17. $x^4 - 6x^3 + 10x^2 - 6x + 9$ **19.** $x^4 - 6x^3 + 14x^2 - 16x + 8$ **20.** Not
possible because $1 - i$ must also be a zero   **21.** Not possible
22. $x^4 + 13x^2 + 36$ **23.** $\pm 2, \pm 2i$ **25.** $\sqrt{2} \pm \sqrt{2}i, -\sqrt{2} \pm \sqrt{2}i$ **27.** $\pm i$,
$1, 3$ **29.** $-2, 1 \pm \sqrt{3}i$ **30.** $-3, 2 \pm i$ **32.** A polynomial of odd degree
has an odd number of zeros but the complex zeros appear in conjugate
pairs.

Section 9-4 (page 381)

1. $32(\cos 5\pi/6 + i\sin 5\pi/6)$ **3.** $\cos(-495°) + i\sin(-495°)$ **5.** $(-1 + \sqrt{3}i)/2$
7. -1 **9.** $-128 + 128\sqrt{3}i$ **11.** $3125(\cos 4.6 + i\sin 4.6)$
13. $28{,}561(\cos 17.3 + i\sin 17.3)$ **15.** $\sqrt{1} = \pm 1$; $\sqrt[3]{1} = 1, (-1 \pm \sqrt{3}i)/2$;
$\sqrt[4]{1} = \pm 1, \pm i$; $\sqrt[5]{1} = 1, \cos 2\pi/5 \pm i\sin 2\pi/5, \cos 4\pi/5 \pm i\sin 4\pi/5$;
$\sqrt[7]{1} = 1, \cos 2\pi/7 \pm i\sin 2\pi/7, \cos 4\pi/7 \pm i\sin 4\pi/7, \cos 6\pi/7 \pm i\sin 6\pi/7$
17. $2, -1 \pm \sqrt{3}i$ **19.** $(\sqrt{3} \pm i)/2, \pm i, (-\sqrt{3} \pm i)/2$
21. $\cos \pi/10 + i\sin \pi/10, i, \cos 9\pi/10 + i\sin 9\pi/10, \cos 13\pi/10 + i\sin 13\pi/10,$
$\cos 17\pi/10 + i\sin 17\pi/10$ **23.** $\cos\left(\dfrac{\pi}{6} + \dfrac{2\pi k}{7}\right) + i\sin\left(\dfrac{\pi}{6} + \dfrac{2\pi k}{7}\right),$
$k = 0, 1, \ldots, 6$ **25.** $\pm(4.5 + 2.2i)$ **27.** $(.5 + 2.2i)/2$ or $(-8.5 - 2.2i)/2$

Chapter 10

Section 10-1 (page 393)

1.

$(x + 1)^2 + (y - 2)^2 = 9$

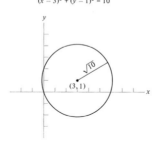

5.

$(x - 3)^2 + (y - 1)^2 = 10$

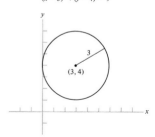

9.

$(x - 3)^2 + (y - 4)^2 = 9$

13.

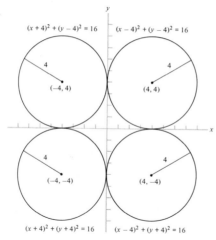

$(x + 4)^2 + (y - 4)^2 = 16$ $(x - 4)^2 + (y - 4)^2 = 16$

$(x + 4)^2 + (y + 4)^2 = 16$ $(x - 4)^2 + (y + 4)^2 = 16$

15.

$(x - \frac{1}{2})^2 + (y - 3)^2 = \frac{1}{4}$

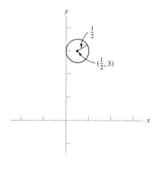

19.

$x^2 + y^2 - 2x - 4y - 20 = 0$ or
$(x - 1)^2 + (y - 2)^2 = 25$

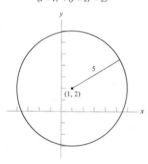

23.

$x^2 + (y - 1)^2 = 1$

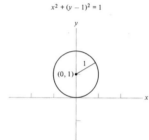

25.

$(x - 3)^2 + (y + 4)^2 = 25$

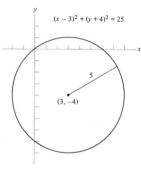

27.

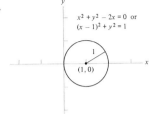

$x^2 + y^2 - 2x = 0$ or
$(x - 1)^2 + y^2 = 1$

29.

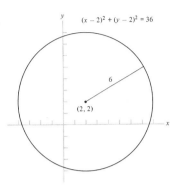

$(x - 2)^2 + (y - 2)^2 = 36$

31.

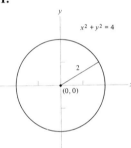

$x^2 + y^2 = 4$

33.

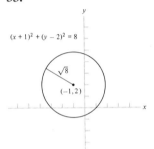

$(x + 1)^2 + (y - 2)^2 = 8$

37.

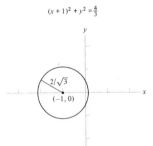

$(x + 1)^2 + y^2 = \frac{4}{3}$

39. No solution   **41.** $x^2 = 9 \cos^2 t$, $y^2 = 9 \sin^2 t$; therefore,
$x^2 + y^2 = 9(\cos^2 t + \sin^2 t) = 9$ **42.** $x - h = r \cos t$ and $y - k = r \sin t$;
therefore, $(x - h)^2 + (y - k)^2 = r^2$ **43.** The path is a circle with center $(4, -3)$
and radius 2; the particle is at $(6, -3)$ when $t = 0$ and at $(4, -1)$ when $t = \pi/2$.
44. $y = 2x$ **46.** Let m be the slope; the coordinates of the point of tangency
will be (x, mx). Now use the fact that the tangent line is perpendicular to the
radius. ANSWER: $y = \pm(4/3)x$

Section 10-2 (page 403)

1.

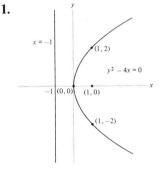

$x = -1$
$(1, 2)$
$y^2 - 4x = 0$
$(0, 0)$ $(1, 0)$
$(1, -2)$

3.

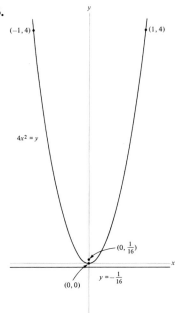

5.

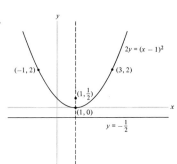

7.

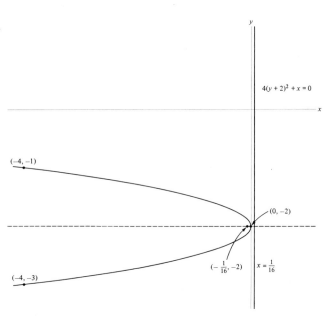

9.

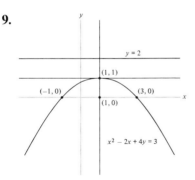

11.

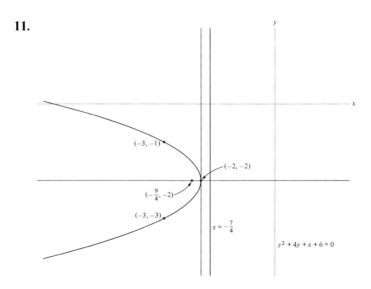

13. $x^2 = 12y$ **15.** $(x + 1)^2 = 16(y - 4)$ **17.** $7(x + 1)^2 = (y + 3)$
19. $(x - 6)^2 = -8(y - 1)$ **21.** $2(x - 1)^2 = y - 1$
23. $x = at$, $y = bt^2$; therefore, $x^2 = a^2t^2 = (a^2/b)bt^2 = (a^2/b)y$
24. $x = at$, $y = bt^2 + ct + d$; therefore, $t = x/a$ and
$y = b(x/a)^2 + c(x/a) + d = (b/a^2)[x^2 + (ca/b)x + (c^2a^2)/4b^2] + d - (c^2/4b) = (b/a^2)[x + (ca/2b)]^2 + (4bd - c^2)/4b$. The vertex is at the point $(-(ca/2b), (4bd - c^2)/4b)$ **25.** Refer to Exercise 24; $x = at$ and $y = bt^2 + ct + d$
with $a = v_0\cos\theta$, $b = -16$, $c = v_0\sin\theta$, and $d = 0$ **26.** Refer to Exercise 25;
$v_0 = 1000$, $\theta = 30°$ so $a = 500\sqrt{3}$, $b = -16$, $c = 500$, and $d = 0$.
Now refer to Exercise 24; the maximum height is the y-coordinate of the vertex;
$(4bd - c^2)/4b = 250{,}000/64 \approx 3906$ ft. It will strike the ground
$250{,}000\sqrt{3}/16 \approx 27{,}063$ ft away in $500/16 \approx 31$ sec.

27. The x-coordinate $-ca/2b$ of the vertex is half the distance; thus, $2500 = -(1000 \cos \theta)(1000 \sin \theta)/(-32) = 10^6 \sin 2\theta/64$. The cannon should be aimed at an angle of $4°36'$.

Section 10-3 (page 414)

1.

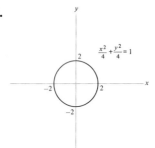

3.

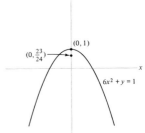

5.

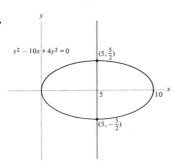

7. $\frac{(x+1)^2}{5} + \frac{(y-4)^2}{7} = 1$

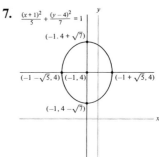

9. No solution

11.

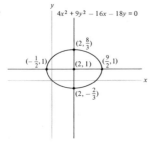

13.

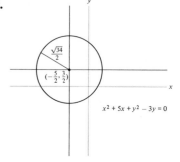

15. $(-2, -1)$ **17.** $(x - 2)^2 + \dfrac{(y - 2)^2}{4} = 1$

19. $\dfrac{(x + 1)^2}{36} + \dfrac{(y - 2)^2}{32} = 1$ **21.** $\dfrac{(x - 2)^2}{9} + \dfrac{(y - 3)^2}{5} = 1$

23. $\dfrac{(x + 3)^2}{16} + \dfrac{(y + 2)^2}{4} = 1$ **25.** $\dfrac{(x - 2)^2}{3} + \dfrac{(y - 1)^2}{4} = 1$

27. $x = 2 \cos t$, $y = 3 \sin t$; therefore, $9x^2 + 4y^2 = 9(4 \cos^2 t) + 4(9 \sin^2 t) = 36(\cos^2 t + \sin^2 t) = 36$ **28.** $x - h = a \cos t$, $y - k = b \sin t$; therefore, $\dfrac{(x - h)^2}{a^2} + \dfrac{(y - k)^2}{b^2} = 1$ **29.** 7.4×10^7 miles, 11.2×10^7 miles.

Section 10-4 (page 427)

1.

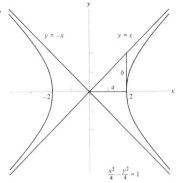

$$\frac{x^2}{4} - \frac{y^2}{4} = 1$$

3.

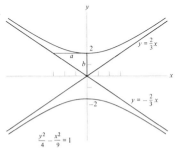

$$\frac{y^2}{4} - \frac{x^2}{9} = 1$$

5.

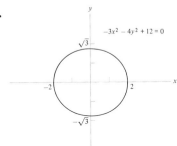

$-3x^2 - 4y^2 + 12 = 0$

7.

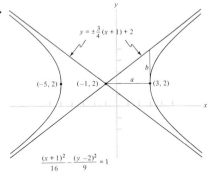

$$\frac{(x + 1)^2}{16} - \frac{(y - 2)^2}{9} = 1$$

9.

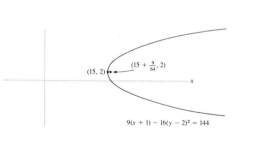

$9(x + 1) - 16(y - 2)^2 = 144$

11.

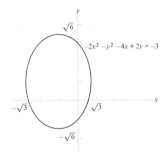

$-2x^2 - y^2 - 4x + 2y = -3$

13.

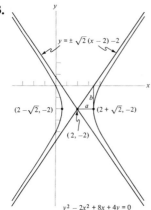

$y = \pm \sqrt{2}(x-2) - 2$

$(2-\sqrt{2}, -2)$ $(2+\sqrt{2}, -2)$

$(2, -2)$

$y^2 - 2x^2 + 8x + 4y = 0$

15.

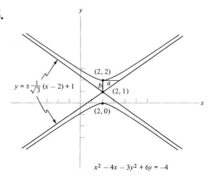

$(2, 2)$

$y = \pm \frac{1}{\sqrt{3}}(x-2) + 1$ $(2, 1)$

$(2, 0)$

$x^2 - 4x - 3y^2 + 6y = -4$

17. $15x^2 - y^2 = 15$ **19.** $5y^2 - 4(x-1)^2 = 20$

21. $36(x+1)^2 - 4(y-2)^2 = 144$ **23.** $5(y-3)^2 - 20x^2 = 64$

26. $(x-h)/a = \sec t$ and $(y-k)/b = \tan t$; therefore, $\dfrac{(x-h)^2}{a^2} - \dfrac{(y-k)^2}{b^2} =$

$\sec^2 t - \tan^2 t = 1$ **27.** $(x-h)/a = \cosh t$ and $(y-k)/b = \sinh t$; therefore,

$\dfrac{(x-h)^2}{a^2} - \dfrac{(y-k)^2}{b^2} = \cosh^2 t - \sinh^2 t = 1$

Section 10-5 (page 437)

1.

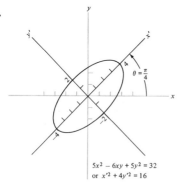

$\theta = \frac{\pi}{4}$

$5x^2 - 6xy + 5y^2 = 32$
or $x'^2 + 4y'^2 = 16$

3.

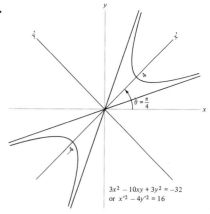

$\theta = \frac{\pi}{4}$

$3x^2 - 10xy + 3y^2 = -32$
or $x'^2 - 4y'^2 = 16$

5. No solution   **7.** Parabola: $4\left(y' + \dfrac{3\sqrt{2}}{4}\right)^2 = 3\sqrt{2}\left(x' + \dfrac{3\sqrt{2}}{64}\right)$

9. Ellipse: $4x'^2 + 9y'^2 = 36$ **11.** Hyperbola: $x'^2 - y'^2 = 10$

13. Two lines: $4x''^2 - y''^2 = 0$ **15.** Parabola: $x''^2 = -4\sqrt{5}y''$ **17.** Hyperbola

19. Ellipse   **21.** Hyperbola

Appendix A
Section A-1 (page 444)

1. For $n = 1$, $1 = 1(2 \cdot 1 - 1)$. If it is true for k, then add $4(k + 1) - 3$ to both sides of S_k. Thus,

$$1 + 5 + 9 + \ldots + (4k - 3) + [4(k + 1) - 3]$$
$$= k(2k - 1) + [4(k + 1) - 3]$$
$$= 2k^2 + 3k + 1$$
$$= (k + 1)(2k + 1)$$
$$= (k + 1)[2(k + 1) - 1]$$

This is S_{k+1} and completes the proof.

3. True for $n = 1$. If it is true for k, then add $3(k + 1)$ to both sides of S_k. The right side will be

$$\tfrac{3}{2}k(k + 1) + 3(k + 1) = (k + 1)(\tfrac{3}{2}k + 3) = \tfrac{3}{2}(k + 1)[(k + 1) + 1]$$

8. Add $\dfrac{1}{(k + 1)(k + 2)}$ to both sides of S_k. The right side will be

$$\frac{k}{k + 1} + \frac{1}{(k + 1)(k + 2)} = \frac{k(k + 2) + 1}{(k + 1)(k + 2)} = \frac{(k + 1)^2}{(k + 1)(k + 2)} = \frac{k + 1}{k + 2}.$$

10. Multiply both sides of S_k by

$$\left(1 + \frac{1}{k + 1}\right) = \frac{k + 2}{k + 1}$$

The right side will be

$$(k + 1)\left(\frac{k + 2}{k + 1}\right) = k + 2$$

11. True for $n = 1: 3^{2 \cdot 1} - 1 = 8$. Assume it is true for k; that is, assume that $3^{2k} - 1$ is divisible by 8. It follows that there is some integer m such that $3^{2k} = 8m + 1$. Multiply both sides of this equation by $3^2 = 9$ and then subtract 1 to obtain $3^{2(k+1)} - 1 = 72m + 8$, which is divisible by 8.

14. True for $n = 4$. Assume it is true for k; $2^k + 10k < 3^k$. Then $2^{(k+1)} + 10(k + 1) < 2(2^k + 10k) < 2 \cdot 3^k < 3^{k+1}$

Section A-2 (page 451)

1. $a_{20} = a_1 + d(n - 1) = -3 + 6(20 - 1) = 111$; $s_{10} = \dfrac{n}{2}(2a_1 + d(n - 1)) =$

$\dfrac{10}{2}(2(-3) + 6(10 - 1)) = 240$ **3.** $a_{20} = -74$; $s_{10} = -160$ **5.** $a_{20} = \tfrac{43}{10}$; $s_{10} = 14$

7. $a_5 = a_1 r^{n-1} = (\tfrac{1}{4})(\tfrac{1}{2})^4 = \tfrac{1}{64}$; $s_6 = \dfrac{a_1(1 - r^n)}{1 - r} = \dfrac{\tfrac{1}{4}(1 - (\tfrac{1}{2})^6)}{1 - (\tfrac{1}{2})} = \tfrac{63}{128}$

9. $a_5 = \frac{1}{32}; s_6 = \frac{819}{128}$ **11.** $a_5 = \frac{1}{81}; s_6 = \frac{364}{243}$ **13.** $n = 35$; sum $= \frac{35}{2}(-2 + 100) =$
1715 **15.** 255 **17.** 10,100 **19.** -6222 **21.** $\frac{63}{32}$
24. True for $n = 1$; $a_1 = a_1 + d(1 - 1) = a_1$. Suppose S_k is true; that is, suppose
$a_k = a_1 + d(k - 1)$. Then $a_{k+1} = a_k + d = a_1 + d(k - 1) + d = a_1 + dk =$
$a_1 + d[(k + 1) - 1]$; thus, S_{k+1} is true.

Section A-3 (page 456)

1. 3 **3.** 21 **5.** 1 **7.** 1 **9.** $4^4 = 256$ **11.** $6^4 = 1296$ **13.** $2 \cdot 10^3 \cdot 26^3 = 35{,}152{,}000$

14. $2^6 = 64$ **15.** $\binom{6}{1} = 6$; $\binom{6}{3} = 20$ **16.** 3^{10}; $1/3^{10} \approx .000017$ **17.** $\binom{7}{4} = 35$

18. $\binom{5}{2} + \binom{5}{1} = 15$ **20.** $2^3 = 8$ **22.** $\binom{4}{3} \cdot \frac{48 \cdot 40}{2} = 3840$

23. $(13)(3840) = 49{,}920$ **24.** There are $4^5 = 1024$ ways of getting an Ace,
2, 3, 4, 5 straight: a straight can begin with any card from an Ace through a 10;
therefore, there are $10 \cdot 4^5 = 10{,}240$ ways of getting a straight. (Some of these
will also be flushes; that is, straight flushes.) **25.** 5148

27. $\binom{n}{r} + \binom{n}{r + 1} = \dfrac{n!}{r!(n - r)!} + \dfrac{n!}{(r + 1)![n - (r + 1)]!}$

$= \dfrac{n!(r + 1)}{(r + 1)!(n - r)!} + \dfrac{n!(n - r)}{(r + 1)!(n - r)!}$

$= \dfrac{n!(n - r + r + 1)}{(r + 1)![(n + 1) - (r + 1)]!}$

$= \binom{n + 1}{r + 1}$

Section A-4 (page 461)

1. $a^3 + 3a^2b + 3ab^2 + b^3$ **3.** $16x^4 - 32x^3y + 24x^2y^2 - 8xy^3 + y^4$
5. $s^8 + 4s^6y^3 + 6s^4y^6 + 4s^2y^9 + y^{12}$
7. $\dfrac{1}{u^5} - \dfrac{5v}{u^4} + \dfrac{10v^2}{u^3} - \dfrac{10v^3}{u^2} + \dfrac{5v^4}{u} - v^5$
11. $1 + 4(.01) + 6(.01)^2 + 4(.01)^3 + (.01)^4 = 1.04060401$
13. $1 + 3(-.01) + 3(-.01)^2 + (-.01)^3 = .970299$
16. $\binom{8}{4}(2x)^4(-y)^4 = 1120x^4y^4$ **18.** $-56x^{10}y^9$

Appendix B
Section B-4 (page 484)

1. -1 **3.** -13 **5.** -7

Index